D1295422

THE AUTHOR

Nathan Keyfitz is Professor of Sociology at the University of Chicago, where he received the Ph.D. degree in 1952. Professor Keyfitz served on the faculty of the University of Toronto from 1959 to 1963. He is an Associate of the Society of Actuaries, a Fellow of the American Statistical Association, a Fellow of the Royal Society of Canada, and a member of the International Statistical Institute.

INTRODUCTION TO THE MATHEMATICS OF POPULATION

NATHAN KEYFITZ
University of California, Berkeley

ADDISON-WESLEY
PUBLISHING COMPANY
Reading, Massachusetts
Menlo Park, California · London · Don Mills, Ontario

This book is in the
ADDISON-WESLEY SERIES IN BEHAVIORAL SCIENCE:
QUANTITATIVE METHODS

Consulting Editor
Frederick Mosteller

 Printed in the United States of America. Published simultaneously in Canada. Library of Congress Catalog Card No. 68-25926.

FOR BEATRICE

PREFACE

The inexactitude of our methods of measurement has no more reason in statistics than it has in physics to dim our conception of that which we measure.

R. A. Fisher, *The Genetical Theory of Natural Selection*

Public and scholarly recognition of population as a practical problem has grown in recent years in response to the increase in the number of human beings on our planet. This recognition has not so far expressed itself in any unified presentation of the mathematics of population. Only one short book by A. J. Lotka, written in French and published in 1939, suggests what ought and ought not to be included of the material available thirty years ago.

The annual excess of births over deaths in the world is now of the order of 70,000,000 which means, numerically speaking, that a new United States is brought into existence every three years. The new United States does not enjoy the amenities of the existent United States to which it aspires, and this time of supreme aspiration may also be one of retrogression to the misery of the most primitive periods of history. Much is being done toward population limitation, and much more needs to be done to turn the tide in the direction of progress.

This book, however, is concerned with a wholly different aspect of the enterprise of human betterment: ascertaining the demographic situation. Even within this field of knowledge its aim is limited. Its subject is not facts as such, but how to handle them. It tries to gather together, and as far as possible to systematize, the most relevant parts of that large body of mathematical theory concerned with the growth processes of human and animal populations.

Though no books have been written on it, the richness of the subject is evident in the many hundreds of papers scattered throughout fifty or more journals, and selection was necessary if this book was to have a degree of coherence and to be of reasonable length. The path of exposition selected starts with the life table or stationary model, and goes on through the more general one-sex model, with discrete and then with continuous age intervals; in Chapters 12 to 14 the single-sex populations enter into interaction with each other. All these are treated in the deterministic fashion usual in demography, but Chapters 15 to 18 recognize random variation and derive in some simple cases variances of the distributions with whose expected values the preceding chapters deal.

The argument is as self-contained as space limitations permit; for the reader whose background is demographic rather than mathematical, matrices, differential equations, and the Laplace Transform are explained in some detail and worked examples of their use given. I have not supposed a knowledge of Markov chains, but introduced in elementary terms such of their ideas as were needed.

My teaching procedure was to attempt only a fraction of the manuscript with any single class. For a one-quarter course (30 lecture hours) with students interested in numerical results, I have stayed with the discrete case (principally Chapters 1 through 4) and included some Fortran programming of the matrix model and selected techniques from Chapters 10 and 11. For students whose interest was more theoretical, I have worked through the renewal equation (Chapters 5, 6, and 8) and then gone on to Chapters 12 and 13. For more advanced students I have taught a course emphasizing two-sex populations and probability, consisting of Chapters 12 through 14 and 16 through 18. Thus at least three largely separate courses are contained here, each requiring a quarter or semester.

Though it was developed in courses and seminars, the book is primarily designed for the lone reader. I have tried to challenge him by questions interspersed throughout the exposition. The proofs are intended to be complete and self-contained in the sense that they may be followed without extensive mathematical knowledge or reference to other books. But the reader is assumed to have pencil and paper at hand and himself to bridge the interval from one typeset formula to the next. Numerical examples can be verified on a desk calculator. The reader interested in developing computer programs will find specimen data and results that should enable him to test his programs (and mine). Results shown here were separately rounded from computations to eight places of decimals.

Theory is rendered understandable, to the writer as well as to readers, by application to data. I have done my utmost to illustrate the theory with real data concerning human populations, and to avoid hypothetical examples. Where the source of any set of data is a single publication, that is cited. For most of the tables, however, a variety of sources enter, and to cite them all would have taken more space than could be allowed in a book concerned with logic rather than with substantive results. The United Nations *Demographic Yearbooks* from 1948 to 1966 have been important in supplying raw data; so also have been the national official publications contained in the library of the University of Chicago, and correspondence with national statistical agencies. Two sets of computations were made for the United States: one from birth registrations as published, the other from the registrations as adjusted by the official source, the National Center for Health Statistics; the latter are distinguished by a footnote. Detailed sources of all data are contained in the author's files.

A much more extensive series of computations, with which the ones here contained are consistent, is provided in *World Population*, by the present author and Wilhelm Flieger, published by the University of Chicago Press in 1968.

"Truth emerges more readily from error than from confusion," says Bacon in the *Novum Organum*. I do not know in what measure my work avoids confusion, but it undoubtedly contains errors. I shall be glad to be informed of these.

Over the five years in which this book was my nearly exclusive preoccupation, I have received help from many people. Fred Mosteller not only promoted the entire project, but he read the sequence of drafts and made numerous comments, all of which contributed to cogency and clarity. Chapters were rewritten many times in an effort to meet his standards of exposition. Divakar Sharma verified many of the proofs, and asked questions which caused me to realize better what assumptions underlay my arguments. Others to whom I am grateful for suggestions include Carl Bajema, R. N. Battacharya, Arthur A. Campbell, Norman Carrier, Chin Long Chiang, Ansley J. Coale, Wilhelm Flieger, Leo A. Goodman, Morris H. Hansen, P. Das Gupta, R. W. Hodge, Barbara Keyfitz, Leslie Kish, Evelyn Kitagawa, John S. Lew, R. C. Lewontin, Alvaro Lopez, David McFarland, Paul Meier, Walter Mertens, Felix Moore, E. M. Murphy, Jay Palmore, Andrei Rogers, Norman Ryder, Mindel C. Sheps, Mortimer Spiegelman, Leon Tabah, and William Taylor. In the last search for errors at the proof stage, I had valuable help from Robert Retherford.

Students at Chicago, Duke, and Berkeley provided numerical results on real data and so assessed the correctness as well as the applicability of some pieces of theory. Those who did substantial amounts of programming, the results of which do not always appear explicitly, were Eduardo Arriaga, Roger Avery, Frank Bean, Beth Berkov, Linda Bourque, Chen-Tung Chang, Jere Cohen, William Cummings, Thomas G. Donnelly, Linda Drass, Jeffery Evans, Wilhelm Flieger, Prithwis Das Gupta, Barbara Heyns, Joginder Kumar, Ronald Lee, William Lindeman, George Masnick, Susan McDougall, Maurice Moore, Effat Moussa, James Mulherin, E. M. Murphy, Dhruva Nagnur, Pierre Nakache, Terry Nichols, Frank Oechsli, A. Okorafor, Jay Palmore, James Porter, Robert Retherford, Hardeo Sahai, Diego Salazar, R. S. S. Sarma, Susan Borker Schwarz, J. M. Sehgal, William J. Serow, S. N. Sinha, Peter Smith, Shannon Stokes, P. P. Talwar, William Taylor, Andrea Tyree, Eliezer Uche, Daniel Vandeportaele and Nancy Wang. Even where the result of the programming was merely to convince me that no useful application to real data was in sight, so that I dropped the theory out of the volume, I am grateful for printouts which substantially aided my thinking.

The National Science Foundation supported this computational work financially. Many incidental expenses were covered by a grant from the Population Council. A Ford Foundation grant relieved me of some of the usual teaching load.

The ultimate debt of any writer is to the classics of his subject. Lotka, Volterra, Leslie, Feller, Kendall, Coale, Goodman, and others framed the issues expounded in this book. None of them, whether his help was in writing or oral, is responsible for the use here made of his work.

While the largest part of the book is expository, an assembly of relatively well-known material, some gaps have been filled and some new theory and techniques are developed. The parts of several chapters containing what is novel in the argument have been presented in preliminary form in *Behavioral Science*, *Biometrics*, *Demography*, *Human Biology*, *The Journal of the American Statistical Association*, *The Journal of the Royal Statistical Society*, *Population*, *Population Studies*, and *The Re-*

view of the International Statistical Institute. My thanks go to the editors of these journals for raising points of substance as well as of exposition, and for permission to reuse material.

Most of the work was carried out at the University of Chicago. I was not the first newcomer to that community to feel, under the stimulus of colleagues and students, a dissatisfaction with what I thought I already knew. From such a dissatisfaction the impulse to search more deeply develops naturally, even in individuals for whom in other surroundings new knowledge was not of special importance. Of all my obligations, the greatest is to the University of Chicago.

Berkeley, California
February 1968

N.K.

ACKNOWLEDGMENTS

Chapter 1, Section 1.2, pp. 19–23, is a drastically altered version of "A life table that agrees with the data," *Journal of the American Statistical Association* **61,** Part I, 305–312 (June 1966).

Chapters 2 and 3 overlap with the following: "Matrix multiplication as a technique of population analysis," *The Milbank Memorial Fund Quarterly* **42,** No. 4, 68–84 (October 1964); "The population projection as a matrix operator," *Demography* **1,** No. 1, 57–73 (1964); "Estimating the trajectory of a population," *Proceedings of the Fifth Berkeley Symposium on Mathematical Statistics and Probability* **4,** 81–113 (1966).

Chapter 4, Section 4.4, pp. 88–89, contains a device first published in "Criteria for data adjustment," United Nations World Population Conference, Belgrade, 1965 (B. 6/I/E/323) (with E. M. Murphy).

Chapter 5 includes some of the methods from "The intrinsic rate of natural increase and the dominant root of the projection matrix," *Population Studies* **18,** No. 3, 293–308 (March 1965).

Chapters 5 and 6 overlap with "The integral equation of population analysis," *Review of the International Statistical Institute* **35,** No. 3, 213–246 (1967).

Chapter 7, Section 7.4, pp. 189–193, includes material from "Changing vital rates and age distribution," *Population Studies* 22, No. 1 (July 1968); "On the interpretation of age distributions," *Journal of the American Statistical Association* **62,** 862–874 (September 1967), (with Dhruva Nagnur and Divakar Sharma).

A preliminary version of Chapter 8 appeared as "Reconciliation of population models: matrix, integral equation, and partial fraction," *Journal of the Royal Statistical Society*, Series A (General) **130,** Part 1, 61–83 (1967).

Chapter 10, Sections 10.1, 10.2, and 10.5 overlap with "A unified approach to interpolation and graduation," *Demography* **3,** No. 2, 528–536 (1966).

Chapter 11 overlaps with "Finite approximations in demography," *Population Studies* **19,** No. 3, 281–295 (March 1966).

Parts of Chapter 12 were included in a paper, "Volterra and Lotka up-dated: the study of multiple populations," given at the December 1967 meeting of the American Statistical Association.

A very early and brief version of Chapter 13 appeared as "On the interaction of populations," *Demography* **2,** 276–288 (1965).

Chapter 14, Section 14.1, pp. 328–330, contains material from "Matrix and multiple decrement in population analysis," *Biometrics* **23,** No. 3, 485–503 (September 1967), (with E. M. Murphy); pp. 331–332 were published in "Matrix models in sociology," *et al.*, **1,** No. 1, 3, 8–9 (Fall 1967).

An early version of Chapter 15 appeared as "Sampling variance of demographic characteristics," *Human Biology* **38,** No. 1, 22–41 (February 1966).

Chapter 18 was published in part in "Computerization of the branching process," *Behavioral Science* **12,** 329–336 (1967) (with Andrea Tyree).

Many of the computations in all chapters appear in *World Population: An Analysis of Vital Data*, University of Chicago Press, 1968 (with Wilhelm Flieger).

CONTENTS

Part I

THE LIFE TABLE

CHAPTER 1

THE STATIONARY POPULATION MODEL

1.1. AN ACCOUNT OF THE LIFE TABLE

The life table is a scheme for expressing the facts of mortality in terms of probabilities. It is also a population model, covering the simplest case which is worth discussing: a cohort or group of people born at the same moment, closed to migration, and followed through successive ages until they die. Like other successful models, the life table has given its shape to the natural world; we are incapable of thinking of population change and mortality from any other starting point. Its description includes a considerable part of the notation that will be used throughout this book.

Age-Specific Rates and Probabilities

If in a past year, in a *closed population* (one which loses none of its members by emigration nor receives new ones by immigration), there were K members present or *exposed* on the average during the year, and D deaths occurred in the year, then the proportion of deaths is $M = D/K$. For the United States in 1964 the midyear resident population was officially estimated at $K = 191{,}372{,}000$ (*Statistical Abstract*, 1965,* p. 5), and registered deaths numbered $D = 1{,}798{,}051$ (*ibid.*, p. 56). Hence

$$M = \frac{1{,}798{,}051}{191{,}372{,}000} = 0.00940 \quad \text{or} \quad 9.40 \text{ per thousand}\,.$$

This is the *crude death rate*, crude because it confounds the mortality condition with the age distribution.

Statistical averages are more meaningful when they refer to homogeneous groups. A big step toward homogeneity is to narrow down the scope of the ratio from the entire population to one age group for a given sex. Suppose the males from age x to $x + 1$ (i.e., the group aged x at last birthday) number K_x at the middle of the calendar year, and deaths among them over the calendar year number D_x; then we define the *age-specific* death rate for males at age x as $M_x = D_x/K_x$. In the United States on July 1, 1964, there were estimated to be 1,081,000 men aged 32 at last birthday, and the number of men who died at

* U. S. Bureau of the Census, *Statistical Abstract of the United States: 1965*, 86th Ed. (Washington: Government Printing Office, 1965); referred to throughout as *Statistical Abstract*, with the year.

this age during 1964 was estimated at 2317, making an age-specific death rate of

$$M_{32} = \frac{D_{32}}{K_{32}} = \frac{2317}{1{,}081{,}000} = 0.002143 \quad \text{or} \quad 2.143 \text{ per thousand population}\,.$$

(Data are as shown in Table 1.3 in five-year age groups, graduated to single years of age by Greville multipliers, a procedure discussed in Section 10.4.)

The life table is a means of presenting information on population numbers and deaths of some past interval of time, age by age, in such fashion that conclusions on prospective probabilities of death and survivorship can be conveniently drawn. The question is how to go from M_x, the observed age-specific death rates, to probability statements regarding the futures of individuals. We are willing to tolerate, provisionally, the assumption that future mortality will be the same as past mortality. Any group of people who at midyear average age $x + \frac{1}{2}$ must at the beginning of the year have averaged age x. If the deaths D_x were evenly distributed through the year of time and age, so that one half of them would have occurred in the first half of the year, then the number of people at the beginning of the year must have been $K_x + \frac{1}{2}D_x$. We now look at the matter prospectively: among a group numbering initially $K_x + \frac{1}{2}D_x$ persons, say on January 1, D_x die during the subsequent 12 months. The probability as of January 1 of any individual dying during the subsequent 12 months is thus

$$q_x = \frac{D_x}{K_x + \frac{1}{2}D_x} = \frac{M_x}{1 + \frac{1}{2}M_x}\,,$$

the last expression being obtained by dividing both numerator and denominator by K_x. For United States males aged 32 in 1964, the probability of dying during the succeeding 12 months is estimated to be

$$q_{32} = \frac{2317}{1{,}081{,}000 + 1158} = 0.002141\,,$$

slightly less than M_{32}.

From the probabilities of dying within a year at each age, q_x, we get the complements, $p_x = 1 - q_x$, the probabilities of living through each year of age. These p_x can be chained for successive years to find the probability ${}_np_x$ of an individual aged x living through n years,

$${}_np_x = (p_x)(p_{x+1}) \cdots (p_{x+n-1})\,.$$

In particular, the chance of living through the first year of life for a child just born is p_0, the chance of living through the first two years of life for a child just born is p_0p_1, of living through the first x years of life is ${}_xp_0 = p_0p_1 \cdots p_{x-1}$.

It is customary to write the cumulative product of the probabilities as $l_x = l_0p_0p_1 \cdots p_{x-1}$, where l_0, called the *radix*, is an arbitrary constant such as unity or 100,000.

This set of l_x is spoken of as *the stationary population*, almost as though it had a real contemporary existence and $(l_x + l_{x+1})/2$ persons could be counted at age x last birthday. Deaths between ages x and $x + 1$ are $d_x = l_x - l_{x+1}$; between x and $x + n$, ${}_nd_x = l_x - l_{x+n}$. The total deaths each year in this constructed "population" are l_0. Since the stationary model is defined as closed to migration, and since births are equal to deaths, births also are l_0.

The same l_x-column may be interpreted as survivors of an initial set of babies. A group or *cohort* of l_0 children just born, if subject to the mortality of the observed population at the several ages, would have an expected number of survivors at age 1 equal to $l_0p_0 = l_1$, at age 2 equal to $l_0p_0p_1 = l_2$, etc. In due course the last of the cohort of l_0 would die—this is ensured by making $q_{\omega-1} = 1$, or $p_{\omega-1} = 0$, for ω some age such as 90 or 100. The observations on which the table is based are usually a cross section through all ages at a given slice of time, say the calendar year 1963, and the resulting life table then deals with careers of cohorts in a metaphorical sense only. Such cohorts are called *synthetic*.

Continuous Life Table Functions

Functions of continuous variables are the principal means of looking more deeply into age at death and many other demographic matters. Whenever we mean to use x as a continuous variable rather than for a discrete set of values, this intent will be suggested by the functional notation $l(x)$ in place of l_x. We define $\mu(x)$, the instantaneous death rate or *force of mortality*, as the limiting value of the death rate when the age interval becomes very short. Since the life table deaths in the age interval x to $x + \Delta x$ are $l(x) - l(x + \Delta x)$, and the exposure is $l(x)\,\Delta x$, we have

$$\mu(x) = \lim_{\Delta x\to 0} \frac{l(x) - l(x + \Delta x)}{l(x)\,\Delta x} = \frac{-dl(x)}{l(x)\,dx} = -\frac{d\ln l(x)}{dx}, \tag{1.1.1}$$

where ln stands for the natural logarithm of the quantity following it.

The life table may be constructed from a knowledge of $\mu(x)$, the force of mortality defined in (1.1.1). For the differential equation $\mu(x)\,dx = -d\ln l(x)$ can serve as a definition of $l(x)$, and integrating it gives

$$l(x) = C\exp\left[-\int_0^x \mu(t)\,dt\right]. \tag{1.1.2}$$

Putting $x = 0$ shows the (arbitrary) *radix* or initial value of the life table number-living column, $C = l_0$. The chance of living n years for a person aged x is $l(x + n)/l(x)$, and this may be obtained from (1.1.2) as

$$\frac{l(x+n)}{l(x)} = \exp\left[-\int_x^{x+n} \mu(t)\,dt\right].$$

When the l_0 individuals are taken as a synthetic cohort they are subject to an annual diminution by death according to the observed mortality of the given year. The number who die between ages x and $x + dx$ is $l(x)\mu(x)\,dx$, and this, or its value integrated over one year, $d_x = \int_0^1 l(x+t)\mu(x+t)\,dt$, is known as the *decrement*. Though this chapter deals with a cohort subject only to the single decrement of death, the concept is applicable to entry into the work force, marriage, having a child, etc., and a number of such decrements may be incorporated in one table (Jordan, 1952, pp. 251–269; Chapter 14 below).

When we think of $l(x)$ as an age distribution of individuals alive at a given moment, the number of persons alive between ages x and $x + dx$ in this hypothetical stationary population is $l(x)\,dx$, and between x and $x + n$ is

$$ {}_nL_x = \int_0^n l(x+t)\,dt\,. $$

On the other hand, when the life table represents a cohort, the integral ${}_nL_x$ is the person-years lived by that cohort between ages x and $x + n$. The total person-years, T_x, in prospect for the group numbering l_x who have attained age x on the radix l_0 will be the same integral to the maximum age to which anyone can live, say ω:

$$ T_x = \int_0^{\omega-x} l(x+t)\,dt\,. $$

For each of the l_x individuals the share of this total will be, on the average,

$$ T_x/l_x = \mathring{e}_x\,, $$

known as the *complete expectation of life* at age x.

The reader may wish to derive formulas for obtaining the several columns of the life table starting from any one of l_x, ${}_nL_x$, T_x, $\mathring{e}_x$. Two ways of setting out the construction are possible, one in the continuous version, as theory, the other in the discrete version for computation.

We can show that $\mathring{e}_x$, the average prospective lifetime of an individual aged x, is also formally identical with the mean or centroid used in statistics and physics:

$$ \mathring{e}_x = \frac{\int_0^{\omega-x} t\,l(x+t)\mu(x+t)\,dt}{\int_0^{\omega-x} l(x+t)\mu(x+t)\,dt}\,, \qquad (1.1.3) $$

where the numerator is arranged to assign to each of the $l(x+t)\mu(x+t)\,dt$ persons dying at age $x + t$ the number of years t that he has lived beyond age x; the ratio of integrals in (1.1.3) is the average of t. Applying the definition of $\mu(x+t)$ in (1.1.1), integrating by parts in the numerator of (1.1.3), and using the fact that everyone dies before age ω, the ratio (1.1.3) becomes

$$ \begin{aligned} \mathring{e}_x &= \frac{-\int_{t=0}^{t=\omega-x} t\,dl(x+t)}{l_x} \\ &= \frac{-[tl(x+t)]_0^{\omega-x} + \int_0^{\omega-x} l(x+t)\,dt}{l_x} \\ &= \frac{T_x}{l_x}\,. \end{aligned} \qquad (1.1.4) $$

This proves the equivalence of the two forms of $\mathring{e}_x$ given at the right of (1.1.3) and (1.1.4). The total number in the stationary population generated by l_0 births per year is $T_0 = \int_0^\omega l(t)\,dt$, and its annual deaths number

$$l_0 = \int_0^\omega l(t)\mu(t)\,dt\,.$$

Hence its death rate is

$$l_0/T_0 = 1/\mathring{e}_0\,.$$

Mortality Comparison by the Life Table and by Standardization

The expectation $\mathring{e}_0$ is frequently used in comparing mortality between times and places. Its value for the United States in 1964 was 66.9 years for males and 73.7 for females, a difference of 6.8 years in favor of females. In the three-year period centered on 1930 the male expectation was 57.3 years and the female 60.7, a difference of 3.4 years. Increases in expectation have averaged 2.8 years per decade for males and 3.8 years per decade for females. The most recent tables show some tapering off, with females increasing by only 0.1 of a year between 1964 and 1965, and males decreasing by 0.03. Examination of age-specific rates suggests that the fall of deaths at ages under 70 has been mainly responsible for stretching the expectation by 3 or 4 years per decade. The probability ${}_5q_{25}$ for American women dropped from 0.02142 in 1930 to 0.00439 in 1964, a reduction of 80%. On the other hand, $\mathring{e}_{70}$ for United States males was 9.2 in 1930, and 10.5 in 1964, a gain of one and one-third years in a third of a century. As deaths at youthful ages approach zero, a resumption of the upward trend in $\mathring{e}_0$ will require medical advances on a new front, the ailments of people over 70.

An alternative way of comparing mortality between two places, sexes, or times is the *directly standardized death rate* whose continuous form is

$$(\text{sd}) = \frac{\int_0^\omega K'(x)M(x)\,dx}{\int_0^\omega K'(x)\,dx}\,,$$

where the set of weights $K'(x)$ is the age distribution of the *standard* population, and the $M(x)$ are the death rates by age of the *given* population. The *indirectly standardized death rate* may be defined as

$$(\text{isd}) = \left(\frac{\int_0^\omega K(x)M(x)\,dx}{\int_0^\omega K(x)M'(x)\,dx}\right)d'\,,$$

where again the prime distinguishes the standard population and d' is the crude death rate of the standard population. The reader may exhibit (sd) and (isd) in discrete form. He may then show that if death rates are replaced by prices, and population numbers by quantities purchased, (sd)/d' is a base-weighted aggregative price index, and (isd)/d' the corresponding current-weighted index (Duncan, Cuzzort, and Duncan, 1961, p. 177; Kitagawa, 1964).

Table 1.1 Crude, life table, and standardized death rates per thousand population, males*

	CRUDE DEATH RATE	LIFE-TABLE DEATH RATE $1000/\mathring{e}_0$	DEATH RATE INDIRECTLY STANDARDIZED ON		
			ENGLAND AND WALES 1960-62	UNITED STATES 1959-61	MEXICO 1959-61
CANADA 1940-42	10.64	16.06	14.43	12.48	9.76
1964	8.88	14.57	10.95	9.70	7.32
1965	8.87	14.54	10.99	9.74	7.40
ENGLAND AND WALES 1960-62	12.46	14.68	12.46	11.07	9.53
1963	12.81	14.73	12.90	11.45	9.79
FRANCE 1851	22.37	26.09	33.47	28.38	21.58
1959-63	11.91	14.82	12.34	11.02	9.30
MEXICO 1959-61	11.97	17.97	25.49	21.08	11.97
SWEDEN 1783-87	28.57	29.78	50.12	41.40	27.49
1958-62	10.36	13.98	9.45	8.54	7.67
UNITED STATES 1919-21	12.91	18.35	22.60	18.82	13.08
1939-41	11.87	16.36	16.23	13.96	11.15
1959-61	10.85	14.96	12.22	10.85	8.52
1963	11.08	14.99	12.47	11.10	8.80
1964	10.83	14.95	12.16	10.84	8.63
1965	10.88	14.95	12.22	10.91	8.74

* Data on population and deaths by age from United Nations *Demographic Yearbook*, 1948–66, and official national sources. Standardization programmed by Wilhelm Flieger; life tables programmed by Wilhelm Flieger and William Cummings, using method of Section 1.2.

Table 1.1 shows indirectly standardized rates on three standards for a number of male populations, along with crude and life table death rates. The reader is invited to compare results and to comment on the effect of the life table's implicit weighting by a stationary age distribution which (1) is different from that prevailing in a rapidly growing population, and (2) in any case differs among the populations being compared. Which of the five columns shown best indicates the improvement in United States mortality? in Swedish mortality? How does the United States compare with England and Wales in 1963? Show the advantage in a tight comparison of knowing *both* directly and indirectly standardized rates. What standard would be best for comparing male with female mortality at a given place and time?

The Lexis Diagram

The life table, or more strictly its number-living column, has been spoken of as

a) a set of probabilities, l_{x+n}/l_x, that an individual aged x will live to age $x + n$;
b) the survivors l_x out of a cohort of l_0 babies born at the same time and going through life together;
c) a population, stationary in total numbers as well as in age distribution, which includes at any one time ${}_nL_x = \int_0^n l(x + t)\,dt$ persons between exact ages x and $x + n$.

Aid in application along any of these lines, as well as in calculating the life table itself, is given by the presentation known as a *Lexis* diagram (Lexis, 1875, p. 302). Time is laid out along the horizontal axis, and age along the vertical. Each individual member of the population is represented by a line at 45° to either axis, starting at $x = 0$ and at the moment of birth in t, and terminating at a point which corresponds to both his age and time of death. When the lines stand for a population, the density of their starting points along the t-axis is proportional to the frequency of births in time (Fig. 1.1).

Vital statistics provide the number of deaths, D_x^z, which occurred in the calendar year z in which the deceased was x years of age at last birthday. These deaths took place in the square *ABCD*, and strictly we should relate them to the number of person-years of exposure in the same square—the number of persons within the scope of our registration system during the calendar year z, each counted as exposed from when he passed his xth birthday to when he passed his $(x + 1)$th birthday, or whatever part of that interval was within the year. In practice, outside of insurance companies no records are kept which would permit statistics of exposure in this precise sense, and various approximations are used.

Such approximations are based on a census of the number of persons, for example K_x^t aged x at time t, the beginning of calendar year z, or $K_x^{t+1/2}$ at time $t + \frac{1}{2}$, the middle of the year. K_x^t is the number of life lines crossing AD, $K_x^{t+1/2}$

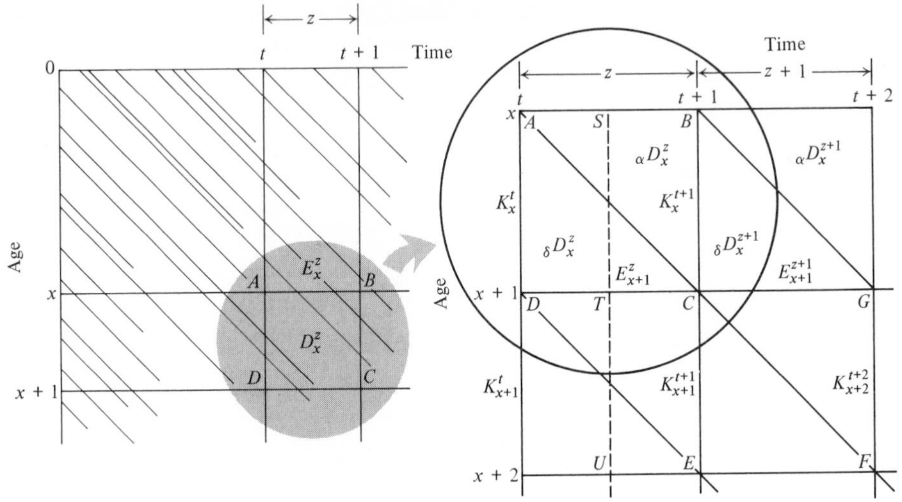

Fig. 1.1 Lexis diagram showing life lines in age-time plane.

the number crossing ST. Censuses taken at other dates may be adjusted to these without appreciable loss of precision.

A further group recognized in the diagram is the number E_{x+1}^z of individuals whose life lines cross DC, that is, those who reach their $(x + 1)$th birthday during the year z.

Three ways of proceeding from the observations to the probabilities of dying are discussed in the actuarial literature (Wolfenden, 1954, pp. 100, 101). The first is to take the deaths in the triangle ABC plus those in the triangle BCG and relate these to the lines crossing AB; the ratio of the deaths in the parallelogram $ABGC$ to the lines crossing AB is equal to q_x if the population is closed to migration:

$$q_x = \frac{{}_\alpha D_x^z + {}_\delta D_x^{z+1}}{E_x^z},$$

where ${}_\alpha D_x^z$ is the part of D_x^z in the upper triangle ABC, and ${}_\delta D_x^{z+1}$ the part of D_x^{z+1} in the lower triangle BCG. Though the formula is exact for age at last birthday x, it mixes two calendar years.

The second procedure refers to deaths of a single calendar year, but mixes deaths of two years of age. It is

$$q_x = 1 - \frac{K_{x+1}^{t+1}}{K_x^t} = \frac{{}_\delta D_x^z + {}_\alpha D_{x+1}^z}{K_x^t},$$

$1 - q_x$ being the survivors who cross CE divided by those who have crossed AD.

The third ratio falls within the square $ABCD$ and uses the deaths, clearly defined by time and age, of the calendar year z and age x last birthday. This consists of two triangles, the upper *ABC* which contains the ${}_{\alpha}D_x^z$ deaths of individuals who passed their xth birthday in the given calendar year, and *ACD*, the ${}_{\delta}D_x^z$ deaths of those who passed their xth birthday in the preceding calendar year. From these, q_x is estimated by

$$q_x = 1 - \left[\frac{E_{x+1}^z}{K_x^t}\right]\left[\frac{K_x^{t+1}}{E_x^z}\right] = 1 - \left[1 - \frac{{}_{\delta}D_x^z}{K_x^t}\right]\left[1 - \frac{{}_{\alpha}D_x^z}{E_x^z}\right] \doteqdot \frac{{}_{\delta}D_x^z}{K_x^t} + \frac{{}_{\alpha}D_x^z}{E_x^z},$$

where $\doteqdot$ signifies approximate equality. This preferred method finds the probability that individuals entering *ABCD* by crossing either of the arms *AB* or *AD* will die within the square.

During most of the ages of life the deaths for a large population are sufficiently spread through the year of age that it suffices to consider that half of those in *ABCD* are in *ACD* and the other half in *ABC*. But this is not true for the beginning of the life table, and the diagrammatic considerations above are helpful in determining how to proceed from the observations to the life table probabilities.

When for those dying under one year of age at each month we know the month of birth, then the triangles ${}_{\alpha}D_x^z$ and ${}_{\delta}D_x^z$ may be approximated and the *separation factor*

$$f_x^z = \frac{{}_{\delta}D_x^z}{{}_{\alpha}D_x^z + {}_{\delta}D_x^z}, \tag{1.1.5}$$

established (Wolfenden, 1954, p. 97). The factor f_0^z is that fraction of the deaths under one year of age which are to births occurring in the preceding year $z - 1$. When information on this point is lacking, the separation factor of some other time or place may be assumed, though separation factors in practice vary from 0.15 to 0.30. The point is of importance in the degree in which a sharp change occurs in the number of births from one year to the next. (An application appears at the end of section 1.2 below.)

Period and Generation

So far we have thought of mortality data referring to a period, typically of a single year; our cohorts have been constructed or *synthetic*. The $l(x)$-column of the life table for a given *real cohort* is a distribution of decreasing density along a given 45-degree line in Fig. 1.1 from upper left to lower right of the coordinate system. What is known as a cohort or *generation* life table shows the mortality to which a given individual is successively exposed. This is in direct contrast with the *period* life tables, based on data referring to a given year or other calendar interval, that have concerned us up to this point.

The difference between period results on the one hand and generation results on the other is illustrated in Table 1.2 with 19th century data for Sweden. The measures presented, $\mathring{e}_0$ and l_{50}/l_0, are on the whole more favorable for the real cohort born in a given interval than for the cross section of mortality in that

Table 1.2 Excerpt from life tables for Swedish males, showing $\mathring{e}_0$ and l_{50}/l_0, 1805–40*

MIDPOINT OF FIVE-YEAR PERIOD AND TIME WHEN COHORT WAS 0-4 YEARS OLD	EXPECTATION OF LIFE AT AGE 0 = $\mathring{e}_0$		PROBABILITY OF ATTAINING AGE 50 = l_{50}/l_0	
	PERIOD	REAL COHORT OR GENERATION	PERIOD	REAL COHORT OR GENERATION
1805	37.81	36.84	0.4384	0.4062
1810	28.99	34.78	0.2926	0.3852
1815	37.33	39.08	0.4279	0.4417
1820	37.42	40.76	0.4252	0.4674
1825	41.96	44.24	0.4832	0.5075
1830	36.77	42.11	0.4034	0.4830
1835	40.25	44.43	0.4531	0.5150
1840	39.97	44.20	0.4516	0.5133

* Data on populations and deaths by age provided by Erland von Hofsten; cohort data were assembled from period data in five-year intervals of age and time. Programmed by Wilhelm Flieger.

interval, as is to be expected when mortality is subject to a secular trend of improvement; the cohort result refers to a time considerably more recent.

Somewhat more surprising is the relative smoothness of the cohorts. Evidently some of the causes of mortality—disease, famine, and war—struck at all ages, or at least a wide range of ages, at a certain moment of time; the cohort results average a number of time periods, as does the experience of the individual.

Calculation Procedures

The total person-years ${}_nL_x$ lived by the stationary population in the age-interval x to $x + n$ may be decomposed into years lived by the l_{x+n} who survive (n years each), and years lived by the ${}_nd_x = l_x - l_{x+n}$ who die in the interval. Suppose that the average number of years lived in the interval by those who die in it is ${}_na_x$. Then the decomposition of ${}_nL_x$ is the identity

$${}_nL_x = nl_{x+n} + {}_nd_x\,{}_na_x\,,$$

from which

$${}_na_x = \frac{{}_nL_x - nl_{x+n}}{{}_nd_x}\,. \tag{1.1.6}$$

(The uniform distribution of deaths assumed earlier leads to ${}_na_x = n/2$, but this is not acceptable for careful work when the age interval n is as wide as 5 years.)

The result (1.1.6) may incidentally be applied to compare the increases in longevity attributable to different portions of the life span. The United States male $\mathring{e}_1$ went up from 60.7 years in the three years about 1930 to 67.8 in 1964, a gain of 7.1 years. This gain consists of three elements:

1) The average years lived beyond 1 year by those of the synthetic cohort dying between age 1 and age 70 in 1964 was, from (1.1.6),

$$ {}_{69}a_1 = \frac{{}_{69}L_1 - 69l_{70}}{l_1 - l_{70}} = 54.4 \text{ years} , $$

as compared with 48.0 years in 1930, an improvement of 6.4 years.
2) The improvement in $\mathring{e}_{70}$, the number of years lived by men dying above age 70, was 1.3 years, to 10.5 from 9.2.
3) Finally, more men survived to age 70; l_{70}/l_1 was 0.532 in 1964 and 0.421 in 1930.

The reader may examine in what sense these three elements account for the overall gain of 7.1 years in $\mathring{e}_1$, using the identity

$$ l_1\mathring{e}_1 = (l_1 - l_{70})\,{}_{69}a_1 + l_{70}\mathring{e}_{70} + 69l_{70} , $$

along with Table 1.3 and the following items from the 1929–31 life table:

$$ l_1 = 92{,}775 ; \qquad l_{70} = 39{,}102 ; \qquad T_1 = 5{,}632{,}457 ; \qquad T_{70} = 359{,}405 . $$

Alternatively we can introduce ${}_na_x$ in terms of the continuous model. The number of individuals in the stationary population who die between ages $x + t$ and $x + t + dt$ $(t \le n)$ is $l(x + t)\mu(x + t)\,dt$. Each of these has lived t years in the interval x to $x + n$; hence the average number of years ${}_na_x$ lived in the interval by those who die in it is the ratio

$$ {}_na_x = \frac{\int_0^n tl(x + t)\mu(x + t)\,dt}{\int_0^n l(x + t)\mu(x + t)\,dt} , \qquad n > 0 , \tag{1.1.7} $$

a mean value which is the same as the expression for $\mathring{e}_x$ in (1.1.3) except that the upper limit of the integrals is now more general. The denominator of (1.1.7) is ${}_nd_x$. The numerator may be integrated by parts as in (1.1.4) to give

$$ \begin{aligned} -\int_{t=0}^{t=n} t\,dl(x + t) &= -[tl(x + t)]_{t=0}^{n} + \int_0^n l(x + t)\,dt \\ &= -nl_{x+n} + {}_nL_x . \end{aligned} \tag{1.1.8} $$

Entering the rightmost expression of (1.1.8) in place of the numerator of (1.1.7) and ${}_nd_x$ in place of its denominator gives (1.1.6) once again.

The ratio in the life table corresponding to observed ${}_nM_x$ is ${}_nd_x/{}_nL_x$. In recognition of the fact that the distribution within the age group is not the same for the life table as for the observed population (especially where mortality is changing rapidly from age to age and the observed population is far from stationary), a notational distinction is made: ${}_nm_x$ is written for ${}_nd_x/{}_nL_x$, the age-specific rate in the life table, while ${}_nM_x$ stands for ${}_nD_x/{}_nK_x$, the corresponding ratio from the observations. A commonly used approximation, especially when the age interval n is 1 year or less, is to assume the equality of ${}_nm_x$ and ${}_nM_x$. In Section 1.2 we will derive an iterative process for making a life table which avoids this assumption. In Section 10.4 graduation into intervals of 0.2 of a year makes the assumption innocuous.

The average ${}_na_x$ serves as a means of proceeding from the life table age-specific death rate ${}_nm_x = {}_nd_x/{}_nL_x$, the deaths divided by the number living, to the probability of dying during the subsequent n years for a person aged x. Writing $l_{x+n} = l_x - {}_nd_x$ in (1.1.6), the reader may establish that as a pure consequence of the definitions (Chiang, 1960),

$$ {}_nq_x = \frac{n\,{}_nm_x}{1 + (n - {}_na_x)\,{}_nm_x} . \qquad (1.1.9) $$

Since the value of ${}_nq_x$ is not very sensitive to ${}_na_x$, it is possible to guess the a's (for example, set ${}_na_x = n/2$) to make a first draft of the life table. A better approximation to ${}_na_x$ can then be obtained from the draft ${}_nd_x$, using a formula derived from (1.1.7), and these a's may be entered in (1.1.9) for an improved set of ${}_nq_x$. Monroe Sirken (1964) has suggested that the a's may be found from a reference life table worked out in single years of age.

From ${}_nq_x$ calculated by (1.1.9) with the observed ${}_nM_x$ in place of ${}_nm_x$, or other means, and an arbitrary l_0, usually 100,000, the life table is constructed by working down the column of l's and d's, applying the recurrence equations

$$ {}_nd_x = l_x\,{}_nq_x , \qquad l_{x+n} = l_x - {}_nd_x . \qquad (1.1.10) $$

The procedure for going from the observed age-specfic death rates ${}_nM_x$ to the ${}_nm_x$ and ${}_nq_x$ is the first of two parts of making a life table in which a choice must be made among a number of options. The second point of choice is in the integration of $l(x)$ over the interval from x to $x + n$ to find ${}_nL_x$:

$$ \int_0^n l(x + t)\,dt = {}_nL_x . $$

A variety of formulas are available, of which the most popular is obtained by the integration from x to $x + n$ of a third-degree curve through four values, $l_{x-n}, l_x, l_{x+n}, l_{x+2n}$:

$$ \begin{aligned} {}_nL_x &= n/2\cdot(l_x + l_{x+n}) + n/24\cdot({}_nd_{x+n} - {}_nd_{x-n}) , \\ &= 13n/24\cdot(l_x + l_{x+n}) - n/24\cdot(l_{x-n} + l_{x+2n}) , \end{aligned} \qquad (1.1.11) $$

derivable by the method of Chapter 10, a special case being (10.2.14).

Table 1.3 Iterative life table, obtained by successive adjustment of ${}_nq_x$, for United States males, 1964*

AGE x	${}_nK_x$ 000's	${}_nD_x$	${}_nq_x$	ℓ_x	${}_nd_x$	${}_nL_x$
0	2,069	57,368	0.027146	100,000	2,715	97,902
1	8,486	8,881	0.004173	97,285	406	387,958
5	10,341	5,314	0.002561	96,879	248	483,777
10	9,371	4,926	0.002644	96,631	256	482,599
15	8,188	10,792	0.006623	96,376	638	480,414
20	6,279	11,614	0.009226	95,737	883	476,523
25	5,432	9,799	0.008984	94,854	852	472,167
30	5,434	11,754	0.010760	94,002	1,011	467,593
35	5,916	17,804	0.014942	92,991	1,389	461,709
40	6,007	28,027	0.023089	91,601	2,115	453,112
45	5,517	41,098	0.036681	89,486	3,282	439,839
50	5,084	61,328	0.058784	86,204	5,067	419,189
55	4,358	81,835	0.090098	81,136	7,310	388,369
60	3,653	102,084	0.131311	73,826	9,694	345,946
65	2,857	121,225	0.192694	64,132	12,358	290,536
70	2,289	135,642	0.258748	51,774	13,396	225,565
75	1,520	126,801	0.345253	38,378	13,250	158,449
80	791	97,707	0.473113	25,128	11,888	95,915
85	398	83,779	1.000000	13,239	13,239	62,468
TOT.	93,990	1,017,778				

AGE x	${}_nm_x$	${}_na_x$	T_x	${}_nr_x$	$\mathring{e}_x$	${}_nM'_x = {}_nM_x = {}_nD_x/{}_nK_x$
0	0.027727	0.227	6,690,031	0.000	66.900	0.027727
1	0.001047	1.086	6,592,130	0.000	67.761	0.001047
5	0.000513	2.500	6,204,171	0.011	64.040	0.000514
10	0.000529	2.818	5,720,394	0.023	59.198	0.000526
15	0.001329	2.705	5,237,796	0.039	54.348	0.001318
20	0.001854	2.550	4,757,382	0.039	49.692	0.001850
25	0.001805	2.531	4,280,859	0.013	45.131	0.001804
30	0.002163	2.611	3,808,692	0.000	40.517	0.002163
35	0.003009	2.666	3,341,098	0.000	35.929	0.003009
40	0.004668	2.686	2,879,389	0.002	31.434	0.004666
45	0.007463	2.687	2,426,277	0.009	27.113	0.007449
50	0.012089	2.666	1,986,438	0.011	23.044	0.012063
55	0.018823	2.632	1,567,249	0.014	19.316	0.018778
60	0.028022	2.608	1,178,880	0.016	15.968	0.027945
65	0.042535	2.562	832,933	0.016	12.988	0.042431
70	0.059391	2.514	542,397	0.016	10.476	0.059258
75	0.083623	2.476	316,833	0.016	8.256	0.083422
80	0.123945	2.500	158,384	0.016	6.303	0.123523
85	0.211938	4.718	62,468	0.016	4.718	0.210500

* Programmed by Wilhelm Flieger on data of National Center for Health Statistics.

The remainder of the life table follows from the definitions

$$T_x = {}_nL_x + {}_nL_{x+n} + \cdots ; \qquad \mathring{e}_x = T_x/l_x ; \qquad {}_np_x = 1 - {}_nq_x .$$

An illustration showing all the columns mentioned except ${}_np_x$ is given as Table 1.3, a more detailed exposition of the method of calculation used being provided in Section 1.2. At this point the reader may wish to verify on a desk calculator that the relations (1.1.4), (1.1.6), (1.1.9), (1.1.10), and (1.1.11) hold from ages 15 onward in Table 1.3, and that ${}_5d_x = l_x\,{}_5q_x$ and ${}_5m_x = {}_5d_x/{}_5L_x$. (The verification is limited by rounding in the printout, especially for ${}_na_x$ at ages of low ${}_nd_x$.)

Applications

If the life table is not the best way of comparing the mortality of populations, it does serve to calculate a variety of probabilities and expectations for individual and group lives. To find, on the given mortality, the chance of X who is x years of age still being alive at the end of m years, and Y who is y being alive at the end of n years, it is necessary only to multiply l_{x+m}/l_x by l_{y+n}/l_y, provided the probabilities for the two individuals are independent, which they will not be if X and Y go on a submarine trip together. No additional difficulty is created if X and Y belong to groups of recognizably different mortality, say male and female, and l^*_{x+m}/l^*_x is taken from one life table, l_{y+n}/l_y from another. An asterisk in the upper right will distinguish male survivorship. Then to find the expected married life together of a couple of which the man is now x years of age and the woman y years, $x \geq y$, we note that the probability of the couple both being alive between t and $t + dt$ years from now is

$$\left[\frac{l^*(x+t)}{l^*(x)}\right]\left[\frac{l(y+t)}{l(y)}\right],$$

and in this time they will have dt years together; the expected value of their years together is thus

$$\int_0^{\omega-x} \frac{l^*(x+t)l(y+t)}{l^*(x)l(y)}\,dt ,$$

neglecting the possibility of separation or divorce.

Joint probabilities can account for a demographic phenomenon such as the present large excess of widows over widowers in the older population. Suppose that at the time when the persons now 65 were marrying, the groom was five years older than his bride. The chance that a bride of 20 and a groom of 25 will still be alive 40 years later is

$$\left[\frac{l_{60}}{l_{20}}\right]\left[\frac{l^*_{65}}{l^*_{25}}\right],$$

the first factor being taken from a female table, the second from a male table.

For the United States, 1964, these were

$$\left[\frac{84{,}572}{96{,}955}\right]\left[\frac{64{,}132}{94{,}854}\right] = 0.5898 .$$

The chance that the wife is alive and the husband dead is

$$\left[\frac{l_{60}}{l_{20}}\right]\left[1 - \frac{l^*_{65}}{l^*_{25}}\right] = 0.2825 ,$$

and that the husband is alive and the wife dead,

$$\left[1 - \frac{l_{60}}{l_{20}}\right]\left[\frac{l^*_{65}}{l^*_{25}}\right] = 0.0864 .$$

The percentages of married couples, widows, and widowers among the living on these assumptions would be 62%, 29%, and 9%, respectively. In fact, the numbers of the three categories in the population as of March 1964 were 75%, 21%, and 4% (roughly estimated for ages 55–64 years from data in *Statistical Abstract*, 1965, p. 31). Some of the difference is due to our taking typical ages rather than an age distribution, some to the use of 1964 period mortality instead of that of the relevant cohorts, some to migration, but probably most to remarriage. The reader may examine the relation of orphanhood to demographic factors and in particular to the cohort life table (Lotka, 1931c).

The life table forms the basis of actuarial science. Actuaries must include a factor in $v = 1/(1 + i)$, i being the annual rate of interest and v the present value of a payment of unity one year from now at rate of interest i. The present discounted value of one dollar payable in t years is v^t dollars. If one dollar a year hence is now worth v dollars, then one dollar a year hence to a man now aged x, if he is still alive, is worth $v(l_{x+1}/l_x)$ dollars, an expected value. A payment of one dollar if he dies between $x + t$ and $x + t + dt$ is now worth (Jordan, 1952, p. 67)

$$\frac{1}{l_x} v^t l(x + t)\mu(x + t)\, dt \quad \text{dollars} .$$

Hence a single life insurance on a person of age x is worth

$$\bar{A}_x = \frac{1}{l_x}\int_0^{\omega - x} v^t l(x + t)\mu(x + t)\, dt$$

dollars per dollar of insurance; a continuous annuity at the rate of one dollar per year is worth

$$\bar{a}_x = \frac{1}{l_x}\int_0^{\omega - x} v^t l(x + t)\, dt \quad \text{dollars} ;$$

the annual premium for an insurance of K dollars payable at death must be K times the first of these divided by the second, or

$$P_x = \frac{K\bar{A}_x}{\bar{a}_x} = \frac{K\int_0^{\omega-x} v^t l(x+t)\mu(x+t)\,dt}{\int_0^{\omega-x} v^t l(x+t)\,dt} \text{ dollars}\,.$$

Far more complicated questions can be answered in terms of the life table. An annuity of K dollars per year payable to a couple of ages x and y while they are both alive is valued at

$$\bar{a}_{xy} = \frac{K\int_0^{\omega-x} v^t l^*(x+t)l(y+t)\,dt}{l^*(x)l(y)}\,, \quad x \geq y\,.$$

A life insurance of K dollars payable to a wife now aged y on the death of her husband now aged x has a present value

$$\frac{K\int_0^{\omega-x} v^t l^*(x+t)\mu^*(x+t)l(y+t)\,dt}{l^*(x)l(y)}\,, \quad x \geq y\,.$$

If it were to be payable only while her son, now aged z, is a minor, the integrand would have a further factor, $l^*(z+t)/l^*(z)$, and the upper limit of the integral would be not $\omega - x$ but $21 - z$. Actuarial textbooks contain many other examples (Spurgeon, 1932).

The most common demographic application of the life table is for *population projection*: the calculation of the expected value of the number of persons alive at future dates, given the number now alive and age-specific mortality. The expected value of the number of survivors at the end of t years among $k(x)\,dx$ persons of age x to $x + dx$ now alive is

$$k(x)\frac{l(x+t)}{l(x)}\,dx\,.$$

In practice we observe not $k(x)\,dx$, the number between ages x and $x + dx$, but the finite

$${}_nK_x^{(0)} = \int_0^n k(x+v)\,dv\,,$$

the number between ages x and $x + n$, and among these,

$${}_nK_{x+t}^{(t)} = \int_0^n k(x+v)\frac{l(x+t+v)}{l(x+v)}\,dv \tag{1.1.12}$$

will be alive at the end of t years. A commonly used approximation to (1.1.12) is

$${}_nK_{x+t}^{(t)} = {}_nK_x^{(0)}\frac{{}_nL_{x+t}}{{}_nL_x}\,. \tag{1.1.13}$$

A closer approximation to the survival factor is given by (11.1.15) through (11.1.18).

To correspond to the fact that such projections are customarily made in intervals of time which are the same length as those of age, the projected, or estimated, or expected value of the population initially x to $x + n$ years of age in n years is (1.1.13) with t replaced by n. Equation (1.1.13) will reappear frequently from Chapter 2 onward. To conform to the context in which it is applied, n may be specialized to 5 and omitted. The unit of age will continue to be one year, but that of time will be 5 years, so that (1.1.13) will be

$$K_{x+5}^{(1)} = K_x^{(0)} \cdot (L_{x+5}/L_x) \, . \tag{1.1.14}$$

While the language of this chapter has been that of human populations, nothing in the logic of the life table restricts it to these. Pearl, Park, and Miner (1941) made laboratory observations to produce life tables for the flour beetle, *tribolium confusum*, and Deevey (1947) applied the technique to data obtained in field observation.

1.2. A LIFE TABLE THAT ITERATES TO THE DATA

The concepts presented above facilitate the calculation of a life table that iterates to the data, so that the completed life table reproduces exactly the age-specific mortality rates which are its basis. This does not mean that the age-specific death rates, ${}_nd_x/{}_nL_x = {}_nm_x$, of the life table will be the same as ${}_nD_x/{}_nK_x = {}_nM_x$ of the population; allowance must be made for the different distribution of population and deaths within age groups, which depends on r, the rate of population increase. We will approximate by supposing that within a given age group, at age x the population is proportional to

$$k(x) = e^{-rx}l(x) \, ; \tag{1.2.1}$$

the rationale of this will appear in Chapter 3 and subsequently in the discussion of stable population theory. For the present we describe an age distribution $e^{-rx}l(x)$, where r may be different from one five-year age interval to another, as *stable in sections*.

Our task is to create from the life table sectionally stable population and deaths. These will incorporate an r dependent on age, designated ${}_nr_x$. In each iterate of the life table we will obtain an ${}_nM'_x$ comparable with observed ${}_nM_x$, and use the ratio ${}_nM_x/{}_nM'_x$ to adjust the ${}_nq_x$. From the adjusted value, say ${}_nq_x^*$, the other columns are calculated, a new ${}_nM'_x$ is worked out, and ${}_nq_x^*$ is in its turn adjusted.

As ${}_5M'_x$ is the ratio of deaths ${}_5D'_x$ to population ${}_5K'_x$ (both on the assumption of sectional stability), we need to define these in a way that will be calculable from any draft of the life table. If the stable population is $k(x)\,dx = e^{-rx}l(x)\,dx$ between ages x and $x + dx$, then we need the integral

$${}_5K'_x = \int_0^5 k(x + t)\,dt = \int_0^5 e^{-r(x+t)}l(x + t)\,dt \, . \tag{1.2.2}$$

For the deaths we need a continuous curve corresponding to $l(x)$, which might be represented as $l(x)\mu(x)$, such that

$$ {}_5d_x = \int_0^5 l(x+t)\mu(x+t)\,dt \,. $$

In fact $l(x)\mu(x)$ is simply $-(dl(x)/dx)$ from (1.1.1). To represent ${}_5D'_x$, the deaths in a population growing at rate r, we write

$$ {}_5D'_x = \int_0^5 e^{-r(x+t)} l(x+t)\mu(x+t)\,dt = -\int_0^5 e^{-r(x+t)}\,dl(x+t) \,. $$

Fortunately this latter may be integrated by parts to provide

$$ {}_5D'_x = e^{-rx} l_x - e^{-r(x+5)} l_{x+5} - r\int_0^5 e^{-r(x+t)} l(x+t)\,dt \,, \tag{1.2.3} $$

in which the only integral is the same ${}_5K'_x$ of (1.2.2).

Our age-specific rate of ${}_5M'_x$ as worked out from the life table for an increasing population being

$$ {}_5M'_x = {}_5D'_x/{}_5K'_x \,, $$

we enter ${}_5D'_x$ from (1.2.3) and ${}_5K'_x$ from (1.2.2) to find the basic result

$$ {}_5M'_x = \frac{{}_5D'_x}{{}_5K'_x} = \frac{e^{-rx} l_x - e^{-r(x+5)} l_{x+5}}{\int_0^5 e^{-r(x+t)} l(x+t)\,dt} - r \,. \tag{1.2.4} $$

Note that no approximations are required to reach (1.2.4) once we have r and the l_x of the previous iteration. An approximation will of course enter for the integral ${}_5K'_x$ of (1.2.4). The agreement of the life table with the data is mediated only by how we ascertain this integral, and different formulas for the integral will produce different life tables.

An explicit form of (1.2.4), not containing the integral sign, may be shown for a cubic through k_{x-5}, k_x, k_{x+5}, and k_{x+10}. The approximate integral (1.1.11), used with $e^{-rx} l_x$ written for l_x and 5 for n, gives ${}_5K'_x$. For this special case (1.2.4) becomes, after the e^{-rx} are canceled out,

$$ {}_5M'_x = \frac{l_x - e^{-5r} l_{x+5}}{\frac{65}{24}(l_x + e^{-5r} l_{x+5}) - \frac{5}{24}(e^{-10r} l_{x+10} + e^{5r} l_{x-5})} - r \,. \tag{1.2.5} $$

The object has been to make each draft of the life table produce an ${}_nM'_x$ which is directly comparable with the ${}_nM_x$ of the data. This permits a correction of the life table ${}_nq_x$ to

$$ {}_nq^*_x = {}_nq_x({}_nM_x/{}_nM'_x) \,. \tag{1.2.6} $$

The corrected ${}_nq^*_x$ results from reducing (increasing) ${}_nq_x$ in proportion as the death rates ${}_nM'_x$ of the first draft have proved too high (low). The iterations continue until the ${}_nM'_x$ of the table is the same as the ${}_nM_x$ of the data to the six decimal places used; since the highest ages take longest to converge, it suffices to test on the age group 75 through 79.

The result is invariant with respect to the starting values. In one experiment the starting values ${}_5q_x = 5\,{}_5M_x$ were tried, and 9 iterations resulted in ${}_5M'_{75} - {}_5M_{75} < 10^{-6}$; with the starting value ${}_5q_x = 0.1$ for all x, 11 iterations were required to meet the same criterion of convergence. Evidently we need not know how to *make* a life table; it suffices to know how to *improve* one.

One other point remains to be settled: the r or rate of increase that is to be used. The options include a single value, for example the present rate of increase of the population as a whole, or rates of increase which differ from one section of the table to another. The latter is favored by the consideration that an age distribution such as that of the contemporary United States reflects very different birth rates in the cohorts now age 30 and those 10 or 70. Why not then allow the age distribution, which is part of the data required in any case, to determine the r, and to determine it "locally" for each age of the table? The calculation is readily made by an extension of the assumption of stability that led to (1.2.2); if steady increase is assumed through three successive 5-year age groups, and if ${}_5K_x$ is the number in the population from age x to $x + 5$, and A is a suitable constant, then approximately

$$ {}_5K_{x-5} = Ae^{-(x-2.5)r}\,{}_5L_{x-5}\,, \qquad {}_5K_{x+5} = Ae^{-(x+7.5)r}\,{}_5L_{x+5}\,, $$

and therefore by division and the taking of natural logarithms, we obtain

$$ {}_5r_x = (0.1)\ln \frac{{}_5K_{x-5}/{}_5L_{x-5}}{{}_5K_{x+5}/{}_5L_{x+5}}\,. \tag{1.2.7} $$

In practice, negative ${}_5r_x$ has been replaced by zero, and the ${}_5r_x$ for ages 60 and over have been averaged. The e^{-10r} required for (1.2.5) is

$$ e^{-10r} = \frac{{}_5K_{x+5}/{}_5L_{x+5}}{{}_5K_{x-5}/{}_5L_{x-5}}\,; $$

e^{-5r} is the square root of this, and e^{5r} the reciprocal of e^{-5r}.

As an example of the procedure consider the calculation of ${}_5M'_{25}$ in the iteration shown in Table 1.3. From the column of ${}_5K_x$ and ${}_5L_x$ for $x = 20$ and $x = 30$ we establish

$$ e^{-10r} = \frac{5434/467{,}593}{6279/476{,}523} = 0.881952\,; $$

the square root of this is $e^{-5r} = 0.939123$; the reciprocal of the latter is $e^{5r} = 1.064823$. A table of logarithms* and any of the above exponentials provides $r = 0.0125617$. Entering these numbers in (1.2.5) along with l_{20}, l_{25}, l_{30}, l_{35} from Table 1.3 gives ${}_5M'_{25} = 0.0143656 - 0.0125617 = 0.0018039$, as against ${}_5M'_{25} = 0.001804$ in the table, which agrees with ${}_5M_{25} = {}_nD_{25}/{}_nK_{25}$.

---

* Exponentials sufficient to provide six-place logarithms are given in the appendix; an example of their use appears in Table 5.3.

Once convergence has been attained, the remaining columns can be worked out, in our example ${}_nm_x$, T_x, and $\mathring{e}_x = T_x/l_x$.

Table 1.3 for United States males in 1964 starts with the observed population and deaths, no other information than that given in the first two columns being used. The ${}_nM'_x$ at the end of the ta' 'e, obtained from the ${}_nr_x$, ${}_nd_x$, and ${}_nL_x$ of the final iteration, agrees to six decimal places with the ${}_nM_x$ obtained by dividing ${}_nD_x$ by ${}_nK_x$. With the help of a desk calculator the reader has verified that ${}_5d_x = l_x\,{}_5q_x$; ${}_5m_x = {}_5d_x/{}_5L_x$; $\mathring{e}_x = T_x/l_x$; now he may examine numerically the relations (1.2.5) and (1.2.7). The table to which the iterative process converges is like a seamless web; the complex of relationships discussed in this chapter all hold simultaneously. The iteration is indispensable; any single cycle of calculation would permit one or more of the relations to hold only approximately.

Minor variations, not discussed in the preceding statement, are possible in the construction of an iterative life table. To see what they amount to numerically, four young demographers were asked to make a life table for United States males, 1963, more or less independently; their values for three of the $\mathring{e}_x$ are:

	$\mathring{e}_0$	$\mathring{e}_{10}$	$\mathring{e}_{30}$
Wilhelm Flieger	66.729	59.089	40.332
James Mulherin	66.767	59.098	40.339
Christina Olsen	66.753	59.094	40.338
Peter Uhlenberg	66.754	59.099	40.342

For $\mathring{e}_0$ the values are in a range of 0.04; for $\mathring{e}_{10}$ and $\mathring{e}_{30}$ of 0.010.

Given a set of age-specific death rates, the life table described above agrees with them, the agreement being mediated only by the choice of integration procedure for ${}_nL_x$ and the value of r taken to approximate the increase of the population from cohort to cohort, and special procedures at the youngest and oldest ages. These choices are apparently unavoidable, and experiment shows that within a considerable range they have little influence.

Even using r equal to zero throughout does not greatly alter the result. The interested reader may show that the effect on ${}_5M'_x$ of a change Δr in r is approximately

$$\Delta_5M'_x = -\frac{5\,{}_5m_x}{24}\left(\frac{{}_5d_{x+5} - {}_5d_{x-5}}{{}_5d_x} + \frac{{}_5L_{x-5} - {}_5L_{x+5}}{{}_5L_x}\right)\Delta r\,.$$

Use this result with Table 1.3 to show that putting $r = 0$ at age 45 instead of the 0.009 actually used would raise ${}_5M'_{45}$ by 0.000015, and compare with the difference of tabulated values ${}_5m_{45} - {}_5M'_{45} = 0.000014$.

More serious is the problem of *which* data the life table is to agree with, when more than one set is available. For most ages in most countries, the data consist exclusively of a population counted or calculated to midyear, and deaths over a one-, three-, or five-year period around that midyear point. But at the youngest ages, birth statistics are an alternative source on exposure. If we have the births (occurring in part before the period which the deaths cover) to which deaths under one year of age are related, then q_0 is obtained directly by the division of deaths by such births. (Refer to the parallelogram $ABGC$ in Fig. 1.1.) If the births are known or calculable to higher accuracy than the population under one year of age at midyear, which is commonly understated in censuses, they should be taken into account. United States male deaths under one year of age in 1964 were 57,368, and in 1965 were 53,437; 1964 registered births were 2,060,000. If the separation factor f_0^z is 0.2, so that 0.2 of the deaths under one year were to births of the preceding year, then the probability of dying in the first year of life for a child born in 1964 is

$$q_0 = \frac{(57{,}368)(0.8) + (53{,}437)(0.2)}{2{,}060{,}000} = 0.02747 \,,$$

or 1.2% above the q_0 of Table 1.3. An alternative calculation, which corresponds to the time period for deaths of calendar year 1964 used in Table 1.3, is to take births of 1963 and 1964 and find

$$q_0 = \frac{57{,}368}{(2{,}102{,}000)(0.2) + (2{,}060{,}000)(0.8)} = 0.02774 \,,$$

or 2.7% higher than the q_0 of Table 1.3. If the supposition $f_0^z = 0$ can be tolerated, then

$$q_0 = \frac{57{,}368}{2{,}060{,}000} = 0.2785 \,,$$

which is an overstatement of mortality insofar as births were falling in the period covered.

Those with detailed knowledge of United States census and vital statistics may be able to say which q_0 is closest to the truth among these and the $q_0 = 0.027146$ of Table 1.3. (See Section 10.4.)

1.3. LEVELS OF DISCOURSE

This chapter has been written from a demographic viewpoint, and as such I trust it appears reasonably homogeneous and consistent; yet from a statistical viewpoint, it shifts among several levels of discourse. In some places it refers to real data, in others to hypothetical models which may be capable of representing data only more or less closely. It argues in terms of probabilities for individuals, but wherever a number of individuals are exposed, it changes to expected values. Most awkward of all from a statistical viewpoint, it makes no distinction between samples and the populations from which these are drawn, using the word "population" for both just as long as a plurality of individuals is involved. (The last ambiguity will cause special difficulty when we do talk about sampling, in

Chapter 15.) This book has some of its roots in actuarial science, whose classical theory of life contingencies was based on expected values. Today, however, under the heading of individual and collective risk theory, modern probability is making important headway in actuarial circles. It is still true that the sheer mathematical difficulties have caused demographers, including this writer, to close their eyes to the confusion of levels whose existence is here acknowledged. In later chapters some attempts will be made to meet these difficulties; the last four chapters of the book are specifically concerned with probability distributions.

Part II

DISCRETE ANALYSIS FOR ONE SEX

CHAPTER 2

THE BASIC SET OF RECURRENCE EQUATIONS

2.1. POPULATION PROJECTION

A population projection, introduced in Chapter 1, is the calculation of the expected number of persons, age by age for each sex, at points in time subsequent to a census or other starting point. The set of birth and death rates used may be those of some past period, or they may be an extrapolation from the past; the extrapolation may follow a mathematically specified method, or it may be intuitive. This and the following chapter will treat projection with the rates of a period of observation taken as fixed. The object is to understand the past rather than to predict the future; apparently the way to think effectively about an observed set of birth and death rates is to ask what it would lead to if continued.

A census of the United States enumerated in mid-1964 would have shown about 5,614,000 ($= {}_5K_{25}$) women aged 25 to 29 at last birthday; the life table constructed on deaths and population for 1964 gives the probability of a woman 25 to 29 living five years as

$$\frac{{}_5L_{30}}{{}_5L_{25}} = \frac{479{,}486}{482{,}030} = 0.99472$$

(Table 2.1). The product of the probability of surviving and the 1964 number alive is the expected number of women 30–34 in 1969,

$$\begin{aligned}\frac{{}_5L_{30}}{{}_5L_{25}}\,{}_5K_{25}^{(0)} &= (0.99472)(5{,}614{,}000)\\ &= 5{,}584{,}000\\ &= {}_5K_{30}^{(1)}\,,\end{aligned}$$

assuming that the territory remains the same and is closed to migration, that mortality is unchanged from 1964, and using the approximation of (1.1.13) of Chapter 1. Here as elsewhere, a superscript will be placed on the upper right to signify the point in time to which the symbol refers, the lower limit of the age interval will be written on the lower right, and the length of the age interval on the lower left. Thus ${}_nK_x^{(t)}$ is the population at time t whose ages are between x and $x + n$. In what follows below, $n = 5$ and will be omitted.

Among those alive at $t = 0$, survivors to $t = 1$ are calculated as

$$\begin{aligned} \frac{L_5}{L_0} K_0^{(0)} &= K_5^{(1)} , \\ \frac{L_{10}}{L_5} K_5^{(0)} &= K_{10}^{(1)} , \\ &\vdots \\ \frac{L_{85}}{L_{80}} K_{80}^{(0)} &= K_{85}^{(1)} , \end{aligned} \qquad (2.1.1)$$

using a calendar in which the starting point is time 0 (in place of 1964), and the unit of time is five years.

The typical age interval of the set (2.1.1) is from x at last birthday to $x + 4$, where x is a multiple of 5; the Eq. (2.1.1) may be written

$$(L_{x+5}/L_x)K_x^{(0)} = K_{x+5}^{(1)} , \qquad x = 0, 5, \ldots, \omega - 5 , \qquad (2.1.2)$$

ω being the maximum possible age taken as a multiple of 5. Evidently the same operation of multiplying by an expected proportion surviving will on the same assumptions give the expected number alive 10 years after the starting date:

$$\frac{L_{x+10}}{L_{x+5}} K_{x+5}^{(1)} = \frac{L_{x+10}}{L_x} K_x^{(0)} = K_{x+10}^{(2)} ,$$

and similarly for later points of time.

This projects the population already alive at the time zero, and to it must be added an allowance for births subsequent to that date. We will suppose that age-specific birth rates F_x are obtained by observing the number of births to mothers x to $x + 4$ years of age at last birthday and dividing this by the average number of women in the same age group over the period of observation. For the United States in 1964, 1,007,362 births were registered to women 25–29 (Table 2.1). To follow the female population, the number of births of girl babies is required, and we will assume that the fraction female is the same for all ages of mother—an assumption which is incorrect but does not greatly affect the calculation (see Tables 5.2 and 5.3). The ratio of female to total births for 1964 was

$$\frac{1{,}967{,}328}{4{,}027{,}490} = 0.488475 ,$$

and hence female births for women 25–29 are estimated at

$$1{,}007{,}362 \times 0.488475 = 492{,}071 .$$

The number of women 25–29 living in mid-1964 being taken as the same 5,614,000 mentioned above, the age-specific female birth rate was

$$F_{25} = \frac{492{,}071}{5{,}614{,}000} = 0.08765 .$$

Table 2.1 Information used in calculating the projection matrix **M**, upper left 10 × 10 portion of **L** in (2.1.9), for United States females, 1964

x	$_5L_x$	$_5K_x/1000$ POPULATION		$_5B_x$ BIRTHS
0	488,970	10,136		0
5	487,312	10,006		0
10	486,502	9,065		7,816
15	485,484	8,045		585,710
20	483,940	6,546		1,439,486
25	482,030	5,614		1,007,362
30	479,486	5,632		585,006
35	475,789	6,193		309,814
40	470,394	6,345		87,626
45	462,418	5,796		4,670
			MALE	2,060,162
			FEMALE	1,967,328
			TOTAL	4,027,490

x	$F_x = \frac{_5B_x}{_5K_x}\, 0.488475$	$_5\phi_x = \frac{_5L_x\, F_x}{\ell_0}$	$\frac{_5\phi_x + {_5\phi_{x+5}}}{2}$
5			0.00102
10	0.00042	0.00205	0.08735
15	0.03556	0.17265	0.34624
20	0.10742	0.51983	0.47117
25	0.08765	0.42250	0.33289
30	0.05074	0.24328	0.17978
35	0.02444	0.11627	0.07400
40	0.00675	0.03173	0.01678
45	0.00039	0.00182	0.00091
	TOTAL	1.51014 = R_0	1.51014

The ratio F_x is to be multiplied (Barclay, 1958, p. 235) by the arithmetic mean of the initial and final population of ages x to $x + 4$ taken from (2.1.1),

$$\frac{K_x^{(0)} + K_x^{(1)}}{2} = \frac{1}{2}\left(K_x^{(0)} + \frac{L_x}{L_{x-5}} K_{x-5}^{(0)}\right), \tag{2.1.3}$$

and since this number is exposed for 5 years, we multiply also by 5. The women aged x to $x + 4$ together with those $x + 5$ to $x + 9$ at last birthday will make a contribution to the number of births during the 5-year time period from 0 to 1 of

$$\frac{5}{2}\{K_x^{(0)} + K_x^{(1)}\}F_x + \frac{5}{2}\{K_{x+5}^{(0)} + K_{x+5}^{(1)}\}F_{x+5}\,. \tag{2.1.4}$$

Adding through all ages and rearranging somewhat gives

$$\frac{5}{2}\sum_{\alpha-5}^{\beta-5}\left(F_x + \frac{L_{x+5}}{L_x} F_{x+5}\right) K_x^{(0)}, \tag{2.1.5}$$

where α is the youngest age of childbearing and β the oldest, both assumed to be multiples of 5. This will serve to calculate births in the five-year interval of age and time, on the assumption of fixed vital rates, and pending an improved approximation to be introduced in Chapter 11.

The term in parentheses in (2.1.5) may be interpreted as a crude but not unreasonable approximation to the number of births expected in the 5-year period by a woman initially x to $x + 4$ at last birthday; it assigns her an exposure at the rate F_x of her initial age group for the first half of the time period, and if she survives 5 years she is taken as exposed at the rate for the next higher age group, F_{x+5}, for the other half of the period.

Births are not quite what we want, however; the projection requires expected population surviving at the end of the interval, for which (2.1.5) must be multiplied by a survivorship factor. If a child is born at moment t $(0 \le t \le 1)$, then the probability that she will live to the end of the interval, which is to say to age $x = 5(1 - t)$, is $l(x)/l_0 = l(5 - 5t)/l_0$. Summing this through the five-year interval of time and age, as though births are uniformly distributed in time within the five years, gives the proportion of survivors among children born throughout the interval:

$$\frac{\int_0^1 l(5 - 5t)\,dt}{l_0} = \frac{\int_0^5 l(x)\,dx}{5l_0} = \frac{{}_5L_0}{5l_0}\,. \tag{2.1.6}$$

Multiplying (2.1.5) by (2.1.6) gives $K_0^{(1)}$, which was the term needed to complete the population projection (2.1.1).

The Difference Equations and Their Matrix Presentation

The conditions of birth and death set up in the preceding paragraphs enable us to show the relation between the population at time $t + 1$ and that at time t

(where t is in units of 5 years) as a set of linear, first-order, homogeneous difference equations with constant coefficients:

$$
\begin{aligned}
&\frac{L_0}{2l_0}[\{K_{15}^{(t)} + K_{15}^{(t+1)}\}F_{15} + \{K_{20}^{(t)} + K_{20}^{(t+1)}\}F_{20} + \cdots \\
&\qquad\qquad + \{K_{40}^{(t)} + K_{40}^{(t+1)}\}F_{40}] = K_0^{(t+1)}\,, \\
&\left(\frac{L_5}{L_0}\right) K_0^{(t)} = K_5^{(t+1)}\,, \\
&\quad\vdots \\
&\left(\frac{L_{85}}{L_{80}}\right) K_{80}^{(t)} = K_{85}^{(t+1)}\,,
\end{aligned}
\tag{2.1.7}
$$

where for concreteness the childbearing span is taken as $\alpha = 15$ to $\beta = 45$. (Modification of (2.1.7) for a different age span either of reproduction or of life presents no difficulty.) In the first equation of (2.1.7) the age-specific fertility rates F_{15}, etc., are applied to the number of woman-years of exposure over the period, $\frac{5}{2}\{K_{15}^{(t)} + K_{15}^{(t+1)}\}$, etc.; the factor allowing for the children born during 5 years to survive to the end of the period is $L_0/5l_0$.

We can use the equations of (2.1.7) below the first to find $K_{15}^{(t+1)}$, and so substitute for $K_{15}^{(t+1)}$, etc., in the left-hand side of the first equation. The entire set can now be compactly written with superscript (t) on the left and $(t+1)$ on the right, as

$$
\mathbf{L}\{\bar{\mathbf{K}}^{(t)}\} = \{\bar{\mathbf{K}}^{(t+1)}\}\,,
\tag{2.1.8}
$$

where $\{\bar{\mathbf{K}}^{(t)}\}$ is the vertical vector of the age distribution at time t,

$$
\bar{\mathbf{K}}^{(t)} = \begin{Bmatrix} K_0^{(t)} \\ K_5^{(t)} \\ \vdots \\ K_{80}^{(t)} \end{Bmatrix},
$$

and $\mathbf{L}$ is the matrix of the coefficients of $K_x^{(t)}$ in (2.1.7) after the $K_x^{(t+1)}$ are eliminated on the left:

$$
\mathbf{L} = \begin{bmatrix}
0 & 0 & \frac{L_0}{2l_0}\left(\frac{L_{15}}{L_{10}}F_{15}\right) & \frac{L_0}{2l_0}\left(F_{15} + \frac{L_{20}}{L_{15}}F_{20}\right) & \cdots & 0 & 0 \\
\frac{L_5}{L_0} & 0 & 0 & 0 & \cdots & 0 & 0 \\
0 & \frac{L_{10}}{L_5} & 0 & 0 & \cdots & 0 & 0 \\
\vdots & & & & & & \vdots \\
0 & 0 & 0 & 0 & \cdots & \frac{L_{85}}{L_{80}} & 0
\end{bmatrix}.
\tag{2.1.9}
$$

Braces, $\{\bar{\mathbf{K}}\}$, will be used as a reminder that the vector is vertical in (2.1.8), and the bar that all ages to the end of life are included. To say that (2.1.8) is the same as (2.1.7) assumes nothing beyond the row-by-column rule for the multiplication of matrices.*

The population projection at which we have arrived has long been an important instrument of the working demographer (Cannan, 1895; Bowley, 1924; Whelpton, 1936). Cannan's method was identical with ours on survivorship; on births it differed only in using a single ratio applied to all persons 20 to 40 years of age. The matrix form was suggested by Bernardelli (1941) and Lewis (1942), and thoroughly investigated by Leslie (1945, 1948a, 1948b), from whose results most of Chapter 3 is taken. An example of **M**, the upper left 10×10 of **L** based on the 1964 estimate of female population in the United States, and births and deaths by age for the calendar year 1964, is shown as Table 2.2.

Given the excerpts from the life table, the distribution of women by age, and the distribution of women bearing children by age shown as Table 2.1, the corresponding elements of the projection matrix **M** may be calculated by the reader, and the projection of Table 2.3 verified.

Consider (Table 2.3) the prospective female population under 45 years of age of the United States if age-specific rates of birth and death are constant at 1964 levels. The number 20–24 increases 20% in the first five-year period, slows down to a near stop in the 1980's, then accelerates again in the 1990's. The age group 30–34 does the same, except that its most rapid rate of increase is not reached until the late 1970's. These oscillations reflect the drop in the birth rate in the 1930's and its increase in the 1940's. They have important consequences for college enrollment and labor-market entrance in the 1960's and 1970's. The fashion in which historical changes in births are reflected in the age distributions of subsequent periods, for example the degree to which they are damped, depends on the nature of the projection matrix **M**, to be investigated in Chapter 3.

Three Populations Compared

Before going on to discuss the theoretical properties of the matrix, **M** and $\{\mathbf{K}^{(0)}\}$ will be shown for three female populations observed for the year 1963 (Table 2.4). The three, Denmark, New Zealand, and Costa Rica, are listed in a rising sequence of birth rates, but much more than this is reflected in the first rows of their matrices. New Zealand birth rates exceed those of Denmark in a ratio which is especially great at the youngest and oldest ages of reproduction. Costa Rican fertility is, in turn, about one-half higher than New Zealand at the ages up to 25, but beyond that the ratio rises sharply.

---

* If primes indicate the operation of transposing, i.e., of interchanging rows and columns, then we could have used the horizontal vector of ages $\{\bar{\mathbf{K}}^{(t)}\}'$ and the transpose $\mathbf{L}'$ to express (2.1.8) in the form $\{\bar{\mathbf{K}}^{(t)}\}'\mathbf{L}' = \{\bar{\mathbf{K}}^{(t+1)}\}'$. There is little preference in either direction, and we will stay with (2.1.8) throughout this discussion.

Table 2.2 Projection matrix **M**, upper left 10 × 10 portion of **L** in (2.1.9), United States females, 1964

0	0.00103	0.08779	0.34873	0.47607	0.33769	0.18333	0.07605	0.01744	0.00096
0.99661	0	0	0	0	0	0	0	0	0
0	0.99834	0	0	0	0	0	0	0	0
0	0	0.99791	0	0	0	0	0	0	0
0	0	0	0.99682	0	0	0	0	0	0
0	0	0	0	0.99605	0	0	0	0	0
0	0	0	0	0	0.99472	0	0	0	0
0	0	0	0	0	0	0.99229	0	0	0
0	0	0	0	0	0	0	0.98866	0	0
0	0	0	0	0	0	0	0	0.98304	0

INFORMATION FOR COMPLETING MATRIX $\underset{\sim}{L}$ FOR UNITED STATES FEMALES, 1964

x	${}_5L_{x+5}/{}_5L_x$	x	${}_5L_{x+5}/{}_5L_x$	x	${}_5L_{x+5}/{}_5L_x$	x	${}_5L_{x+5}/{}_5L_x$
45	0.97416	55	0.94430	65	0.86938	75	0.68817
50	0.96222	60	0.91410	70	0.80060	80	0.76848*

* ${}_{15}L_{85}/{}_5L_{80}$.

Table 2.3 Female population of the United States for 1964, projected over five-year intervals to 1999 at 1964 birth and death rates (thousands)

AGE x	1964 $\{\underset{\sim}{K}^{(0)}\}$	1969 $\{\underset{\sim}{K}^{(1)}\}$	1974 $\{\underset{\sim}{K}^{(2)}\}$	1979 $\{\underset{\sim}{K}^{(3)}\}$	1984 $\{\underset{\sim}{K}^{(4)}\}$	1989 $\{\underset{\sim}{K}^{(5)}\}$	1994 $\{\underset{\sim}{K}^{(6)}\}$	1999 $\{\underset{\sim}{K}^{(7)}\}$
0	10,136	10,244	11,623	13,075	14,227	15,047	16,003	17,397
5	10,006	10,102	10,209	11,584	13,030	14,178	14,996	15,949
10	9,065	9,989	10,085	10,192	11,564	13,009	14,155	14,971
15	8,045	9,046	9,968	10,064	10,170	11,540	12,981	14,125
20	6,546	8,019	9,017	9,937	10,032	10,138	11,504	12,940
25	5,614	6,520	7,988	8,982	9,898	9,992	10,098	11,458
30	5,632	5,584	6,486	7,946	8,934	9,845	9,939	10,045
35	6,193	5,589	5,541	6,436	7,884	8,865	9,769	9,863
40	6,345	6,123	5,525	5,478	6,363	7,795	8,765	9,659
45	5,796	6,237	6,019	5,432	5,386	6,255	7,663	8,616
50	5,336	5,646	6,076	5,863	5,291	5,246	6,093	7,465
55	4,642	5,134	5,433	5,847	5,642	5,091	5,048	5,863
60+	14,023	15,532	17,042	18,443	19,862	20,809	20,927	20,784
ALL AGES	97,379	103,765	111,013	119,277	128,284	137,812	147,942	159,137

In comparison with the substantial differences in both the levels and the age incidence of fertility appearing in the top rows of the matrices of Table 2.4, the differences in survivorship, shown by the subdiagonals, are trifling. The probability of surviving from age 45–49 to 50–54, which is the 10th element of the 11th row of **M**, is 0.98051 for Denmark, 0.97687 for New Zealand, and 0.97276 for Costa Rica. More important for population increase is the first subdiagonal element m_{21} for the probability of passing from age 0–4 to 5–9; the lowest of these is Costa Rica's $m_{21} = 0.97827$, while the highest is 0.99703, a small range. Additional mortality is concealed in the top row, which gives a kind of net fertility—not the births but the survivors to the end of the five-year period among the births. But even here the lowest L_0 is Costa Rica's 457,546, against Denmark's 491,427 (not shown in Table 2.4). The probability of dying varies more in proportion from one country to another than does the probability of surviving, but the latter is what the projection requires.

The age vectors $\{\mathbf{K}^{(0)}\}$ for women are shown at the right of the table. The Danish distribution is nearly flat; that of New Zealand drops from 151,000 girls 0–4 to 66,000 women 50–54; the Costa Rican drops from 123,000 girls 0–4 to 21,000 women 50–54. The contrast in slopes results from very different rates of increase over the lifetimes of the individuals recorded. The Danish birth rate was falling in the 15 years before 1963, and this is reflected in its $K_0^{(0)}$ being below its $K_{15}^{(0)}$, in contrast to New Zealand, which maintained its postwar level of births and shows a steady fall from $K_0^{(0)}$ to $K_{25}^{(0)}$.

Methods of Solution

Two approaches to (2.1.8) are possible. The more obvious is to treat it as though it were an equation in scalars, and solve, without any deeper analysis, by

$$\mathbf{L}\{\bar{\mathbf{K}}^{(0)}\} = \{\bar{\mathbf{K}}^{(1)}\}\,,\ \mathbf{L}\{\bar{\mathbf{K}}^{(1)}\} = \{\bar{\mathbf{K}}^{(2)}\}\,, \ldots . \tag{2.1.10}$$

This is what was done in Table 2.3, where at each point of time the population was calculated from that at the preceding time. The solution can be improved for analytical purposes by writing (2.1.10) as

$$\{\bar{\mathbf{K}}^{(t)}\} = \mathbf{L}^t\{\bar{\mathbf{K}}^{(0)}\}\,, \tag{2.1.11}$$

which enables one to study the effects of the pattern of fertility and mortality contained in **L** and $\mathbf{L}^t$, in separation from the initial age distribution $\bar{\mathbf{K}}^{(0)}$.

The other approach to the solution of (2.1.8) is to analyze the matrix of the coefficients in terms of its latent roots. This is analogous to what is done in factor analysis. In our case it will turn out that the first three roots contain most of the meaning; this being so, some simplification, and hence understanding, may be gained by an analytical form of solution which permits the separation of the effects of these three main roots.

It is convenient to express the argument in terms of a partition of **L**. In fact **L** and its powers may be written as four submatrices by a split at a point

Table 2.4 Projection matrices **M** and age distributions $\{\mathbf{K}^{(0)}\}$ for Denmark, New Zealand, and Costa Rica, females, 1963

AGE	PROJECTION MATRIX $\underset{\sim}{M}$: SUBDIAGONAL*	PROJECTION MATRIX $\underset{\sim}{M}$: FIRST ROW**	OBSERVED POPULATION (THOUSANDS) $\{\underset{\sim}{K}^{(0)}\}/1000$
	DENMARK		
0	0.99703	0	183
5	0.99876	0.0000	180
10	0.99848	0.0555	185
15	0.99791	0.2649	209
20	0.99746	0.4055	164
25	0.99595	0.3031	145
30	0.99362	0.1543	140
35	0.99081	0.0596	150
40	0.98669	0.0131	157
45	0.98051	0.0008	150
50		0.0000	153
55+			546
TOTAL			2361
	NEW ZEALAND		
0	0.99634	0	151
5	0.99826	0.0013	136
10	0.99820	0.1034	123
15	0.99737	0.3628	106
20	0.99724	0.5554	86
25	0.99614	0.4688	73
30	0.99389	0.2612	75
35	0.99111	0.1133	78
40	0.98498	0.0279	77
45	0.97687	0.0017	71
50		0.0000	66
55+			224
TOTAL			1265
	COSTA RICA		
0	0.97827	0	123
5	0.99557	0.0009	108
10	0.99628	0.1388	85
15	0.99480	0.5288	66
20	0.99245	0.8101	53
25	0.99003	0.7609	44
30	0.98846	0.6022	39
35	0.98454	0.3760	34
40	0.97767	0.1351	27
45	0.97276	0.0194	23
50		0.0001	21
55+			48
TOTAL			670

*${}_5L_{x+5}/{}_5L_x$.

**$(L_0/2\ell_0)(F_x + F_{x+5}\ {}_5L_{x+5}/{}_5L_x)$.

which corresponds to the highest age of reproduction β,

$$\mathbf{L} = \begin{bmatrix} \mathbf{M} & \mathbf{0} \\ \mathbf{A} & \mathbf{B} \end{bmatrix}, \qquad \mathbf{L}^2 = \begin{bmatrix} \mathbf{M}^2 & \mathbf{0} \\ \mathbf{AM} + \mathbf{BA} & \mathbf{B}^2 \end{bmatrix}, \qquad \mathbf{L}^t = \begin{bmatrix} \mathbf{M}^t & \mathbf{0} \\ \mathbf{A}_t & \mathbf{B}^t \end{bmatrix},$$

where $\mathbf{A}_t$ is a function of **A**, **B**, and **M** whose explicit form is not required. The important feature of the partitioning is that the upper right-hand submatrix is zero, and it remains zero at all positive integral powers of **L**, as may be verified by application of the rules of matrix multiplication. If now the age vector $\{\bar{\mathbf{K}}\}$ is also split at the same highest age of reproduction, say as

$$\{\bar{\mathbf{K}}\} = \begin{Bmatrix} \mathbf{K} \\ \mathbf{D} \end{Bmatrix},$$

then $\{\bar{\mathbf{K}}^{(t)}\}$ becomes

$$\{\bar{\mathbf{K}}^{(t)}\} = \mathbf{L}^t\{\bar{\mathbf{K}}^{(0)}\} = \begin{bmatrix} \mathbf{M}^t & \mathbf{0} \\ \mathbf{A}_t & \mathbf{B}^t \end{bmatrix} \begin{Bmatrix} \mathbf{K}^{(0)} \\ \mathbf{D}^{(0)} \end{Bmatrix}$$

$$= \begin{Bmatrix} \mathbf{M}^t\mathbf{K}^{(0)} \\ \mathbf{A}_t\mathbf{K}^{(0)} + \mathbf{B}^t\mathbf{D}^{(0)} \end{Bmatrix} = \begin{Bmatrix} \mathbf{K}^{(t)} \\ \mathbf{D}^{(t)} \end{Bmatrix}, \tag{2.1.12}$$

from which it is evident that the **A**, **B** and **D**, referring to the ages beyond reproduction, i.e., beyond β, never affect the ages younger than β. Our subsequent work will be largely in terms of the matrix $\mathbf{M}^t$ and the vector $\{\mathbf{K}^{(t)}\}$ covering the interval from birth to the end of the fertile ages only, rather than $\mathbf{L}^t$ and $\{\bar{\mathbf{K}}^{(t)}\}$, which deal with the whole of life.

As an introduction to the analysis of the following chapter we will create a numerical example (in which age intervals are 15 years wide) whose arithmetic could be carried out on a desk calculator. The results which follow were obtained by computer, and numbers were rounded to four decimal places as they were copied from the printout. Convenience is served by supposing no reproduction beyond the age interval 40–44; the small number of births to women 45–49 were transferred to the 40–44. This procedure may be shown by the techniques of Chapter 11, for a population increasing at rate r, to raise the apparent rate of increase of the projection process by only $re^{-45r}{}_5F_{45}$, or less than 0.000004 for the United States female population discussed below.

2.2. CONDENSATION OF THE MATRIX

To derive a usable 3×3 matrix we start with **M**, compiled in nine five-year age groups to age 45, and cube it to obtain $\mathbf{M}^3$. Table 2.5 shows $\mathbf{M}^3$ for United States females, 1965, with a partitioning into 9 submatrices sketched in dotted lines. In parallel to the notation introduced earlier, where

$$\mathbf{M}\{\mathbf{K}^{(0)}\} = \{\mathbf{K}^{(1)}\},$$

Table 2.5 Matrix $\mathbf{M}^3$ along with observed $\{\mathbf{K}^{(0)}\}$ and first stable vector $\{\mathbf{K}_1\}$, for United States females, 1965*

$$\underset{\sim}{M}^3 = \left[\begin{array}{ccc:ccc:ccc}
0.0856 & 0.3208 & 0.4305 & 0.3082 & 0.1696 & 0.0712 & 0.0174 & 0.0001 & 0.0000 \\
0.0010 & 0.0856 & 0.3203 & 0.4299 & 0.3078 & 0.1692 & 0.0710 & 0.0173 & 0 \\
0 & 0.0010 & 0.0856 & 0.3204 & 0.4306 & 0.3085 & 0.1698 & 0.0714 & 0.0175 \\
\hdashline
0.9930 & 0 & 0 & 0 & 0 & 0 & 0 & 0 & 0 \\
0 & 0.9932 & 0 & 0 & 0 & 0 & 0 & 0 & 0 \\
0 & 0 & 0.9909 & 0 & 0 & 0 & 0 & 0 & 0 \\
\hdashline
0 & 0 & 0 & 0.9878 & 0 & 0 & 0 & 0 & 0 \\
0 & 0 & 0 & 0 & 0.9833 & 0 & 0 & 0 & 0 \\
0 & 0 & 0 & 0 & 0 & 0.9759 & 0 & 0 & 0
\end{array}\right]$$

$$\text{OBSERVED } \{\underset{\sim}{K}^{(0)}\} = \left\{\begin{array}{c} 10.13 \\ 10.22 \\ 9.44 \\ 8.51 \\ 6.88 \\ 5.77 \\ 5.64 \\ 6.17 \\ 6.46 \end{array}\right\}$$

AGES 45 AND OVER, 30.76 PERCENT

$$\text{STABLE } \{\underset{\sim}{K}_1\} = \left\{\begin{array}{c} 10.10 \\ 9.45 \\ 8.85 \\ \hdashline 8.29 \\ 7.76 \\ 7.26 \\ \hdashline 6.77 \\ 6.31 \\ 5.86 \end{array}\right\}$$

AGES 45 AND OVER, 29.35 PERCENT

* Programmed by D. Nagnur. Births adjusted.

we write the same symbols with a bar below when they refer to the 3×3 matrix, i.e., to the condensation into 15-year age groups and 15-year time intervals:

$$\underline{\mathbf{M}}\{\underline{\mathbf{K}}^{(0)}\} = \{\underline{\mathbf{K}}^{(1)}\}\,. \tag{2.2.1}$$

The jth element of the ith row of $\underline{\mathbf{M}}$ is $\underline{m}_{ij}$, and the ith element of $\{\underline{\mathbf{K}}^{(0)}\}$ is $\underline{k}_i^{(0)}$, $i = 1, 2, 3$; $j = 1, 2, 3$, so that explicitly (2.2.1) is

$$\begin{bmatrix} \underline{m}_{11} & \underline{m}_{12} & \underline{m}_{13} \\ \underline{m}_{21} & \underline{m}_{22} & \underline{m}_{23} \\ \underline{m}_{31} & \underline{m}_{32} & \underline{m}_{33} \end{bmatrix} \begin{Bmatrix} \underline{k}_1^{(0)} \\ \underline{k}_2^{(0)} \\ \underline{k}_3^{(0)} \end{Bmatrix} = \begin{Bmatrix} \underline{k}_1^{(1)} \\ \underline{k}_2^{(1)} \\ \underline{k}_3^{(1)} \end{Bmatrix}.$$

The $\underline{m}_{ij}$ from the elements of $\mathbf{M}^3$ which we call $m_{ij}^{(3)}$ and the k_i, $i = 1, 2, \ldots, 9$, $j = 1, 2, \ldots, 9$, must meet two conditions.

The first is that as nearly as possible each 15-year age group in the population as projected once (through 15 years) by the small matrix $\underline{\mathbf{M}}$ be equal to the sum of the corresponding three ages in the population as projected three times (each through 5 years) by the large matrix $\mathbf{M}$. If $\{\mathbf{K}^{(3)}\} = \mathbf{M}^3\{\mathbf{K}^{(0)}\}$ is to be equivalent to $\{\underline{\mathbf{K}}^{(1)}\} = \underline{\mathbf{M}}\{\underline{\mathbf{K}}^{(0)}\}$, then

$$\underline{k}_1^{(1)} = k_1^{(3)} + k_2^{(3)} + k_3^{(3)}\,,$$

since both sides stand for the population under 15 years of age, at 15 calendar years after the zero point. Similarly for $\underline{k}_2^{(1)}$ and $\underline{k}_3^{(1)}$.

The second condition is the demographic one, implicit in the aging of a closed population, that the cohorts each move into the following 15-year age group over the 15-year period of projection by the small matrix. We make each element of the small matrix $\underline{\mathbf{M}}$ depend only on the corresponding square in the partition of $\mathbf{M}^3$; $\underline{m}_{11}$ will depend only on the upper left 3×3 of $\mathbf{M}^3$, for example, and will in no way be affected by birth and death in the range outside of that 3×3 matrix.

The equation representing the two conditions for the upper left of the nine submatrices into which $\mathbf{M}$ is divided is

$$\begin{aligned} &m_{11}^{(3)}k_1 + m_{12}^{(3)}k_2 + m_{13}^{(3)}k_3 \\ &+ m_{21}^{(3)}k_1 + m_{22}^{(3)}k_2 + m_{23}^{(3)}k_3 \\ &+ m_{31}^{(3)}k_1 + m_{32}^{(3)}k_2 + m_{33}^{(3)}k_3 \\ &= \underline{m}_{11}(k_1 + k_2 + k_3)\,, \end{aligned} \tag{2.2.2}$$

and on solving for $\underline{m}_{11}$ we have

$$\underline{m}_{11} = \frac{k_1 \sum_{i=1}^{3} m_{i1}^{(3)} + k_2 \sum_{i=1}^{3} m_{i2}^{(3)} + k_3 \sum_{i=1}^{3} m_{i3}^{(3)}}{k_1 + k_2 + k_3}\,. \tag{2.2.3}$$

A similar argument applies to the remainder of the $\underline{m}_{ij}$, $i = 1, 2, 3$, $j = 1, 2, 3$.

The calculation of $\underline{m}_{ij}$ by formulas typified by (2.2.3), and hence the construction of the 3×3 matrix $\underline{\mathbf{M}}$, now requires only a decision on the k_1, k_2, and k_3. One obvious possibility is the use of $k_1^{(0)}$, $k_2^{(0)}$, $k_3^{(0)}$, the three five-year age groups taken from the initial given population $\{\mathbf{K}^{(0)}\}$. However, this offends against the objective of making projection matrices depend only on mortality and fertility, and not on the initial conditions of age distribution, which may be thought of as arbitrary or accidental in relation to our present analysis. Hence we have chosen the k's for (2.2.3) as that age distribution which would be reached by the continued operation of the matrix $\mathbf{M}$. This is known as the stable population (Section 3.1) in which the k's are only available to within a multiplicative constant, and it is seen from the form of (2.2.3) that they are needed only to within such a constant. They depend in no way on the initial age distribution though they will be calculated as $\{\mathbf{K}_1\} = \mathbf{M}^t\{\mathbf{K}^{(0)}\}$ with $t = 128$.

The stable vector $\{\mathbf{K}_1\}$ for the United States, 1965, is included in Table 2.5, its elements expressed (arbitrarily) as percentages of the female population under age 95. With these numbers as the k_i ($i = 1, 2, \ldots, 9$) of (2.2.3) and similar expressions for the other elements of $\underline{\mathbf{M}}$, we are in a position to calculate the elements $\underline{m}_{ij}$ ($i = 1, 2, 3$; $j = 1, 2, 3$) of $\underline{\mathbf{M}}$. For example, the first element of the second row of $\underline{\mathbf{M}}$ is, from (2.2.3) and Table 2.5,

$$\frac{8.29(0.9930) + 7.76(0.9932) + 7.26(0.9909)}{8.29 + 7.76 + 7.26} = 0.9924\,,$$

as shown in Table 3.1 for United States females in 1965.

In Chapter 3 the matrix analysis will be exemplified with arithmetic on $\underline{\mathbf{M}}^t$, and then the decomposition of $\mathbf{M}^t$, the general projection matrix put through successive multiplications by itself, will be studied. In Chapter 4 something will be said about what happens when the matrix is not held constant according to initial mortality and fertility but is altered (to reflect assumed changing mortality and fertility) in each successive premultiplication of the age vector. In Chapters 5 and 6 the age groups are in effect made indefinitely small, and the system (2.1.7) becomes an integral equation, which permits the derivation of some results not available in the matrix formulation. Chapter 8 suggests a further variant in the analysis, the consolidation of the set of first-order equations obtained as $\mathbf{M}\{\mathbf{K}^{(t)}\} = \{\mathbf{K}^{(t+1)}\}$ of (2.1.7) above into a single higher-order equation in one variable; it also compares this and the earlier treatments with one another.

CHAPTER 3

GENERAL ANALYSIS OF THE PROJECTION MATRIX

Having seen how the changing age distribution of a population under a given regime of mortality and fertility may be formulated in a set of linear recurrence equations, we went on to represent that set as a matrix equation, and found a method for condensing the matrix from 9×9 to 3×3. This chapter starts with an arithmetical example of the 3×3 matrix being raised through successive powers, including a decomposition useful in later analysis. The argument which justifies these procedures is standard matrix algebra, outlined in Section 3.2.

Population subsequent to a given date is determined by (a) the age distribution at that date, (b) the age-specific birth and death rates of that date, and (c) subsequent changes in birth and death rates. The strategy of analysis is to separate these three effects. The use of matrices, especially to separate (a) and (b), is principally due to P. H. Leslie (1945).

3.1. A NUMERICAL EXAMPLE FOR THE 3 × 3 MATRIX

The $\underline{\mathbf{M}}$ resulting from equations such as (2.2.3) for United States females, 1965, is given in Table 3.1. The interpretation to be put on the elements is analogous to that for the larger matrix **M** of Table 2.2: m_{11} or 0.4271 is the number of girl children alive at the end of the 15-year period expected to be born to a girl child now 0–14 years of age at last birthday; m_{21} or 0.9924 is the probability of survival over the next 15 years of a girl 0–14 years of age from the initial population.

The matrix **M** is of such a character that when taken to powers it stabilizes. (The underline is now dropped, since the argument which follows treats only the 3×3 matrix.) The second power corresponds to projection through 30 years, the third through 45 years, and so forth. We can see concretely what stability means by looking at the square of **M**,

$$\mathbf{M}^2 = \begin{bmatrix} 1.0257 & 0.4880 & 0.0544 \\ 0.4238 & 0.8434 & 0.1264 \\ 0.9751 & 0 & 0 \end{bmatrix},$$

and the square of this, which is $\mathbf{M}^4$:

$$\mathbf{M}^4 = \begin{bmatrix} 1.3120 & 0.9122 & 0.1175 \\ 0.9154 & 0.9181 & 0.1296 \\ 1.0002 & 0.4759 & 0.0530 \end{bmatrix}.$$

Table 3.1 Condensed matrix $\underline{\mathbf{M}}$ for United States and three other female populations, showing also latent roots*

UNITED STATES 1965**

$$\begin{bmatrix} 0.4271 & 0.8498 & 0.1273 \\ 0.9924 & 0 & 0 \\ 0 & 0.9826 & 0 \end{bmatrix} \qquad \begin{matrix} \lambda_1 = 1.2093 & r_1 = 0.01267 \\ \lambda_2 = -0.6154 & \lambda_3 = -0.1668 \end{matrix}$$

ENGLAND AND WALES 1960-62

$$\begin{bmatrix} 0.3391 & 0.8425 & 0.1308 \\ 0.9942 & 0 & 0 \\ 0 & 0.9875 & 0 \end{bmatrix} \qquad \begin{matrix} \lambda_1 = 1.1581 & r_1 = 0.00978 \\ \lambda_2 = -0.6479 & \lambda_3 = -0.1711 \end{matrix}$$

HUNGARY 1965

$$\begin{bmatrix} 0.2971 & 0.4922 & 0.0486 \\ 0.9927 & 0 & 0 \\ 0.\ 0 & 0.9855 & 0 \end{bmatrix} \qquad \begin{matrix} \lambda_1 = 0.8993 & r_1 = -0.00708 \\ \lambda_2 = -0.4954 & \lambda_3 = -0.1067 \end{matrix}$$

THE ABOVE ARE IN 15-YEAR INTERVALS OF AGE AND TIME. USING A SIMILAR PROCEDURE, THE FOLLOWING MATRIX WAS CALCULATED FOR PROJECTING IN 10-YEAR INTERVALS:

TAIWAN 1965

$$\begin{bmatrix} 0.0201 & 0.6838 & 1.1245 & 0.3723 & 0.0371 \\ 0.9891 & 0 & 0 & 0 & 0 \\ 0 & 0.9892 & 0 & 0 & 0 \\ 0 & 0 & 0.9831 & 0 & 0 \\ 0 & 0 & 0 & 0.9725 & 0 \end{bmatrix}$$

$\lambda_1 = 1.3240$ $\qquad$ $r_1 = 0.02807$

$\lambda_2, \lambda_3 = -0.1935 \pm 0.0506i$ $\qquad$ $\lambda_4, \lambda_5 = -0.4585 \pm 0.6672i.$

* Programmed by D. Nagnur and P. P. Talwar.
** Births adjusted.

The zeros have filled in, and the columns are evidently becoming more nearly proportional to one another. Squaring again gives $\mathbf{M}^8$, and squaring $\mathbf{M}^8$ gives $\mathbf{M}^{16}$:

$$\mathbf{M}^{16} = \begin{bmatrix} 12.1886 & 9.6072 & 1.2833 \\ 10.0021 & 7.8846 & 1.0533 \\ 8.1274 & 6.4054 & 0.8556 \end{bmatrix},$$

which is as high as we need go for results correct to three or four decimal places.

The matrix $\mathbf{M}^{16}$ is approximately stable, both in the sense that its rows are proportional to one another, and its columns likewise, and also in the sense that each higher power is proportional, element by element, to $\mathbf{M}^{16}$. Thus the first element of the first row of $\mathbf{M}^{17}$ is obtained by taking the first row of $\mathbf{M}$ times the first column of $\mathbf{M}^{16}$, in the form of the inner product:

$$m_{11}^{(17)} = m_{11}m_{11}^{(16)} + m_{12}m_{21}^{(16)} + m_{13}m_{31}^{(16)},$$

which works out to 14.740; the ratio of this to the first element of the first row of $\mathbf{M}^{16}$ is

$$m_{11}^{(17)}/m_{11}^{(16)} = 14.740/12.1886 = 1.2093 .$$

A similar calculation for the first element of the second row is

$$m_{21}^{(17)}/m_{21}^{(16)} = 12.096/10.0021 = 1.2094 ,$$

or very nearly the same. These would agree to several further decimal places if we had squared once again to obtain $\mathbf{M}^{32}$ and then taken the ratio $m_{ij}^{(33)}/m_{ij}^{(32)}$. We will denote the common value of the ratio in the limit by λ_1, the principal *latent* or *characteristic* root of $\mathbf{M}$, also known as an *eigenvalue*. The cube of the λ_1 obtained in similar fashion directly from the 9×9 matrix for United States females, 1965, is 1.2093. The condensation preserves this root, though not the others to be found below.

Having $\mathbf{M}^{16}$ and λ_1, we can obtain a constant matrix, not a function of time, by dividing $\mathbf{M}^{16}$ by λ_1^{16}:

$$\mathbf{Z}_1 = \frac{\mathbf{M}^{16}}{\lambda_1^{16}} = \begin{bmatrix} 0.5824 & 0.4591 & 0.0613 \\ 0.4779 & 0.3767 & 0.0503 \\ 0.3883 & 0.3061 & 0.0409 \end{bmatrix}, \quad \lambda_1 = 1.2093 .$$

This is the first stable matrix, often called a *spectral component*. It may be thought of as somehow containing that part of the matrix $\mathbf{M}$ associated with the root λ_1, which *dominates* the other roots in the sense that they are smaller in absolute value and so disappear when $\mathbf{M}$ is raised to powers.

Now we *deflate* $\mathbf{M}$ by removing from it the portion associated with the first root λ_1, the deflated matrix $\mathbf{N}$ being $\mathbf{M} - \lambda_1\mathbf{Z}_1$:

$$\mathbf{N} = \mathbf{M} - \lambda_1\mathbf{Z}_1 = \begin{bmatrix} -0.2772 & 0.2946 & 0.0532 \\ 0.4145 & -0.4556 & -0.0609 \\ -0.4696 & 0.6124 & -0.0494 \end{bmatrix}.$$

Unlike **M**, the deflated matrix **N** contains negative as well as positive terms, but it may be treated in the same way. It approaches stability when taken to powers, and in fact stabilizes more quickly, so that we need only go as high as $\mathbf{N}^8$. The second latent root is found from **N** by the ratio of any element of the 9th power to the corresponding element of the 8th power, and turns out to be $\lambda_2 = -0.6154$. Using this to normalize the 8th power we find

$$\mathbf{Z}_2 = \frac{\mathbf{N}^8}{\lambda_2^8} = \begin{bmatrix} 0.4627 & -0.4860 & -0.0957 \\ -0.7461 & 0.7838 & 0.1544 \\ 1.1912 & -1.2513 & -0.2465 \end{bmatrix}, \quad \lambda_2 = -0.6154\,,$$

the second spectral component.

Removing the effect of this second component from **N** gives the twice deflated $\mathbf{N} - \lambda_2\mathbf{Z}_2 = \mathbf{M} - \lambda_1\mathbf{Z}_1 - \lambda_2\mathbf{Z}_2$. This turns out to be stable at the outset, even in its first power, and λ_3 may be ascertained by the ratio of any element of its square to the corresponding element of the twice deflated $\mathbf{N} - \lambda_2\mathbf{Z}_2$. Finding in this way $\lambda_3 = -0.1668$, we have the third and last spectral component

$$\mathbf{Z}_3 = \frac{\mathbf{N} - \lambda_2\mathbf{Z}_2}{\lambda_3} = \begin{bmatrix} -0.0451 & 0.0270 & 0.0344 \\ 0.2682 & -0.1605 & -0.2047 \\ -1.5795 & 0.9452 & 1.2056 \end{bmatrix}, \quad \lambda_3 = -0.1668\,.$$

The three components $\mathbf{Z}_1$, $\mathbf{Z}_2$, and $\mathbf{Z}_3$ exhaust the matrix, leaving nothing in it. Thus any element of **M** may be reconstructed by adding the corresponding elements of $\mathbf{Z}_1$, $\mathbf{Z}_2$, and $\mathbf{Z}_3$, each weighted by its root λ; **M** may be seen arithmetically (subject to rounding) to satisfy

$$\lambda_1\mathbf{Z}_1 + \lambda_2\mathbf{Z}_2 + \lambda_3\mathbf{Z}_3 = \mathbf{M}\,.$$

In respect to the first element of the first row, for example, the numbers are

$$(1.2093)(0.5824) + (-0.6154)(0.4627) + (-0.1668)(-0.0451) = 0.4271\,,$$

and this is the same as m_{11} of the first matrix of Table 3.1.

Moreover the **Z**'s add up to the identity matrix:

$$\mathbf{Z}_1 + \mathbf{Z}_2 + \mathbf{Z}_3 = \mathbf{I}\,.$$

The first elements of the first rows of the three **Z**'s add to one:

$$0.5824 + 0.4627 - 0.0451 = 1.0000\,,$$

and similarly for other sets of diagonal elements. Off-diagonal elements add to zero; in the case of the first elements of the second rows, we have

$$0.4779 - 0.7461 + 0.2682 = 0\,.$$

When any pair of the **Z**'s are multiplied by the rules of matrix multiplication which we have been applying, the product equals zero. For example the (inner) product of the first row of $\mathbf{Z}_1$ and the first column of $\mathbf{Z}_2$ is

$$(0.5824)(0.4627) + (0.4591)(-0.7461) + (0.0613)(1.1912) = 0 .$$

The $\mathbf{Z}$'s are mutually *orthogonal* in that $\mathbf{Z}_i\mathbf{Z}_j = 0$, $i \neq j = 1, 2, 3$.

The next of the properties with which we will be concerned is that the $\mathbf{Z}$'s are not altered by being raised to powers. To satisfy oneself that $\mathbf{Z}_1^2 = \mathbf{Z}_1$, consider for example the first element of the first row of the product $\mathbf{Z}_1^2$, obtained as the inner product of the first row by the first column of $\mathbf{Z}_1$. It is

$$(0.5824)(0.5824) + (0.4591)(0.4779) + (0.0613)(0.3883) = 0.5824 ,$$

which is the same as the first element of the first row of $\mathbf{Z}_1$. The $\mathbf{Z}$'s are called *idempotent* because they are equal to powers of themselves.

The result of squaring both sides of

$$\mathbf{M} = \lambda_1\mathbf{Z}_1 + \lambda_2\mathbf{Z}_2 + \lambda_3\mathbf{Z}_3$$

is simplified by the orthogonal and idempotent properties:

$$\mathbf{M}^2 = \lambda_1^2\mathbf{Z}_1 + \lambda_2^2\mathbf{Z}_2 + \lambda_3^2\mathbf{Z}_3 ,$$

which may be verified arithmetically for $m_{11}^{(2)}$ as

$$(1.4625)(0.5824) + (0.3788)(0.4627) + (0.0278)(-0.0451) = 1.0257 ,$$

in agreement with the upper left element of $\mathbf{M}^2$. Similar results are obtained for $\mathbf{M}^3$, $\mathbf{M}^4$, etc.

The feature of the $\mathbf{Z}$'s that most clearly entitles them to be called stable is that $\mathbf{M}\mathbf{Z}_i = \lambda_i\mathbf{Z}_i$, $i = 1, 2, 3$. For example, the first element of the first row of $\mathbf{M}\mathbf{Z}_1$ is

$$(0.4271)(0.5824) + (0.8498)(0.4779) + (0.1273)(0.3883) = 0.7043 ,$$

which is equal to λ_1 times 0.5824, the first element of $\mathbf{Z}_1$. A numerically different (since the matrices are not symmetrical) aspect of stability is given by $\mathbf{Z}_i\mathbf{M}$, which also turns out to be equal to $\lambda_i\mathbf{Z}_i$, $i = 1, 2, 3$.

This numerically illustrates some ways in which matrices are different from ordinary numbers. The results are not merely paradoxical, but are understandable in terms of a perfectly consistent matrix theory, whose general form is the subject of the later sections of the present chapter.

The first of the spectral components $\mathbf{Z}_1$ is of special demographic interest. Each of its columns is proportional to the *stable population*, denoted $\{\mathbf{K}_1\}$, the age distribution to which a closed population would evolve if its age-specific rates of birth and death were to continue indefinitely. Populations which have been subjected to relatively unchanging rates in the past actually have age distributions close to their $\{\mathbf{K}_1\}$. Agreement between stable and observed ages

Table 3.2 Observed and stable age distributions, three countries, showing index of dissimilarity Δ

	OBSERVED PERCENT	STABLE PERCENT	STABLE MINUS OBSERVED
ENGLAND AND WALES 1960-62			
MALES			
0-14	24.3	27.6	3.3
15-29	20.2	23.7	3.5
30-44	20.6	20.1	-0.5
45+	34.8	28.6	-6.2
TOTAL	100.0	100.0	0.0
			Δ = 6.8
FEMALES			
0-14	21.7	26.3	4.6
15-29	18.5	22.6	4.1
30-44	19.5	19.3	-0.2
45+	40.3	31.8	-8.5
TOTAL	100.0	100.0	0.0
			Δ = 8.7
HONDURAS 1959-61, FEMALES			
0-14	46.3	44.7	-1.6
15-29	25.8	26.3	0.5
30-44	15.2	15.2	0.0
45+	12.6	13.8	1.2
TOTAL	100.00	100.00	0.0
			Δ = 1.6
JAPAN 1959-61, FEMALES			
0-14	29.0	18.8	-10.2
15-29	27.2	19.3	-7.9
30-44	20.5	19.7	-0.8
45+	23.3	42.2	18.9
TOTAL	100.0	100.0	0.0
			Δ = 18.9

testifies to the fixity of the preceding regime of fertility and mortality, and a difference between stable and observed shows that the regime has been changing, or else that migration has taken place. The stable population has meaning as a set of proportions, not of absolute numbers.

The percent distributions of observed and stable ages in the United States, 1965, were shown in Table 2.5, and Table 3.2 contains condensed versions of four other stable age distributions. Japan, 1959–61, shows an extreme departure from stability, while for Honduras the observed and stable are nearly identical. These reflect preceding alterations in birth rates, or absence of such alterations. A convenient measure of the departure of the stable from the observed age distributions is Δ, the sum of the positive differences of the percentages, known as the *index of dissimilarity*. Verify for England and Wales, females, 1960–62, with the help of the matrix of Table 3.1, that the stable population $\{\mathbf{K}_1\}$ of Table 3.2 is indeed the stable population in that it satisfies $\mathbf{M}\{\mathbf{K}_1\} = \lambda_1\{\mathbf{K}_1\}$, and check the index of dissimilarity shown.

3.2. MATRIX ALGEBRA OF THE PROJECTION PROCESS

Having worked a simple arithmetical example, we retrace our steps and go over the argument in more systematic fashion. The starting point is a characteristic or stable vector, a line of fixed direction in the space of the age distribution, defined by the property of being unaltered when premultiplied by the matrix operator $\mathbf{M}$. To find it we solve the linear equations $\mathbf{M}\{\mathbf{K}\} = \lambda\{\mathbf{K}\}$, or set out more fully,

$$\begin{aligned} m_{11}k_1 + m_{12}k_2 + \cdots + m_{1n}k_n &= \lambda k_1\,, \\ m_{21}k_1 + m_{22}k_2 + \cdots + m_{2n}k_n &= \lambda k_2\,, \\ \vdots \qquad\qquad & \quad \vdots \\ m_{n1}k_1 + m_{n2}k_2 + \cdots + m_{nn}k_n &= \lambda k_n\,, \end{aligned} \tag{3.2.1}$$

where the m's are the elements of the projection matrix $\mathbf{M}$, and $k_1, k_2, \ldots, k_n$ are the numbers of persons in the first age group, the second age group, etc., represented as a vertical vector $\{\mathbf{K}\}$. Typically the theory is applied to 5-year age intervals, n in number, extending from zero to $\beta = 5n$, the end of the reproductive period.

A set of k's which are not all zero and which satisfy the n homogeneous linear equations (3.2.1) in n variables exists only if the several equations are consistent, the condition for which is obtained by subtracting λk_i from both sides of the ith equation and then writing the coefficients of the k's as a determinant (Chrystal, 1961, Vol. I, p. 375):

$$\begin{vmatrix} m_{11} - \lambda & m_{12} & \cdots & m_{1n} \\ m_{21} & m_{22} - \lambda & \cdots & m_{2n} \\ \vdots & & & \vdots \\ m_{n1} & m_{n2} & \cdots & m_{nn} - \lambda \end{vmatrix} = 0\,. \tag{3.2.2}$$

A more compact expression of the *characteristic equation* (3.2.2) is

$$f(\lambda) = |\mathbf{M} - \lambda\mathbf{I}| = 0 \, ,$$

where $\mathbf{I}$ is the $n \times n$ matrix with ones in the diagonal and zeros elsewhere.

Because the nonzero elements of $\mathbf{M}$ are typically m_{1j}, $j = 3, 4, \ldots, n$, and $m_{i+1,i}$, $i = 1, 2, \ldots, n-1$, we can evaluate $|\mathbf{M} - \lambda\mathbf{I}| = 0$ as

$$\begin{aligned} &\lambda^n - m_{21}m_{32}m_{13}\lambda^{n-3} - m_{21}m_{32}m_{43}m_{14}\lambda^{n-4} - \cdots \\ &\quad - m_{21}m_{32} \cdots m_{n,n-1}m_{1n} = 0 \, , \end{aligned} \tag{3.2.3}$$

or explicitly in terms of survivorship L_x and age-specific fertility rates F_x,

$$f(\lambda) = l_0\lambda^n - \tfrac{1}{2}(L_{15}F_{15})\lambda^{n-3} - \tfrac{1}{2}(L_{15}F_{15} + L_{20}F_{20})\lambda^{n-4} - \cdots - \tfrac{1}{2}(L_{5n-5}F_{5n-5}) = 0 \, . \tag{3.2.4}$$

This will be referred to as Method A (Chap. 11).

That there is at most one positive root of (3.2.3) follows from Descartes' rule (Burnside and Panton, 1960, Vol. I, p. 28) that the number of positive roots of a polynomial equation cannot be greater than the number of changes of sign in its coefficients. Show that the characteristic equation of any matrix having zeros everywhere except in its top row and subdiagonal has only one change of sign, immediately following the term in the highest power of λ, irrespective of the size of the matrix, if nonzero terms are positive.

Polynomial equations such as (3.2.4) may be solved by various iterative procedures. Especially easy to program is the secant method (Ralston, 1965, p. 323). According to this method, if λ' and λ'' are two approximations to a root of $f(\lambda) = 0$, then the straight line through the points $(\lambda', f(\lambda'))$ and $(\lambda'', f(\lambda''))$ intersects with the abscissa where

$$\frac{0 - f(\lambda'')}{f(\lambda'') - f(\lambda')} = \frac{\lambda - \lambda''}{\lambda'' - \lambda'} \, , \qquad \text{or} \qquad \lambda = \lambda'' - \frac{\lambda'' - \lambda'}{f(\lambda'') - f(\lambda')} f(\lambda'') \, ,$$

which may be designated λ''', an improved approximation. About five iterations suffice to evaluate λ_1, the real dominant root, almost irrespective of how far out the initial approximations are.

Equation (3.2.3) for the first 3×3 matrix of Table 3.1 is

$$f(\lambda) = \lambda^3 - 0.4271\lambda^2 - 0.8433\lambda - 0.1241 = 0 \, .$$

It may be verified that the λ_1, λ_2, and λ_3 shown satisfy this equation. The characteristic equation (3.2.4) for the 1964 United States data of Table 2.1 is

$$\begin{aligned} &\lambda^{10} - 0.00102\lambda^8 - 0.08735\lambda^7 - 0.34624\lambda^6 - \cdots - 0.01678\lambda \\ &\quad - 0.00091 = 0 \, , \end{aligned}$$

the coefficients being the column of the table designated $({}_5\phi_x + {}_5\phi_{x+5})/2$. Using the secant method and starting with the arbitrary $\lambda' = 1.05$ and $\lambda'' = 1.10$, we obtain $f(1.05) = -0.27363$ and $f(1.10) = 0.21368$. Then λ''' is 1.07808. Three more iterations bring us to $\lambda = 1.08184$, which is correct to the places shown. The same method is usable for the complex roots, and a program has been devised for searching the plane of λ, which finds all the roots in due course. The problem is to find starting points for the iterations which converge to the successive roots systematically, and do not repeatedly fall into the earlier roots (Coale, 1967). Each root can be swept out as discovered, and the next following root located by the reduced equation. We must avoid rounding error, of course, and to do this the full original equation should be used for the final iteration on every root.

Programs for eigenvalues of a general matrix have also been applied; however, they perform extended computation to bring the determinant down to (3.2.3), which is a very simple operation in the case of our matrix **M** whose nonzero terms are in the top row and subdiagonal. Another iterative approach for the λ, the stable vectors, and stable matrices was used in Section 3.1 and is extended to complex roots in Section 3.3, based on the theory to be developed below. Further methods, also applicable here, are given in Section 5.3, and one recommended strongly is the functional iteration of (5.3.5), a Fortran program for which is shown in Table 5.10.

Let the roots for a 9×9 projection matrix be $\lambda_1, \lambda_2, \ldots, \lambda_9$. Those for Mexico and the United States, both for females in 1960, are given in Table 3.3. The dominant root λ_1 is the ratio by which the population increases in each five years when the effect of the initial age distribution has worn off; the Mexican λ_1 corresponds to a five-years increase two-thirds greater than that of the United States. The second and third roots will be shown (Section 3.4 and Chapters 5 and 6) to give a damped harmonic component, whose period is the length of a generation, 25 to 30 years. Figure 8.1 presents a typical configuration of the roots in the complex plane.

Vertical Stable or Characteristic Vectors

When we replace λ in the set (3.2.1) by a specific root, say λ_j, we can find a solution in the k, say the vector

$$\{\mathbf{K}_j\} = \begin{Bmatrix} k_{1j} \\ k_{2j} \\ \vdots \\ k_{nj} \end{Bmatrix}, \quad j = 1, 2, \ldots, n,$$

specified except for multiplication by an arbitrary factor, the j being included as the second subscript where a reminder is required that the vector pertains to the jth root. The elements of $\{\mathbf{K}_j\}$ are proportional to the cofactors of any row of $\mathbf{M} - \lambda_j\mathbf{I}$ (Frazer, Duncan, and Collar, 1963, p. 65), but this general method of finding cofactors is not necessary for the particular matrix **M** with which we are dealing.

Table 3.3 Characteristic equations and latent roots $\lambda_1, \lambda_2, \ldots, \lambda_9$, for female population, Mexico and United States, 1960

CHARACTERISTIC EQUATIONS $|\underset{\sim}{M} - \lambda \underset{\sim}{I}| = 0$

MEXICO, 1960: $|\underset{\sim}{M} - \lambda \underset{\sim}{I}| = \lambda^9 - 0.0008\lambda^7 - 0.1086\lambda^6 - 0.4144\lambda^5 - 0.6230\lambda^4 - 0.5840\lambda^3 - 0.4604\lambda^2 - 0.2800\lambda - 0.0872 = 0,$

U. S., 1960: $|\underset{\sim}{M} - \lambda \underset{\sim}{I}| = \lambda^9 - 0.0010\lambda^7 - 0.1066\lambda^6 - 0.4115\lambda^5 - 0.5408\lambda^4 - 0.3685\lambda^3 - 0.1998\lambda^2 - 0.0842\lambda - 0.0202 = 0.$

	ROOTS	
	MEXICO*	UNITED STATES**
λ_1	1.18167	1.11183
λ_2, λ_3	0.4412 ± 0.7911i	0.3016 ± 0.7974i
λ_4, λ_5	0.0037 ± 0.7344i	0.0347 ± 0.5379i
λ_6, λ_7	-0.4477 ± 0.4925i	-0.4019 ± 0.3899i
λ_8, λ_9	-0.5881 ± 0.1747i	-0.4903 ± 0.1845i

TO REDUCE MATRIX TO 9 × 9 SIZE, FERTILITY AT AGES 45 AND OVER WAS ASSIGNED TO WOMEN 40-44. NOTE DIFFERENCE IN UNITED STATES ROOTS FROM FIRST CASE OF TABLE 8.2, WHICH RECOGNIZES FERTILITY TO AGE 49.

* Census ages 0–4 adjusted.
** Adjusted births.

Our stable vectors are readily calculable by recurrence relations derived from **M** and the λ_j. Because the relevant nonzero elements of **M** are in the subdiagonal, it follows for the jth root, from row-by-column multiplication in the equation

$$\mathbf{M}\{\mathbf{K}_j\} = \lambda_j\{\mathbf{K}_j\}\,,$$

that

$$m_{i+1,i}k_i = \lambda_j k_{i+1}\,, \quad i = 1, 2, \ldots, n-1\,,$$

and dividing by λ_j we have

$$k_{i+1} = \frac{m_{i+1,i}\,k_i}{\lambda_j} = \frac{{}_5L_{5i}\,k_i}{\lambda_j\,{}_5L_{5i-5}}\,, \tag{3.2.5}$$

since the subdiagonal elements $m_{i+1,i}$ are the probabilities of surviving over five years.

If we arbitrarily take k_1 as ${}_5L_0/\sqrt{\lambda_j}$, and apply (3.2.5) successively, then the stable vector corresponding to λ_j is

$$\{\mathbf{K}_j\} = \begin{Bmatrix} {}_5L_0\,\lambda_j^{-1/2} \\ {}_5L_5\,\lambda_j^{-3/2} \\ {}_5L_{10}\,\lambda_j^{-5/2} \\ \vdots \\ {}_5L_{5n-5}\,\lambda_j^{-(n-1/2)} \end{Bmatrix}, \tag{3.2.6}$$

on the life table of radix l_0. The first of the n vectors $\{\mathbf{K}_j\}$ is the stable population, determined to within a multiplicative constant only, of which abridged examples appear in Table 3.2.

If the $\{\mathbf{K}_j\}$ are arranged side by side to constitute a matrix,

$$\mathbf{K} = [\{\mathbf{K}_1\}\quad\{\mathbf{K}_2\}\cdots\{\mathbf{K}_n\}] = \begin{bmatrix} k_{11} & k_{12} & \cdots & k_{1n} \\ k_{21} & k_{22} & \cdots & k_{2n} \\ \vdots & & & \vdots \\ k_{n1} & k_{n2} & \cdots & k_{nn} \end{bmatrix}, \tag{3.2.7}$$

then using the fact that the column components of the matrix $\mathbf{K}$ are $\{\mathbf{K}_j\}$, and that $\mathbf{M}\{\mathbf{K}_j\} = \{\mathbf{K}_j\}\lambda_j$, the reader may satisfy himself that

$$\mathbf{MK} = \mathbf{K}\begin{bmatrix} \lambda_1 & 0 & \cdots & 0 \\ 0 & \lambda_2 & \cdots & 0 \\ \vdots & & & \vdots \\ 0 & 0 & \cdots & \lambda_n \end{bmatrix}, \tag{3.2.8}$$

or

$$\mathbf{MK} = \mathbf{K\Lambda}\,,$$

where $\mathbf{\Lambda}$ stands for the diagonal matrix of the roots of the characteristic equation. From (3.2.8) we obtain by multiplying on the right by $\mathbf{K}^{-1}$

$$\mathbf{M} = \mathbf{K\Lambda K}^{-1}\,. \tag{3.2.9}$$

The roots λ_i are always distinct in demographic applications. This is true at least empirically, though the conditions under which it is true mathematically are not expressible in elementary terms. From the distinctness of the roots follows the independence of the vectors (Ralston, 1965, p. 470). For suppose that two vectors $\{\mathbf{K}_1\}$ and $\{\mathbf{K}_2\}$ are not independent, i.e., are connected by a linear relation

$$a_1\{\mathbf{K}_1\} + a_2\{\mathbf{K}_2\} = \mathbf{0}\,, \tag{3.2.10}$$

in which a_1 and a_2 are not both zero. Multiply on the left by $\mathbf{M}$ and obtain

$$a_1\lambda_1\{\mathbf{K}_1\} + a_2\lambda_2\{\mathbf{K}_2\} = \mathbf{0}\,. \tag{3.2.11}$$

If $\lambda_1 \neq \lambda_2$, Eqs. (3.2.10) and (3.2.11) can be simultaneously satisfied only by $a_1 = a_2 = 0$; this proves that (3.2.10) cannot hold for nonzero a_1 and a_2 and hence that $\{\mathbf{K}_1\}$ and $\{\mathbf{K}_2\}$ are linearly independent. The property may be extended by induction to the set of n vectors. The columns of $\mathbf{K}$ being linearly independent, its determinant cannot be zero, and hence the inverse $\mathbf{K}^{-1}$ always exists.

The factoring of $\mathbf{M}$ described by (3.2.9) leads easily to the factoring of any power of $\mathbf{M}$. For

$$\mathbf{M}^2 = (\mathbf{K\Lambda K}^{-1})(\mathbf{K\Lambda K}^{-1}) = \mathbf{K\Lambda}(\mathbf{K}^{-1}\mathbf{K})\mathbf{\Lambda K}^{-1} = \mathbf{K\Lambda}^2\mathbf{K}^{-1},$$

and repeating the multiplication proves that

$$\mathbf{M}^t = \mathbf{K\Lambda}^t\mathbf{K}^{-1} \tag{3.2.12}$$

if $t > 0$ is an integer. Thus to raise $\mathbf{M}$ to a power, given $\mathbf{K}$ and $\mathbf{K}^{-1}$, one need merely raise $\mathbf{\Lambda}$, whose powers are calculated as

$$\mathbf{\Lambda}^t = \begin{bmatrix} \lambda_1^t & 0 \cdots 0 \\ 0 & \lambda_2^t \cdots 0 \\ \vdots & \vdots \\ 0 & 0 \cdots \lambda_n^t \end{bmatrix}.$$

This helps with further theory, as we will see. Its practical use in hand computation is restricted by the fact that the columns of $\mathbf{K}$, except $\{\mathbf{K}_1\}$, are in general complex, and so are the rows beyond the first of $\mathbf{K}^{-1}$.

All of the preceding can be said also for multiplication on the left by a new set of vectors $[\mathbf{H}]$, horizontal this time. Corresponding to (3.2.1) we would have $[\mathbf{H}]\mathbf{M} = \lambda[\mathbf{H}]$, and the condition of consistency is the same equation in λ, $|\mathbf{M} - \lambda\mathbf{I}| = 0$, producing the same latent roots. For each latent root λ_i we find $[\mathbf{H}_i]$, determined except for a constant multiplier by the set of linear equations

$$[h_{i1} \quad h_{i2} \ldots h_{in}] \begin{bmatrix} m_{11} & m_{12} \cdots m_{1n} \\ m_{21} & m_{22} \cdots m_{2n} \\ \vdots & \vdots \\ m_{n1} & m_{n2} \cdots m_{nn} \end{bmatrix} = \lambda_i[h_{i1} \quad h_{i2} \ldots h_{in}], \tag{3.2.13}$$

or more compactly,

$$[\mathbf{H}_i]\mathbf{M} = \lambda_i[\mathbf{H}_i].$$

Reproductive Value

Recurrence equations may be obtained for the successive elements of the stable horizontal vector as for the vertical vector, though the equations are somewhat more complicated than (3.2.5). Both m_{1j} and $m_{j+1,j}$ can be nonzero, and the typical member of the set (3.2.13) for the ith root is (omitting the i subscript)

$$h_1 m_{1k} + h_{k+1}m_{k+1,k} = \lambda h_k, \quad k = 1, 2, \ldots, n-1.$$

One of the h is at our choice, and h_1 can be put equal to unity to give

$$h_{k+1} = \frac{\lambda h_k - m_{1k}}{m_{k+1,k}} = \frac{{}_5L_{5k-5}}{{}_5L_{5k}} (\lambda h_k - m_{1k}) .$$

This recurrence equation has been used for computation.

For studying the meaning of the h_k, an alternative arrangement, starting at the oldest age of reproduction and using the fact that $h_{n+1} = 0$, is more helpful. Now with h_1 arbitrarily set at $5l_0\sqrt{\lambda}/{}_5L_0$, we have from (3.2.13)

$$h_k = \left(\frac{{}_5L_{5k}}{{}_5L_{5k-5}}\right)\left(\frac{h_{k+1}}{\lambda}\right) + \frac{5l_0}{{}_5L_0\sqrt{\lambda}} m_{1k} . \tag{3.2.14}$$

In words: h_k, the reproductive value for ages $5k - 5$ to $5k$, is equal to the probability of surviving 5 years, times the reproductive value h_{k+1} for ages $5k$ to $5k + 5$, discounted over 5 years by dividing by λ; the whole added to the expected births in the approaching 5-year interval, discounted over $2\frac{1}{2}$ years by dividing by $\sqrt{\lambda}$. For example, we can construct the reproductive value for age 25–29 by

$${}_5H_{25} = \left(\frac{{}_5L_{30}}{{}_5L_{25}}\right)\left(\frac{{}_5H_{30}}{\lambda}\right) + \frac{5l_0}{{}_5L_0\sqrt{\lambda}} m_{1,6} ,$$

where ${}_5H_{25}$ (analogous to ${}_5L_{25}$ and ${}_5K_{25}$) is the same as h_6, and $m_{1,6}$ is the sixth element of the first row of $\mathbf{M}$. With data of Tables 2.1 and 2.2 for United States females, 1964, whose λ is 1.0818, this becomes

$${}_5H_{25} = (0.9947)\left(\frac{0.264}{1.0818}\right) + \frac{5(0.3377)}{(4.8897)(1.0401)} = 0.243 + 0.332 = 0.575 ,$$

as shown in Table 3.4.

The real eigenvector $[\mathbf{H}_1]$ is the discrete version of R. A. Fisher's (1930, p. 29) reproductive value of a woman, $v(x)$, defined as

$$v(x) = \frac{1}{l_x} \int_x^\beta \lambda_1^{-(a-x)/5} l(a)m(a)\, da , \tag{3.2.15}$$

where $m(a)\,da$ is the chance of bearing a child for a woman between ages a and $a + da$. As before, for a woman of a given age, reproductive value is the total prospective number of girl children that would be born, with the net maternity function $p(a)m(a)$ prevailing, discounted at the intrinsic rate of natural increase r, where $e^{5r} = \lambda$, or $r = (\ln \lambda)/5$. The definition (3.2.15) will be studied in the context of the continuous treatment in Section 5.2. Prove that the part of the column for $[\mathbf{H}_1]$ corresponding to ages below reproduction is proportional to the reciprocal of the stable population $\{\mathbf{K}_1\}$. Verify $[\mathbf{H}_1]$ for United States females, 1964, with the matrix of Table 2.2, using the equation $[\mathbf{H}_1]\mathbf{M} = \lambda_1[\mathbf{H}_1]$, with $\lambda_1 = 1.08184$.

Table 3.4 Reproductive value $[\mathbf{H}_1]$ and $[\mathbf{H}_1]\{\mathbf{K}\}^{(0)}$ for Chile, West Germany, and the United States, 1964

	CHILE, 1964 FEMALES	FEDERAL REPUBLIC OF GERMANY, 1964 FEMALES	UNITED STATES, 1964	
			FEMALES	MALES
	REPRODUCTIVE VALUE PER CHILD JUST BORN			
0-4	1.186	1.040	1.063	1.075
5-9	1.347	1.076	1.154	1.178
10-14	1.503	1.111	1.250	1.289
15-19	1.581	1.121	1.261	1.391
20-24	1.406	0.975	0.997	1.276
25-29	1.029	0.638	0.575	0.884
30-34	0.633	0.305	0.264	0.487
35-39	0.297	0.108	0.091	0.230
40-44	0.088	0.025	0.018	0.094
45-49	0.014	0.002	0.001	0.035
50-54	0.002	0.000	0.000	0.010
	AGGREGATE REPRODUCTIVE VALUE (THOUSANDS)			
0-4	736	2,495	10,779	10,895
5-9	733	2,209	11,550	11,790
10-14	736	2,118	11,329	11,687
15-19	659	1,926	10,148	11,187
20-24	520	2,139	6,526	8,352
25-29	319	1,436	3,225	4,964
30-34	178	558	1,486	2,742
35-39	75	219	565	1,423
40-44	19	56	114	599
45-49	2	4	5	204
50-54	0	0	0	52
TOTAL $= \frac{V}{1000} = \frac{[\underset{\sim}{H}_1]\{\underset{\sim}{K}^{(0)}\}}{1000}$	3,976	13,160	55,728	63,896

The horizontal stable vector $[\mathbf{H}_1]$ along with the age distribution tell us about the reproductive potential of a population. We could compare two observed age distributions from this viewpoint by applying to them a common $[\mathbf{H}_1]$ (Vincent, 1945). The aggregate reproductive value is obtained by multiplying unit values by the number of women, and may be written $V = [\mathbf{H}_1]\{\mathbf{K}^{(0)}\}$. Use the population distribution $\{\mathbf{K}^{(0)}\}$ of Table 2.1 along with the unit values in Table 3.4 to verify $V = 55{,}728{,}000$ for United States females, 1964.

Table 3.4 permits an examination of reproductive value by age for populations of different growth rates. The value per individual woman rises to a maximum at age 15–19 in all three countries. The drop after reproduction starts is more rapid for the United States than for Chile; to what feature of United States fertility is this due? Why does the Federal Republic of Germany show total female reproductive value higher at ages 20–24 than at 15–19?

Like every other aspect of the one-sex model, the projection matrix, and hence its stable vectors, are as appropriate to males as they are to females. Table 3.4 includes $[\mathbf{H}_1]$ for United States males, 1964, on a unit of one boy child just born. Note the differences between the male and female schedules, including the fact that men reach a higher peak and retain reproductive value to an older age.

Factors of M and Analysis of an Observed Age Distribution

A stable row vector $[\mathbf{H}_i]$ corresponds to each of the λ_i, and if the $[\mathbf{H}_i]$ are arrayed one beneath the other to make

$$\mathbf{H} = \begin{Bmatrix} [\mathbf{H}_1] \\ [\mathbf{H}_2] \\ \vdots \\ [\mathbf{H}_n] \end{Bmatrix},$$

then

$$\mathbf{HM} = \mathbf{\Lambda H}\,.$$

Multiplying by $\mathbf{H}^{-1}$ on the left gives

$$\mathbf{M} = \mathbf{H}^{-1}\mathbf{\Lambda H}\,, \qquad (3.2.16)$$

which is the same equation as (3.2.9), since $\mathbf{HK} = \mathbf{I}$; as will be shown below.

We know the stable vectors only to within a multiplicative constant. If the column vector for the ith root as originally calculated is $\{\mathbf{K}_i\}$, and the row vector for the same root is $[\mathbf{H}_i]$, then it may be convenient to normalize by the divisor $[\mathbf{H}_i]\{\mathbf{K}_i\}$, writing

$$[\bar{\mathbf{H}}_i] = \frac{[\mathbf{H}_i]}{[\mathbf{H}_i]\{\mathbf{K}_i\}}\,. \qquad (3.2.17)$$

When $[\bar{\mathbf{H}}_i]$ is from (3.2.17) and $i = j$, the product $[\bar{\mathbf{H}}_i]\{\mathbf{K}_j\}$ is 1.

The stable vectors possess an orthogonality property by which if $i \neq j$, then $[\mathbf{H}_i]\{\mathbf{K}_j\} = 0$. For

$$\mathbf{M}\{\mathbf{K}_j\} = \lambda_j\{\mathbf{K}_j\}, \tag{3.2.18}$$

by the definition of the stable column vector. Multiplying (3.2.18) on the left by $[\mathbf{H}_i]$ we have

$$[\mathbf{H}_i]\mathbf{M}\{\mathbf{K}_j\} = \lambda_j[\mathbf{H}_i]\{\mathbf{K}_j\}. \tag{3.2.19}$$

But it is also true by the definition of the stable row vector that

$$[\mathbf{H}_i]\mathbf{M} = \lambda_i[\mathbf{H}_i]. \tag{3.2.20}$$

Multiplying (3.2.20) on the right by $\{\mathbf{K}_j\}$ gives

$$[\mathbf{H}_i]\mathbf{M}\{\mathbf{K}_j\} = \lambda_i[\mathbf{H}_i]\{\mathbf{K}_j\}. \tag{3.2.21}$$

Equations (3.2.19) and (3.2.21) are the same on the left and differ by having scalars, λ_j and λ_i respectively on the right, where $\lambda_j \neq \lambda_i$. Subtracting (3.2.21) from (3.2.19) and dividing through by $\lambda_j - \lambda_i$ leaves

$$[\mathbf{H}_i]\{\mathbf{K}_j\} = 0, \quad i \neq j. \tag{3.2.22}$$

This fact enables us to express an observed age distribution, say the column of frequencies $\{\mathbf{K}^{(0)}\}$ obtained from a census, as a sum of the stable vectors, each multiplied by a constant:

$$\{\mathbf{K}^{(0)}\} = c_1\{\mathbf{K}_1\} + c_2\{\mathbf{K}_2\} + \cdots + c_n\{\mathbf{K}_n\}. \tag{3.2.23}$$

To find c_i premultiply (3.2.23) by the normalized row vector $[\bar{\mathbf{H}}_i]$; the result is

$$[\bar{\mathbf{H}}_i]\{\mathbf{K}^{(0)}\} = c_i, \tag{3.2.24}$$

or in terms of the nonnormalized vectors,

$$c_i = \frac{[\mathbf{H}_i]\{\mathbf{K}^{(0)}\}}{[\mathbf{H}_i]\{\mathbf{K}_i\}}. \tag{3.2.25}$$

The expansion (3.2.23) is a means of analyzing changes in age distribution under a given regime of fertility and mortality. Multiplying (3.2.23) by $\mathbf{M}$ on the left, we have

$$\begin{aligned}\mathbf{M}\{\mathbf{K}^{(0)}\} &= c_1\mathbf{M}\{\mathbf{K}_1\} + c_2\mathbf{M}\{\mathbf{K}_2\} + \cdots + c_n\mathbf{M}\{\mathbf{K}_n\} \\ &= \lambda_1 c_1\{\mathbf{K}_1\} + \lambda_2 c_2\{\mathbf{K}_2\} + \cdots + \lambda_n c_n\{\mathbf{K}_n\},\end{aligned}$$

since $\mathbf{M}\{\mathbf{K}_1\} = \lambda_1\{\mathbf{K}_1\}$, etc., and by a t-fold repetition of the multiplication,

$$\{\mathbf{K}^{(t)}\} = \mathbf{M}^t\{\mathbf{K}^{(0)}\} = \lambda_1^t c_1\{\mathbf{K}_1\} + \lambda_2^t c_2\{\mathbf{K}_2\} + \cdots + \lambda_n^t c_n\{\mathbf{K}_n\}, \tag{3.2.26}$$

where $t > 0$ is integral.

The 3×3 matrix of Section 3.1 and its $\mathbf{Z}_1$, $\mathbf{Z}_2$, and $\mathbf{Z}_3$ enable us to apply (3.2.23) to decompose the observed 15-year age groups with a desk calculator. The United States 1965 population included 29,413,000 girls under 15; 20,886,000 women 15–29; 18,040,000 women 30–44. Using as the stable $\{\mathbf{K}_i\}$, $i = 1, 2, 3$, the first column of $\mathbf{Z}_1$, and as $[\mathbf{H}_i]$ the first row of $\mathbf{Z}_i$, and entering these in (3.2.25), gives $c_1 = 47{,}776{,}000$; $c_2 = 3{,}744{,}000$; $c_3 = 3{,}149{,}000$. For example,

$$\begin{aligned} c_1 &= \frac{[\mathbf{H}_1]\{\mathbf{K}^{(0)}\}}{[\mathbf{H}_1]\{\mathbf{K}_1\}} \\ &= 1000\,\frac{(0.5824)(29{,}413) + (0.4591)(20{,}886) + (0.0613)(18{,}040)}{(0.5824)(0.5824) + (0.4591)(0.4779) + (0.0613)(0.3883)} \\ &= 47{,}776{,}000\,. \end{aligned}$$

The equation (3.2.23) is then, in thousands,

$$\begin{Bmatrix} 29{,}413 \\ 20{,}886 \\ 18{,}040 \end{Bmatrix} = 47{,}776 \begin{Bmatrix} 0.5824 \\ 0.4779 \\ 0.3883 \end{Bmatrix} + 3744 \begin{Bmatrix} 0.4627 \\ -0.7461 \\ 1.1912 \end{Bmatrix} + 3149 \begin{Bmatrix} -0.0451 \\ 0.2682 \\ -1.5795 \end{Bmatrix},$$

to within errors of rounding. Show the decomposition (3.2.26) after 15 years, i.e., with $t = 1$.

Suppose, as before, $[\mathbf{H}_1]$ to have been multiplied by a factor which makes its first element $(5l_0/{}_5L_0)\sqrt{\lambda_1}$; it is then nearly consistent with a unit of reproductive value equal to one girl child just born (or one boy child if the calculation is for males). Again arbitrarily, suppose $\{\mathbf{K}_1\}$ to have been multiplied by a factor which makes it unity in total. Then, as in Table 3.4, total reproductive value is $[\mathbf{H}_1]\{\mathbf{K}^{(0)}\}$, and we may define reproductive value per person in the stable age distribution as $A = [\mathbf{H}_1]\{\mathbf{K}_1\}$. The reader who is familiar with the argument of Section 5.2 below can show for the continuous case that A is the product of the birth rate and the mean age of childbearing when both are taken from the stable population. The more difficult task of proving this for the discrete case of the present chapter is accomplished by Goodman (1967c).

With these definitions we can say that c_1 of (3.2.25) is equal to V/A. And with the definition used for $\{\mathbf{K}_1\}$ by which it is unity in total, c_1, in the light of (3.2.26), may be called the *stable equivalent* population. For after a long enough time has passed (in practice 50 to 100 years), the first term only of (3.2.26) counts, and it may be written with our vectors

$$\{\mathbf{K}^{(t)}\} = \lambda_1^t c_1\{\mathbf{K}_1\}\,.$$

The total of the elements in $\{\mathbf{K}_1\}$ is unity, and hence the population of all ages at time t is $c_1\lambda_1^t$ on the projection with fixed rates. The closeness of approximation is seen for United States females in 1964, where $c_1\lambda_1^{20} = 91{,}655(1.08184)^{20} = 442{,}000$ thousands, while the full projection to the end of 100 years, $\mathbf{M}^{20}\{\mathbf{K}^{(0)}\}$, totals 442,100 thousands.

This justifies our speaking of c_1 as the stable equivalent population; it is the total which, if distributed according to the stable age distribution, would increase under the given regime of mortality and fertility at the same rate as the observed $\{\mathbf{K}^{(0)}\}$ projected by the matrix $\mathbf{M}$ as $\mathbf{M}^t\{\mathbf{K}^{(0)}\}$. The ratio $\mathbf{M}^t\{\mathbf{K}^{(0)}\}/\lambda_1^t c_1$ asymptotically equals the vector $\{\mathbf{K}_1\}$ whose elements add to unity.

Table 3.5 Population K, total reproductive value V, mean reproductive value in stable population A, and stable equivalent c_1

	POPU-LATION K/1000	REPRO-DUCTIVE VALUE V/1000	STABLE MEAN VALUE $A = V/c_1$	STABLE EQUI-VALENT c_1/1000
FEMALE				
AUSTRALIA 1965	5,632	3,186	0.56	5,659
BULGARIA 1964	4,076	1,665	0.34	4,888
CANADA 1965	9,479	5,995	0.61	9,839
CHILE 1964	4,280	3,976	0.89	4,452
GREECE 1965	4,393	2,057	0.40	5,185
HONDURAS 1965	1,148	1,353	1.15	1,174
HUNGARY 1964	5,231	1,889	0.27	7,011
MAURITIUS 1965	369	387	1.07	363
PORTUGAL 1965	4,805	2,942	0.60	4,890
TAIWAN 1965	6,049	5,888	0.94	6,294
UNITED STATES 1964	97,379	55,728	0.61	91,655
MALE				
CHILE 1964	4,111	4,805	1.18	4,088
HUNGARY 1964	4,889	2,306	0.39	5,901
UNITED STATES 1964	93,990	63,896	0.75	85,713

The quantities referred to are shown in Table 3.5 for 14 populations, 11 female and 3 male. The fact that c_1 is higher than K for Bulgaria and Hungary is due to their recent decline in fertility which leaves them with age distributions temporarily favorable to reproduction. The United States is in the opposite position of suffering from a hollow in the fertile ages, the result of which shows in Table 3.5 both for males and for females.

Nonnegative Matrices

The matrix **M** with which we are dealing is of the kind which Frobenius (1912) called *nonnegative*; i.e., its elements are all positive or zero. Nonnegative matrices that may be written

$$\mathbf{A} = \begin{bmatrix} \mathbf{B} & \mathbf{0} \\ \mathbf{C} & \mathbf{D} \end{bmatrix},$$

after permutation of rows and of corresponding columns, where **B** and **D** are square matrices, are called *reducible*; all others are *irreducible*. The matrix **L** of the complete projection introduced in Chapter 2 is reducible; **M**, in which the last element of the top row is positive, is irreducible.

Some properties of irreducible nonnegative matrices relevant to demography will be cited here. For proofs, the reader is referred to Gantmacher (1959, Vol. II, Chapter 13). First, an irreducible matrix always has a real positive latent root λ_1 that is distinct; the absolute values of all other roots are less than or equal to λ_1, which is to say that the other roots are either complex or else less than λ_1. Second, corresponding to λ_1 is an eigenvector $\{\mathbf{K}_1\}$ whose elements are nonnegative; no other eigenvector of nonnegative elements exists, disregarding multiples of $\{\mathbf{K}_1\}$.

The matrix **M** used in demography falls in a restricted subclass of irreducible nonnegative matrices: those that are *primitive*, which have no other root whose absolute value is equal to that of the unique positive root λ_1. A primitive matrix may be recognized by the powers of λ in its characteristic equation $|\mathbf{M} - \lambda\mathbf{I}| = 0$, of the nth degree if **M** is $n \times n$. If $|\mathbf{M} - \lambda\mathbf{I}| = 0$ contains terms in λ^{n_1} and λ^{n_2}, with nonzero coefficients, and such that $n - n_1$ and $n - n_2$ have no common factor greater than 1, then **M** is primitive. Our matrix **M** satisfies this condition, as may be seen by inspection of (3.2.3), provided only that at least two ages of nonzero fertility exist in positions in the first row which are relatively prime (Bernardelli, 1941). A primitive matrix raised to a sufficiently high power becomes positive—all its elements are greater than zero. (A method of proof of this for our **M** will be outlined in Section 4.5.)

Thus some of the important properties of **M** arise because it is a primitive, irreducible, nonnegative matrix. In particular, the real root we call dominant, λ_1, exceeds in absolute value all other roots. (Descartes' rule applied to (3.2.3) permitted the statement that no positive root other than λ_1 exists.)

Because λ_1 is larger than any other of the λ's in absolute value, the first term on the right-hand side of (3.2.26) will increase in relative magnitude as t increases. The age distribution $\{\mathbf{K}^{(0)}\}$ premultiplied by $\mathbf{M}^t$ will approach closer and closer to $c_1\lambda_1^t\{\mathbf{K}_1\}$, which is called the stable population and does not depend on the original age distribution $\{\mathbf{K}^{(0)}\}$. This is the *ergodic* property in demography, the tendency of a population to forget its initial age distribution. Lotka's more elementary demonstration of it for the continuous case follows from equation (5.2.3) below.

Spectral Decomposition

By virtue of the orthogonality property (3.2.22) of the stable vectors, **HK** is a diagonal matrix, and when the vectors are in their normal form we have $\mathbf{HK} = \mathbf{I}$, the unit $n \times n$ matrix. For the ith row of **H** is $[\mathbf{H}_i]$, and the jth column of **K** is $\{\mathbf{K}_j\}$; the product of these is unity when $i = j$ and zero when $i \neq j$. That **H** as well as **K** is nonsingular follows from the fact that the roots are distinct.

The relation $\mathbf{HK} = \mathbf{I}$ is commutative for any nonsingular $\mathbf{H}$ and $\mathbf{K}$, i.e., is the same as the relation $\mathbf{KH} = \mathbf{I}$. For multiplying $\mathbf{HK} = \mathbf{I}$ on the left by $\mathbf{H}^{-1}$ and on the right by $\mathbf{H}$ results in

$$\mathbf{H}^{-1}\mathbf{HKH} = \mathbf{H}^{-1}\mathbf{H}\,,$$

or

$$\mathbf{KH} = \mathbf{I}\,. \tag{3.2.27}$$

If $\mathbf{HK} = \mathbf{I}$ then multiplication on the right by $\mathbf{K}^{-1}$ gives $\mathbf{K}^{-1} = \mathbf{H}$, and recalling (3.2.9), which was

$$\mathbf{M} = \mathbf{K\Lambda K}^{-1}\,,$$

we have on substituting $\mathbf{H}$ for $\mathbf{K}^{-1}$,

$$\mathbf{M} = \mathbf{K\Lambda H}\,. \tag{3.2.28}$$

The rules of matrix multiplication hold when the elements are matrices just as when they are scalars (Frazer, Duncan, and Collar, 1963, p. 14). The reader may show that multiplying out $\mathbf{K\Lambda}$ puts (3.2.38) in the form

$$\mathbf{M} = [\lambda_1\{\mathbf{K}_1\} \quad \lambda_2\{\mathbf{K}_2\} \cdots \lambda_n\{\mathbf{K}_n\}]\mathbf{H}\,,$$

and partitioning $\mathbf{H}$ by rows gives

$$\begin{aligned}\mathbf{M} &= \lambda_1\{\mathbf{K}_1\}[\mathbf{H}_1] + \lambda_2\{\mathbf{K}_2\}[\mathbf{H}_2] + \cdots + \lambda_n\{\mathbf{K}_n\}[\mathbf{H}_n] \\ &= \lambda_1\mathbf{Z}_1 + \lambda_2\mathbf{Z}_2 + \cdots + \lambda_n\mathbf{Z}_n\,,\end{aligned} \tag{3.2.29}$$

no matrices appearing on the right except $\mathbf{Z}_i = \{\mathbf{K}_i\}[\mathbf{H}_i]$, $i = 1, 2, \ldots, n$, the spectral operators or components introduced by an arithmetical example for United States females, 1965, in Section 3.1.

The argument that we have here used to decompose $\mathbf{M} = \mathbf{K\Lambda K}^{-1}$ applies also to $\mathbf{M}^t = \mathbf{K\Lambda}^t\mathbf{K}^{-1}$ of (3.2.12). Substituting $\mathbf{K}^{-1} = \mathbf{H}$, we have $\mathbf{M}^t = \mathbf{K\Lambda}^t\mathbf{H}$, and this is

$$\mathbf{M}^t = \mathbf{K\Lambda}^t\mathbf{H} = \sum_i \lambda_i^t\{\mathbf{K}_i\}[\mathbf{H}_i] = \sum_i \lambda_i^t\mathbf{Z}_i\,, \tag{3.2.30}$$

a special case of Sylvester's theorem (Frazer, Duncan, and Collar, 1963, p. 78) for analyzing a function of a matrix into spectral operators.

Equation (3.2.30) may be multiplied by a constant scalar, say a_t. If a number of equations such as (3.2.30) for powers $t, t-1, \ldots, 1$, are each multiplied by an arbitrary constant and then added, we have

$$a_t\mathbf{M}^t + a_{t-1}\mathbf{M}^{t-1} + \cdots + a_0\mathbf{I} = \sum_i [(a_t\lambda_i^t + a_{t-1}\lambda_i^{t-1} + \cdots + a_0)\{\mathbf{K}_i\}[\mathbf{H}_i]]\,,$$

which is to say that $f(\mathbf{M})$, any polynomial function of the matrix $\mathbf{M}$, may be expanded as

$$f(\mathbf{M}) = f(\lambda_1)\mathbf{Z}_1 + f(\lambda_2)\mathbf{Z}_2 + \cdots + f(\lambda_n)\mathbf{Z}_n\,. \tag{3.2.31}$$

Rational or transcendental functions of a matrix, insofar as they may be approximated by polynomial functions, may similarly be expanded in terms of the spectral components **Z**.

If $f(\lambda)$ is the characteristic function $|\mathbf{M} - \lambda\mathbf{I}|$, then

$$f(\lambda_1) = f(\lambda_2) = \cdots = f(\lambda_n) = 0\,,$$

and hence from (3.2.31),

$$f(\mathbf{M}) = 0\,.$$

This is the important Cayley-Hamilton theorem that a matrix satisfies its own characteristic equation, which we have proved for the special case of the λ_i distinct. The characteristic equation of the 3×3 matrix for United States females, 1965, was shown above as an illustration of (3.2.3). From it we can write

$$f(\mathbf{M}) = \mathbf{M}^3 - 0.4271\mathbf{M}^2 - 0.8433\mathbf{M} - 0.1241\mathbf{I} = 0\,.$$

If $f(\mathbf{M})$ is to vanish, then it must vanish when the upper left-hand cells, for example, of $\mathbf{M}^3$, $\mathbf{M}^2$, $\mathbf{M}$, and $\mathbf{I}$ of Section 3.1, are entered. This means that

$$0.9224 - (0.4271)(1.0257) - (0.8433)(0.4271) - 0.1241$$

must equal zero, which it does to within 0.0001. Eight other arithmetic identities may be formed in similar fashion. Conversely, one may square any of the 3×3 matrices of Table 3.1 and then use the Cayley-Hamilton theorem to ascertain its cube.

If $\mathbf{M}$ is nonsingular, the fact that $f(\mathbf{M}) = 0$ may also be used to find the reciprocal $\mathbf{M}^{-1}$ from $\mathbf{M}$ and $\mathbf{M}^2$. Show the equation for this and apply it to the 3×3 matrix for Hungary, 1965, given in Table 3.1. Then infer that the inverse of any matrix of the form

$$\mathbf{M} = \begin{bmatrix} a & b & c \\ d & 0 & 0 \\ 0 & e & 0 \end{bmatrix}, \quad c, d, e \neq 0\,,$$

is

$$\mathbf{M}^{-1} = \begin{bmatrix} 0 & 1/d & 0 \\ 0 & 0 & 1/e \\ 1/c & -a/cd & -b/ce \end{bmatrix},$$

and verify the $\mathbf{M}^{-1}$ obtained by the Cayley-Hamilton theorem, both in general and for the Hungarian data.

The matrix $\mathbf{M}$ looks as though it may be used to project the population backward, by multiplying successively by $\mathbf{M}^{-1}$ and obtaining (3.2.26) with t negative. Write out explicitly the elements of $\mathbf{M}^{-1}$ for five-year age groups. Analyze what happens if projection by $\mathbf{M}^{-1}$ is attempted, using the eigenvalues to judge the degree of instability. Is the instability lessened by using wider age groups and correspondingly dropping the minor eigenvalues? Compare this backward projection with working back along cohort lines, and express in common-sense terms how each makes the inference; in what sense is the problem of saying from what the age distribution emerged more difficult than saying where it is going? (See Goodman, 1968a.)

Spectral operators are *idempotent*: they are equal to powers of themselves. Our $\mathbf{Z}_i$ satisfy this condition, for

$$\mathbf{Z}_i^2 = (\{\mathbf{K}_i\}[\mathbf{H}_i])(\{\mathbf{K}_i\}[\mathbf{H}_i]) = \{\mathbf{K}_i\}([\mathbf{H}_i]\{\mathbf{K}_i\})[\mathbf{H}_i] = \{\mathbf{K}_i\}[\mathbf{H}_i] = \mathbf{Z}_i\,,$$

if we have normalized according to (3.2.17) to make $[\mathbf{H}_i]\{\mathbf{K}_i\} = 1$. By repeating the argument, we obtain

$$\mathbf{Z}_i^k = \mathbf{Z}_i\,, \tag{3.2.32}$$

where k is any positive integer. What can be said when k is a negative integer?

Spectral operators are orthogonal. The matrices $\mathbf{Z}_i$ and $\mathbf{Z}_j$ also satisfy this condition:

$$\mathbf{Z}_i\mathbf{Z}_j = \{\mathbf{K}_i\}[\mathbf{H}_i]\{\mathbf{K}_j\}[\mathbf{H}_j] = \{\mathbf{K}_i\}([\mathbf{H}_i]\{\mathbf{K}_j\})[\mathbf{H}_j] = 0, \quad i \neq j\,,$$

since the expression $[\mathbf{H}_i]\{\mathbf{K}_j\}$ in parentheses is zero by the orthogonality property (3.2.22) with $i \neq j$.

Finally the sum of the spectral operators is the unit matrix. The total of our $\mathbf{Z}$'s,

$$\sum_i \mathbf{Z}_i = \{\mathbf{K}_1\}[\mathbf{H}_1] + \{\mathbf{K}_2\}[\mathbf{H}_2] + \cdots + \{\mathbf{K}_n\}[\mathbf{H}_n]\,, \tag{3.2.33}$$

is equal to **KH**, as may be seen by partitioning **KH** into the vectors by which **K** and **H** were defined, and then multiplying as though the vectors were scalar elements:

$$\mathbf{KH} = [\{\mathbf{K}_1\} \quad \{\mathbf{K}_2\} \cdots \{\mathbf{K}_n\}]\begin{Bmatrix} [\mathbf{H}_1] \\ [\mathbf{H}_2] \\ \vdots \\ [\mathbf{H}_n] \end{Bmatrix}. \tag{3.2.34}$$

The right-hand side of this multiplies to

$$\{\mathbf{K}_1\}[\mathbf{H}_1] + \{\mathbf{K}_2\}[\mathbf{H}_2] + \cdots + \{\mathbf{K}_n\}[\mathbf{H}_n] = \sum_i \mathbf{Z}_i\,.$$

But we proved earlier that the product on the left of (3.2.34) is $\mathbf{KH} = \mathbf{HK} = \mathbf{I}$, and hence we now have that $\sum_i \mathbf{Z}_i = \mathbf{I}$. This completes the theory lying behind the arithmetical relation of the $\mathbf{Z}$'s presented in Section 3.1. We go on now to theory for computing the $\mathbf{Z}$'s themselves.

3.3. ITERATIVE CALCULATION OF MATRIX COMPONENTS

Since λ_1 is larger in absolute value than the other roots, $\mathbf{Z}_1$ is computed readily by dividing (3.2.30) by λ_1^t to obtain

$$\frac{\mathbf{M}^t}{\lambda_1^t} = \mathbf{Z}_1 + \left(\frac{\lambda_2}{\lambda_1}\right)^t \mathbf{Z}_2 + \cdots + \left(\frac{\lambda_n}{\lambda_1}\right)^t \mathbf{Z}_n ,$$

so that if t is sufficiently large,

$$\mathbf{Z}_1 \doteqdot \mathbf{M}^t/\lambda_1^t ,$$

a fact that was exploited in Section 3.1. For 1964 United States male data, shown in Table 3.6, find λ_1, using $m_{11}^{(64)}$ and $m_{21}^{(64)}$ along with m_{21}, then check whether stability has been attained by finding whether $m_{21}^{(64)}$, $m_{31}^{(64)}$, and m_{32} produce the same λ_1. Verify some values of $\mathbf{Z}_1$, which was found as $\mathbf{M}^{64}/\lambda_1^{64}$.

From $\lambda_1 = 1.09149$ and $\lambda_2 = 0.3975 + 0.7891i$, we ascertain $|\lambda_2|/|\lambda_1| = 0.809$, and can apply (3.2.30) to find an upper limit to the error in $\mathbf{Z}_1$ when it is calculated as $\mathbf{M}^{64}/\lambda_1^{64}$. In fact $(0.809)^{64} = 1.3 \times 10^{-6}$, and hence the neglected terms are of the order of one-millionth of those included.

From λ_1 and the subdiagonal of the matrix $\mathbf{M}$ reproduce some of the ratios of successive column elements in $\mathbf{Z}_1$. Find the stable age distribution from the portion of $\mathbf{M}^{64}$ shown in Table 3.6, and verify that the number at age x to $x + 4$ at last birthday, $x = 5, 10, 15, \ldots$, is proportional to $\lambda^{-(x+2.5)/5}\,{}_5L_x$, where ${}_5L_x$ is taken from Table 1.3. Use any row of $\mathbf{Z}_1$ to verify the reproductive value for United States males shown in Table 3.4.

Since $\mathbf{Z}_1 = \{\mathbf{K}_1\}[\mathbf{H}_1]$, its rows are proportional to one another; it can have no nonvanishing determinant of second or higher order, which is to say it is of rank unity. (This is a special case of the rule that the rank of a product of matrices is less than or equal to the rank of each factor.) The rank of a matrix is unaffected by multiplication of all terms by a constant; in particular, $\mathbf{M}^t = \lambda_1^t\mathbf{Z}_1$ must be of the same rank as $\mathbf{Z}_1$ when t is large enough. Our computer program for the calculation of $\mathbf{Z}_1$ was controlled by the magnitude of the second-order determinant in the upper left of $\mathbf{M}^t$, this determinant being evaluated for each of the successive squarings of $\mathbf{M}$. When t was such that

$$\frac{\begin{vmatrix} m_{11}^{(t)} & m_{12}^{(t)} \\ m_{21}^{(t)} & m_{22}^{(t)} \end{vmatrix}}{m_{11}^{(t)} m_{12}^{(t)}} = \frac{m_{22}^{(t)}}{m_{12}^{(t)}} - \frac{m_{21}^{(t)}}{m_{11}^{(t)}}$$

became less than 0.000001, the program stopped squaring, calculated λ_1 by

$$\lambda_1 = m_{21}^{(t+1)}/m_{21}^{(t)} ,$$

and then divided all terms of $\mathbf{M}^t$ by λ_1^t to obtain $\mathbf{Z}_1$. In this instance, we can reasonably take the risk of supposing all two-by-two determinants to vanish when one does.

Table 3.6 Matrix **M**, principal spectral component $\mathbf{Z}_1$, and powers of **M** and $\mathbf{N} = \mathbf{M} - \lambda_1 \mathbf{Z}_1$, United States males, 1964*

$100{,}000\underset{\sim}{M} =$

0	2	2131	23472	48038	44940	28323	14717	6414	2709	986
99571	0	0	0	0	0	0	0	0	0	0
0	99757	0	0	0	0	0	0	0	0	0
0	0	99547	0	0	0	0	0	0	0	0
0	0	0	99190	0	0	0	0	0	0	0
0	0	0	0	99086	0	0	0	0	0	0
0	0	0	0	0	99031	0	0	0	0	0
0	0	0	0	0	0	98742	0	0	0	0
0	0	0	0	0	0	0	98138	0	0	0
0	0	0	0	0	0	0	0	97071	0	0
0	0	0	0	0	0	0	0	0	95305	0

$100{,}000 \dfrac{\underset{\sim}{M}^{64}}{\lambda_1^{64}} = 100{,}000\underset{\sim}{Z}_1 =$

17408	19083	20879	22520	20662	14321	7884	3722	1529	569	157
15880	17408	19047	20544	18849	13064	7193	3396	1395	519	144
14514	15910	17408	18776	17227	11940	6574	3103	1275	475	131
13237	14510	15876	17124	15711	10890	5995	2830	1163	433	120
12029	13186	14428	15562	14278	9896	5448	2572	1057	393	109
10920	11970	13098	14127	12962	8984	4946	2335	959	357	99
9908	10861	11883	12818	11760	8151	4488	2118	870	324	90
8963	9825	10750	11595	10639	7374	4060	1916	787	293	81
8059	8834	9666	10426	9565	6630	3650	1723	708	264	73
7167	7857	8596	9272	8507	5896	3246	1532	630	234	65
6258	6860	7506	8096	7428	5148	2834	1338	550	205	56

* Programmed by William Lindeman and Belinda Bourque.

Table 3.6 (continued)

$$\underset{\sim}{M}^{64} = \begin{bmatrix} 47.211 & 51.753 & \cdots & 0.426 \\ 43.068 & 47.211 & \cdots & 0.389 \\ 39.362 & 43.149 & \cdots & 0.356 \\ 35.899 & 39.353 & \cdots & 0.324 \\ 32.624 & 35.762 & \cdots & 0.295 \\ 29.616 & 32.465 & \cdots & 0.268 \\ 26.870 & 29.455 & \cdots & 0.243 \\ 24.309 & 26.647 & \cdots & 0.220 \\ 21.856 & 23.959 & \cdots & 0.197 \\ 19.437 & 21.308 & \cdots & 0.176 \\ 16.972 & 18.605 & \cdots & 0.153 \end{bmatrix} \qquad \underset{\sim}{M}^{65} = \begin{bmatrix} 51.531 & 56.488 & \cdots & 0.466 \\ 47.009 & 51.530 & \cdots & 0.425 \\ 42.963 & 47.096 & \cdots & 0.388 \\ 39.184 & 42.953 & \cdots & 0.354 \\ 35.609 & 39.034 & \cdots & 0.322 \\ 32.325 & 35.435 & \cdots & 0.292 \\ 29.329 & 32.150 & \cdots & 0.265 \\ 26.532 & 29.084 & \cdots & 0.240 \\ 23.855 & 26.150 & \cdots & 0.216 \\ 21.216 & 23.257 & \cdots & 0.192 \\ 18.525 & 20.307 & \cdots & 0.167 \end{bmatrix}$$

$$10^6\underset{\sim}{N}^{64} = \begin{bmatrix} -45.464 & \cdots \\ 111.237 & \cdots \\ 170.848 & \cdots \\ 31.680 & \cdots \\ -184.107 & \cdots \\ -225.650 & \cdots \\ 3.871 & \cdots \\ 286.555 & \cdots \\ 281.562 & \cdots \\ -71.380 & \cdots \\ -402.962 & \cdots \end{bmatrix} \qquad 10^6\underset{\sim}{N}^{65} = \begin{bmatrix} -123.348 & \cdots \\ -45.269 & \cdots \\ 110.966 & \cdots \\ 170.074 & \cdots \\ 31.424 & \cdots \\ -182.424 & \cdots \\ -223.464 & \cdots \\ 3.823 & \cdots \\ 281.218 & \cdots \\ 273.314 & \cdots \\ -68.029 & \cdots \end{bmatrix} \qquad 10^6\underset{\sim}{N}^{66} = \begin{bmatrix} -62.561 & \cdots \\ -122.819 & \cdots \\ -45.159 & \cdots \\ 110.464 & \cdots \\ 168.697 & \cdots \\ 31.136 & \cdots \\ -180.656 & \cdots \\ -220.653 & \cdots \\ 3.752 & \cdots \\ 272.982 & \cdots \\ 260.482 & \cdots \end{bmatrix}$$

To use the analog of $\mathbf{Z}_1 = \mathbf{M}^t/\lambda_1^t$ for finding the next pair of components $\mathbf{Z}_2$, $\mathbf{Z}_3$, we first remove $\lambda_1\mathbf{Z}_1$, that is, calculate the deflated

$$\mathbf{M} = \lambda_1\mathbf{Z}_1 = \lambda_2\mathbf{Z}_2 + \lambda_3\mathbf{Z}_3 + \cdots + \lambda_n\mathbf{Z}_n = \mathbf{N}\,,$$

and take $\mathbf{N}$ to a high power. We need not go as high as for the first latent root, because the drop in absolute value from the third to the fourth roots is greater than from the first to the second. The ratio of the fourth to the third for United States males, 1964, is $|\lambda_4|/|\lambda_3| = 0.6$, which is less than the square of $|\lambda_2|/|\lambda_1| = 0.809$, the ratio of the second to the first. Less than half the power t used for λ_1 will therefore serve. Verify this also on the roots for Mexican and United States females given in Table 3.3, and compare with λ_2/λ_1 and λ_3/λ_2 in the abridged example for the United States, 1965, of Section 3.1.

Because the λ_2 and λ_3 are of the same absolute value they cannot be separated by taking a single high power of $\mathbf{N}$. We need altogether three powers, say $\mathbf{N}^t$, $\mathbf{N}^{t+1}$, $\mathbf{N}^{t+2}$. Then if t is large enough that other terms are negligible, we have

$$\begin{aligned}\mathbf{N}^t &= \lambda_2^t\mathbf{Z}_2 + \lambda_3^t\mathbf{Z}_3\,,\\ \mathbf{N}^{t+1} &= \lambda_2^{t+1}\mathbf{Z}_2 + \lambda_3^{t+1}\mathbf{Z}_3\,,\\ \mathbf{N}^{t+2} &= \lambda_2^{t+2}\mathbf{Z}_2 + \lambda_3^{t+2}\mathbf{Z}_3\,.\end{aligned} \tag{3.3.1}$$

The same equations apply to any one element, say the jth of the ith row. Eliminating the corresponding element of $\mathbf{Z}$ gives

$$\begin{vmatrix} n_{ij}^{(t)} & \lambda_2^t & \lambda_3^t \\ n_{ij}^{(t+1)} & \lambda_2^{t+1} & \lambda_3^{t+1} \\ n_{ij}^{(t+2)} & \lambda_2^{t+2} & \lambda_3^{t+2} \end{vmatrix} = 0\,.$$

Dividing through by $\lambda_2^t\lambda_3^t(\lambda_2 - \lambda_3)$ and evaluating the determinant results in

$$n_{ij}^{(t+2)} - (\lambda_2 + \lambda_3)n_{ij}^{(t+1)} + (\lambda_2\lambda_3)n_{ij}^{(t)} = 0\,. \tag{3.3.2}$$

If $i = 1, 2$, and $j = 1$, we have the pair

$$\begin{aligned} n_{11}^{(t+2)} - (\lambda_2 + \lambda_3)n_{11}^{(t+1)} + (\lambda_2\lambda_3)n_{11}^{(t)} &\doteqdot 0\,,\\ n_{21}^{(t+2)} - (\lambda_2 + \lambda_3)n_{21}^{(t+1)} + (\lambda_2\lambda_3)n_{21}^{(t)} &\doteqdot 0\,.\end{aligned} \tag{3.3.3}$$

A convenient way of solving (3.3.3) for the unknown λ_2 and λ_3 follows from noting that λ_2 and λ_3 are the roots in x of $(x - \lambda_2)(x - \lambda_3) = 0$, or

$$x^2 - (\lambda_2 + \lambda_3)x + \lambda_2\lambda_3 = 0\,. \tag{3.3.4}$$

Eliminating $\lambda_2 + \lambda_3$ and $\lambda_2\lambda_3$ from (3.3.3) and (3.3.4) provides a quadratic

$$\begin{vmatrix} x^2 & x & 1 \\ n_{11}^{(t+2)} & n_{11}^{(t+1)} & n_{11}^{(t)} \\ n_{21}^{(t+2)} & n_{21}^{(t+1)} & n_{21}^{(t)} \end{vmatrix} = 0\,, \tag{3.3.5}$$

whose roots in x must be λ_2 and λ_3. Equation (3.3.5) for United States males, 1964, comes out to

$$x^2 - 0.7949x + 0.7807 = 0\,, \tag{3.3.6}$$

on using the printout of Table 3.6 once again, with $t = 64$. By completing the square in (3.3.6) we find

$$x = -0.3975 \pm 0.7891i = \lambda_2, \lambda_3\,.$$

Form similar quadratic equations from other elements, and solve them, so illustrating that λ_2, λ_3 do not depend on which elements are chosen.

When the power required is low, economy is served by starting with an arbitrary vector and repeatedly multiplying it by the matrix. This method, written symbolically as $\mathbf{M}(\mathbf{M}(\cdots(\mathbf{MK}))\cdots)$, does not permit the shortcut of successive squaring which may be described as $\mathbf{M}^{(2^s)}$, but each matrix multiplication requires only $1/n$ as many scalar multiplications as a squaring of an $n \times n$ matrix. The reader may show that the break-even point on the number of scalar multiplications is at $2^s n^2 = sn^3 + n^2$, where 2^s is the power required. By making a table of $n = (2^s - 1)/s$, the value of s can be read off for each n. The preferred method depends on how high a power we need: with an $n \times n = 9 \times 9$ matrix, successive squaring is cheaper for 64th and higher powers.

The method of finding the roots, real and complex, described in these pages is applicable where an arbitrary vector is repeatedly premultiplied by the given matrix $\mathbf{M}$. If $\{\mathbf{K}^{(0)}\}$ is the arbitrary vector, and $k_i^{(t)}$ the typical member of $\mathbf{M}^t\{\mathbf{K}^{(0)}\}$, then $\lambda_1 \doteqdot k_i^{(t+1)}/k_i^{(t)}$ for t large; the reader may wish to devise a solution for λ_2 and λ_3 by this alternative procedure.

The calculation of the second and third spectral components is not difficult once λ_2 and λ_3 are available. When the deflated matrix, from which the first spectral component has been subtracted,

$$\mathbf{N} = \mathbf{M} - \lambda_1\mathbf{Z}_1\,,$$

is raised to the $(t + 1)$th power, it is

$$\mathbf{N}^{t+1} \doteqdot \lambda_2^{t+1}\mathbf{Z}_2 + \lambda_3^{t+1}\mathbf{Z}_3\,;$$

to the $(t + 2)$th power it is

$$\mathbf{N}^{t+2} \doteqdot \lambda_2^{t+2}\mathbf{Z}_2 + \lambda_3^{t+2}\mathbf{Z}_3\,.$$

Subtracting the first of these multiplied by λ_3 from the second gives

$$\mathbf{N}^{t+2} - \lambda_3\mathbf{N}^{t+1} = (\lambda_2^{t+2} - \lambda_3\lambda_2^{t+1})\mathbf{Z}_2\,,$$

so that

$$\mathbf{Z}_2 = \frac{\mathbf{N}^{t+2} - \lambda_3\mathbf{N}^{t+1}}{\lambda_2^{t+2} - \lambda_3\lambda_2^{t+1}}\,, \tag{3.3.7}$$

and $\mathbf{Z}_3$ is obtained from this by interchanging subscripts.

Table 3.7 Projection Matrix **M**, and its first two spectral components $\mathbf{Z}_1$ and $\mathbf{Z}_2$, Canadian females, 1965

AGE	PROJECTION MATRIX $\underset{\sim}{M}$: SUBDIAGONAL	PROJECTION MATRIX $\underset{\sim}{M}$: FIRST ROW	FIRST SPECTRAL COMPONENT $\underset{\sim}{Z}_1$: COLUMN $\{\underset{\sim}{K}_1\}$	FIRST SPECTRAL COMPONENT $\underset{\sim}{Z}_1$: ROW $[\underset{\sim}{H}_1]'$
0	0.99651	0.00000	0.10618	1.059
5	0.99820	0.00024	0.09832	1.144
10	0.99802	0.05861	0.09119	1.233
15	0.99729	0.28608	0.08456	1.267
20	0.99694	0.44791	0.07836	1.064
25	0.99621	0.36399	0.07259	0.673
30	0.99460	0.22259	0.06719	0.340
35	0.99184	0.10457	0.06210	0.131
40	0.98700	0.02826	0.05723	0.030
45	0.97899	0.00240	0.05248	0.002

AGE	SECOND SPECTRAL COMPONENT $\underset{\sim}{Z}_2$: COLUMN $\{\underset{\sim}{K}_2\}$	SECOND SPECTRAL COMPONENT $\underset{\sim}{Z}_2$: ROW $[\underset{\sim}{H}_2]'$
0	0.1642 + 0.0854i	0.1642 + 0.0854i
5	0.1738 - 0.1300i	-0.0049 + 0.1577i
10	-0.0490 - 0.2503i	-0.1228 + 0.0545i
15	-0.2898 - 0.0757i	-0.0968 - 0.0791i
20	-0.2276 + 0.2680i	-0.0222 - 0.1280i
25	0.1674 + 0.3771i	0.0163 - 0.1028i
30	0.4835 + 0.0150i	0.0250 - 0.0567i
35	0.2614 - 0.5022i	0.0162 - 0.0209i
40	-0.3958 - 0.5294i	0.0048 - 0.0043i
45	-0.7535 + 0.1474i	0.0004 - 0.0003i

We will need $\lambda_2\mathbf{Z}_2 + \lambda_3\mathbf{Z}_3$ to deflate $\mathbf{N}$ and continue the process. From (3.3.7) this is

$$\lambda_2\mathbf{Z}_2 + \lambda_3\mathbf{Z}_3 = \frac{1}{\lambda_2 - \lambda_3}\left(\frac{\mathbf{N}^{t+2} - \lambda_3\mathbf{N}^{t+1}}{\lambda_2^t} - \frac{\mathbf{N}^{t+2} - \lambda_2\mathbf{N}^{t+1}}{\lambda_3^t}\right). \tag{3.3.8}$$

If $\lambda_2 = e^{x+iy}$ we may express (3.3.8) in real terms. Using the fact that $e^{x+iy} = e^x(\cos y + i \sin y)$, and also that $\sin(A + B) = \sin A \cos B + \cos A \sin B$, we finally arrive at

$$\lambda_2\mathbf{Z}_2 + \lambda_3\mathbf{Z}_3 = \frac{\mathbf{N}^{t+1}e^{-tx}\sin(t+1)y - \mathbf{N}^{t+2}e^{-(t+1)x}\sin ty}{\sin y}. \tag{3.3.9}$$

(Verify this by finding its limiting value, if $\lambda_4 = \lambda_5 = \cdots = 0$ for $t = 0$ and $t = 1$, and see whether it applies to the real root by making y tend to zero. Remember that the limit of $\sin ty/\sin y$ as y tends to zero is t.) The method risks serious rounding error after the first three roots.

3.4. INTERPRETATION OF RESULTS

A numerical application of the methods of this chapter is published in detail for United States females, 1963 (Keyfitz, 1967), and need not be repeated here. Instead, an abridged result of decomposition is shown for a different population: Canadian females, 1965. Table 3.7 gives the original matrix $\mathbf{M}$, the vertical vector $\{\mathbf{K}_1\}$ normed to a total of unity, the stable population as a percentage distribution, and the horizontal stable vector $[\mathbf{H}_1]'$ (i.e., transposed for convenience in printing) with a girl child just born as the unit. These are proportional to the columns and rows respectively of the first stable matrix $\mathbf{Z}_1$. Corresponding numbers for the second stable matrix $\mathbf{Z}_2$ are also shown.

Now we need only the numbers c_1, and c_2, c_3 from (3.2.25) in order to work out the decomposition of the observed $\{\mathbf{K}^{(0)}\}$ in Table 3.8. They are $c_1 = 9{,}838{,}600$ and $c_2, c_3 = 83{,}669 \pm 252{,}529i$, and it may be verified that, multiplied by the column vectors in Table 3.7, these produce the two main components of Table 3.8.

The first component allows for that part of $\{\mathbf{K}^{(0)}\}$ which is stable. Departures from stability whose periodicity is the generation are covered by the contributions of the second and third roots. Because the low births of the late 1930's are separated by about a generation, the wavelength of the second root, from the dip of the 1960's, the second component has much weight in the decomposition according to (3.2.23), shown as Table 3.8. Verify the second and third columns of Table 3.8 from the c's given at the bottom of the table and the stable vectors of Table 3.7. You will find, for instance, that for age 10 the element of the first component $c_1\{\mathbf{K}_1\}$ is

$$(9{,}838{,}600)(0.09119) = 897{,}000\ ,$$

Table 3.8 Decomposition of observed age 42 distribution $\{\mathbf{K}^{(0)}\}$ into three components by (3.2.23), Canadian females, 1965 (thousands)

AGE	OBSERVED POPULATION $\{K^{(0)}\}$	CONTRIBUTION OF: DOMINANT TERM CONTAINING REAL ROOT $c_1\{K_1\}$	SECOND AND THIRD TERMS $c_2\{K_2\}+c_3\{K_3\}$	FOURTH TO NINTH TERMS $c_4\{K_4\} + \cdots + c_9\{K_9\}$
0	1067	1045	-16	38
5	1051	967	95	-11
10	966	897	118	-49
15	847	832	-10	25
20	665	771	-173	67
25	581	714	-162	30
30	589	661	73	-145
35	621	611	297	-287
40	615	563	201	-149
45	528	516	-200	212
50	469	470	-470	469
55+	1480	1791		
TOTAL	9479	9838		

$$c_1 = 9{,}838{,}600,$$

$$c_2,\ c_3 = 83{,}669 \pm 252{,}529i.$$

and of the second and third components is

$$(83{,}669 + 252{,}529i)(-0.0490 - 0.2503i) + (83{,}669 - 252{,}529i)(-0.0490 + 0.2503i) = 118{,}216\ ,$$

a real quantity rounded in Table 3.8 to 118,000.

Table 3.9 shows two components of the projection as carried out by (3.2.26). The relative and absolute decline of the effect of roots beyond the first is conspicuous. Find the ratio of absolute values $|\lambda_2|/|\lambda_1|$ from the roots for Canada,

Table 3.9 Projection from 1965 to 2015 and to 2065 on fixed age-specific rates, showing effects of dominant and of other roots according to (3.2.26), Canadian females (thousands)

AGE	2015		2065	
	DOMINANT TERM CONTAINING REAL ROOT $c_1\lambda_1^{10}\{\underset{\sim}{K}_1\}$	OTHER TERMS $\sum_{i=2}^{9} c_i\lambda_i^{10}\{\underset{\sim}{K}_i\}$	DOMINANT TERM CONTAINING REAL ROOT $c_1\lambda_1^{20}\{\underset{\sim}{K}_1\}$	OTHER TERMS $\sum_{i=2}^{9} c_i\lambda_i^{20}\{\underset{\sim}{K}_i\}$
0	2170	29	4557	9
5	2010	36	4219	4
10	1864	1	3914	-2
15	1729	-23	3629	1
20	1602	-15	3363	6
25	1484	27	3115	9
30	1373	55	2884	1
35	1269	25	2665	-11
40	1170	-39	2456	-14
45	1073	-94	2252	-1
50	976	24	2049	14
55+	3722	-26	7814	-16

1965, of Table 3.10 and see whether the powers of this ratio explain the decline in the second column of Table 3.9 from 1965 to 2015 and from 2015 to 2065.

The λ are less readily interpreted than their logarithms. If λ_1 is the ratio of a stable population at a given time to that five years earlier, then $r_1 = 0.2 \ln \lambda_1$ is the annual rate of increase compounded momently. For a complex root, say $\lambda = u + iv$, suppose the corresponding $r = 0.2 \ln \lambda = 0.2 \ln (u + iv)$ is $x + iy$. Then we have by Demoivre's theorem (Chrystal, 1961, Vol. I, p. 235)

$$e^{5(x+iy)} = e^{5x}(\cos 5y + i \sin 5y) = u + iv\ ,$$

so that the absolute value or *modulus* is

$$|\lambda| = \sqrt{u^2 + v^2} = e^{5x}\ ,$$

Table 3.10 Principal characteristic roots $r = 0.2 \ln \lambda$, Canadian and United States female populations*

	$r_1 = 0.2 \ln \lambda_1$	$r_2, r_3 = 0.2 \ln (\lambda_2, \lambda_3)$ $x \pm iy$
CANADA		
1965	0.01469	-0.0326 ± 0.2244i
1964	0.01843	-0.0285 ± 0.2264i
1963	0.02002	-0.0275 ± 0.2274i
1960-62	0.02131	-0.0274 ± 0.2275i
1950-52	0.01698	-0.0293 ± 0.2179i
1940-42	0.00735	-0.0351 ± 0.2078i
1930-32	0.00904	-0.0317 ± 0.2029i
UNITED STATES**		
1965	0.01267	-0.0390 ± 0.2346i
1964	0.01613	-0.0346 ± 0.2370i
1963	0.01753	-0.0335 ± 0.2387i
1962	0.01929	-0.0323 ± 0.2405i
1959-61	0.02119	-0.0317 ± 0.2418i
1949-51	0.01440	-0.0406 ± 0.2330i
1939-41	0.00094	-0.0513 ± 0.2189i
1929-31	0.00251	-0.0499 ± 0.2096i

* Programmed by Wilhelm Flieger.
** Births adjusted.

and the *argument* is

$$\arg \lambda_2 = \arctan (v/u) = 5y\,.$$

Now (3.2.26) becomes

$$\mathbf{M}^t\{\mathbf{K}^{(0)}\} = e^{5r_1t}c_1\{\mathbf{K}_1\} + e^{5r_2t}c_2\{\mathbf{K}_2\} + \cdots + e^{5r_9t}c_9\{\mathbf{K}_9\}\,, \qquad (3.4.1)$$

$$= e^{5r_1t}c_1\{\mathbf{K}_1\} + \sum_{s=2}^{9} c_s e^{5x_st}(\cos 5y_st + i \sin 5y_st)\{\mathbf{K}_s\}\,. \qquad (3.4.2)$$

All the elements of each even-numbered term are *complex conjugates* of the next following odd-numbered term, that is, the successive even and odd terms are of the form $a + ib$ and $a - ib$ respectively, where a and b are real. This is proved by the method of (5.2.3) below. Satisfy yourself that multiplication and exponentiation performed on complex conjugates results in complex conjugates, and hence that the right-hand side of (3.4.2) is necessarily a sum of real vectors.

We can thus see what happens for any of the r with the increase of t by breaking out $\lambda^t = e^{5rt}$ in terms of $r = x + iy$. The real part x is negative, and e^{5xt} is therefore an exponential dying-away curve, which determines the rate of damping of the waves. When t has increased by $2\pi/y$ the quantities $\cos yt$ and $\sin yt$ of (3.4.2) are back in the same phase. Hence $2\pi/y$ is their wavelength and y their frequency.

The record for Canadian and United States female population from 1930 to the 1960's is shown in Table 3.10. The real root, $r_1 = 0.2 \ln \lambda_1$, is the rate, compounded continuously, at which the female population would increase if the age-specific rates of mortality and fertility of the year in question were maintained long enough for the initial age distribution to wear off. As between the United States and Canada, movement of r_1 in recent years is very similar, but about 1930 the United States was considerably more "advanced," which is to say lower, by $0.00904 - (0.00251)$ or about $\frac{2}{3}\%$ per annum.

For the United States the real part x of the first complex root $r_2 = x + iy$ moves from -0.0513 in 1939–41 to -0.0317 in 1959–61; this corresponds to the narrowing of the range of ages within which reproduction takes place: the narrower this range of ages, the less rapid the damping of waves arising from disturbances in the age distribution (Section 6.4).

The imaginary part y, on the other hand, has increased; thus the period of the waves caused in later generations by a disturbance in the age distribution, which is equal to $2\pi/y$ years, tends to diminish. The upward trend in y shown in Table 3.10, from 0.2189 in 1939–41 to 0.2418 in 1959–61, corresponds to a decline in the wavelength from $2\pi/0.2189 = 28.70$ years to $2\pi/0.2418 = 25.99$ years. These periods are related to the mean age of women at childbearing, a theme to be investigated in Chapter 6. The changes are more consistent in the United States figures than in the Canadian.

CHAPTER 4

PROJECTION MATRIX CHANGING THROUGH TIME

4.1. EXPERIMENTS ON THE EFFECTS OF CHANGE IN BIRTH AND DEATH RATES

The analysis up to this point has consisted in premultiplication of a given age vector by powers of a fixed matrix. But just as the usual population projection can incorporate changing birth and death rates, so can the matrix formulation of that projection. The projected population after two cycles will not be $\mathbf{M}^2\{\mathbf{K}^{(0)}\}$ but $\mathbf{M}^{(1)}\mathbf{M}^{(0)}\{\mathbf{K}^{(0)}\}$, where $\mathbf{M}^{(0)}$ is made from the set of mortality and fertility rates expected to apply over the first period, and $\mathbf{M}^{(1)}$ from the set over the second. It will sometimes be of interest to suppose that the premultiplying matrix changes over time in a given systematic fashion.

As an example, consider the birth rates of an under-developed country and suppose that in the future they decline until they are at a level appropriate to its low death rates. Mexico's 1960 crude birth rate of 46.0 per thousand is not appropriate to its death rate of 11.5, as proved by the fact that the continuation of these rates would multiply the population by $(1.0 + 0.0460 - 0.0115)^{100} = 29.7$ during the course of a century, bringing it to $(34{,}923{,}000)(29.7) = 1{,}038{,}000{,}000$, and by the end of a second century to 30.8×10^9, or nine times the present population of the planet. Since change, preferably in the form of a decline of birth rates, is certain to occur, we ask how much difference it makes to the ultimate population whether the change takes place slowly or quickly, over 15 years or over 40 years. The following pages describe a computer program that would be suitable for any two sets of fertility and mortality patterns, in order to study the changing distribution by age as an initially given population moves more or less rapidly from one set of rates to the other. It will suffice to trace the female population 0–44 years of age, and the discussion is confined to this group.

The data used in the illustration are for Mexico, 1960, and the United States, 1940. Table 4.1 shows the two matrices. We may think of the Mexico, 1960, matrix as at the midpoint of a *demographic transition* (Notestein *et al.*, 1944), where mortality has fallen but fertility remains high. The United States, 1940, may be thought of as the endpoint of such a transition, in which births have fallen to where deaths are barely replaced. Mexico, 1960, had a female domi-

Table 4.1 Matrices $\mathbf{M}_0$ (Mexico, 1960) and $\mathbf{M}_1$ (United States, 1940) representing the assumed initial and final conditions of mortality and fertility for females in hypothetical demographic transition

$$
\underset{\sim}{M}_0 = \begin{bmatrix}
0 & 0 & 0.1145 & 0.4413 & 0.6689 & 0.6383 & 0.5132 & 0.3197 & 0.1025 \\
0.9650 & 0 & 0 & 0 & 0 & 0 & 0 & 0 & 0 \\
0 & 0.9902 & 0 & 0 & 0 & 0 & 0 & 0 & 0 \\
0 & 0 & 0.9923 & 0 & 0 & 0 & 0 & 0 & 0 \\
0 & 0 & 0 & 0.9888 & 0 & 0 & 0 & 0 & 0 \\
0 & 0 & 0 & 0 & 0.9811 & 0 & 0 & 0 & 0 \\
0 & 0 & 0 & 0 & 0 & 0.9805 & 0 & 0 & 0 \\
0 & 0 & 0 & 0 & 0 & 0 & 0.9765 & 0 & 0 \\
0 & 0 & 0 & 0 & 0 & 0 & 0 & 0.9715 & 0
\end{bmatrix}
$$

$$
\underset{\sim}{M}_1 = \begin{bmatrix}
0 & 0 & 0.0633 & 0.2199 & 0.2987 & 0.2384 & 0.1498 & 0.0737 & 0.0203 \\
0.9909 & 0 & 0 & 0 & 0 & 0 & 0 & 0 & 0 \\
0 & 0.9959 & 0 & 0 & 0 & 0 & 0 & 0 & 0 \\
0 & 0 & 0.9942 & 0 & 0 & 0 & 0 & 0 & 0 \\
0 & 0 & 0 & 0.9909 & 0 & 0 & 0 & 0 & 0 \\
0 & 0 & 0 & 0 & 0.9886 & 0 & 0 & 0 & 0 \\
0 & 0 & 0 & 0 & 0 & 0.9864 & 0 & 0 & 0 \\
0 & 0 & 0 & 0 & 0 & 0 & 0.9830 & 0 & 0 \\
0 & 0 & 0 & 0 & 0 & 0 & 0 & 0.9800 & 0
\end{bmatrix}
$$

nant root $\lambda_1 = 1.182$ corresponding to an annual increase of 33.9 per thousand; the United States in 1940 was very nearly stationary, i.e., with $\lambda_1 = 1$. The curve of change assumed arbitrarily for the future of Mexico implies a birth rate which first declines slowly, then declines rapidly, and finally levels off. This S-shaped curve, similar to the *logistic* of Eq. (9.2.4) and portrayed in Fig. 9.1, has been several times applied in demography (Verhulst, 1838; Pearl and Reed, 1920).

We will define our variant of the logistic by considering the initial and final forms of the projection matrix, and showing a simple way of establishing a transition from the one to the other. If the initial projection matrix, applicable to Mexico in 1960, is called $\mathbf{M}_0$, and the final one, derived from the United States 1940, is $\mathbf{M}_1$, then suppose the difference $\mathbf{M}_0 - \mathbf{M}_1$ to be divided into seven (not all equal) portions. The projection from 1960 to 1964 will be by $\mathbf{M}_0$, that between 1965 and 1969 by $\mathbf{M}_0$ less the first of these portions, that for 1970–74 by M_0 less the first and second of these portions, etc., and over the period 1995–99 and subsequently by M_0 less all of these portions, or by $\mathbf{M}_0 - (\mathbf{M}_0 - \mathbf{M}_1) = \mathbf{M}_1$. The change in the premultiplying matrix in any period is related to the distance from the start and also to that from the end of the transition. For 1965–69 the deduction from M_0 is proportional to $(1)(7) = 7$; for 1970–74 the further deduction is proportional to $(2)(6) = 12$; for 1975–79 to $(3)(5) = 15$, etc. The total of

$$7 + 12 + 15 + 16 + 15 + 12 + 7 = 84$$

provides the denominator for the cumulative fractions

$$\tfrac{0}{84},\ \tfrac{7}{84},\ \tfrac{19}{84},\ \tfrac{34}{84},\ \tfrac{50}{84},\ \tfrac{65}{84},\ \tfrac{77}{84},\ \tfrac{84}{84}.$$

Thus the matrices used were

$$\begin{aligned}
&\text{for } 1960\text{–}64, && \mathbf{M}_0 - \tfrac{0}{84}(\mathbf{M}_0 - \mathbf{M}_1) = \mathbf{M}_0 = \mathbf{M}^{(0)}, \\
&\text{for } 1965\text{–}69, && \mathbf{M}_0 - \tfrac{7}{84}(\mathbf{M}_0 - \mathbf{M}_1) = \tfrac{77}{84}\mathbf{M}_0 + \tfrac{7}{84}\mathbf{M}_1 = \mathbf{M}^{(1)}, \\
&\text{for } 1970\text{–}74, && \mathbf{M}_0 - \tfrac{19}{84}(\mathbf{M}_0 - \mathbf{M}_1) = \tfrac{65}{84}\mathbf{M}_0 + \tfrac{19}{84}\mathbf{M}_1 = \mathbf{M}^{(2)}, \\
&\quad\vdots && \\
&\text{for } 1990\text{–}94, && \mathbf{M}_0 - \tfrac{77}{84}(\mathbf{M}_0 - \mathbf{M}_1) = \tfrac{7}{84}\mathbf{M}_0 + \tfrac{77}{84}\mathbf{M}_1 = \mathbf{M}^{(6)}, \\
&\text{for } 1995\text{–}99, && \mathbf{M}_0 - \tfrac{84}{84}(\mathbf{M}_0 - \mathbf{M}_1) = \mathbf{M}_1 = \mathbf{M}^{(7)}.
\end{aligned}$$

In general, where the transition is spread not over 7 but over s cycles or $5s$ years, the matrix used to project from $1960 + 5i$ to $1960 + 5(i + 1)$ would be

$$\mathbf{M}_0 - \left[\frac{(i)(i+1)(3s-2i+2)}{(s)(s+1)(s+2)}\right](\mathbf{M}_0 - \mathbf{M}_1). \tag{4.1.1}$$

This uses the fact that

$$(1)(s) + (2)(s-1) + \cdots + (s)(1) = (s)(s+1)(s+2)/6,$$

which the reader may derive by equating the two forms of the coefficient of x^{s-1} in the identity $(1-x)^{-2}(1-x)^{-2} = (1-x)^{-4}$.

Given the following age vector for Mexican females,

$$\{\mathbf{K}^{(0)}\} = 1000\begin{Bmatrix} 2840 \\ 2611 \\ 2124 \\ 1796 \\ 1542 \\ 1309 \\ 1043 \\ 962 \\ 687 \end{Bmatrix},$$

totalling 14,914,000 girls and women under 45 years of age in 1960, along with the matrix $\mathbf{M}_0$ of Table 4.1, verify the common first row for 1965 of Table 4.2. Use $\mathbf{M}_1$ to verify the figures for the year 2000 under the 15-year transition.

Over the time when the matrix is assumed changing, verification requires a weighted mean of $\mathbf{M}_0$ and $\mathbf{M}_1$. For the change from 1975 to 1980 we have from (4.1.1) for $i = 3$ and $s = 5$

$$\mathbf{M}^{(3)} = \frac{13\mathbf{M}_0 + 22\mathbf{M}_1}{35}.$$

For the projection from 0–4 to 5–9 this gives

$$m_{12} = \frac{(13)(0.9650) + (22)(0.9909)}{35} = 0.9813,$$

and (4062)(0.9813) is 3986 for age 5–9 in 1980 as shown. For age 0–4 in 1980, we need the weighted mean of all elements of the first row. For example, the first nonzero element is

$$\frac{(13)(0.1145) + (22)(0.0633)}{35} = 0.08232.$$

Then for the number 0–4 in 1980 for $s = 5$ we have

$$(0.08232)(3668) + (0.30213)(2697) + \cdots + (0.05083)(1223) = 3808$$

as shown.

The three examples, $s = 3$, $s = 5$, $s = 7$, of Table 4.2 all end up with the same rates, but the consequence of having the change take place over 15 years is a population of 27,308,000 women 0–44 years of age by the end of the century, while having it take place over 25 years results in 31,664,000, or 16% more.

Table 4.2 Projected female population of Mexico, 1965–2000, assuming transition starting 1965 from mortality and fertility of Mexico, 1960, to mortality and fertility of United States, 1940, over 15, 25, and 35 years (thousands)

YEAR	0-4	5-9	10-14	15-19	20-24	25-34	35-44	0-44
	TRANSITION SPREAD OVER 15 YEARS: s = 3							
1965	3816	2740	2585	2108	1776	2796	1953	17,775
1970	3663	3712	2718	2567	2085	3232	2248	20,226
1975	3044	3601	3690	2701	2542	3776	2685	22,040
1980	2467	3016	3587	3669	2677	4542	3119	23,077
1985	2890	2445	3004	3566	3636	5125	3651	24,316
1990	3243	2864	2435	2986	3534	6204	4392	25,658
1995	3333	3214	2852	2421	2959	7039	4954	26,772
2000	3198	3303	3200	2836	2399	6372	6000	27,308
	TRANSITION SPREAD OVER 25 YEARS: s = 5							
1965	3816	2740	2585	2108	1776	2796	1953	17,775
1970	4080	3696	2716	2566	2085	3229	2245	20,617
1975	4062	3977	3668	2697	2540	3765	2676	23,384
1980	3808	3986	3952	3644	2670	4522	3101	25,683
1985	3510	3760	3966	3928	3610	5104	3628	27,506
1990	3371	3478	3744	3944	3893	6170	4369	28,968
1995	3726	3340	3464	3723	3908	7368	4934	30,463
2000	3887	3692	3327	3444	3689	7659	5967	31,664
	TRANSITION SPREAD OVER 35 YEARS: s = 7							
1965	3816	2740	2585	2108	1776	2796	1953	17,775
1970	4238	3690	2715	2566	2085	3227	2244	20,766
1975	4512	4115	3659	2695	2538	3761	2672	23,952
1980	4615	4401	4084	3634	2667	4511	3091	27,004
1985	4628	4525	4373	4057	3598	5087	3611	29,879
1990	4552	4559	4500	4346	4019	6141	4344	32,460
1995	4375	4501	4538	4474	4306	7471	4907	34,572
2000	4264	4335	4483	4512	4433	8173	5934	36,134

A more extensive series of totals for the year 2000 than is shown in Table 4.2 is given below.

Drop spread over: Cycles	Drop spread over: Years	No. of women under 45 by 2000 A.D.
$s = 3$	15	27,308,000
$s = 4$	20	29,504,000
$s = 5$	25	31,664,000
$s = 6$	30	33,850,000
$s = 7$	35	36,134,000
$s = 8$	40	38,572,000

Each additional five years over which the decline is spread, assuming that it starts immediately after 1965, brings about some 2.2 million more women by the end of the century. This may be compared with the effect of postponing the onset of the decline and then proceeding through it at a given pace: a five-year postponement would add 18% (or in general the fraction $\lambda_1 - 1$) to the population.

The waves induced by decline in the birth rate, which hardly appear in the 35-year transition, are conspicuous in the 15-year transition. In the latter ${}_5K_0$, the number of girls under five, declines sharply from 3,816,000 in 1965 to 2,467,000 in 1980, then rebounds to 3,333,000 in 1995; the column 15–19 peaks at 3,669,000 in 1980, and then declines to 2,421,000 in 1995; this is followed by a rise to 3,271,000 in 2010 (not shown in the table).

Such hypothetical computations have a place intermediate between empirical investigation and theory, without strictly being either. The two main results of the preceding example are the waves induced when the change of rates is over a short period like 15 years, and the degree in which a slower transition increases the population at the end. The art of this kind of demographic work is in framing clearcut questions, which are, however, not simple enough that they can be answered readily in theory. Important work along this line is the simulation due to Orcutt and his colleagues (1961).

Frank Oechsli asked what happens to various characteristics of a population if fertility drops sharply in a five-year period while mortality remains constant. He brought the Taiwan 1950–59 average population forward to 1961, and then subjected it to the age-specific fertility of Japan 1963, projecting both sexes on births by age of mother. The reader may comment on the results I have extracted from Oechsli's work (Table 4.3). He may surmise why the crude rate of natural increase takes fully 60 years to become negative; why the percent of the population under age 15 falls to its final level rapidly but the percent over 65 rises slowly and at an accelerating pace; why the dependency ratio oscillates; why the sex ratio changes so considerably. Aid in answering such questions will be given in the theory of Chapters 7, 13 and elsewhere.

Table 4.3 Projection of the 1956 population of China (Taiwan), supposing mortality unchanged and fertility dropping between 1961 and 1966 to the age-specific rates of Japan in 1963*

YEAR	POPU-LATION (000's)	CRUDE BIRTH RATE	CRUDE DEATH RATE	CRUDE RATE OF NATURAL INCREASE	PERCENT AT AGES			DEPEN-DENCY RATIO**	Δ†	MALES PER 100 FEMALES
					0–14	15–64	65+			
1961	11,095	40.1	6.7	33.4	46.2	50.8	3.0	0.969	3.2	103.5
1966	11,595	15.3	5.8	9.5	39.4	57.2	3.4	0.748	26.5	103.0
1971	12,150	16.7	6.4	10.3	30.0	66.2	3.9	0.511	23.4	102.5
1976	12,846	20.3	7.1	13.2	21.6	73.8	4.5	0.355	21.2	101.9
1981	13,762	23.4	7.8	15.6	24.3	70.6	5.0	0.416	20.4	101.3
1991	15,367	15.0	8.8	6.2	26.6	67.1	6.3	0.490	17.8	100.2
2001	15,925	13.6	10.3	3.3	20.4	71.3	8.3	0.403	13.7	99.1
2011	16,451	16.0	12.5	3.5	20.0	70.1	9.9	0.426	11.1	98.2
2021	16,542	13.1	14.7	-1.6	21.0	64.0	15.1	0.563	8.8	97.2
2031	16,016	13.4	16.7	-3.3	19.1	64.9	16.0	0.542	7.4	96.6
2041	15,598	14.5	16.9	-2.4	19.9	66.8	13.3	0.496	5.5	96.8
2051	15,252	13.4	15.0	-1.6	20.3	64.3	15.4	0.556	3.8	97.0
2061	14,851	13.7	16.6	-2.9	19.5	65.2	15.3	0.533	3.0	96.6
2111	13,106	13.7	16.1	-2.4	19.9	65.0	15.1	0.538	0.8	96.8
2161	11,554	13.8	16.2	-2.4	19.9	65.3	14.9	0.532	0.3	96.8

* Programmed by Frank Oechsli.

** Percent at ages 0–14 and 65+, divided by percent at 15–64.

† Departure of observed from stable ages as measured by index of dissimilarity Δ: sum of positive differences in percentages.

4.2. ANALYSIS OF COLLECTIONS OF LIFE TABLES

Interpolation may be applied among life tables or fertility patterns as well as among matrices to find intermediate or typical sets. Because of their more common use the following discussion will be in terms of life tables. In the absence of data regarding a country or territory one is tempted to resort to another country whose population may be presumed similar, and to import its life table. If one has reason to believe that the country of interest has a certain $\mathring{e}_0$, for example, he may search for an age pattern of mortality derived from vital statistics in other countries which have the same $\mathring{e}_0$. *Model life tables* are a way of systematizing this search.

They are also a way of studying mortality change through time. Swedish life tables are available over the whole of the nineteenth century. Do these form a single parameter system; i.e., do intermediate tables fall on a straight line of interpolation between the first and last? A simple way of examining this is to use two extreme tables to generate an intermediate set. If the index to be used is $\mathring{e}_{10}$, we may note, for example, that Swedish males for the 5 years about 1800 showed $\mathring{e}_{10} = 45.86$, and for the 5 years about 1900, $\mathring{e}_{10} = 52.93$. Then by straight-line interpolation a set of tables can be made, say at intervals of one year on $\mathring{e}_{10}$.

Interpolation may be put simply in terms of a weight w. We weight our 1900 table with w_i and our 1800 table with $1 - w_i$, so that

$$52.93w_i + 45.86(1 - w_i) = i\,, \qquad (4.2.1.)$$

where i is the $\mathring{e}_{10}$ or index of the model table. Solving (4.2.1) for w_i gives

$$w_i = \frac{i - 45.86}{52.93 - 45.86}\,,$$

or if $\mathring{e}_{10}$ and $\mathring{e}'_{10}$ are the two observed expectations and i is the $\mathring{e}_{10}$ of the desired model, we have

$$w_i = (i - \mathring{e}'_{10})/(\mathring{e}_{10} - \mathring{e}'_{10})\,. \qquad (4.2.2)$$

The weights w_i and $1 - w_i$ would then be applied to the q_x column of the two observed tables to find the intermediate q_x, and from these latter the remainder of the model table calculated in the usual way. [Would it reproduce the aimed-at intermediate $\mathring{e}_{10}$ exactly? What can be said about the linearity of the process of life-table computation?]

For the interpolated $\mathring{e}_{10} = i = 49.00$ the weights are $1 - w = 0.5559$ on the year 1800 and $w = 0.4441$ on 1900. These were applied to the q_x of the 1800 and 1900 observed tables: $(0.5559)({}_5q_x) + (0.4441)({}_5q'_x)$ to obtain the ${}_5q_x$ for the interpolated table aimed at $\mathring{e}_{10} = 49.00$.

The question is how close this fictional table comes to the observed table for Sweden whose $\mathring{e}_{10}$ is approximately 49.00. That for 1858–62 shows an $\mathring{e}_{10}$ of 48.99. Its $\mathring{e}_0$ is 43.07 (against the 42.16 of the interpolated table); its $q_0 = 0.1481$ (against 0.1747); $q_{20} = 0.0348$ (against 0.0376); $q_{40} = 0.0578$ (against 0.0593).

Changes in Swedish mortality through the nineteenth century did not take place linearly at all ages. (An alternative way of examining essentially the same question is presented in Tables 7.6 to 7.8 and the discussion of Section 7.4.).

The discrepancies from the straight line are sometimes great enough to suggest that a two-parameter set might be required to represent the changes over the period. We now deal not with a straight line but with three points in a triangle, from which we can fill in the plane linearly. If we index on $\mathring{e}_{10}$ and q_0, and observe tables with $\mathring{e}_{10}, q_0$; $\mathring{e}'_{10}, q'_0$; $\mathring{e}''_{10}, q''_0$, then the appropriate weights, w, w', $1 - w - w'$, are found for the model table with $\mathring{e}_{10} = i$, $q_0 = j$, by solving

$$w\mathring{e}_{10} + w'\mathring{e}'_{10} + (1 - w - w')\mathring{e}''_{10} = i\,,$$
$$wq_0 + w'q'_0 + (1 - w - w')q''_0 = j\,, \tag{4.2.3}$$

for the two unknowns, w and w' (Fig. 4.1).

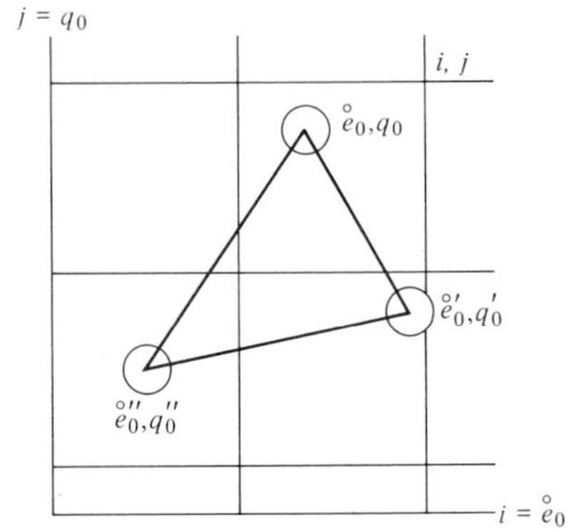

Fig. 4.1 Interpolation among three given life tables.

The above interpolatory scheme serves for a preliminary study of the age-incidence of mortality change, but is not usable in practice to make model tables because it is statistically inefficient—no easy way exists of incorporating a large number of observed tables into it.

Regression does constitute a way of incorporating relevant observations, and it is the basis of the two sets of model tables now available, one published by the United Nations (1955, 1956) and the other by the Princeton Office of Population Research (Coale and Demeny, 1966). The United Nations set has a single parameter; given the infant death rate, a unique table is indicated. The Princeton set is more flexible; given the expectation of life at age ten, four tables are available, labeled North, South, East, and West, which represent different age patterns of mortality for the same $\mathring{e}_{10}$.

In the Princeton procedure, reliable existing tables were assembled and arranged in the four homogeneous sets. Within each of the sets a regression was worked out of the q_x on $\mathring{e}_{10}$, of the form $q_x = A_x + B_x\mathring{e}_{10}$. Once the A_x and B_x were on hand, a set of q_x and hence a life table could be constructed for each $\mathring{e}_{10}$. Stable populations (i.e., the vector $\{\mathbf{K}_1\}$) were constructed by assigning intrinsic rates of increase. The set of model tables can be entered by a number of characteristics, including crude birth and death rates or the net reproduction rate.

The usefulness of statistical study of groups of life tables representing a sequence in time or a cross section, shown by the work of Coale and Demeny (1966), has encouraged William Cummings and the writer to make the calculation for three such groups. The first (a) consists of 50 historical tables for

Table 4.4 Mean and standard deviation for three groups of male life tables:
(a) 50 tables for Swedish and other European countries, from 1780 to 1910,
(b) 40 tables for Latin American countries, from 1945,
(c) 83 tables for developed countries, from 1945*

	MEAN			STANDARD DEVIATION		
	(a) 50 SWEDISH AND OTHER EUROPEAN FROM 1780 TO 1910	(b) 40 LATIN AMERICAN FROM 1945	(c) 83 DEVELOPED COUNTRIES FROM 1945	(a) 50 SWEDISH AND OTHER EUROPEAN FROM 1780 TO 1910	(b) 40 LATIN AMERICAN FROM 1945	(c) 83 DEVELOPED COUNTRIES FROM 1945
$\mathring{e}_{10}$	48.92	57.54	60.18	3.82	2.84	1.88
q_0	0.1622	0.0743	0.0395	0.0438	0.0276	0.0201
q_{10}	0.0196	0.0066	0.0030	0.0087	0.0029	0.0010
q_{20}	0.0364	0.0160	0.0084	0.0096	0.0074	0.0028
q_{30}	0.0430	0.0225	0.0096	0.0130	0.0083	0.0030
q_{40}	0.0614	0.0341	0.0183	0.0177	0.0085	0.0044
q_{50}	0.0966	0.0616	0.0481	0.0243	0.0143	0.0093
q_{60}	0.1727	0.1271	0.1185	0.0336	0.0385	0.0193
q_{70}	0.3475	0.2452	0.2606	0.0480	0.0663	0.0309

* Tables 4.4, 4.5, and 4.6 programmed by William Cummings. He began with population and deaths by age assembled from national sources by Wilhelm Flieger, constructed some 250 male life tables by the method of Section 1.2, rejected those tables which were far from the regression line of their respective groups, and with the remaining tables calculated the constants here shown.

Table 4.5 Coefficient of correlation of q_x with $\mathring{e}_{10}$ for three groups of male life tables

q_x	(a) 50 SWEDISH AND OTHER EUROPEAN FROM 1780 TO 1910	(b) 40 LATIN AMERICAN FROM 1945	(c) 83 DEVELOPED COUNTRIES FROM 1945
q_0	-0.8515	-0.1759	-0.5534
q_{10}	-0.8300	-0.1907	-0.5326
q_{20}	-0.8379	-0.3933	-0.6308
q_{30}	-0.9722	-0.5068	-0.7621
q_{40}	-0.9793	-0.7905	-0.8943
q_{50}	-0.9420	-0.8869	-0.9499
q_{60}	-0.8981	-0.6722	-0.8931
q_{70}	-0.8870	-0.6754	-0.8967

Sweden and other European countries covering a period from 1780 to 1910. The second (b) is 40 contemporary Latin American tables, referring to mortality of the last decade or two. The third (c) is also contemporary, being 83 tables of developed countries of Europe, plus the United States, Canada, and Australia. The method of computation of individual tables is that of Section 1.2 above.

Mortality falls from the first to the second, and from the second to the third, as shown by the section of Table 4.4 giving means; the mean of $\mathring{e}_{10}$ rises from 48.92 for (a) the historical tables, to 57.54 for (b) Latin America, to 60.18 for (c) contemporary developed countries. The improvement is mostly at young ages: a drop in q_{10} by two thirds appears from the first to the second group, and by one half from the second to the third; the oldest ages, on the other hand, show no such spectacular differences.

Variance among countries seems to decline with mortality. The standard deviation of $\mathring{e}_{10}$ is 3.82 years for (a) the historical tables, 2.84 for (b) Latin America, and 1.88 for (c) the developed countries (Table 4.4). Such a decline in variance is to be expected if mortality were pushing against a ceiling; the closer it gets, the less room for chance variation.

The coefficients of correlation measuring the extent to which the several q_x are predictable from the $\mathring{e}_{10}$ are decidedly higher for the historical series than for the other two (Table 4.5). This is related to the greater range of mortality (shown by the higher variance) of the historical series; the more homogeneous tables combined together in the two contemporary series offer less scope for correlation.

Table 4.6 Regression of q_x on $\mathring{e}_{10}$ for three groups of male life tables

(a) 50 SWEDISH AND OTHER EUROPEAN LIFE TABLES FROM 1780 TO 1910	(b) 40 LATIN AMERICAN LIFE TABLES FROM 1945	(c) 83 LIFE TABLES OF DEVELOPED COUNTRIES FROM 1945
$q_0 = 0.6393 - 0.00975\mathring{e}_{10}$	$q_0 = 0.1726 - 0.00171\mathring{e}_{10}$	$q_0 = 0.3955 - 0.00592\mathring{e}_{10}$
$q_1 = 0.4382 - 0.00704\mathring{e}_{10}$	$q_1 = 0.2079 - 0.00289\mathring{e}_{10}$	$q_1 = 0.1014 - 0.00155\mathring{e}_{10}$
$q_5 = 0.1963 - 0.00332\mathring{e}_{10}$	$q_5 = 0.0532 - 0.00073\mathring{e}_{10}$	$q_5 = 0.0246 - 0.00035\mathring{e}_{10}$
$q_{10} = 0.1116 - 0.00188\mathring{e}_{10}$	$q_{10} = 0.0177 - 0.00019\mathring{e}_{10}$	$q_{10} = 0.0201 - 0.00028\mathring{e}_{10}$
$q_{15} = 0.0975 - 0.00148\mathring{e}_{10}$	$q_{15} = 0.0593 - 0.00085\mathring{e}_{10}$	$q_{15} = 0.0381 - 0.00054\mathring{e}_{10}$
$q_{20} = 0.1392 - 0.00210\mathring{e}_{10}$	$q_{20} = 0.0745 - 0.00102\mathring{e}_{10}$	$q_{20} = 0.0644 - 0.00093\mathring{e}_{10}$
$q_{25} = 0.1706 - 0.00270\mathring{e}_{10}$	$q_{25} = 0.1150 - 0.00167\mathring{e}_{10}$	$q_{25} = 0.0742 - 0.00109\mathring{e}_{10}$
$q_{30} = 0.2047 - 0.00331\mathring{e}_{10}$	$q_{30} = 0.1081 - 0.00149\mathring{e}_{10}$	$q_{30} = 0.0820 - 0.00120\mathring{e}_{10}$
$q_{35} = 0.2355 - 0.00379\mathring{e}_{10}$	$q_{35} = 0.1747 - 0.00256\mathring{e}_{10}$	$q_{35} = 0.1049 - 0.00154\mathring{e}_{10}$
$q_{40} = 0.2837 - 0.00454\mathring{e}_{10}$	$q_{40} = 0.1695 - 0.00235\mathring{e}_{10}$	$q_{40} = 0.1444 - 0.00210\mathring{e}_{10}$
$q_{45} = 0.3247 - 0.00510\mathring{e}_{10}$	$q_{45} = 0.2519 - 0.00361\mathring{e}_{10}$	$q_{45} = 0.2181 - 0.00314\mathring{e}_{10}$
$q_{50} = 0.3888 - 0.00597\mathring{e}_{10}$	$q_{50} = 0.3187 - 0.00447\mathring{e}_{10}$	$q_{50} = 0.3315 - 0.00471\mathring{e}_{10}$
$q_{55} = 0.4355 - 0.00632\mathring{e}_{10}$	$q_{55} = 0.3412 - 0.00453\mathring{e}_{10}$	$q_{55} = 0.4766 - 0.00664\mathring{e}_{10}$
$q_{60} = 0.5590 - 0.00790\mathring{e}_{10}$	$q_{60} = 0.6507 - 0.00910\mathring{e}_{10}$	$q_{60} = 0.6727 - 0.00921\mathring{e}_{10}$
$q_{65} = 0.7169 - 0.00965\mathring{e}_{10}$	$q_{65} = 0.9562 - 0.01372\mathring{e}_{10}$	$q_{65} = 0.8852 - 0.01179\mathring{e}_{10}$
$q_{70} = 0.8921 - 0.01113\mathring{e}_{10}$	$q_{70} = 1.1516 - 0.01575\mathring{e}_{10}$	$q_{70} = 1.1503 - 0.01478\mathring{e}_{10}$
$q_{75} = 1.0244 - 0.01109\mathring{e}_{10}$	$q_{75} = 1.6273 - 0.02284\mathring{e}_{10}$	$q_{75} = 1.4449 - 0.01768\mathring{e}_{10}$
$q_{80} = 1.1312 - 0.00994\mathring{e}_{10}$	$q_{80} = 1.4629 - 0.01753\mathring{e}_{10}$	$q_{80} = 1.6294 - 0.01809\mathring{e}_{10}$

The correlations throughout are high enough, however, that we are invited to compute regressions of the q's on $\mathring{e}_{10}$ (Table 4.6). (You can verify Table 4.6. from Tables 4.4. and 4.5, subject to errors of rounding). On a first impression the variation among groups (a), (b) and (c) is disconcerting, both in the absolute term of the regression and in the coefficient of $\mathring{e}_{10}$. This variation is somewhat deceptive however; the three lines can have different slope and intercept and yet agree reasonably well in the limited range of $\mathring{e}_{10}$ which is of interest. Charts may be made to judge the agreement of the lines.

Further help in judging them is obtained from sampling error. Writing the standard error beside each coefficient, we have for q_{30}:

a) 50 historical tables

$$q_{30} = 0.2047 \pm 0.0056 - (0.00331 \pm 0.00012)\mathring{e}_{10} ,$$

b) 40 Latin American tables

$$q_{30} = 0.1081 \pm 0.0236 - (0.00149 \pm 0.00041)\mathring{e}_{10} ,$$

c) 83 tables of developed countries

$$q_{30} = 0.0820 \pm 0.0068 - (0.00120 \pm 0.00011)\mathring{e}_{10} .$$

Variation is greatest in Latin America, as corresponds to the low correlations of Table 4.4. To what extent this is due to different degrees of completeness of registration and to what extent to genuine variation cannot be said without further information. The differences among (a), (b), and (c) are not all explainable by sampling variability.

The method described above amounts to stratifying the data, i.e., the life tables representing observations, and, within strata, working with regression of q_x on $\mathring{e}_{10}$. An alternative might be to retain all the data in a single stratum, and to calculate multiple regressions of the q_x on two indicators, say $\mathring{e}_{10}$ and q_0. The statistical properties of this alternative are under study.

4.3. EXTRAPOLATION TO FUTURE POPULATIONS

An exposition of the mathematics of population is not more directly concerned with prediction of future changes than a book on hydrodynamics is concerned with the prediction of floods. The most one can hope is that theoretical formulations will give the practitioners who do the predicting some help in thinking about their problem. Its importance is suggested by the entire meeting given over to prediction at the United Nations World Population Conference of 1965. Speakers referred warmly to the increasing public demand for population forecasts. They also agreed that population forecasting is impossible (P.R. Cox, 1965). Said an early forecaster, Edwin Cannan (1895, p. 505), in this very connection: "It is a good deal easier to utter warnings against prophecy than to abstain from it."

In making statements about the matrix $\mathbf{M}$, and in asserting that $\mathbf{M}^t\{\mathbf{K}^{(0)}\}$ gives the age distribution $5t$ years hence on the assumption of a fixed regime of births and deaths, one is not predicting, but rather analyzing the nature of the (past) rates embodied in $\mathbf{M}$. This may be useful in simply telling us that existing rates cannot continue, as we argued for Mexico above. One need not go abroad for such illustrations—the maintenance of United States, 1960 female age-specific rates acting on the United States, 1960 female population would produce 3.4 billion people of both sexes in 150 years. (In fact the 1960 rate did not continue, and the 1965 rate would result in less than 1.4 billion in 150 years.)

One would often like to see in detail the consequences for future population of a given supposed course of change of the regime of mortality and fertility. One way of assembling the supposition is to extend recent past changes into the future by fitting a polynomial. If $\mathbf{M}^{(1)}$ is the projection matrix based on 1960–64 mortality and fertility and $\{\mathbf{K}^{(1)}\}$ is the age distribution on January 1, 1960, then $\mathbf{M}^{(1)}\{\mathbf{K}^{(1)}\}$ will be the age distribution on January 1, 1965. Suppose $\mathbf{M}^{(0)}$ is the projection matrix based on 1955–59 fertility. If the difference between $\mathbf{M}^{(0)}$ and $\mathbf{M}^{(1)}$ is to be continued as a straight line, and $\Delta\mathbf{M}^{(0)} = \mathbf{M}^{(1)} - \mathbf{M}^{(0)}$ is the matrix of differences, then the 1965 population would be projected to 1970 with

$$\mathbf{M}^{(2)} = \mathbf{M}^{(0)} + 2\,\Delta\mathbf{M}^{(0)}\,.$$

The 1955 + $5s$ population on a polynomial extrapolation of the matrix would be written symbolically

$$\{\mathbf{K}^{(s+1)}\} = \mathbf{M}^{(s)}\{\mathbf{K}^{(s)}\} = (1 + \Delta)^s\mathbf{M}^{(0)}\{\mathbf{K}^{(s)}\}\,, \tag{4.3.1}$$

where $(1 + \Delta)^s\mathbf{M}^{(0)}$ is to be interpreted as

$$(1 + \Delta)^s\mathbf{M}^{(0)} \equiv \mathbf{M}^{(0)} + s\,\Delta\mathbf{M}^{(0)} + \frac{(s)(s-1)}{2}\,\Delta^2\mathbf{M}^{(0)} + \cdots$$

The reader may outline a calculation of finite differences for matrices in application to demography. This calculation would be identical in result with applying the extrapolation formula to each element of the projection matrix individually.

A computer program has been devised which incorporates as arguments the current information on age distribution, fertility, mortality, and migration, and prospective changes according to the intuition of the user. The user enters in a table his opinion of the percentage change during the five years subsequent to the latest data, during the five years following that, etc., in births, deaths, and net migration—percent changes which may be designated Δb, Δd, and Δn respectively.

The initial projection matrix $\mathbf{M}$, representing the latest observations, is decomposed into three components: a matrix $\mathbf{B}$ for births with nonzero elements in its top row only, a matrix $\mathbf{S}$ for survivorships whose only nonzero elements are in its subdiagonal, and $\mathbf{N}$, also zero except in the subdiagonal, to allow for net migration. In symbols,

$$\mathbf{M} = \mathbf{U} - (\mathbf{U} - \mathbf{S}) + \mathbf{B} + \mathbf{N}\,,$$

$\mathbf{U}$ being a matrix with 1's in its subdiagonal and 0's elsewhere.

In each cycle the component matrices actually used are the matrices as they stood in the preceding cycle adjusted by the percentages Δb, Δd, and Δn:

$$\mathbf{M}^{(t+1)} = \mathbf{U} - (\mathbf{U} - \mathbf{S}^{(t)})\left(1 + \frac{\Delta d}{100}\right) + \mathbf{B}^{(t)}\left(1 + \frac{\Delta b}{100}\right) + \mathbf{N}^{(t)}\left(1 + \frac{\Delta n}{100}\right). \qquad (4.3.2)$$

Prediction being too difficult a subject for theoretical demography, the most that a volume such as this can contribute is a variety of models among which the predictor can select the one he believes appropriate. Unfortunately the models of the mathematical literature on which this volume is based mostly concern cross sections of data for a given period of time—say a calendar year. Only now and again is reference made to following a cohort through its reproductive life. But if the decision on the number of children to whom they will give birth is made by each couple in respect of its whole career, then year-to-year fluctuations in the period aggregates are of little consequence (Ryder, 1964). This is implicit in the U.S. Bureau of the Census projections, which suppose certain numbers of births in completed families—3.35 down to 2.45 per woman by the end of childbearing (*Statistical Abstract of the United States*, 1966, p. 6). A thoroughgoing incorporation of this cohort approach is part of the mathematical demography of the future.

4.4. ADJUSTMENT OF DATA

Filling out the demographic history of a population in which data on births and deaths are missing or of doubtful accuracy may be possible through the use of censuses. If good periodic censuses are available and migration is known or can be neglected, then inferences on births and deaths may be relatively accurate. In principle, age-specific death rates can be calculated from a pair of successive censuses, and also crude rates of birth, but not birth rates by age. The latter are not *identifiable*: the given performance in the two censuses is consistent with a variety of age patterns of birth. (Johnston, 1963, pp. 249 *et seq.*, and other textbooks on econometrics discuss identifiability. See also Blalock, 1964).

If $\mathbf{M}^{(t)}$ of (4.3.2) is used to predict, not the unknown future, but a census which was actually taken at time $t + 1$, discrepancies between the predicted $\mathbf{M}^{(t)}\{\mathbf{K}^{(t)}\}$ and $\{\mathbf{K}^{(t+1)}\}$, the census at time $t + 1$, occur in each age category and provide information bearing on the quantities Δd, Δb, and Δn of (4.3.2), which in this context we think of as overall corrections of the observed birth, death, and migration data.

The problem is how to use systematically the redundancy which is contained in any set of (in practice inconsistent) information on population, births, deaths, and migration in order to improve the data. That such improvement is possible is shown by Coale and Zelnik (1963) for the United States; their success depended on their making assumptions, which further work confirmed, on what was more likely to be in error and in which direction. They knew, for instance, that birth rates and census populations under five years of age are more likely to be understated than overstated, and that of the successive censuses through which an individual lives he is more likely to be caught in one when he is aged 10 than when he is aged 20.

Suppose that an investigator has contrived a set of rules or assumptions which may be objectively applied to replace the inconsistent data with a consistent set, and to arrive at a collection of life tables, population totals, births, and deaths such that starting with the adjusted population of any date, subtracting adjusted deaths and adding adjusted births and net immigration brings him exactly to the adjusted population at the next census date, age by age and for each sex. This very large fitting operation is entirely feasible with the computer. Call this new set, the first adjustment, A_1. With different rules one might arrive at another adjustment, say A_2, again perfectly consistent with itself but different from the raw data and from A_1 on all or practically all figures.

A scoring system will be required for choosing between A_1 and A_2. One such system would score each discrepancy between the original and the adjusted figure by an amount equal to its square, say with a weight of 10 if the adjusted figure was lower than the original census or other count, and a weight of 1 if it was higher than the original count; perhaps with a weight of 5 for discrepancies in birth and death against 1 for discrepancies in migration and population number. Relative to the scoring system the comparison of two sets of adjustments is perfectly objective, and it is possible to say which of the systems of adjustment, A_1 or A_2, is on the whole better by noting which has the lower score. The choice may be extended to further systems of adjustment, A_3, A_4, etc.

So far we have arrived only at a way of adjusting inconsistencies. If all data are low (say by omission of one region of the country from all census, birth, and death statistics), the above procedure will not discover this fact. Any such knowledge of under-enumeration or under-registration should be applied as a correction at the outset, and the above fitting would be to the corrected rather than to the originally observed figures. Our formal procedure remains a way of adjusting inconsistencies rather than eliminating errors.

4.5. ON STRONG AND WEAK ERGODICITY

Exercises in short-term projection suggest the question of what would happen if projection were indefinitely continued at the age-specific rates observed in a given period. This question has fascinated students of the subject, and a large literature deals with it (Sharpe and Lotka, 1911; Haldane, 1927; Leslie, 1945).

There are several ways of demonstrating Lotka's theorem that a population subjected to fixed rates of mortality and fertility will asymptotically approach an age distribution which depends only on the schedule of mortality and fertility, one of which is discussed with the help of the properties of nonnegative matrices in Section 3.2, another taken up for the continuous case in Section 5.2. The ultimate age distribution is fixed and depends neither on the original age distribution nor even on the age-specific rates of fertility, except as these latter are reflected in the intrinsic rate r_1 (Chapter 5) or the real root λ_1 (Chapter 3). This tendency to forget the past age distribution under the action of a fixed set of vital rates may be referred to as *strong ergodicity*, following Hajnal (1958).

Of comparable interest is *weak ergodicity*, a property of age distributions subject to changing mortality and fertility. A substantial generalization of Lotka's theorem is possible: if two or more populations are subject to age schedules of mortality and fertility which may change in time but are the same for the two populations, then after a long enough period their age distributions will come to resemble one another as closely as one cares to specify. This proposition was conjectured by Coale and demonstrated by Lopez (1961). The weak ergodic property embraces the strong ergodic, but the ultimate age distribution for strong ergodicity is compactly specified (as $\{\mathbf{K}_1\}$, the vertical stable vector for the dominant root), while that for weak is not. Because of its generality and the insight which it provides into the nature of a population projection, the Coale-Lopez argument is worth following in some detail.

A sequence of matrices $\mathbf{M}^{(t)}$ (in which the jth element of the ith row of the tth matrix is $m_{ij}^{(t)}$) is given, each $\mathbf{M}^{(t)}$ having at least two consecutive positive elements in the first row in fixed positions, none but positive elements in the subdiagonal, and zeros elsewhere. We will think of the one-year representation, so that each time $\mathbf{M}^{(t)}$ premultiplies the vertical vector of ages, it carries the population into the following year. People are taken at their age at last birthday; they jump one year every 365 days. The range of ages is finite; everyone dies by age ω at the latest.

The two different initial age distributions on which the matrices of the sequence will act are $\{\mathbf{G}^{(0)}\}$ and $\{\mathbf{K}^{(0)}\}$, whose typical elements, representing the number of individuals a years of age at last birthday, are $g_a^{(0)}$ and $k_a^{(0)}$. After t premultiplications the vectors will be $\{\mathbf{G}^{(t)}\}$ and $\{\mathbf{K}^{(t)}\}$:

$$\begin{aligned}\{\mathbf{G}^{(t)}\} &= \mathbf{M}^{(t-1)}\mathbf{M}^{(t-2)} \cdots \mathbf{M}^{(0)}\{\mathbf{G}^{(0)}\}\,,\\ \{\mathbf{K}^{(t)}\} &= \mathbf{M}^{(t-1)}\mathbf{M}^{(t-2)} \cdots \mathbf{M}^{(0)}\{\mathbf{K}^{(0)}\}\,,\end{aligned} \tag{4.5.1}$$

with typical elements $g_a^{(t)}$ and $k_a^{(t)}$. The two vectors are said to represent the same age distribution if for any two ages a and b

$$\frac{g_a^{(t)}}{k_a^{(t)}} = \frac{g_b^{(t)}}{k_b^{(t)}}\,, \quad a = 0, 1, \ldots, \omega - 1\,, \quad b = 0, 1, \ldots, \omega - 1\,. \tag{4.5.2}$$

The weak ergodic property is proved if the difference

$$\frac{g_a^{(t)}}{k_a^{(t)}} - \frac{g_b^{(t)}}{k_b^{(t)}} \tag{4.5.3}$$

becomes arbitrarily small when t is sufficiently large, for all a and b up to $\omega - 1$ at last birthday. The vectors $\{\mathbf{G}^{(t)}\}$ and $\{\mathbf{K}^{(t)}\}$ would come to have the same (generally changing) direction though their lengths can differ by any amount.

The proof will assume that there is a clump of at least two fixed consecutive ages, say $\beta - 1$ and β, at which fertility is always greater than some positive number ε. This eliminates from consideration such hypothetical populations as those having a single age of reproduction, for which any initial departures from the stable age distribution will be indefinitely continued (Bernardelli, 1941). The proof goes up only to the age β which has a positive chance of childbearing in all matrices, but it may be shown that if two populations of the same fertility and mortality history have the same age distribution in the ages up to the end of the clump $\beta - 1$, β, then they will have the same age distribution beyond that (Lopez, 1961, p. 60). The initial age distributions will be assumed positive in all ages up to the end of the reproductive period, so that all of the ratios in (4.5.3) are finite numbers, between some $\varepsilon > 0$ and $A < \infty$; the proof may be extended to initial distributions containing zeros.

The proof begins by replacing the one-year steps of the projection by a lumped step, covering r years. Our first objective is to show that for some r the product of matrices

$$\mathbf{P}^{(r)} = \mathbf{M}^{(r)}\mathbf{M}^{(r-1)} \cdots \mathbf{M}^{(1)} \tag{4.5.4}$$

when expressed as a single matrix is strictly positive, i.e., has no zero elements. Can a number $r = r_0$ be found above which the product (4.5.4) is a matrix having no zeros?

The proof that there is a lumped step to which corresponds a product matrix such as (4.5.4) all of whose elements are nonzero starts by considering an arbitrary element of (4.5.4), say $p_{ij}^{(r)}$. In the nature of matrix multiplication this must be constituted by a sum through all possible paths that begin in the ith row of $\mathbf{M}^{(r)}$ and end in the jth column of $\mathbf{M}^{(1)}$. Thus

$$p_{ij}^{(2)} = \sum_{\nu} m_{i\nu}^{(2)} m_{\nu j}^{(1)}$$

for the product of two matrices, and

$$p_{ij}^{(r)} = \sum_{\nu_1\nu_2\cdots\nu_{r-1}} m_{i\nu_1}^{(r)} m_{\nu_1\nu_2}^{(r-1)} \cdots m_{\nu_{r-1},j}^{(1)}, \tag{4.5.5}$$

for a product of r matrices. The object of the following argument is to see under what circumstances a path such as that of (4.5.5) can avoid passing through zero elements.

We are supposing that the nonzero elements of each matrix are at least $m_{1,\beta-1}$, $m_{1,\beta}$, and $m_{i,i-1}$, where β is the last age in which reproduction is nonzero in all matrices, and i ranges over all values 2, 3, . . . , β. We want a product of r matrices which will give a nonzero value for $p_{ij}^{(r)}$, the jth element of the ith row, and we would like this to be nonzero for all orders r beyond r_0 of the product. The $p_{ij}^{(r)}$ that we seek can be made up starting with $m_{i,i-1}$ in the product

$$m_{i,i-1}m_{i-1,i-2} \cdots m_{2,1}m_{1,\beta-1}\,, \tag{4.5.6}$$

which could equally well end with $m_{1,\beta}$, and either way contains i factors. [If $i = 1$, we would take $m_{1,\beta-1}$ for (4.5.6).] We could continue with

$$m_{\beta-1,\beta-2}m_{\beta-2,\beta-3} \cdots m_{2,1}m_{1,\beta-1}\,, \tag{4.5.7}$$

which contains $\beta - 1$ factors, and is thought of as written on the right of (4.5.6). Moreover, we could in some instances terminate with $m_{1,\beta}$ instead:

$$m_{\beta-1,\beta-2}m_{\beta-2,\beta-3} \cdots m_{2,1}m_{1,\beta}\,, \tag{4.5.8}$$

which also contains $\beta - 1$ factors, but would be followed by

$$m_{\beta,\beta-1}m_{\beta-1,\beta-2} \cdots m_{2,1}m_{1,\beta}\,, \tag{4.5.9}$$

which contains β factors. Suppose (4.5.7) and (4.5.8) are together applied $p - 1$ times, making altogether $(p - 1)(\beta - 1)$ factors, and that there are q sets of (4.5.9) that contain β factors each. Finally suppose that we end with

$$m_{\beta,\beta-1}m_{\beta-1,\beta-2} \cdots m_{j+1,j}\,,$$

which contains $\beta - j$ factors, unless $j = \beta$, in which case this product would be omitted. The combined product, $\mathbf{P}^{(r)}$, which constitutes a route such that $p_{ij}^{(r)}$ is nonzero for all i, j, contains

$$\begin{aligned} r &= i + (p - 1)(\beta - 1) + q\beta + \beta - j \\ &= p(\beta - 1) + q\beta + i - j + 1 \end{aligned} \tag{4.5.10}$$

factors.

The question is now whether all $r > r_0$ can be decomposed into the expression (4.5.10) for given β, for any i and j, by a suitable selection of p and q. This is the same as asking whether $r' = r - (i - j + 1)$ can be constituted by $p(\beta - 1) + q\beta$ merely by choice of p and q.

It will suffice to show that for some number r_0' all integers r' greater than r_0' can be represented by $p(\beta - 1) + q\beta$, $p \geq 1$, $q \geq 0$. In fact the representation is possible for all $r' \geq (\beta - 1)^2$. To represent any $r' \geq (\beta - 1)^2$ divide r' by $\beta - 1$; suppose it goes u times with v left over, $u \geq \beta - 1 > v \geq 0$. In that case, $r' = u(\beta - 1) + v = (u - v)(\beta - 1) + v\beta$. Since $r' \geq (\beta - 1)^2$ we know that $u - v$ is positive; hence it is always possible to represent r' by $(u - v)(\beta - 1) + v\beta$ with $u - v$ positive and v nonnegative. This is the

$r' = p(\beta - 1) + q\beta$ which we sought, and which gives

$$r = r_0' + \max(i - j + 1) = (\beta - 1)^2 + \max(i - j + 1),$$

so that for all $r > r_0$ and for all i and j we have $p_{ij}^{(r)} > 0$. The largest possible $(i - j + 1)$ is β, so that if r is greater than the fixed quantity $(\beta - 1)^2 + \beta$, every element of $P^{(r)}$ is greater than zero. Essentially the same proof would apply if the two nonzero elements of the first row were not the $(\beta - 1)$th and βth, but the sth and βth, where s and β have no common factor. The proof given is readily adapted if any two first-row elements, in positions prime to each other, are nonzero.

We have spoken only of the first $\mathbf{P}^{(r)}$, but such lumping may be done throughout; if r is chosen large enough, the first r matrices when multiplied together will make a matrix of positive elements, so will the second r, the third r, etc., so long as the otherwise dissimilar matrices have nonzero terms in the places specified.

The reader may use essentially the same method to ascertain r on the stronger assumption that $\beta > 2\alpha$ and the ages from α to β are all of nonzero fertility, and show that this r is smaller than that of the preceding paragraphs.

Having established that the projection can be consolidated into lumped steps for the changing regime, such that the matrix for the lumped step consists of positive elements throughout, Lopez (1961, pp. 55–57) goes on to consider the successive multiplication of the original age distribution by the lumped matrices. If the matrix for the Tth lumped step is $\mathbf{H}^{(T)}$, where the unit of time is not years but r-year steps, then in the projection at that stage the $g_a^{(T+1)}$ and $k_a^{(T+1)}$, the ath age groups of the two vectors whose convergence we are trying to demonstrate, will be

$$g_a^{(T+1)} = h_{a1}^{(T)}g_1^{(T)} + h_{a2}^{(T)}g_2^{(T)} + \cdots + h_{a\beta}^{(T)}g_\beta^{(T)},$$
$$k_a^{(T+1)} = h_{a1}^{(T)}k_1^{(T)} + h_{a2}^{(T)}k_2^{(T)} + \cdots + h_{a\beta}^{(T)}k_\beta^{(T)},$$

and the bth age groups will be similar expressions with b replacing a. Now consider the ratios of the numbers in the two populations at the several ages, $g_a^{(T)}/k_a^{(T)}$, and take the age at which the ratio is smallest, say a, and the age at which it is largest, say b; call the two ratios r_T and R_T respectively. Then for any age i,

$$r_T = \frac{g_a^{(T)}}{k_a^{(T)}} \le \frac{g_i^{(T)}}{k_i^{(T)}} \le \frac{g_b^{(T)}}{k_b^{(T)}} = R_T .$$

When we have for $i = 0, 1, 2, \ldots, \beta$, the ratios $g_i^{(T)}/k_i^{(T)}$ intermediate between two numbers r_T and R_T, and take a weighted total of the numerators and divide it by the same weighted total of the denominators, all the weights being nonzero, we will have a fraction which is again intermediate. Indeed

$$r_T = \frac{g_a^{(T)}}{k_a^{(T)}} \le \frac{g_i^{(T+1)}}{k_i^{(T+1)}} \le \frac{g_b^{(T)}}{k_b^{(T)}} = R_T .$$

It follows that the minima r_T will be a monotonically ascending sequence in T (though consecutive elements may be equal), and similarly R_T will be a monotonically descending sequence in T. (This sequence in steps of r years constitutes a subsequence of that in single years.) We are not yet sure that the sequence rising from below, r_T, will ever meet that declining from above, R_T. Lopez (1961, pp. 55–57) concludes his demonstration by proving that the two sequences converge to the same limit. He has since (1967) worked out a means of demonstrating weak ergodicity in the continuous case, a substantial generalization of the next chapter (Chapter 5).

The above argument concerning weak ergodicity is of course applicable to strong ergodicity. Note that the proof depends on elementary ideas; at no point is the apparatus of eigenvalues and spectral decomposition brought into play. Since eigenvalues arise from algebraic considerations which have little to do with demography, their avoidance here seems a merit. A technique which forces us to think specifically about the demographic problem as expressed in our particular matrix having nonzero elements in its first row and subdiagonal only seems preferable to one which is more general. Kemeny and Snell (1960, p. v) rightly consider it an adyantage that they could develop the theory of finite Markov chains without eigenvalues.

The weak ergodic theorem of Coale and Lopez enables us to understand (without eigenvalues) why nonsustained migration has only a transient effect on the age distribution of a population, so long as the migratory movements do not affect the prevailing patterns of fertility and mortality. It also enables us to see why the matrix $\mathbf{M}^t$ of Chapter 3 comes to have columns which are proportional to one another as t becomes large: what applies to the successively premultiplied vectors of this chapter will apply to each column of the matrix of Chapter 3. It follows too from the weak ergodic theorem that two initially different age structures, acted on by the same regime of mortality and fertility, will ultimately take on the same (crude) birth and death rates.

Part III

THE CONTINUOUS ANALYSIS

CHAPTER 5

THE RENEWAL EQUATION: GENERAL SOLUTION

The population projection, calculation of the prospective closed population of one sex on given age-specific rates of mortality and fertility, has been our preoccupation up to this point. The analysis will continue under most of the same assumptions, but instead of the finite age intervals, usually five years, used heretofore, age intervals will be made small. This will provide some results that are not accessible to matrix theory.

5.1. POPULATION PROJECTION IN THE CONTINUOUS CASE

The vector of observed numbers in the several age groups, $\{\mathbf{K}^{(0)}\}$, now gives place to a continuous function, $k(x)$, $0 \leq x \leq \omega$, such that the number of individuals between x and $x + dx$ is $k(x)\,dx$. Survivorship is according to the continuous version of the life table $l(x)$ defined in Chapter 1. The expected number of survivors t years later of those between x and $x + dx$ at the outset is

$$k(x)\,\frac{l(x+t)}{l(x)}\,dx\,, \qquad \text{or} \qquad k(x)\,\frac{p(x+t)}{p(x)}\,dx\,,$$

where $p(x) = l(x)/l_0$ is the number-living column of the life table with radix unity. The probability of a woman x years of age having a child in the interval x to $x + dx$ will be $m(x)\,dx$.

With these definitions, the continuous form of the projection may be followed on the adaptation of the Lexis diagram given as Fig. 5.1. The population alive at time zero is a density function along the x-axis, and the $k(x)\,dx$ individuals at age x to $x + dx$ suffer attrition through mortality; the survivors among them are reduced as we follow them down the diagonal toward the lower right to the number

$$k(x)\,\frac{p(x+t)}{p(x)}\,dx\,,$$

which is the element of density along the horizontal line for time t. The number of children per year who would be born to these at time t is their number multiplied by $m(x + t)$. The children born at time t for all parents surviving from time zero, obtained by summing over the initial ages x, are at the annual rate

$$G(t) = \int_{\alpha-t}^{\beta-t} k(x)\,\frac{p(x+t)}{p(x)}\,m(x+t)\,dx\,,$$

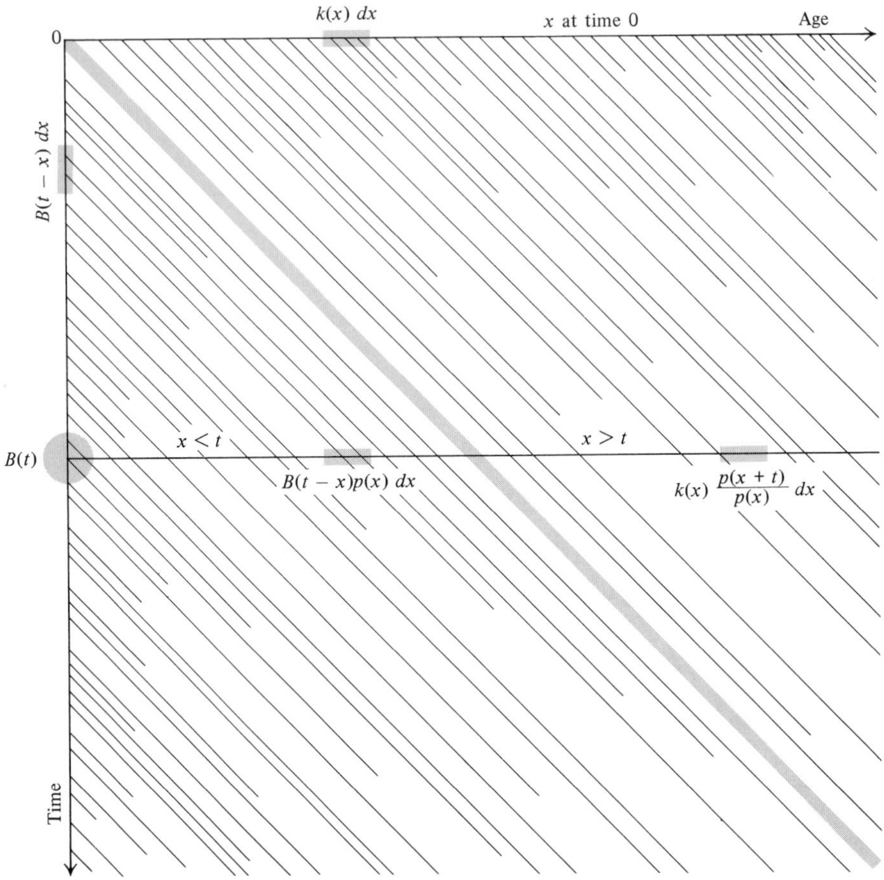

Fig. 5.1 Lexis diagram for aging and reproduction, with density functions of age distribution and birth.

where α and β are the youngest and oldest ages respectively of childbearing, the integral being unaffected if we use the limits 0 to β or 0 to ∞.

The quantity $G(t)$ is the number of births to the initial population, but if t is more than α there will also be births at time t to women who themselves were born since time zero. We find these by an analogous argument. If the density of births is given by $B(t)$ along the time axis on the left of Fig. 5.1, then the number of women of ages x to $x + dx$ at time t, born since time zero, will be the survivors of children born x years ago, $B(t - x)p(x)\,dx$, $x \leq t$. These women would have at time t a number of children equal to

$$B(t - x)p(x)m(x)\,dx$$

per year.

Integrating $B(t - x)p(x)m(x)\,dx$ through all x and adding the allowance $G(t)$ for births to those already alive at time zero gives the fundamental equation

$$B(t) = G(t) + \int_0^t B(t - x)p(x)m(x)\,dx\,. \tag{5.1.1}$$

Of the two terms on the right, the first, $G(t)$, applies to the part of the Lexis diagram above the heavy diagonal line, and the integral applies below the line.

The discussion of (5.1.1) will occupy us through this and the succeeding chapter. It is an *integral equation*; the unknown function $B(t)$ appears both under and outside the integral sign. Integral equations are similar to differential equations, and indeed can be converted into them. We could convert (5.1.1) by differentiating both sides with respect to t, but this does not bring us closer to a solution for the unknown birth trajectory $B(t)$.

The Homogeneous Equation

The term $G(t)$ in (5.1.1) is awkward, and fortunately

$$G(t) = 0 \qquad \text{for} \qquad t \geq \beta\,.$$

Our initial strategy will be to consider Eq. (5.1.1) with $G(t)$ omitted:

$$B(t) = \int_0^t B(t - x)p(x)m(x)\,dx\,, \quad t \geq \beta\,; \tag{5.1.2}$$

any solution that we find to (5.1.2) applies to (5.1.1) for all $t \geq \beta$, that is, sufficiently far down in Fig. 5.1 that we need not consider the possibility of children being born to the women on the right of the heavy diagonal line. In general, the solution to (5.1.2) will contain an infinite number of arbitrary constants which are at our disposal. We will choose them so that in addition to satisfying (5.1.2), $B(t)$ also satisfies (5.1.1).

What makes (5.1.2) convenient is that it is *homogeneous*, which is to say that the solution remains a solution when it is multiplied by a constant: if $B(t)$ is a solution, so also is $cB(t)$. Moreover, solutions are *additive*: if $B_1(t)$ and $B_2(t)$ are solutions, so is $B_1(t) + B_2(t)$. These two properties, easily verified for (5.1.2) by reference to the elementary properties of integrals, are sometimes referred to together as *linearity*. If a number of functions can be found that satisfy (5.1.2), then from these special answers a more general solution can be built up. To anticipate somewhat, if e^{rt} is a solution to (5.1.2) for $r = r_1, r_2, \ldots$, then, subject to the condition of convergence,

$$B(t) = Q_1 e^{r_1 t} + Q_2 e^{r_2 t} + \cdots \tag{5.1.3}$$

will be a solution to (5.1.2) for all values of the arbitrary constants $Q_1, Q_2, \ldots$; the Q_i may then be chosen to satisfy (5.1.1) for the given $k(x)$ implicitly contained in $G(t)$.

5.2. SOLUTION BY ELEMENTARY CALCULUS

To try the function e^{rt}, we substitute it for $B(t)$ in (5.1.2); on replacing $B(t)$ by e^{rt} and $B(t-x)$ by $e^{r(t-x)}$, then canceling out e^{rt} from both sides, we obtain from (5.1.2)

$$\int_0^t e^{-rx}p(x)m(x)\,dx = 1\,, \quad t \geq \beta\,, \tag{5.2.1}$$

or since $m(x) = 0$ except for $\alpha \leq x \leq \beta$,

$$\psi(r) = \int_\alpha^\beta e^{-rx}p(x)m(x)\,dx = 1\,, \tag{5.2.2}$$

whose relation to the characteristic equation for the matrix, $|\mathbf{M} - \lambda\mathbf{I}| = 0$ of Chapter 3, is very close and will be discussed in Chapter 8. The dummy variable for age will often be written a rather than x, and $p(x)m(x)$ will be shortened to $\phi(x)$, known as the *net maternity function.*

Insofar as e^{rt} is an appropriate form for $B(t)$ our problem has been reduced from (5.1.2) to (5.2.2). This is a major advance, since the unknown in (5.1.2) is a function $B(t)$, while that in (5.2.2) is a variable r. A number of procedures will be given for the numerical solution of (5.2.2), but before discussing these, we will take up some of its general properties.

Equation (5.2.2) can have only one real root. This follows from the fact that the integrand of $\psi(r)$ on the left-hand side of (5.2.2) consists of nonnegative factors; if the integral is equal to unity for r, it cannot also be equal to unity for $\rho > r$, since $e^{-\rho a}$ is less than e^{-ra} for every a. In the same way, a real number less than r cannot be a root. Since $\phi(a) = p(a)m(a)$ is positive or zero for all a, and, for any given a, e^{-ra} is a decreasing function of r, the integral $\psi(r)$ must be a decreasing function of r. It is helpful to think of the graph of $\psi(r)$ plotted as the ordinate against r on the abscissa (Table 5.1 and Fig. 5.2).

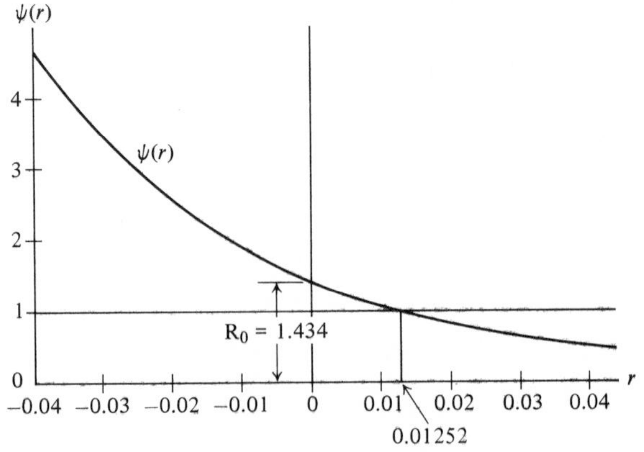

Fig. 5.2 Curve of $\psi(r) = \int_\alpha^\beta e^{-ra}p(a)m(a)\,da$ plotted against r for Netherlands females, 1965.

Table 5.1 Values of $\psi(r)$ for Netherlands females, 1965*

VALUES FROM r = -0.20 TO r = 0.10		DETAIL ABOUT r = 0	
r	ψ(r)	r	ψ(r)
-0.20	1018.277	-0.010	1.91870
-0.18	491.867	-0.008	1.80951
-0.16	241.261	-0.006	1.70678
-0.14	120.220	-0.004	1.61012
-0.12	60.876	-0.002	1.51914
-0.10	31.330	0.000	1.43350
-0.08	16.387	0.002	1.35288
-0.06	8.710	0.004	1.27697
-0.04	4.702	0.006	1.20548
-0.02	2.577	0.008	1.13816
0.00	1.434	0.010	1.07474
0.02	0.809	0.012	1.01499
0.04	0.462	0.014	0.95870
0.06	0.267	0.016	0.90565
0.08	0.157	0.018	0.85565
0.10	0.093	0.020	0.80851

$$* \ \psi(r) = \int_\alpha^\beta e^{-ra}p(a)m(a)\,da \doteq 0.0001e^{-12.5r} + 0.0498e^{-17.5r} + 0.3334e^{-22.5r} + 0.4912e^{-27.5r} + 0.3267e^{-32.5r} + 0.1716e^{-37.5r} + 0.0559e^{-42.5r} + 0.0048e^{-47.5r}\,.$$

The figure could be used to solve $\psi(r) = 1$ but we will find more convenient ways in Section 5.3. A solution by interpolation in Table 5.1 appears as an application of Eq. (10.2.5).

To prove formally that $\psi(r)$ is monotonically decreasing, we observe that its derivative is

$$\psi'(r) = -\int_\alpha^\beta ae^{-ra}\phi(a)\,da\,,$$

which is always negative, since all three factors of the integrand are nonnegative, and over some range are positive. A constantly decreasing function can cross the line $\psi(r) = 1$ only once, at the real root r_1. Since

$$\psi''(r) = \int_\alpha^\beta a^2 e^{-ra}\phi(a)\,da$$

is positive, $\psi(r)$ must be concave upward throughout.

Prove that $-\psi'(r)/\psi(r)$ evaluated at $r = 0$ is μ, the mean age of childbearing in the stationary population, and that $-\psi'(r)$ evaluated where $\psi(r) = 1$ is A_r, the mean age of childbearing in the stable population, which is the age distribution proportional to $e^{-rx}p(x)$, the continuous analog of (3.2.6). The quantity $\psi(0) = R_0$, the integral of $\phi(a) = p(a)m(a)$, is called the *net reproduction rate* (NRR); it is the number of (girl) children expected to be born to a (girl) child at existing age-specific rates of birth and death, or the analog for males. Locate R_0 on Table 5.1 for Netherlands females, 1965, and use the table to estimate the two ages μ and A_r with any small h. A formula for the derivative of tabular values for this purpose is

$$\psi'(r) \doteq \frac{\psi(r + h) - \psi(r - h)}{2h}\,.$$

By the geometrical considerations of the preceding paragraph show that $\mu > A_r$ if $r > 0$.

Examination of (5.2.2) shows that if $R_0 = \int_\alpha^\beta \phi(a)\,da > 1$, then the real root, r_1, must be positive. For only a positive r makes e^{-ra} less than unity, and if $\int_\alpha^\beta \phi(a)\,da = R_0$ is greater than unity, the other factor under the integrand of (5.2.2), e^{-ra}, must be less than unity. Similarly if $R_0 < 1$, then r_1 must be negative. The converse also holds. Thus we can say that if and only if

$$\begin{aligned} R_0 &< 1\,, &\quad \text{then}\quad r_1 &< 0\,,\\ R_0 &= 1\,, &\quad \text{then}\quad r_1 &= 0\,,\\ R_0 &> 1\,, &\quad \text{then}\quad r_1 &> 0\,. \end{aligned}$$

The complex roots must come in conjugate pairs. For suppose $u + iv$ is a root. From DeMoivre's theorem

$$e^{ra} = e^{ua+iva} = e^{ua}[\cos(va) + i\sin(va)]\,,$$

and hence (5.2.2) is

$$\psi(r) = \int_\alpha^\beta e^{-ua}[\cos(va) - i\sin(va)]\phi(a)\,da = 1\,. \tag{5.2.3}$$

Since there is no imaginary portion on the right-hand side, that on the left must vanish,

$$\int_\alpha^\beta e^{-ua}\sin(va)\phi(a)\,da = 0\,,$$

and hence $u - iv$ must also be a root.

Moreover, the value of u in the complex root $u + iv$ must be less than r_1, the real root. For equating real parts on the two sides of (5.2.3),

$$\int_\alpha^\beta e^{-ua} \cos(va)\phi(a)\, da = 1 ,$$

gives the same equation as (5.2.2), which was satisfied by the real root, except that now we have a factor $\cos(va)$. The cosine being always less than unity, whatever real value its argument may take other than multiples of 2π, e^{-ua} must be larger than the corresponding factor in the integrand of (5.2.2); hence u must be smaller than r_1. If $R_0 < 1$, then the real root is negative and all the complex roots have negative real elements; when $R_0 > 1$, and therefore $r_1 > 0$, they could have positive elements as far as this argument goes, though in practice this does not occur. Out of 480 populations for which the calculation was made, u was closest to positive for Taiwan females, 1964, at $u = -0.0059$.

Lotka's argument that persistence of a fixed set of age-specific fertility and mortality rates will result in a stable age distribution rests on the fact proved above that the real part of any complex root must be less than the real root. For if the real part u_s is less than r_1, then the factor $e^{u_s t}$ in (5.2.6) below will be less than $e^{r_1 t}$, and hence the term $Q_s e^{r_s t}$ involving the factor $e^{u_s t}$ will become indefinitely small in absolute value compared with the leading term $Q_1 e^{r_1 t}$ as t becomes large. Hence, beyond a suitable t the series (5.2.5) may be approximated by its first term, and the births are a simple exponential $Q_1 e^{r_1 t}$. We see below (Chapter 7) that exponential births lead to an exponentially increasing population with stable age distribution. The same ergodic property may be demonstrated from the properties of irreducible nonnegative matrices as suggested in Section 3.2.

The real root of equation (5.2.2) cannot be multiple. For any multiple root would be in common between (5.2.2) and its derivative with respect to r; it would therefore satisfy

$$\int_\alpha^\beta a e^{-ra}\phi(a)\, da = 0 . \tag{5.2.4}$$

But all the factors of the integrand are positive or zero in the admissible range $\alpha \le a \le \beta$; the integral of (5.2.4) cannot be equal to 0 unless $\phi(a) = 0$ almost everywhere in (α, β).

Multiple *complex* roots may indeed exist. Empirically no such cases have turned up in our observation, and the condition under which they could appear is theoretically open (Hadwiger, 1939, p. 7). John S. Lew has suggested in correspondence several forms of the net maternity function that would produce multiple roots. The simplest of his examples is

$$\phi(a) = e^{-ka}\left(\frac{a^5}{60} + \frac{a^3}{2}\right),$$

which by a change of variable in the well-known integral

$$\int_0^\infty e^{-u}u^{n-1}\,du = (n-1)!$$

applied for $n = 6$ and $n = 4$ to give $\psi(r) - 1$, and the result factored, produces

$$\psi(r) = \int_0^\infty e^{-ra}\phi(a)\,da = 1 + \left(\frac{2}{(r+k)^2} - 1\right)\left(\frac{1}{(r+k)^2} + 1\right)^2.$$

Hence the equation $\psi(r) = 1$ has the roots $-k \pm i$, each repeated twice. Distinct roots are required for (5.2.19) below, a step in ascertaining the Q's of (5.1.3) by elementary calculus.

For a proof based on properties of entire functions that the number of roots of (5.2.2) is infinite when $\infty > \beta > \alpha$, that is, when the fertile range is finite, see Hadwiger (1939b, p. 2) or Lopez (1961, p. 15).

The presence of the constants Q is permitted by the linearity of (5.1.2), and there will be as many Q's as there are r's. The general solution of (5.2.2) is

$$B(t) = Q_1e^{r_1t} + Q_2e^{r_2t} + \cdots, \tag{5.2.5}$$

or, if $r_s = u_s + iv_s$,

$$B(t) = Q_1e^{r_1t} + \sum_{s=2}^{\infty} Q_se^{u_st}[\cos(v_st) + i\sin(v_st)]. \tag{5.2.6}$$

Since, as was argued from (5.2.3), each complex root is accompanied by its complex conjugate, which is multiplied by the conjugate coefficient, the imaginary terms in the series will cancel out, and a real trigonometric series remains. This is evidently necessary for our purpose, since the representation of the counts of a real population could hardly include imaginary terms.

The next task is to evaluate the Q's to fit a given $G(t)$.

To find Q_s by direct integration, we start by rewriting (5.1.1) as

$$G(t) = B(t) - \int_0^t B(t-a)\phi(a)\,da. \tag{5.2.7}$$

Following Hertz (1908, p. 84) and Lotka (1939c, p. 86) we introduce the auxiliary quantity

$$P_s = \int_0^\beta e^{-r_st}G(t)\,dt, \tag{5.2.8}$$

and substituting from (5.2.7) for $G(t)$ in (5.2.8), we have

$$P_s = \int_0^\beta e^{-r_st}\left[B(t) - \int_0^t B(t-a)\phi(a)\,da\right]dt. \tag{5.2.9}$$

Now substituting for $B(t)$ in (5.2.9) the series (5.2.5),

$$B(t) = \sum_1^\infty Q_je^{r_jt} = Q_se^{r_st} + \sum_{j\neq s}^\infty Q_je^{r_jt},$$

and similarly for $B(t - a)$, we have

$$P_s = \int_0^\beta e^{-r_s t}\left[Q_s e^{r_s t} - \int_0^t Q_s e^{r_s(t-a)}\phi(a)\,da\right]dt + R_s\,, \tag{5.2.10}$$

where R_s is a sum of the same type of double integral as that which precedes it on the right-hand side of (5.2.10), containing terms in $Q_u e^{r_u t}$, $u \neq s$. (It will later be shown that $R_s = 0$.) From (5.2.10),

$$\begin{aligned} P_s &= Q_s \int_0^\beta \left[1 - \int_0^t e^{-r_s a}\phi(a)\,da\right]dt + R_s \\ &= Q_s \int_0^\beta \left[\int_0^\beta e^{-r_s a}\phi(a)\,da - \int_0^t e^{-r_s a}\phi(a)\,da\right]dt + R_s\,, \end{aligned} \tag{5.2.11}$$

where we use the fact that $\int_0^\beta e^{-r_s a}\phi(a)\,da = 1$; this is so if r_s is one of the roots of (5.2.2). The difference between the two interior integrals of (5.2.11) is

$$\int_t^\beta e^{-r_s a}\phi(a)\,da\,,$$

and entering this in (5.2.11) gives

$$P_s = Q_s \int_0^\beta \int_t^\beta e^{-r_s a}\phi(a)\,da\,dt + R_s\,. \tag{5.2.12}$$

The double integral of (5.2.12) is taken over a right-angled triangle in the ta-plane. Integrating the same function over the same area, which is to say, finding the volume of the same triangular cylinder but changing the order of the variables (Fig. 5.3), must leave the integral in (5.2.12) unchanged. Thus

$$P_s = Q_s \int_0^\beta \int_0^a e^{-r_s a}\phi(a)\,dt\,da + R_s\,. \tag{5.2.13}$$

The integration with respect to t is now merely $\int_0^a dt = a$, and hence

$$P_s = Q_s \int_0^\beta a e^{-r_s a}\phi(a)\,da + R_s\,. \tag{5.2.14}$$

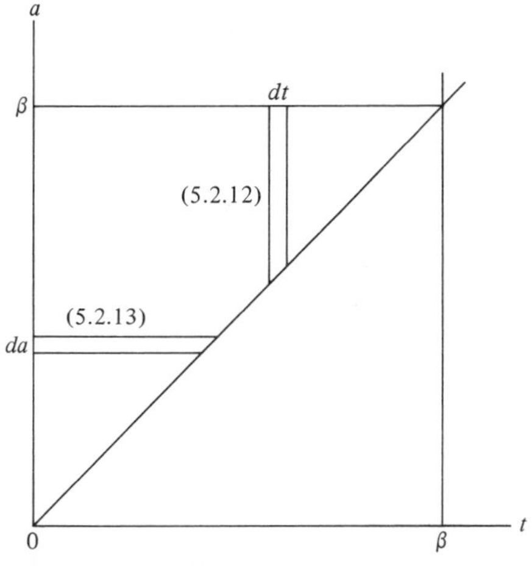

Fig. 5.3 Elementary strips for double integral used in ascertaining Q_1.

It remains only to show that $R_s = 0$. From (5.2.9) and (5.2.10) we see that R_s is made up of terms such as

$$R_{s,u} = Q_u \int_0^\beta e^{-r_s t}\left[e^{r_u t} - \int_0^t e^{r_u(t-a)}\phi(a)\,da\right]dt\,, \tag{5.2.15}$$

where $u \neq s$. Therefore,

$$R_{s,u} = Q_u \int_0^\beta \left[e^{(r_u - r_s)t} - \int_0^t e^{(r_u - r_s)t} e^{-r_u a} \phi(a)\, da \right] dt \,. \tag{5.2.16}$$

As before, we replace 1 by $\int_0^\beta e^{-r_u a}\phi(a)\, da$ after the first integral sign in (5.2.16):

$$R_{s,u} = Q_u \int_0^\beta e^{(r_u - r_s)t} \left[\int_0^\beta e^{-r_u a}\phi(a)\, da - \int_0^t e^{-r_u a}\phi(a)\, da \right] dt$$

$$= Q_u \int_0^\beta e^{(r_u - r_s)t} \left[\int_t^\beta e^{-r_u a}\phi(a)\, da \right] dt \,. \tag{5.2.17}$$

Changing the order of integration as before, we obtain

$$R_{s,u} = Q_u \int_0^\beta e^{-r_u a}\phi(a) \int_0^a e^{(r_u - r_s)t}\, dt\, da \tag{5.2.18}$$

$$= \frac{Q_u}{r_u - r_s} \int_0^\beta e^{-r_u a}\phi(a)(e^{(r_u - r_s)a} - 1)\, da$$

$$= \frac{Q_u}{r_u - r_s} \left[\int_0^\beta e^{-r_s a}\phi(a)\, da - \int_0^\beta e^{-r_u a}\phi(a)\, da \right] \tag{5.2.19}$$

$$= 0 \,,$$

since each integral in (5.2.19) is unity and r_u and r_s are two distinct roots. The same argument applies to all $R_{s,u}$ for $u \neq s$, and hence to R_s, since

$$R_s = \sum_{u \neq s} R_{s,u} \,.$$

Reverting to (5.2.14), now with $R_s = 0$, we have

$$Q_s = \frac{P_s}{\int_0^\beta a e^{-r_s a}\phi(a)\, da} \,, \tag{5.2.20}$$

and incorporating the definition of P_s in (5.2.8) gives finally

$$Q_s = \frac{\int_0^\beta e^{-r_s t} G(t)\, dt}{\int_0^\beta a e^{-r_s a}\phi(a)\, da} \,. \tag{5.2.21}$$

If we know $G(t)$, the births to that portion of the population itself born before or at $t = 0$, and the assumed fixed rates of survivorship and fertility, then (5.2.21) suffices to calculate Q_s. As a special case, consider the daughters of B_0 births occurring at $t = 0$. These daughters will have birth dates distributed as $B_0 p(t) m(t) = B_0 \phi(t)$. Inserting this for $G(t)$ in (5.2.21), we have

$$Q_s = \frac{B_0 \int_0^\beta e^{-r_s t}\phi(t)\, dt}{\int_0^\beta a e^{-r_s a}\phi(a)\, da} = \frac{B_0}{\int_0^\beta a e^{-r_s a}\phi(a)\, da} = \frac{B_0}{-\psi'(r_s)} \,. \tag{5.2.22}$$

If r_s is the real root r_1, (5.2.22) multiplied by $e^{r_1 t}$ tells us the number of births in the population at time t after the effect of the complex roots has become negligible. For such time t,

$$B(t) = Q_1 e^{r_1 t} = B_0 e^{r_1 t}/(-\psi'(r_1)), \tag{5.2.23}$$

where the denominator is the average age of mothers at childbearing in the stable population, designated $A_r = -\psi'(r_1)$.

Spectral Decomposition for the Continuous Population Model

The analysis in Chapter 3, using matrices and age intervals of five years, included the decomposition of an arbitrary age distribution as a weighted sum of stable vectors. All of this has an analogy in the continuous version. To any r_i for which $\psi(r_i) = 1$ corresponds a $\lambda_i = e^{5r_i}$ which approximately satisfies

$$|\mathbf{M} - \lambda\mathbf{I}| = 0 .$$

(The proof that λ_i converges to $e^{s r_i}$ as the interval of time becomes small is given in Chapter 8, and the error of approximation in any finite width of interval in Chapter 11.) To each stable vertical vector $\{\mathbf{K}_i\}$ such that $\mathbf{M}\{\mathbf{K}_i\} = \lambda_i\{\mathbf{K}_i\}$, in the notation of Chapter 3, corresponds a continuous stable age distribution $c_i(x) = b_i e^{-r_i x} p(x)$, where b_i is defined as

$$b_i = \frac{1}{\int_0^\omega e^{-r_i a} p(a)\, da} ;$$

and to each stable horizontal vector $[\mathbf{H}_i]$ satisfying $[\mathbf{H}_i]\mathbf{M} = \lambda_i[\mathbf{H}_i]$ corresponds a function $v_i(x)$, generalized from Fisher's reproductive value of a woman, defined in (3.2.15):

$$v_i(x) = \frac{1}{e^{-r_i x} p(x)} \int_x^\beta e^{-r_i a} p(a) m(a)\, da . \tag{5.2.24}$$

The orthogonality property $[\mathbf{H}_i]\{\mathbf{K}_j\} = 0$, $i \neq j$, has its analog in

$$\int_0^\beta v_i(x) c_j(x)\, dx = 0 , \quad i \neq j ,$$

which the reader may prove by entering the definitions of $v_i(x)$ and $c_j(x)$, changing the order of integration between a and x, and using the fact that

$$\psi(r_i) = \psi(r_j) = 1 .$$

He may similarly evaluate $\int_0^\beta v_i(x) c_i(x)\, dx$ and find it to be $-b_i\psi'(r_i)$. For the real root r_1 this last is the product of the intrinsic birth rate and the mean age of childbearing in the stable population (Goodman, 1967c).

Now the arbitrary age distribution $k(x)$ may be expanded in terms of the stable $c_i(x)$, $i = 1, 2, \ldots$:

$$k(x) = Q_1 c_1(x) + Q_2 c_2(x) + \cdots \tag{5.2.25}$$

To find the constant Q_i we multiply by $v_i(x)$, integrate with respect to x from 0 to β, note that the orthogonality property makes all terms but the ith on the right zero, and obtain

$$\int_0^\beta k(x)v_i(x)\,dx = Q_i \int_0^\beta c_i(x)v_i(x)\,dx\,,$$

so that with $\int_0^\beta c_i(x)v_i(x)\,dx = -b_i\psi'(r_i)$, the result is

$$Q_i = \int_0^\beta k(x)v_i(x)\,dx\Big/\big(-b_i\psi'(r_i)\big)\,. \tag{5.2.26}$$

What does Q_i become for the arbitrary $k(x)$ equal to one birth?

If we write $k(x, t)\,dx$ for the absolute number between ages x and $x + dx$ at time t, then with fixed mortality and fertility an expansion of the form

$$k(x, t) = Q_1c_1(x)e^{r_1t} + Q_2c_2(x)e^{r_2t} + \cdots \tag{5.2.27}$$

should be obtainable. The reader may round off the proof of (5.2.27) by showing in what circumstances the Q_i are the same as those of (5.2.25) given by (5.2.26).

5.3. NUMERICAL SOLUTION OF THE CHARACTERISTIC EQUATION

To ascertain the roots of (5.2.2) from observations which provide a life table and age-specific female birth rates, it is usual to approximate to $l_0\psi(r)$ with

$$l_0\psi(r) = \sum_{\alpha}^{\beta-5} e^{-r(x+2.5)}\,{}_5L_x\,F_x\,, \tag{5.3.1}$$

F_x being the birth rate to women aged x to $x + 5$ where α and β are numbers such as 10 and 50, and summation is over ages x which are multiples of 5. Then Eq. (5.2.2) is approximated by

$$l_0\psi(r) = e^{-12.5r}\,{}_5L_{10}\,F_{10} + e^{-17.5r}\,{}_5L_{15}\,F_{15} + \cdots + e^{-47.5r}\,{}_5L_{45}\,F_{45} = l_0\,, \tag{5.3.2}$$

in which the integral

$$\int_0^5 e^{-r(x+t)}p(x + t)m(x + t)\,dt\,, \quad x = 10, 15, \ldots, 45\,, \tag{5.3.3}$$

is replaced by the product of

1. a mid-value: $e^{-r(x+2.5)}$,
2. an integral: $\displaystyle\int_0^5 \frac{l(x + t)\,dt}{l_0} = \frac{{}_5L_x}{l_0}$,
3. a ratio of two integrals: $\dfrac{\int_0^5 k(x + t)m(x + t)\,dt}{\int_0^5 k(x + t)\,dt} = F_x$,

   $k(x)$ being the observed age distribution.

Table 5.2 Ratio of male to female births at the several ages of mother, for four countries*

AGE	ENGLAND AND WALES 1964	ITALY 1963	JAPAN 1963	UNITED STATES 1964
15-19	1.068	1.045	1.031	1.056
20-24	1.060	1.054	1.057	1.050
25-29	1.065	1.059	1.054	1.047
30-34	1.059	1.052	1.063	1.039
35-39	1.059	1.050	1.055	1.039
40-44	1.041	1.050	1.067	1.029

* Source: United Nations, *Demographic Yearbook*, 1965, Table 13.

The rules of integral calculus do not sanction such a decomposition of an integral over a finite interval. However, the errors happen to be compensating in some degree, and it will be shown in Chapter 11 that (5.3.2) (there called Method B) is not as bad an approximation to (5.2.2) as it seems at first.

We here follow the conventional practice in demographic work of taking the ratio of girl births to total births for all ages of mother and applying this to the births at each age. To check the assumption that the masculinity of births is the same for all ages of mother we present Table 5.2. The sex ratio (males divided by females) at least in some instances diminishes with age of mother. For the United States, 1964, the trend is clear; for England and Wales, 1964, less so; and for Japan, 1963, and Italy, 1963, hardly discernible. [How far could greater masculinity of births after a war be explained by a larger number of births to new brides?]

Insofar as the usual method slightly underestimates the average age μ of mothers at the bearing of girl children, it slightly overestimates the female intrinsic rate, since $r \doteq (\ln R_0)/\mu$, by disregarding r^2 in (6.2.6). (For discussion of μ and other moments see Section 5.6 and Chapter 6.)

For the United States, 1964, the mean age of childbearing was about one part in 1700 too low on the conventional method. But on the other hand, the value of $\ln R_0$ by the conventional method was also too low, by about one part in 1900. The net result of these largely offsetting errors was to make the conventional r too high by about one part in 15,000, evidently a matter of no consequence. Table 5.3 shows the details, and constitutes a justification of the conventional method.

To find ln 1.51014 required for the calculation in Table 5.3 below, look in the body of the table of e^x, given in the appendix, for the largest entry which is less than 1.51014 and find $1.491825 = e^{0.4}$. Divide 1.51014 by 1.491825 to

Table 5.3 Comparison of conventional and correct methods of calculating the intrinsic rate r, United States females, 1964*

	CONVENTIONAL	CORRECT
CHARACTERISTICS OF AGES AT CHILDBEARING IN STATIONARY POPULATION	FEMALE BIRTHS OBTAINED BY APPLICATION OF AVERAGE SEX RATIO TO ALL BIRTHS BY AGE OF MOTHER	OBSERVED FEMALE BIRTHS BY AGE OF MOTHER
R_0	1.51014	1.51047
$\ln R_0$	0.41220	0.41242
μ = MEAN AGE	26.530	26.546
σ^2 = VARIANCE	36.339†	36.390†
$1000r_L$ FROM (6.2.7)	15.706	15.705
$1000r$ FROM (5.3.5)	15.703	15.702

DATA: CONVENTIONAL NET MATERNITY FUNCTION GIVEN IN TABLE 2.1. CORRECT NET MATERNITY FUNCTION AS FOLLOWS:

x	$_5\phi_x$	x	$_5\phi_x$	x	$_5\phi_x$
10	0.00207	25	0.42262	40	0.03201
15	0.17190	30	0.24429	45	0.00181
20	0.51905	35	0.11672	TOTAL	1.51047

* Programmed by Shannon Stokes and James Porter.
† Not corrected for grouping (See Chapter 11).

obtain 1.012277. Now search for the largest entry smaller than this and find $1.012072 = e^{0.012}$. Divide 1.012277 by 1.012072 to obtain 1.000203. This last is approximately $e^{0.000203}$, since $e^x = 1 + x$ for small x. Then the given number 1.51014 is equal to

$$(e^{0.4})(e^{0.012})(e^{0.000203}) = (e^{0.412203}),$$

so that its natural logarithm is 0.412203, as appears, to five decimal places, in the second row of Table 5.3.

The modern iterative approach to the solution of (5.3.2) was first proposed by Ansley Coale (1957). Several routes of iteration suggest themselves:

a) *The rule*

If $\psi(r^*)$ is greater than 1, take r^{**} as $r^* + 0.5|r^* - r|$;
if $\psi(r^*)$ is less than 1, take r^{**} as $r^* - 0.5|r^* - r|$,

r, r^*, and r^{**} being successive iterates.

This requires programming only $\psi(r)$, and gives one binary digit per iteration, starting for example from $r = 0.0$ and $r^* = 0.025$. Fifteen to twenty iterations in practice provide six-decimal-place accuracy. [Why is this so? State the permissible limits on the arbitrary pair of initial values.]

b) *The Newton-Raphson method*

$$r^* = r - \frac{\psi(r) - 1}{\psi'(r)}, \tag{5.3.4}$$

which requires the calculation of the derivative $\psi'(r)$ as well as of $\psi(r)$, and converges in about five cycles. [Derive (5.3.4) from Taylor's expansion, and show r^* explicitly in terms of the $\psi(r)$ of (5.3.2).]

c) *The secant method* [given in Section 3.2]

d) *Functional iteration.* By multiplying the characteristic equation (5.3.2) by $e^{27.5r}$ and transposing, we obtain the alternative form

$$\begin{aligned} e^{27.5r^*} &= e^{15r}\left(\frac{{}_5L_{10}}{l_0}\right)F_{10} + e^{10r}\left(\frac{{}_5L_{15}}{l_0}\right)F_{15} + e^{5r}\left(\frac{{}_5L_{20}}{l_0}\right)F_{20} \\ &+ \left(\frac{{}_5L_{25}}{l_0}\right)F_{25} + e^{-5r}\left(\frac{{}_5L_{30}}{l_0}\right)F_{30} + \cdots + e^{-20r}\left(\frac{{}_5L_{45}}{l_0}\right)F_{45}. \end{aligned} \tag{5.3.5}$$

We start by choosing some arbitrary value for r, evaluating the expression on the right of (5.3.5), then taking 1/27.5 of the logarithm to obtain the improved r^*, substitute r^* for r, and continue. The test for convergence might be that r^* differ from r by less than 0.000001. In practice only about four cycles are necessary for six-decimal-place accuracy.

Verify that $1000r = 15.703$ as shown in Table 5.3 by using the data of Table 2.1 in (5.3.5) and the arbitrary starting value $r = 0.015$, given that $e^{5(0.015)} = e^{0.075} = 1.077884$. The first iteration provides $r^* = 0.015664$. Given that $e^{5r^*} = e^{0.078320} = 1.081469$, try again and find $r^{**} = 0.015701$, low by 2 in the last decimal place. With (6.2.8) below as the start of the first iteration,

$$r \doteq \frac{\ln R_0}{\mu} = \frac{0.4122}{26.53} = 0.01554,$$

a single application of (5.3.5) suffices for most purposes. Devise an iterative form analogous to (5.3.5) for the matrix characteristic equation (3.2.4), and show in a single application of it, starting with $r = 0.015703$, that $r = 0.2 \ln \lambda$ comes out to 0.015733. Differences between such results will be taken up in Chapter 11; (5.3.5), method B, gives a lower r than (3.2.4), method A.

The iterative sequence of (5.3.5) combines ease of programming with economy of computer time. If we form the iterative process by multiplying (5.3.2) by $e^{37.5r}$, and start with $r = 0.02$, some 20 cycles are necessary for United States females, 1964. Waves of slowly diminishing amplitude appear in the successive iterates. When we multiply (5.3.2) by $e^{32.5r}$ convergence to six decimal places requires seven iterations; multiplying by $e^{17.5r}$ requires 12 iterations. Translate these facts into terms of the shape of the curves $e^{27.5r}\psi(r)$, etc. considering especially their slopes. Verify your general remarks numerically with the help of the data of Table 5.1. Prove that the optimum power of e^r by which to multiply is the mean age of childbearing in the stable population, if one knew it. Theory on convergence in functional iteration is provided by Scarborough (1962, p. 206) and Ralston (1965, p. 320), who show that, in the notation of (5.3.5), the requirement is that $\partial r^*/\partial r < 1$ in the relevant range, and the smaller $\partial r^*/\partial r$ the more rapid the convergence.

e) *A solution that dispenses with the characteristic equation.* The method of Daniel Bernoulli (Hildebrand, 1956, p. 458; Ralston, 1965, p. 364) converts a polynomial equation into a recurrence equation in order to solve the former. In demography we start with the recurrence equation (5.1.1). Instead of converting it into the polynomial equation (5.3.2), we should be able to use Bernoulli's method directly.

We seek then a direct solution for (5.1.1) expressed in finite form as

$$B(t) = B(t - 12\tfrac{1}{2})\frac{{}_5L_{10}}{l_0}F_{10} + B(t - 17\tfrac{1}{2})\frac{{}_5L_{15}}{l_0}F_{15} + \cdots + B(t - 47\tfrac{1}{2})\frac{{}_5L_{45}}{l_0}F_{45}\,, \tag{5.3.6}$$

with $G(t) = 0$. The $B(t)$ for values of the argument less than 0 may be put equal to 1 to start the process. Then the first calculated $B(t)$ from (5.3.6) will be $B(0) = R_0$, the net reproduction rate. [Why?] We now move along in the trajectory by adding 2.5 to the arguments of B in all terms of (5.3.6), and find again that $B(2.5) = R_0$. Next we add another 2.5 and so find $B(5)$. The process of increasing the argument of $B(t)$ and evaluating the right-hand side of (5.3.6) continues step by step until stability is reached, for example as tested by

$$\left|\frac{B(t + 2\frac{1}{2})}{B(t)} - \frac{B(t)}{B(t - 2\frac{1}{2})}\right| < 10^{-7}\,.$$

The value of r may then be extracted as

$$r = \tfrac{2}{5}\bigl(\ln B(t + 2\tfrac{1}{2}) - \ln B(t)\bigr)\,,$$

since at stability $B(t + 2\frac{1}{2}) = e^{5r/2}B(t)$.

The method does converge, but too slowly for use. Large waves of gradually diminishing amplitude are generated in $B(t)$, and convergence typically requires about 250 iterations, corresponding to a projection of over 500 years. The main reason for presenting this here is to show that the characteristic equation *is* helpful. To what functional integration formula under (d) does this method correspond?

f) *Simultaneous iteration for r and other constants of the stable population.* This is useful when intrinsic birth and death rates are required as well as r; it converges

Table 5.4 Crude, standardized, and intrinsic rates of increase per thousand population, United States females, 1919–65*

	CRUDE	DIRECTLY STANDARDIZED ON U.S. 1960	INTRINSIC 1000r
1919-21	15.05	4.17	10.23
1924-26	13.68	2.53	9.04
1929-31	10.02	1.10	2.51
1934-36	8.28	0.05	-1.16
1939-41	9.64	2.26	0.94
1944-46	12.55	5.80	6.88
1949-51	15.41	10.42	14.37
1954-56	16.35	14.06	19.88
1959-61	15.03	15.03	21.13
1962	13.71	13.94	19.24
1963	12.84	12.92	17.50
1964	12.41	12.43	16.10
1965	10.78	10.75	12.65

* Births adjusted for underregistration. Programmed by Wilhelm Flieger.

in four or five iterations and produces a number of quantities relating to the stable situation (Section 7.2).

The reader may examine under what circumstances the six methods will give numerically identical answers. How suited is each to finding the complex roots?

To illustrate the real root r_1, regarded as the measure of the intrinsic rate of natural increase of a population, Table 5.4 gives for United States females, 1919–65, crude, standardized, and intrinsic rates per thousand population, based on registrations as adjusted officially. (Note the difference between r for 1964 of Table 5.3 and of Table 5.4, due to adjustment of the data in the latter.) The crude rate is merely births less deaths over a period, divided by the mean population of the period (Section 1.1). The rate standardized on 1960 is the result of applying age-specific mortality and fertility to the 1960 female population of the United States.

In the 1930's the considerable number of mothers remaining from the preceding epoch of high fertility maintained a positive crude rate of increase despite a negative intrinsic rate. The intrinsic rate trebled from the mid-1940's to the mid-1950's, while the crude rate only added 25%. During the 1960's the intrinsic rate has fallen more than the crude rate.

The argument provided by Lotka and reproduced in Section 5.2 is imperfect in several directions, as Feller (1941) showed. To solve first the essentially irrelevant homogeneous equation (5.1.2) and then try to fit the answer to (5.1.1) is roundabout. We used the assumption that the roots are distinct; even though in practice they are distinct, a method that did not assume this would be preferable. That the solution (5.1.3) should be capable of being fitted to the births arising from an arbitrary initial age distribution requires among other things that the number of roots in r of (5.2.2) be infinite, and this need not be so with an infinite range of the net maternity function. Finally, two different net maternity functions could produce the same of set of roots in r, as Feller shows with an example (1941, p. 262). None of these difficulties is of practical consequence, and yet to escape from them, at the same time simplifying the argument, seems worthwhile. With the Laplace transform, much of Section 5.2 is replaced by the few lines from (5.5.4) to (5.5.8) below. In order to make the present account self-contained, the definition of the transform and the few properties that will be needed are set forth in Section 5.4.

5.4. PROPERTIES OF THE LAPLACE TRANSFORM

Given a function $h(t)$, we define its one-sided Laplace transform as

$$h^*(r) = \int_0^\infty e^{-rt}h(t)\,dt \tag{5.4.1}$$

if the improper integral on the right exists. It is common to speak of $h(t)$ as the *original* function and the transform $h^*(r)$ as the *image*. Given the transform, the original is spoken of as its *inverse*. Transforming may be thought of as translating from the variable t to r, from a t-language to an r-language, by means of (5.4.1); the point of doing it is that there are problems, including that expressed in the renewal equation (5.1.1), which become very simple when so translated (Doetsch, 1958, p. 29).

We will need the actual integration of (5.4.1) for certain functions to constitute the dictionary for the change of language. If $h(t)$ is a constant k, then its transform is

$$h_k^*(r) = \int_0^\infty e^{-rt}k\,dt = k/r \tag{5.4.2}$$

if $R(r)$, the real part of r, is positive. If $h(t)$ is t, then

$$h_t^*(r) = \int_0^\infty e^{-rt}t\,dt = 1/r^2\,, \quad R(r) > 0\,,$$

by integration by parts. Repeated integration by parts provides the transform of t^n, n integral,

$$h^*_{t^n}(r) = \int_0^\infty e^{-rt}t^n\,dt = n!/r^{n+1}, \quad R(r) > 0, \tag{5.4.3}$$

and a change of variable gives

$$h^*_{t^n}(r) = \frac{1}{r^{n+1}}\int_0^\infty e^{-rt}(rt)^n\,d(rt) = \frac{\Gamma(n+1)}{r^{n+1}}, \quad R(r) > 0, \tag{5.4.4}$$

as the transform of t^n if n is real. Especially important for our work will be the transform of $h(t) = e^{r_s t}$, where r_s is a special constant, the (real or complex) sth root of the characteristic equation, $\psi(r) = 1$, of (5.2.2):

$$h^*(r) = \int_0^\infty e^{-rt}e^{r_s t}\,dt = \int_0^\infty e^{t(r_s - r)}\,dt = \frac{1}{r - r_s}, \tag{5.4.5}$$

valid for all (complex) r such that $R(r)$, the real part of r, is greater than $R(r_s)$. We will use (5.4.5) in the other direction: the inverse of $1/(r - r_s)$ is $e^{r_s t}$.

A few general rules may be said to constitute the grammar for the translation to which we are leading up. If the transform of $h(t)$ is known to be $h^*(r)$, then that of $Kh(t)$, where K is any constant, is $Kh^*(r)$, as follows from the definition (5.4.1). If the transforms of $h(t)$ and $k(t)$ are $h^*(r)$ and $k^*(r)$ respectively, then the transform of $h(t) + k(t)$ is

$$\begin{aligned}[h(t) + k(t)]^* &= \int_0^\infty e^{-rt}[h(t) + k(t)]\,dt \\ &= \int_0^\infty e^{-rt}h(t)\,dt + \int_0^\infty e^{-rt}k(t)\,dt \\ &= h^*(r) + k^*(r).\end{aligned} \tag{5.4.6}$$

In short, the transform is a linear operator.

One other rule will be needed. The integral in our equation (5.1.1) is known as a *convolution* of the functions B and ϕ; it contains only $B(t - x)$ and $\phi(x)$, the sum of whose arguments is t, which is fixed in relation to the variable of integration. To find the transform of the convolution $\int_0^t B(t - a)\phi(a)\,da$ we have

$$\begin{aligned}\left(\int_0^t B(t - a)\phi(a)\,da\right)^* &= \int_0^\infty e^{-rt}\int_0^t B(t - a)\phi(a)\,da\,dt \\ &= \int_0^\infty\int_0^t e^{-rt}B(t - a)\phi(a)\,da\,dt \\ &= \int_0^\infty\int_0^t e^{-r(t-a)}B(t - a)e^{-ra}\phi(a)\,da\,dt;\end{aligned} \tag{5.4.7}$$

and if the two integrations may be separated this becomes for $t \geq \beta$

$$\left(\int_0^\infty e^{-r(t-a)}B(t - a)\,dt\right)\left(\int_0^\infty e^{-ra}\phi(a)\,da\right) = B^*(r)\phi^*(r). \tag{5.4.8}$$

In words: the convolution of two functions has as its transform the product of the transforms of the two functions. A more careful proof is found in Van der Pol (1964, pp. 39–41). The argument requires that both of the functions $B(t)$ and $\phi(a)$ be bounded in any finite range of positive values; it also requires that both integrals in (5.4.8) be absolutely convergent (Doetsch, 1958, p. 55).

If r is a complex number, as will often be the case in our application, then for $r = x + iy$, where x and y are real,

$$h^*(r) = \int_0^\infty e^{-rt}h(t)\,dt = \int_0^\infty e^{-(x+iy)t}h(t)\,dt = \int_0^\infty e^{-xt}e^{-iyt}h(t)\,dt\,.$$

The convergence of the integral for a given $h(t)$ depends on $x = R(r)$, the real part of r. If there is some value of x, say x_0, for which the integral converges, then it converges for all values of x greater than this, since $e^{-xt} < e^{-x_0t}$ if $x > x_0$; its region of convergence is at least the half-plane to the right of x_0. Within the region of convergence, the transform is unique, and the inverse of a transform is also unique except for a possible null function which does not concern applications. The uniqueness, essential for the argument of Section 5.5 below, is discussed in Van der Pol (1964, pp. 117–120) and proved in Widder (1946, p. 63).

5.5. GENERAL SOLUTION VIA THE LAPLACE TRANSFORM

If the three functions concerned in the integral equation (5.1.1) have Laplace transforms, these may be designated

$$B^*(r) = \int_0^\infty e^{-rt}B(t)\,dt\,, \tag{5.5.1}$$

$$G^*(r) = \int_0^\infty e^{-rt}G(t)\,dt\,, \tag{5.5.2}$$

$$\phi^*(r) = \int_0^\infty e^{-rt}\phi(t)\,dt\,, \tag{5.5.3}$$

and because the transform of a convolution of two functions is the product of the transforms of the two functions, and addition transforms to addition, Eq. (5.1.1) transforms to

$$B^*(r) = G^*(r) + B^*(r)\phi^*(r)\,. \tag{5.5.4}$$

Solving (5.5.4) for $B^*(r)$, we have

$$B^*(r) = \frac{G^*(r)}{1 - \phi^*(r)}\,. \tag{5.5.5}$$

When the right-hand side of (5.5.5) can be inverted, then $B(t)$, the inverse of $B^*(r)$, is the solution to the integral equation (5.1.1). Feller showed that this solution is unique on the condition that $B^*(r)$ can be expressed in partial fractions:

$$B^*(r) = \frac{G^*(r)}{1 - \phi^*(r)} = \frac{Q_1}{r - r_1} + \frac{Q_2}{r - r_2} + \cdots + \frac{Q_k}{r - r_k} + \cdots, \tag{5.5.6}$$

and that $\sum Q_k$ converges absolutely, the r_k being the roots (finite or infinite in number) of $\phi^*(r) = 1$, which is identical with the characteristic equation $\psi(r) = 1$ of (5.2.2).

The ordinary procedure for finding the coefficients of partial fractions will serve here: by putting $r = r_k + \varepsilon$ in (5.5.6) and proceeding to the limit $\varepsilon = 0$, we have, since $\phi^*(r_k) = \psi(r_k) = 1$,

$$Q_k = \lim_{r \to r_k} \left\{ \frac{(r - r_k)G^*(r)}{1 - \phi^*(r)} \right\} = \left. \frac{G^*(r)}{-d(\phi^*(r))/dr} \right|_{r=r_k}. \tag{5.5.7}$$

Equation (5.5.7) is identical with (5.2.21).

The terms of the expansion (5.5.6) are easily inverted. Since the transform of $Q_k e^{r_k t}$ is

$$\int_0^\infty e^{-rt} Q_k e^{r_k t}\, dt = Q_k \int_0^\infty e^{-(r-r_k)t}\, dt = \frac{Q_k}{r - r_k}, \tag{5.5.8}$$

at least for $R(r) > R(r_k)$, then the inverse of $Q_k/(r - r_k)$ is $Q_k e^{r_k t}$. The Laplace transform being unique in the half-plane of convergence, this completes the solution of the integral equation (5.1.1).

5.6. THE SUCCESSION OF GENERATIONS

An alternative way of applying the Laplace transform to the integral equation is by calculating offspring generation by generation. The births of the zeroth generation are $G(t)$, of the first generation $B_1(t) = \int_0^\beta G(t - a)\phi(a)\, da$, of the nth generation $B_n = \int_0^\beta B_{n-1}(t - a)\phi(a)\, da$, by an obvious extension of the argument based on Fig. 5.1. Since the $B_n(t)$ are convolutions, they transform to products. The transform of the births of the

$$\begin{aligned}
&\text{zeroth generation} = G^*(r)\,,\\
&\text{first generation} = B_1^*(r) = G^*(r)\phi^*(r)\,,\\
&\text{second generation} = B_2^*(r) = B_1^*(r)\phi^*(r) = G^*(r)[\phi^*(r)]^2\,,\\
&\quad\vdots\\
&n\text{th generation} = B_n^*(r) = B_{n-1}^*(r)\phi^*(r) = G^*(r)[\phi^*(r)]^n\,, \quad \text{etc.}\\
&\quad\vdots
\end{aligned} \tag{5.6.1}$$

The number of births in all generations at time t is

$$B(t) = B_0(t) + B_1(t) + B_2(t) + \cdots,$$

and its transform is, by the addition rule (5.4.6), extended to a series:

$$\begin{aligned} B^*(r) &= B_0^*(r) + B_1^*(r) + B_2^*(r) + \cdots \\ &= G^*(r) + G^*(r)\phi^*(r) + G^*(r)[\phi^*(r)]^2 + \cdots \\ &= \frac{G^*(r)}{1 - \phi^*(r)} \end{aligned} \tag{5.6.2}$$

by summing the geometric progression, provided there is some area in the r-plane for which $|\phi^*(r)| < 1$. Equation (5.6.2) agrees with (5.5.5).

These results connecting the births of successive generations can be expressed as simple relations among the constants known as cumulants. Since cumulants will be needed in Chapter 6 and elsewhere, their definition and demographic meaning are presented below.

Moments and Cumulants

We have already made use of moments. For the net maternity function $\phi(a) = p(a)m(a)$ the moments taken about zero are defined as

$$\frac{R_n}{R_0} = \frac{\int_\alpha^\beta a^n p(a)m(a)\,da}{\int_\alpha^\beta p(a)m(a)\,da}, \qquad n = 1, 2, \ldots$$

The reader may show that the function $\psi(r)$ of (5.2.2), when divided by $\psi(0)$ and with the sign of r reversed, *generates* these moments in the sense that the nth derivative with respect to r, $\psi^{(n)}(-r)/\psi(0)$, when r is put equal to zero, is equal to R_n/R_0, and $\psi(-r)/\psi(0)$ is an infinite series in which $R_n/(n!\,R_0)$ is the coefficient of r^n.

For the present and many other purposes a further set of constants, $\kappa_1, \kappa_2, \ldots$, turns out to be convenient, obtained from the moments by the formal definition:

$$\kappa_1 r + \kappa_2 \frac{r^2}{2!} + \kappa_3 \frac{r^3}{3!} + \cdots = \ln\left(\frac{\psi(-r)}{\psi(0)}\right). \tag{5.6.3}$$

The κ are called *cumulants* (Kendall and Stuart, Vol. I, pp. 67–74). If the natural logarithm on the right-hand side of (5.6.3),

$$\ln\left(\frac{\psi(-r)}{\psi(0)}\right) = \ln\left(1 + \frac{R_1 r}{R_0} + \frac{R_2 r^2}{R_0 2!} + \cdots\right),$$

is expanded by Taylor's theorem and powers of r are equated, the definition (5.6.3) gives

$$\kappa_1 = \frac{R_1}{R_0}, \quad \kappa_2 = \frac{R_2}{R_0} - \left(\frac{R_1}{R_0}\right)^2, \ldots$$

Evidently the first two cumulants are the same as the mean and the variance, measures of the central position and dispersion respectively of the distribution.

The cumulants after the first are more simply expressed in terms of the moments about the mean,

$$\mu_n = \frac{\int_\alpha^\beta (a - R_1/R_0)^n p(a)m(a)\,da}{R_0}, \quad n = 2, 3, \ldots,$$

that is,

$$\kappa_2 = \mu_2\,, \quad \kappa_3 = \mu_3\,, \quad \kappa_4 = \mu_4 - 3\mu_2^2\,, \ldots$$

The third cumulant, identical with the third moment about the mean, is related to skewness, and the fourth cumulant to peakedness or flatness of the distribution.

Table 5.5 includes figures for females in Sweden, 1778–82, 1868–72, and 1958–62. The younger ages at marriage, narrower range of childbearing ages, and greater positive skewness all appear in the recent pattern. You will note that throughout the table the tendency is for populations of high R_0 to be high on μ and σ^2.

Moments and Cumulants in Successive Generations

Equations (5.6.1) lead to a simple proof of the proposition (Lotka, 1939c, p. 79) that the cumulants of the distribution of birth times in the nth generation are equal to the cumulants of the birth times (i. e., ages) for a girl child, now born, multiplied by n. For the moment-generating function of the births to such a girl child is $\phi^*(r)$ of (5.5.3) with the sign of r changed; the moments of the distribution of women at the birth of their children are generated by (Karmel, 1948, p. 253)

$$\psi(-r) = \phi^*(-r) = \int_0^\infty e^{rt}\phi(t)\,dt\,, \qquad \text{if} \qquad R_0 = \int_0^\infty \phi(t)\,dt = 1\,,$$

and of the birth dates in the nth generation by

$$B_n^*(-r) = \int_0^\infty e^{rt} B_n(t)\,dt\,,$$

whose value in terms of $G^*(-r)$ and $\phi^*(-r)$ is obtainable from (5.6.1). Since, moreover, the logarithm of the moment-generating function generates the cumulants, we may take logarithms of both sides of the nth member of (5.6.1) with the argument $-r$ to obtain

$$\ln B_n^*(-r) = \ln G^*(-r) + n \ln \phi^*(-r)\,. \tag{5.6.4}$$

The term $\ln G^*(-r)$ generates the cumulants of the distribution of the times at which children are born to women already alive at time zero. If these are disregarded, then

$$\ln B_n^*(-r) = n \ln \phi^*(-r)\,. \tag{5.6.5}$$

Table 5.5 Net reproduction rate R_0 and first to fourth cumulants of net maternity (or paternity) function

	R_0	$\kappa_1 = \mu = \frac{R_1}{R_0}$	$\kappa_2 = \sigma^2 = \frac{R_2}{R_0} - \left(\frac{R_1}{R_0}\right)^2$	κ_3	κ_4
FEMALES					
AUSTRALIA 1965	1.397	27.39	33.31	102.2	-161
CANADA 1965	1.496	27.75	37.09	119.0	-398
CHILE 1964	1.824	29.08	48.62	112.0	-1290
COSTA RICA 1963	3.226	29.23	48.80	105.0	-1654
ENGLAND AND WALES 1963	1.343	27.36	31.64	99.8	-99
EUROPE 1961*	1.197	28.07	35.77	114.4	-301
FEDERAL REPUBLIC OF GERMANY 1965	1.170	28.47	32.89	89.7	-110
HONDURAS 1965	2.613	29.12	53.77	106.4	-2208
HUNGARY 1965	0.833	25.65	28.13	123.3	417
MAURITIUS 1964	2.600	28.63	43.86	112.5	-1058
PORTUGAL 1965	1.333	29.61	43.05	100.2	-1253
PUERTO RICO 1964	1.813	27.14	46.33	208.3	-623
SWEDEN 1778-82	1.209	32.24	43.29	26.8	-1152
1868-72	1.327	32.96	39.15	6.8	-1128
1958-62	1.052	27.45	33.87	102.4	-195
UNITED STATES 1964	1.510	26.53	34.26	122.4	-133
1964**	1.526	26.53	34.39	123.1	-137
1965**	1.395	26.52	35.12	123.9	-191
MALES					
CHILE 1964	2.167	33.66	70.58	321.4	-2316
UNITED STATES 1964	1.666	29.62	45.02	266.3	1225

κ_2 corrected for grouping by subtraction of $5^2/12 = 2.08$ from raw variance.
* Omitting Albania, Northern Ireland, and USSR; population of 425.4 millions included.
** Births adjusted.

The disregard of ln $G^*(-r)$ is appropriate if the initial population, what we are calling the zeroth generation, is one girl child just born. (A formal proof of this may be based on (5.7.1) below). Her children will be distributed as $B_1(t)$ which is the same as $\phi(t)$, her grandchildren as $B_2(t) = \int_0^\beta \phi(t - a)\phi(a)\, da$, etc., and the logarithms of the transforms of these with negative argument are $B_1^*(-r) = \phi^*(-r)$ and $B_2^*(-r) = 2 \ln \phi^*(-r)$, etc. Each cumulant for the nth generation is n times the corresponding cumulant of $\phi(a)$, the distribution in the first generation. If the cumulants of $G(t)$ are not zero, they will have to be added to n times the cumulants of $\phi(a)$ to obtain those of $B_n(t)$.

As a numerical example, consider the Canadian population of 1965. The mean age at childbearing in the stationary population being 27.8 years, the mean birth date of grandchildren (through the female line) to a given girl child just born would be 55.5 years after 1965, of great-grandchildren 83.3 years, etc., always assuming the mortality and fertility regime of 1965. The variance of birth dates in the stationary population being 37.1, the variance of grandchildren's birth dates would be 74.2; of great-grandchildren's 111.3, etc. Assuming normal distributions (i. e., cumulants beyond the second all zero) how many great-grandchildren in the female line would be born between 2063 A.D. and 2100 A.D.?

The argument can be extended to the zeroth moment, which for the children of one woman is the expected total or net reproduction rate

$$R_0 = \int_\alpha^\beta p(a)m(a)\, da\,.$$

The expected total of grandchildren would number R_0^2, of great-grandchildren R_0^3, ... For Canadian women in 1965, R_0 was 1.496, R_0^2 2.238, ...

Computation of the numbers in successive generations, discussed by Lotka (1929a), is today easily programmed in the matrix formulation. In order to put into separate arrays of storage (and subsequently print out in separate columns) the offspring of different generations, we have to separate the projection matrix into a component for survivorship and one for birth. If **B** is the birth matrix consisting of nonzero terms in its first row, **S** the survivorship matrix whose nonzero terms are in its subdiagonal, and $\{\mathbf{K}_n^{(t)}\}$ the vector of ages in the nth generation at time t, then we have a simple matrix recurrence equation from which all generations at all time periods may be calculated:

$$\{\mathbf{K}_n^{(t)}\} = \mathbf{S}\{\mathbf{K}_n^{(t-1)}\} + \mathbf{B}\{\mathbf{K}_{n-1}^{(t-1)}\}\,.$$

If $\mathbf{B} + \mathbf{S} = \mathbf{M}$, show that the sum of the $\{\mathbf{K}_n^{(t)}\}$ for all generations is $\mathbf{M}^t\{\mathbf{K}_0^{(0)}\}$.

A program which evaluates this on the CDC 6400 was worked out by Ronald Lee, and a specimen of its output is shown, with the mortality and fertility of United States females, 1964, applied to 1000 babies under 5 years of age as the initial condition (Table 5.6). At $t = 50$ the first generation resembles the top row of the projection matrix with survivorships applied.

Table 5.6 Projection of 1000 girl children under five years of age by United States 1964 female fertility and mortality rates, showing distribution by age and generation after 50, 100, and 250 years*

	TIME = 0	TIME = 50 YEARS				TIME = 100 YEARS					
	GEN.	GENERATION				GENERATION					
AGE	0	0	1	2	3	1	2	3	4	5	6
0-4	1000	0	1	484	9	0	0	124	743	71	0
5-9	0	0	17	384	1	0	0	229	598	23	0
10-14	0	0	74	202	0	0	0	365	403	6	0
15-19	0	0	178	61	0	0	3	501	222	1	0
20-24	0	0	329	8	0	0	12	586	96	0	0
25-29	0	0	464	0	0	0	38	574	31	0	0
30-34	0	0	339	0	0	0	96	459	7	0	0
35-39	0	0	85	0	0	0	196	286	1	0	0
40-44	0	0	1	0	0	0	322	131	0	0	0
45-49	0	0	0	0	0	0	427	41	0	0	0
50-54	0	921	0	0	0	1	446	8	0	0	0
55-59	0	0	0	0	0	15	341	1	0	0	0
60-64	0	0	0	0	0	62	170	0	0	0	0
65-69	0	0	0	0	0	138	47	0	0	0	0
70-74	0	0	0	0	0	222	6	0	0	0	0
75-79	0	0	0	0	0	252	0	0	0	0	0
80-84	0	0	0	0	0	127	0	0	0	0	0
TOTAL	1000	921	1489	1139	10	816	2103	3305	2101	101	0

Table 5.6 (continued)

	TIME = 250 YEARS									
	GENERATION									
AGE	4	5	6	7	8	9	10	11	12	13
0-4	0	0	0	4	384	3,388	4,727	1,281	74	1
5-9	0	0	0	10	612	3,833	3,855	747	30	0
10-14	0	0	0	23	920	4,084	2,940	403	11	0
15-19	0	0	0	48	1,303	4,087	2,090	200	4	0
20-24	0	0	0	94	1,733	3,827	1,377	91	1	0
25-29	0	0	1	173	2,164	3,345	837	38	0	0
30-34	0	0	2	298	2,529	2,718	468	14	0	0
35-39	0	0	6	479	2,758	2,044	239	5	0	0
40-44	0	0	15	718	2,797	1,414	110	1	0	0
45-49	0	0	32	999	2,622	894	46	0	0	0
50-54	0	0	65	1,283	2,258	512	17	0	0	0
55-59	0	0	121	1,516	1,773	263	6	0	0	0
60-64	0	1	203	1,632	1,254	120	2	0	0	0
65-69	0	3	305	1,575	785	47	0	0	0	0
70-74	0	6	405	1,332	425	16	0	0	0	0
75-79	0	12	458	953	191	4	0	0	0	0
80-84	0	19	410	535	66	1	0	0	0	0
TOTAL	0	41	2,024	11,674	24,574	30,598	16,713	2,780	120	1

* Programmed by Ronald Lee.

Any of these numbers can be calculated from the Tables 2.1 and 2.2. For instance, the number 15 to 19 in the first generation at $t = 50$ is obtained by considering the survivors from 0 to time 30, $1000({}_5L_{30}/{}_5L_0)$, multiplying by the top element of $\mathbf{M}$ corresponding to age 30–34, which is 0.18333, then multiplying by ${}_5L_{15}/{}_5L_0$. The product is

$$(479{,}486/488{,}970)(0.18333)(485{,}484/488{,}970) = 178.49\,,$$

rounded in the table to 178. To verify the figures for 100 years from those for 50 years, consider the 131 women aged 40–44 in the third generation at time 100. They are obtained from the survivors of the second generation through five years, whose children are

$$\begin{aligned}&(484)(0.99661)(0.00103) + \cdots + 8(0.99605)(0.33769)\\ &\quad = 0.496 + 33.655 + 70.289 + 28.948 + 2.691 = 136.079\,.\end{aligned}$$

The survivors of these children through another 40 years are

$$136.079 \times 0.96201 = 130.9\,,$$

rounded to 131 in the table.

The projection gives the intrinsic rate r. At the end of 500 years the total number of children 0–4 is 502,910; at the end of 600 years 2,424,290, a ratio of increase of 4.8205. The estimate of r is $(\ln 4.8205)/100 = 0.01573$, slightly higher than the root of (5.3.2) for United States females, 1964, which is 0.01570. The twentieth root of 4.8205 is 1.0818, the same as the solution in λ of $|\mathbf{M} - \lambda\mathbf{I}|$ of (3.2.4). The difference between $\psi(r)$ of (5.3.2) and $|\mathbf{M} - \lambda\mathbf{I}|$ of (3.2.4) will be taken up in Chapters 8 and 11. Given the above information and the mean age of childbearing in the stable population, $-\psi'(r) = 25.974$ (or 5.195 in the five-year unit required here), apply the first term of (5.2.23) to check approximately the column totals of Table 5.7. You will find, for example, at $t = 100$ that $(1000/5.195)(4.8205) = 928$, against the 938 shown.

The Time Interval between Generations

The net reproduction rate R_0 is the number of (her own) girl children by which it is expected, under the current regime of mortality and fertility, that a newly born girl child will be replaced. A reasonable definition of T, the length of generation, is that it is the time in which this replacement occurs. If T satisfies

$$\frac{B(t)}{B(t - T)} = R_0\,,$$

it is the interval of time over which births increase in the ratio R_0, the net reproduction rate (Lotka, 1937c, p. 92). If $B(t)$ is an exponential function of t, say Qe^{rt}, then $B(t)/B(t - T)$ reduces to e^{rT}, and T may be found from $e^{rT} = R_0$, so that $T = (\ln R_0)/r$. Values of T are shown for a number of countries in Table 6.3.

Table 5.7 Projection of an initial 1000 girl children under age 5 at rates for United States females, 1964, showing distribution of girl children 0–4 years of age among generations at time t*

GENERATION	TIME t IN YEARS					
	0	100	200	300	400	500
0	1,000					
1						
2						
3		124				
4		743				
5		71				
6			71			
7			1,393			
8			2,451			
9			556	46		
10			18	1,450		
11				7,766		
12				9,299	32	
13				2,841	1,288	
14				236	12,757	
15				6	37,730	20
16					37,385	1,070
17					13,285	15,800
18					1,763	83,580
19					90	175,290
20					2	155,170
21						60,440
22						10,650
23						860
24						30
TOTAL	1,000	938	4,489	21,644	104,332	502,910
TOTAL AT t = 600: 2,424,290						

* Programmed by Ronald Lee.

To terms in r, T is the arithmetic mean of μ, the mean age of childbearing in the stationary population, and A_r in the stable population. Following is a sketch of the proof of this statement.

From the definition of T we have

$$T = \frac{\ln R_0}{r} = -\frac{1}{r} \ln \left[\frac{\psi(r)}{R_0} \right], \tag{5.6.6}$$

since r is a root of $\psi(r) = 1$. But $\ln [\psi(r)/R_0]$ may as above be interpreted as a cumulant-generating function with the sign of r reversed, so that (5.6.6) becomes

$$\begin{aligned} T &= -\frac{1}{r}\left(-\mu r + \frac{\sigma^2 r^2}{2!} - \frac{\mu_3 r^3}{3!} + \cdots\right) \\ &= \mu - \frac{\sigma^2 r}{2} + \frac{\mu_3 r^2}{6} - \cdots, \end{aligned} \tag{5.6.7}$$

where μ, σ^2, $\mu_3 = \kappa_3$ are the successive cumulants of the distribution of women by age at childbearing in the stationary population.

By definition the mean age at childbearing in the stable population is

$$A_r = \frac{\int_\alpha^\beta x e^{-rx} p(x) m(x)\, dx}{\int_\alpha^\beta e^{-rx} p(x) m(x)\, dx}, \tag{5.6.8}$$

or

$$A_r = \frac{-\psi'(r)}{\psi(r)} = -\frac{d(\ln \psi(r)/R_0)}{dr}, \tag{5.6.9}$$

the derivative (with sign changed) of the cumulant-generating function with argument $-r$. Expanding $\ln \psi(r)$ of (5.6.9) and taking the derivative, we obtain

$$A_r = \mu - \sigma^2 r + \frac{\mu_3 r^2}{2} - \cdots. \tag{5.6.10}$$

Averaging A_r and μ gives

$$\frac{A_r + \mu}{2} = \mu - \frac{\sigma^2 r}{2} + \frac{\mu_3 r^2}{4} - \cdots, \tag{5.6.11}$$

which is larger than T in (5.6.7) by about $\mu_3 r^2/12$. This completes the proof.

For Canadian females in 1965, μ was 27.753 and A_r was 27.192, their arithmetic mean being 27.472. The value of $T = \ln R_0/r$ for this population was 27.470. The difference between these last two numbers, 0.002, may be compared with the difference between the terms in r^2 in (5.6.7) and (5.6.11), i.e., $\mu_3 r^2/12 = (119)(0.01467)^2/12 = 0.0021$. For all practical purposes, T may be taken as the mean of μ and A_r. (Table 6.3 illustrates this among other relations.)

5.7. POINT AND RECTANGULAR DISTRIBUTIONS OF THE NET MATERNITY FUNCTION

The Laplace transform not only permits a simple treatment of the net maternity function presented as an analytic or continuous function, but it also allows us to handle ungraduated forms, for example those which appear graphically as histograms (L. C. Cole, 1954). In order to pursue this application we require rules for the transforms of certain discontinuous functions (Rainville, 1963, p. 24).

RULE 1). If

$$f(x) = 0\,, \quad x < 0\,,$$
$$f(x) = 1\,, \quad x \geq 0\,,$$

then the transform $f^*(x)$ is

$$f^*(r) = \int_0^\infty e^{-rx}\,dx = \frac{1}{r}\,, \qquad R(r) > 0\,.$$

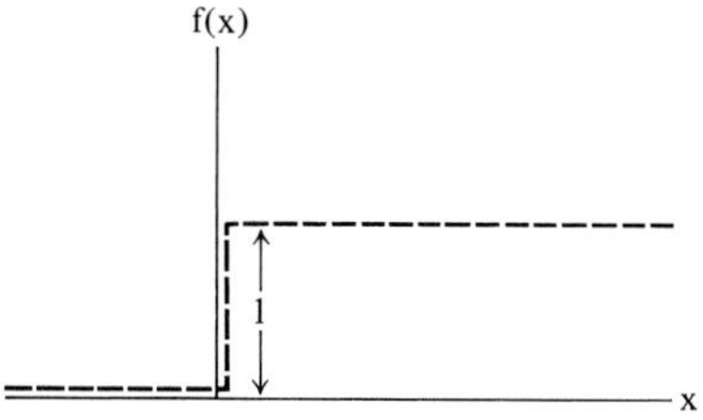

RULE 2). If

$$f(x) = 0\,, \quad x < c\,,$$
$$f(x) = 1\,, \quad x \geq c\,,$$

then

$$f^*(r) = \int_c^\infty e^{-rx}\,dx = \frac{e^{-rc}}{r}\,, \qquad R(r) > 0\,.$$

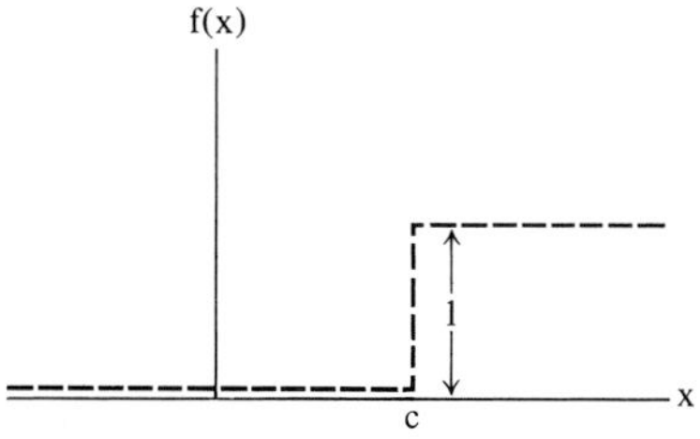

RULE 3). If

$$f(x) = 0\,, \quad x < c_1\,,$$
$$f(x) = 1\,, \quad c_1 < x \leq c_2\,,$$
$$f(x) = 0\,, \quad x > c_2\,,$$

then

$$f^*(r) = \int_{c_1}^{c_2} e^{-rx}\,dx = \frac{e^{-rc_1} - e^{-rc_2}}{r}\,.$$

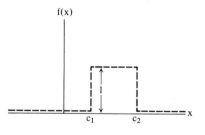

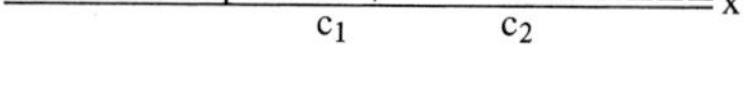

RULE 4). In any of the above, the ordinate might be made k instead of 1, and the transform would accordingly be multiplied by k.

Suppose in Rule 3 that c_2 approaches c_1, and that the ordinate moves upwards so that the area is always unity. Then the transform is

$$f^*(r) = \lim_{c_2 \to c_1} \frac{1}{c_2 - c_1}\left(\frac{e^{-rc_1} - e^{-rc_2}}{r}\right) = e^{-rc_1}\,.$$

The transform of a concentration of density equal to the finite quantity k at the point c is therefore

$$f^*(r) = ke^{-rc} . \tag{5.7.1}$$

Suppose (Cole, 1954, p. 117) that the net maternity function is concentrated at the midpoints of five-year intervals, which is to say at ages 12.5, 17.5, 22.5, . . ., 47.5, and that at these points the weight is $5\,{}_5\phi_{10}$, $5\,{}_5\phi_{15}$, . . ., $5\,{}_5\phi_{45}$ respectively, where ${}_5\phi_{10} = {}_5L_{10}F_{10}/5l_0$ is the net maternity function for ages 10–14, etc. Then, by application of (5.7.1), the transform of the integral equation,

$$B^*(r) = \frac{G^*(r)}{1 - \phi^*(r)} , \tag{5.7.2}$$

can be written as

$$B^*(r) = \frac{G^*(r)}{1 - 5\,{}_5\phi_{10}\,e^{-12.5r} - 5\,{}_5\phi_{15}\,e^{-17.5r} - \dots - 5\,{}_5\phi_{45}\,e^{-47.5}} . \tag{5.7.3}$$

Expressing the right-hand side of (5.7.3) in partial fractions, as before, we find, corresponding to the real root r_1 of $\phi^*(r) = 1$, a fraction $Q_1/(r - r_1)$, of which the inverse is $Q_1e^{r_1t}$. The value of Q_1 is given by the rules for partial fraction decomposition as before:

$$Q_1 = \lim_{r \to r_1} \frac{(r - r_1)G^*(r_1)}{1 - \phi^*(r)} = \frac{G^*(r_1)}{-\psi'(r_1)} ,$$

where $\psi'(r_1)$ is the derivative of $\psi(r) = \phi^*(r)$ defined in (5.2.2). The argument applied to the sth root results in (5.2.21). Not only does this have the same general form as the preceding solution, but the analysis of (5.7.3) into partial fractions would entail the same characteristic equation (5.3.2) in five-year age groups and hence the same approximation (Method B of Chap. 11) to the roots.

Alternatively, the roots beyond the first being complex and in conjugate pairs, there will correspond to each pair in the partial fraction expansion of (5.7.3) a term of the form

$$\frac{a'r + b'}{r^2 + c'r + d'} ,$$

where a', b', c', and d' are real. By completing the square in the denominator and changing the origin of r we find that this becomes

$$\frac{ar + b}{r^2 + c^2} ,$$

whose inverse is

$$a \cos ct + \frac{b}{c} \sin ct , \quad \text{if } R(r) > 0 , \tag{5.7.4}$$

as may be verified by evaluating

$$a \int_0^\infty e^{-rt} \cos ct \, dt + \frac{b}{c} \int_0^\infty e^{-rt} \sin ct \, dt ,$$

or by looking up Chemical Rubber Publishing Co. (1963, p. 328). This is a way of arriving at the trigonometrical series (5.2.6).

The transform is exact. It requires no such unexamined intuitive leap as that which produced (5.3.2) as a practical approximation to the theoretically derived (5.2.2). The fact that we have now come upon (5.3.2) in the denominator of (5.7.3) shows what it was that (5.3.2) really assumed: that the density of the net maternity function is entirely concentrated at midpoints of intervals.

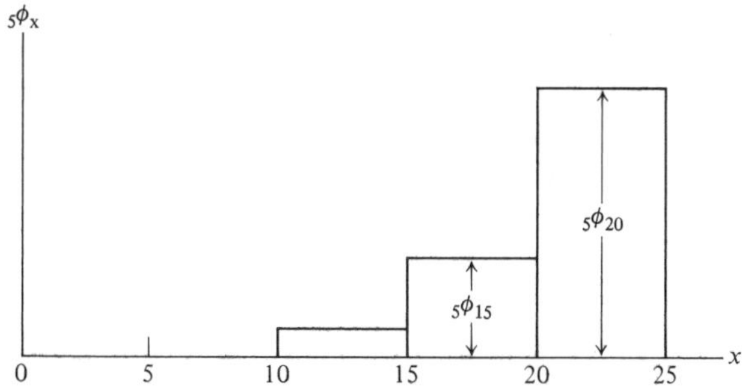

Fig. 5.4 Notation for histogram of net maternity function.

A modification of the preceding argument deals with a net maternity function in the form of a histogram (Fig. 5.4). By the application of the third of the rules in the first paragraph of this section,

$$\phi^*(r) = \frac{_5\phi_{10}}{r}(e^{-10r} - e^{-15r}) + \frac{_5\phi_{15}}{r}(e^{-15r} - e^{-20r}) + \cdots + \frac{_5\phi_{45}}{r}(e^{-45r} - e^{-50r}), \tag{5.7.5}$$

which when equated to unity would provide a different approximation to (5.2.2). The $\phi^*(r)$ of (5.7.5) is the same as $\phi_C(r)$ of Table 11.3, which compares numerical values on several approximations.

We could have obtained (5.7.5) without the Laplace transform by merely integrating e^{-rt} times the histogram form of the net maternity function. Either way the argument shows that no approximation whatever enters the derivation of (5.7.5); it is exact, given the information on mortality and fertility in five-year age groups. However, if the histogram is itself seen as an approximation to a smooth curve, then a correction for grouping is required, and this, which appears in (11.1.23), brings us back to (5.3.2). The histogram is "data" without question, but we usually think of it as an approximation to a smooth curve. May we say that the *exact* solution for the given histogram data is not the *correct* solution?

5.8. FORMULATION THROUGH GENERATING FUNCTIONS AND PARTIAL FRACTIONS

The renewal equation may be approached through generating functions, whose use in relation to probabilities of recurrent events is described by Feller (1957, Chap. 13). The application of this to population mathematics is due to Thompson (1931), Dobbernack and Tietz (1940, p. 239), Lotka (1948, p. 192), and Lamont Cole (1954, p. 112). The result is a discrete form of the renewal equation (5.1.1), but there are three reasons why we introduce the present alternative argument.

1) It is instructive to see the consequence of restating in the fashion here required the probability of a birth occurring at one time in terms of the births at preceding times.

2) The outcome is not numerically identical with that of the methods discussed earlier, but provides a different finite approximation to the intrinsic rate and the other roots of the characteristic equation, which in some circumstances could be more satisfactory, though this point is not investigated.

3) Less mathematical background is called for than in earlier methods.

To exemplify with a very simple population (Cole, 1954, p. 110), consider a pair of rabbits which produces another pair at the end of the first month, and then a second pair in the second month, then remains alive but produces no more offspring. Its descendants follow the same law of reproduction and are likewise subject to zero mortality. The reader may show that the rabbits increase according to the *Fibonacci* numbers u_n, $n = 1, 2, 3, \ldots$:

$$1, 2, 3, 5, 8, 13, 21, 34, 55, 89, 144, 233, \ldots,$$

the nth of which is equal to the sum of the $(n-1)$th and $(n-2)$th numbers:

$$u_n = u_{n-1} + u_{n-2}, \quad n = 3, 4, \ldots$$

The individual reproductive cycle may be represented by $1 - s - s^2$. We may divide out $1/(1 - s - s^2)$ and observe that the result is

$$1 + s + 2s^2 + 3s^3 + 5s^4 + 8s^5 + \cdots, \qquad \text{or} \qquad 1 + \sum u_n s^n .$$

In this sense $1/(1 - s - s^2)$ generates the u_n. We may also expand $1/(1 - s - s^2)$ in partial fractions and hence analyze the Fibonacci numbers into a sum of two geometric series. One of the two series will dominate and constitutes the asymptotic approximation,

$$u_n \sim \frac{1}{\sqrt{5}}\left(\frac{1 + \sqrt{5}}{2}\right)^{n+1} = \frac{(1.618)^{n+1}}{2.236}.$$

This result is surprisingly close even for small values of n. At $n = 4$, the approximation is 4.96 against 5, and at $n = 7$, it is 21.007 against 21. All of this is with an assumed starting population of one pair of rabbits in the first age group. How is the result modified for a starting population of seven pairs of rabbits in the first age group and three pairs in the second?

Reverting now to human reproduction and taking as the starting population one girl baby just born, the number of girl births expected at successive ages 0, 5, 10, 15, . . . , 45, during her lifetime under the given regime of fertility and survivorship may be expressed as the finite sequence

$$f_0 = 0\,, \quad f_1 = 0\,, \quad f_2 = 0\,, \quad f_3 = \frac{5l_{15}}{l_0} F_{12.5}\,, \ldots, \quad f_9 = \frac{5l_{45}}{l_0} F_{42.5}\,. \qquad (5.8.1)$$

In the typical term, $F_{x-2.5}$ is the average chance per year of age of having a child in the interval of age $x - 2.5$ to age $x + 2.5$ centered on x, x being a multiple of 5; it is the age-specific birth rate for the interval $x - 2.5$ to $x + 2.5$. Since the observed age-specific birth rates are usually F_{x-5} for ages $x - 5$ to x, and F_x for ages x to $x + 5$, we will ultimately have to express $F_{x-2.5}$ in terms of F_{x-5} and F_x. The quantity $f_{x/5}$ is the chance of a girl child just born living to the middle of the age interval $x - 2.5$ to $x + 2.5$ *and* having a girl child then.

If u_t is births at time t to this girl *or her female descendants*, including as u_0 her own birth, then

$$\begin{aligned} u_0 &= 1\,, \qquad u_1 = 0, \qquad u_2 = 0\,, \\ u_3 &= u_0 f_3 + u_1 f_2 + u_2 f_1 + u_3 f_0 = u_0 f_3\,, \\ u_4 &= u_0 f_4 + u_1 f_3 + u_2 f_2 + u_3 f_1 + u_4 f_0 = u_0 f_4 + u_1 f_3\,, \end{aligned} \qquad (5.8.2)$$

and so on, for as long as the regime of fertility and mortality persists. If now we multiply the members of (5.8.2) by 1, s, s^2, s^3, etc., and add up the set so multiplied, we have

$$u_0 + u_1 s + u_2 s^2 + \cdots = 1 + (u_0 f_1 + u_1 f_0)s + (u_0 f_2 + u_1 f_1 + u_2 f_0)s^2 + \cdots,$$

an equation which may be represented by

$$U(s) = 1 + U(s)F(s)\,, \qquad (5.8.3)$$

$U(s)$ being the generating function of the u's,

$$U(s) = u_0 + u_1 s + u_2 s^2 + \cdots + u_9 s^9 + \cdots,$$

and $F(s)$ of the f's,

$$F(s) = f_0 + f_1 s + f_2 s^2 + \cdots + f_9 s^9\,.$$

The solution of (5.8.3) for $U(s)$ is

$$U(s) = \frac{1}{1 - F(s)}\,. \qquad (5.8.4)$$

In order to base calculations on (5.8.4), we may expand it in partial fractions. If $s_1, s_2, \ldots, s_9$ are the roots of the ninth-degree polynomial equation

$F(s) = 1$, then the expansion of (5.8.4) is

$$U(s) = \frac{1}{1 - F(s)} = \frac{d_1}{s - s_1} + \frac{d_2}{s - s_2} + \cdots + \frac{d_9}{s - s_9}. \tag{5.8.5}$$

To find d_1, multiply both sides of (5.8.5) by $s - s_1$ and then proceed to the limit $s = s_1$. On the left there is $\lim_{s \to s_1} [(s - s_1)/(1 - F(s))]$, which equals $1/(-F'(s_1))$, by an application of calculus. On the right all terms but d_1 vanish if the roots are distinct. Hence $d_1 = 1/(-F'(s_1))$, and similarly for the remaining $d_2, d_3, \ldots, d_9$. Using this and the fact that each partial fraction may be written as a geometric progression, we have

$$\frac{d_1}{s - s_1} = \frac{-d_1}{(s_1 1 - s/s_1)} = \frac{1}{F'(s_1)}\left(\frac{1}{s_1} + \frac{s}{s_1^2} + \frac{s^2}{s_1^3} + \cdots + \frac{s^t}{s_1^{t+1}} + \cdots\right),$$

which converges in the circle $|s| < |s_1|$. Similar expressions may be found for the remaining terms of (5.8.5). Considering all roots together we have for u_t, the coefficient of s^t in $U(s)$,

$$u_t = \frac{1}{s_1^{t+1}F'(s_1)} + \frac{1}{s_2^{t+1}F'(s_2)} + \cdots + \frac{1}{s_9^{t+1}F'(s_9)}. \tag{5.8.6}$$

Let us examine the nature of the roots $s_1, s_2, \ldots, s_9$. The equation of which they are the solution is established from (5.8.1) as

$$\begin{aligned} F(s) - 1 &= f_0 + f_1 s + \cdots - 1 \\ &= \frac{5l_{15}F_{12.5}}{l_0} s^3 + \frac{5l_{20}F_{17.5}}{l_0} s^4 + \cdots + \frac{5l_{45}F_{42.5}}{l_0} s^9 - 1 = 0, \end{aligned} \tag{5.8.7}$$

If $1/\lambda$ is written in place of s and (5.8.7) multiplied by $-\lambda^9$, we obtain

$$\lambda^9\left(1 - F\left(\frac{1}{\lambda}\right)\right) = \lambda^9 - \frac{5l_{15}F_{12.5}}{l_0}\lambda^6 - \frac{5l_{20}F_{17.5}}{l_0}\lambda^5 - \cdots - \frac{5l_{45}F_{42.5}}{l_0} = 0, \tag{5.8.8}$$

which may be compared with $|\mathbf{M} - \lambda\mathbf{I}| = 0$ of Chapter 3. Hence the roots s are approximately the reciprocals of the eigenvalues of the matrix **M** of Chapter 3. An example is shown in Table 5.9 where, provisionally, $F_{x-2.5}$ is taken as $\frac{1}{2}(F_{x-5} + F_x)$. This is Method D of Chapter 11.

The reader is asked to trace the parallel, point by point, between this demonstration of the partial fraction solution of the renewal problem and the Laplace transform argument which precedes it. How are generating functions related to the transform? What is the advantage of the transform?

Summary and Numerical Example

We have now solved the general equation (5.1.1) by means of (**1**) the Hertz-Lotka argument leading to (5.3.2), and (**2**) the Laplace transform which gave (5.7.5). A different approximation is by means of (**3**) the matrix elaborated in Chapter 3 which corresponds to the usual population projection and resulted

Table 5.8 Constants for population trajectory by integral equation (5.1.3) and by partial fractions (5.8.6) on fertility and mortality of United States females, 1964, starting with 1000 girl births*

ROOTS	COEFFICIENTS
INTEGRAL EQUATION	
$r_1 = 0.01570$	$Q_1 = 38.50$
$r_2 = -0.0287 + 0.2422i$	$Q_2 = 39.76 + 16.98i$
$r_4 = -0.1115 + 0.5160i$	$Q_4 = 29.06 + 30.54i$
PARTIAL FRACTION	
$-0.2 \ln s_1 = 0.01591$	$\frac{1}{s_1 F'(s_1)} = 38.49$
$-0.2 \ln s_2 = -0.0286 + 0.2422i$	$\frac{1}{s_2 F'(s_2)} = 39.77 + 17.02i$
$-0.2 \ln s_4 = -0.1112 + 0.5157i$	$\frac{1}{s_4 F'(s_4)} = 28.79 + 30.47i$

ROOT r_3 IS THE COMPLEX CONJUGATE OF r_2; Q_3 OF Q_2, ETC.; SIMILARLY FOR THE PARTIAL FRACTION SOLUTION.

CALCULATION OF Q_1 VERIFIABLE FROM DATA OF TABLE 2.1 AS FOLLOWS:

x	${}_5\phi_x$ (1)	$(x + 2.5)\,{}_5\phi_x$ (2)	$e^{-r(x+2.5)}$ (3)	(2) × (3) (4)
10	0.00205	0.0256	0.82178	
15	0.17265	3.0214	0.75972	
20	0.51983	11.6962	0.70235	
25	0.42250	11.6188	0.64932	
30	0.24328	7.9066	0.60029	
35	0.11627	4.3601	0.55496	
40	0.03173	1.3485	0.51305	
45	0.00182	0.0865	0.47431	
TOTAL	1.51014	40.0637		25.9744

MEAN AGE IN STABLE POPULATION = $-\psi'(r)$ = 25.9744.
HENCE Q_1 = $1000/-\psi'(r)$ = 1000/25.9744 = 38.499.
(MEAN AGE IN STATIONARY POPULATION = 40.0637/1.51014
= 26.5299.)

* Programmed by Pierre Nakache.

in (3.2.4). Finally, (**4**) a formulation leading to partial fractions has been given in the present section to produce (5.8.7). The four approaches yield four different finite approximations to the continuous equation $\psi(r) = 1$ of (5.2.2). When arranged in the order of (**1**) through (**4**) above, the real roots r_1 turn out to be an ascending sequence. They are studied as methods B, C, A, and D respectivly in Chapter 11. We give here a numerical example of (**1**) and (**4**).

Table 5.8 shows five roots of the characteristic equation (5.3.2) for the integral equation and (5.8.7) for partial fractions. The roots of the partial fraction formulation have been converted into the equivalent r by $r = -0.2 \ln s$ for convenience in comparison. In the same table are given the coefficients Q which are to multiply the tth powers of e^r and $1/s^{1/5}$, for the initial condition of 1000 births. According to (5.2.23), Q_1 ought to be $1000/-\psi'(r_1)$, or 1000 divided by the mean age of childbearing in the stable population. This mean age A_r is calculable as

$$\begin{aligned}-\psi'(r) &= \int_\alpha^\beta ae^{-ra}p(a)m(a)\,da \\ &\doteq 12.5e^{-12.5r}\,{}_5L_{10}F_{10} + 17.5e^{-17.5r}\,{}_5L_{15}F_{15} + \cdots \\ &\quad + 47.5e^{-47.5r}\,{}_5L_{45}F_{45}\,.\end{aligned}$$

From the data of Table 2.1 and $r = 0.01570$, verify that $-\psi'(r) = 25.974$, and hence $Q_1 = 38.50$. (Fitting to an observed age distribution rather than the hypothetical 1000 initial births requires that a double integral be approximated for the Q's, a method for which is found in Chapter 11.) The solutions for the functions $B(t)$ of (5.1.3) and u_t of (5.8.6) are set forth to one, three, and five terms in Table 5.9.

The ordering of the complex roots is not unique, and two principles suggest themselves. The roots represented as $r = x \pm iy$ may be arranged according to decreasing values of x, so that the sequence would be in order of decreasing absolute value of the exponential e^r. The five roots of Table 5.8 are the largest in absolute value.

A logical alternative is to take the roots according to increasing values of y. This means that successive harmonics will be arranged in order of increasing frequency or decreasing wavelength. This arrangement is found in Table 8.2.

All populations show the same order by the two principles for the first three roots. However, the second pair of complex roots according to x is often the third pair according to y, and this happens to be true for the United States 1964. Table 5.8 takes the roots in order of x, so that we deal in Table 5.9 with the five roots of principal absolute value. A harmonic of period about 20 years is omitted in Table 5.8 because the harmonic of period 12 years $(=2\pi/0.5160)$ happens to have a larger x. Turn ahead to Fig. 8.1 and verify this visually. What sequence has been adopted for the numbering in Fig. 8.1?

In Table 5.9 the solutions to the integral equation (5.1.3) and the partial fraction formulation (5.8.6) may be compared with the matrix projection of

Table 5.9 Integral equation and partial fraction forms of solution of renewal equation, using one, three, and five terms, on fertility and mortality of United States females, 1964, starting with 1000 female births; comparison with projection by matrix over 200 years*

t	PROJECTION BY MATRIX	B(t) IN INTEGRAL EQUATION (5.1.3) $Q_1e^{r_1t}$	$\sum_1^3 Q_ie^{r_it}$	$\sum_1^5 Q_ie^{r_it}$	u_t IN PARTIAL FRACTION (5.8.6) ($\tau = t/5$) $\frac{1}{s_1^{\tau+1}F'(s_1)}$	$\sum_1^3 \frac{1}{s_i^{\tau+1}F'(s_i)}$	$\sum_1^5 \frac{1}{s_i^{\tau+1}F'(s_i)}$
0	1000.0	38.5	118.0	176.1	38.5	117.9	175.5
5	0	41.6	38.4	-8.5	41.7	38.3	-8.2
10	0.2	45.0	-16.6	9.7	45.1	-16.7	9.5
15	17.5	48.7	13.6	3.4	48.9	13.6	3.5
20	69.2	52.7	77.5	78.8	52.9	77.9	79.1
25	94.3	57.0	98.5	100.7	57.3	99.0	101.2
30	68.2	61.7	68.3	65.9	62.0	68.8	66.3
35	48.2	66.7	39.6	41.3	67.2	39.9	41.6
40	55.4	72.1	50.6	49.8	72.7	51.0	50.2
45	80.5	78.0	85.2	85.5	78.8	86.0	86.2
50	98.7	84.4	104.9	105.0	85.3	106.0	106.1
60	94.1	98.7	87.7	87.8	100.0	88.8	88.9
70	114.6	115.5	116.5	116.5	117.3	118.2	118.2
80	140.2	135.2	140.4	140.4	137.5	142.8	142.8
90	155.7	158.1	151.8	151.8	161.2	154.7	154.7
100	187.7	185.0	189.3	189.3	189.0	193.4	193.4
150	408.9	405.6	406.3	406.3	418.9	419.6	419.6
200	897.9	889.2	889.3	889.3	928.3	928.3	928.3

* Programmed by Pierre Nakache.

Chapter 3. Theory suggests that for the integral equation or partial fraction solution the five-term approximation ought to be closest for the first three or four cycles of projection, after which the three- and five-term approximations ought to be indifferently close; after about 10 or 15 cycles, i. e., 50 or 75 years, the one-, three-, and five-terms ought all to be indifferently close. The results as shown are consistent with this, if account is taken of the fact that the projection by means of the matrix has a slight upward bias; it implies an r of 0.01573 against the r of the integral equation of 0.01570. This is why the integral equation solution comes close to the matrix and then departs from it again. (At $t = 1000$ years the matrix projection would be about 3% greater than the integral equation trajectory.) The partial fraction approximation as we have used it here at $r = 0.01591$ is higher than the matrix; at the end of 1000 years its path would be about 20% higher.

An explicit account of the cycles represented by the complex roots is obtained as in Section 3.4 by writing (5.1.3) in the form

$$B(t) = Q_1 e^{r_1 t} + Q_2 e^{(x_2+iy_2)t} + Q_3 e^{(x_2-iy_2)t} + \cdots,$$

where x_2 and y_2 are the real and imaginary parts respectively of $r_2 = x_2 + iy_2$. Then

$$B(t) = Q_1 e^{r_1 t} + e^{x_2 t}[(Q_2 + Q_3)\cos(y_2 t) + i(Q_2 - Q_3)\sin(y_2 t)] + \cdots, \tag{5.8.9}$$

where $Q_2 + Q_3, Q_4 + Q_5, \ldots$ are real, and $Q_2 - Q_3, Q_4 - Q_5, \ldots$ pure imaginaries (Sec. 5.2), so that the expression for the trajectory $B(t)$ is real.

This form shows that $B(t)$ consists in sine curves superimposed on an exponential; the principal sine curve is damped by $e^{x_2 t}$ (since x_2 is negative) and is of periodicity $2\pi/y_2$. In terms of the integral equation parameters of Table 5.8, for United States females, 1964,

$$\begin{aligned} B(t) = {} & 38.50e^{0.01570t} \\ & + e^{-0.0287t}(79.52\cos 0.2422t - 33.96\sin 0.2422t) \\ & + e^{-0.1115t}(58.12\cos 0.5160t - 61.08\sin 0.5160t) \\ & + \cdots \end{aligned} \tag{5.8.10}$$

This together with its analog u_t of the partial fraction formulation are the subject of Table 5.9.

Entering $t = 10$ in (5.8.10) we find

$$\begin{aligned} B(10) &= 38.50e^{0.1570} \\ &\quad + e^{-0.287}(79.52\cos 2.422 - 33.96\sin 2.422) \\ &\quad + e^{-1.115}(58.12\cos 5.160 - 61.08\sin 5.160) \\ &= (38.50)(1.1700) + (0.7505)[79.52(-0.7518) - 33.96(0.6594)] \\ &\quad + (0.3279)[58.12(0.4330) + 61.08(0.9014)] \\ &= 45.0 - 61.7 + 26.3\,. \end{aligned}$$

This gives 45.0 for the first term, 45 − 61.7 = −16.7 for the first three terms, and 9.6 for the first five terms. These are as close to the row for $t = 10$ of the computed result, shown in the three columns under "Integral equation" in Table 5.9, as one could expect to attain by hand calculation to four significant figures.

Since the same matrix, shown in Table 2.2, was used for the projection in the first column of Table 5.9 and in Tables 5.6 and 5.7, the results should be the same, and they are if we take account of the different starting points. The ratio of population under five to births is fixed on the fixed life table assumed, and hence $B(t)/B(0)$ should be the same as the ratio of the first element of $\{\mathbf{K}^{(t)}\}$ to the first element of $\{\mathbf{K}^{(0)}\}$.

However, the births $B(t)$ are on an annual basis, while the population under five at a given moment corresponds to births of five years. To translate the annual flow of births $B(t)$ into number of population under the fixed regime assumed, we multiply by five. At 100 years we have

$$5B(100) = (5)(187.7) = 938.5$$

from Table 5.9. And in Tables 5.6 and 5.7 we have 938 children under 5, distributed over three generations, at time 100. Similarly at time 200 the projection of Table 5.9 gives $5B(200) = 4489.5$, against 4489 children under 5 at 200 years of Table 5.7.

A thorough study of the characteristic equation has recently been undertaken by Ansley J. Coale (1967). He found 266 pairs of complex roots, which is to say he took the solution (5.2.5) to 533 terms. Arranging his roots in order of frequency, he found that the first pair always corresponds to waves of period about 25 years; the second pair to waves of 20 years; the third to waves of 13 years. He shows in what degree the complex roots depend on the representation of the net maternity function as a histogram, and how the values of the real and complex parts of successive roots are affected by skewness and kurtosis in the net maternity function.

The scheme for analysis of ages which is implicit in the present chapter provides for two major components. The first is the stable age distribution, represented by the real term $Q_1 e^{r_1 t}$. Insofar as the initial number between ages x and $x + dx$ is the stable $e^{-rx}p(x)\,dx$ all Q's beyond the first will be zero. (This may be readily proved by the orthogonality property of the stable vectors using the argument of Section 5.2 in the continuous version or of Section 3.2 in the discrete form.) The age distribution will be constant through time, and the increase at each age will be exactly the rate r_1 compounded each moment.

The second component of analysis is any perturbation or departure from stability in the initial age distribution. This may be the drop in United States births of the 1930's and subsequent rise, the postwar baby boom in Europe, the high Swedish infant mortality of the Napoleonic war, or any other dip or bump in the succession of cohorts. The perturbation will advance through time in the same fashion as the hypothetical 1000 births which we have traced above, and

Table 5.10 FORTRAN program: iterative computation of intrinsic rate r from (5.3.5)

```
C      DATA ARE THE ARRAY A OF THE NET MATERNITY FUNCTION
C      IN FIVE YEAR INTERVALS FROM 10-14 TO 55-59.
       DIMENSION A(10)
     1 READ (1,2)  ( A(I), I = 1,10 )
     2 FORMAT (10F8.6)
       R = 0.
     3 SUM = 0.
       WRITE (3,4)R
     4 FORMAT (' R =', F10.6 )
       DO 5 I = 1,10
     5 SUM = SUM + A(I) / EXP(R) ** ( 5*I-20 )
       RSTAR = ALOG(SUM) / 27.5
       IF (ABS(RSTAR-R) - .000001) 1,6,6
     6 R = RSTAR
       GO TO 3
       END
```

Table 5.11 FORTRAN program: computation of $\psi(r)$ of (5.2.2) from $r = -0.200$ to $r = 0.200$ by intervals of 0.002

```
C      DATA ARE SAME AS TABLE 5.10
       DIMENSION A(10)
     5 READ (1,6)  (A(I), I = 1,10)
     6 FORMAT (10F8.6)
       R = -.2
     7 PSI = 0.
       DO 8 I = 1,11
       X = I
     8 PSI = PSI + A(I)/EXP(R*(5.*X + 7.5))
       WRITE (3,9)PSI
     9 FORMAT (F20.6)
       R = R + .002
       IF (R - .2) 7,7,5
       END
```

the same waves will follow after it, the principal harmonic having a wavelength equal to the generation. The damped waves, in the absence of changes in mortality and fertility, will be given by the terms $Q_2e^{r_2t} + Q_3e^{r_3t}$ discussed above. In terms of this argument, show why the second and third roots of the 3×3 matrix in Section 3.1 can be real and negative, while those of the 9×9 representation are inevitably complex.

The notion of a stable component on which perturbations are superimposed from time to time, each perturbation being followed by a trail of damped waves, does not allow for all possibilities; it cannot, for example, handle the situation in which birth rates are changing gradually. An attempt to cope with this situation is described in Coale and Zelnik (1963, pp. 82–89) and Keyfitz, Nagnur, and Sharma (1967).

The examples of this book could not have been obtained without machine computation. We cannot take space to show the programs for each table, but Table 5.10 sketches a program for the intrinsic rate r by the iterative (5.3.5), and Table 5.11 for the tracing out of $\psi(r)$ in Table 5.1. These and their elaborations (for instance, of Table 5.10 to complex roots) provided many of the results of the present chapter.

CHAPTER 6

PARAMETRIZATION OF THE RENEWAL PROCESS

6.1. GRADUATING THE NET MATERNITY FUNCTION

The preceding chapter contained a justification of the integral equation

$$B(t) = G(t) + \int_0^t B(t - x)p(x)m(x)\,dx \qquad (6.1.1)$$

as a representation of the process of population renewal, and found three ways of solving it, each giving rise to a different finite approximation. Although the equation is expressed in continuous functions, our solutions were in terms of the five-year intervals of age in which the observations on birth and death are usually presented. Only one sex, typically female, is taken into account.

But 8 specific birth rates ${}_5F_x$ for the relevant ages, plus 8 values of ${}_5L_x$, the life table number-living, as used in the calculations of Chapter 5, can hardly constitute 16 *independent* observations. The human populations to which the theory is applied fall into patterns, and 16 dimensions are not required for their classification. In this chapter we will see how far three parameters can incorporate the relevant facts.

The three parameters will be the zeroth, the first, and the second moments of the net maternity function. In the fundamental equation (6.1.1) we first collapse together $p(x)$, the life table number-living on radix unity, and $m(x)$, the age-specific birth rate, and confine ourselves to their product, $\phi(x) = p(x)m(x)$. We fit to $\phi(x)$ a three-constant curve by the method of moments. Then the three constants for describing $\phi(x)$ will be expressible in terms of R_0, R_1, R_2, defined as

$$R_i = \int_\alpha^\beta x^i\phi(x)\,dx\,, \quad i = 0, 1, 2\,. \qquad (6.1.2)$$

In terms of understandable characteristics, R_0 is the net reproduction rate, the expected number of girl children by which a girl child now born will be replaced under the observed regime of mortality and fertility; $R_1/R_0 = \mu$ is the mean age of childbearing in the stationary population; $R_2/R_0 - (R_1/R_0)^2 = \sigma^2$ is the variance of age at childbearing in the stationary population.

The present chapter will exhibit three graduations, due respectively to Lotka (1939c, p. 70), Wicksell (1931), and Hadwiger (1940). In each instance the substitution of the graduated form of $\phi(x)$ in (6.1.1) leads to a special version of the characteristic equation (5.2.2); solution of this for r gives a special set of roots r_i, and to each of these roots is associated a Q,

$$Q_i = \frac{\int_0^\beta e^{-r_i t} G(t)\,dt}{-\psi'(r_i)}, \quad i = 1, 2, \ldots,$$

to constitute the solution (5.2.5).

The advantage of the graduation is that we can reach values of r and Q which are explicit in terms of the simple functions R_0, μ, and σ^2 of the observations. Although the results are, of course, approximate, with an error dependent on the quality of the fitting to the net maternity function $\phi(x)$, the simplification enables us to answer with sufficient accuracy some questions about the properties of the roots that would be difficult to approach in the general form. In each of the three following sections, some specimen derivations are made to exhibit the methods. A complete set of results for all three graduations is shown in Exhibit 6.1.

6.2. GRADUATION OF THE NET MATERNITY FUNCTION BY THE NORMAL DISTRIBUTION (LOTKA)

First we replace $p(x)m(x)$ in (5.2.2) with the normal or Gaussian,

$$\phi(x) = p(x)m(x) = \frac{K}{\sigma\sqrt{2\pi}} e^{-(1/2\sigma^2)(x-\mu)^2}, \tag{6.2.1}$$

whose three constants may be readily obtained in terms of the observations by integration. We know that the observed and fitted distributions will have the same total numbers if (applying the standard integral $\int_{-\infty}^{+\infty} e^{-x^2}\,dx = \sqrt{\pi}$)

$$\int_\alpha^\beta p(x)m(x)\,dx = R_0 = \int_{-\infty}^{+\infty} \frac{K}{\sigma\sqrt{2\pi}} e^{-(1/2\sigma^2)(x-\mu)^2}\,dx = K.$$

This is the matching of zeroth moments. Matching the first moments gives

$$\int_\alpha^\beta \frac{xp(x)m(x)\,dx}{R_0} = \frac{R_1}{R_0} = \int_{-\infty}^{+\infty} \frac{x}{\sigma\sqrt{2\pi}} e^{-(1/2\sigma^2)(x-\mu)^2}\,dx = \mu; \tag{6.2.2}$$

that is, the mean age of the fitted curve is made equal to the mean age of the observations. The variance of the observations is

$$\int_\alpha^\beta (x-\mu)^2 \frac{p(x)m(x)\,dx}{R_0} = \frac{R_2}{R_0} - \left(\frac{R_1}{R_0}\right)^2, \tag{6.2.3}$$

and to this we equate the variance of the fitted curve:

$$\int_{-\infty}^{+\infty} \frac{(x-\mu)^2}{\sigma\sqrt{2\pi}} e^{-(1/2\sigma^2)(x-\mu)^2}\,dx = \sigma^2.$$

From statistics (Wilks, 1962, p. 157; Kendall and Stuart, 1958, Vol. I, p. 135) we are familiar with the moment-generating function of the normal curve, given by

$$\mathscr{E}(e^{rx}) = \int_{-\infty}^{+\infty} e^{rx} \frac{1}{\sigma\sqrt{2\pi}} e^{-(1/2\sigma^2)(x-\mu)^2} \, dx = e^{r\mu+(1/2)\sigma^2 r^2} . \qquad (6.2.4)$$

This enables us to integrate $\psi(r)$ of the characteristic equation (5.2.2). Replacing r by $-r$ in (6.2.4) gives for (5.2.2) with normal $\phi(x)$

$$\mathscr{E}(e^{-rx}) = \frac{\psi(r)}{R_0} = e^{-r\mu+(1/2)\sigma^2 r^2} = \frac{1}{R_0} , \qquad (6.2.5)$$

or taking natural logarithms, we have

$$\frac{\sigma^2 r^2}{2} - r\mu + \ln R_0 = 0 , \qquad (6.2.6)$$

whose solution for an approximation to the real root is

$$r_L = \frac{\mu - \sqrt{\mu^2 - 2\sigma^2 \ln R_0}}{\sigma^2} , \qquad (6.2.7)$$

obtained by completing the square in (6.2.6).

Lotka (1939c, p. 71) recommended (6.2.7) for finding r. Even if one uses the normal graduation, it is somewhat easier to start with arbitrary r, say $r = 0$, and obtain the improved

$$r^* = \frac{\ln R_0}{\mu - r\sigma^2/2}$$

by rewriting (6.2.6) for an iterative solution. Using either this or (6.2.7), and the data of Table 5.5, show that $r_L = 0.01609$ for United States females, 1964, with adjusted births. (Note that the r_L based on unadjusted births of Table 5.3 is about 2% lower.) Prove that the error of the iterative formula in any cycle cannot in practice be greater than $r\sigma^2/2\mu$ or at most 0.05 of the error in the preceding cycle, and hence that two iterations will provide all necessary accuracy. The interested reader may work out the properties of the process in terms of continued fractions.

On a more practical level, putting $\sigma^2 = 0$ in (6.2.6) gives (Lotka, 1939c, p. 70)

$$r = \frac{\ln R_0}{\mu} . \qquad (6.2.8)$$

This corresponds to a fitting of the net maternity function by a point distribution concentrated at μ, the mean age of childbearing. Despite the unrealistic model underlying it, the value of r obtained by (6.2.8) will rarely be in error by as much as 5%.

Those who have not read Lotka (1939c, p. 69) may reconstruct his argument, and so derive the above results by a different route. He proceeds by expanding the exponential in the characteristic equation (5.2.2) as a Taylor series, integrating term by term to secure moments, then simply dividing both sides by R_0, and taking logarithms. The result is a power series in r in which the coefficients are the cumulants; truncating after r^2 gives a quadratic in r identical with (6.2.6) above. This proves that Lotka's truncation after r^2 is equivalent to replacing the observed net maternity function by the fitted normal.

Bürgdorfer (1932) attempted to solve the characteristic equation of the integral equation by expanding the exponential under the integral in (5.2.2) up to the term in r^2, obtaining moments and hence a quadratic without taking logarithms. Lotka (1932a) pointed out that the solution in terms of cumulants is superior to that in moments about zero, in making the neglected terms smaller. Find an expression for the error arising through neglect of moments about zero beyond the second, showing it to be of the order of $\mu r^2/2$. What result does the Bürgdorfer "method" give for United States females of 1965, whose moments are found in Table 5.5?

Complex as well as real roots are found by admitting the multiple values of the logarithm in the complex plane; on substituting $\ln R_0 \pm 2\pi mi$ for $\ln R_0$, we may write (6.2.6) as

$$\sigma^2 r^2 - 2r\mu + 2 \ln R_0 \pm 4\pi mi = 0 .$$

For $r = u + iv$, u and v real, this becomes

$$\sigma^2(u^2 + 2iuv - v^2) - 2(u + iv)\mu + 2 \ln R_0 \pm 4\pi mi = 0 , \qquad (6.2.9)$$

which, after separation into real and imaginary parts, is

$$\sigma^2(u^2 - v^2) - 2u\mu + 2 \ln R_0 = 0 , \qquad (6.2.10)$$

and

$$\sigma^2 uv - v\mu \pm 2\pi m = 0 . \qquad (6.2.11)$$

Changing the origin for u by writing $u = U + \mu/\sigma^2$ gives

$$U^2 - v^2 = \mu^2/\sigma^4 - 2 \ln R_0/\sigma^2 \qquad (6.2.12)$$

and

$$Uv = \pm 2\pi m/\sigma^2 . \qquad (6.2.13)$$

Equation (6.2.13) describes a set of hyperbolas in the complex plane, one for each value of m. The intersection of these with the curve (6.2.12), also a hyperbola, locates the complex roots arising on the normal graduation of the maternity function (Lotka, 1939c, p. 75, and Fig. 6.1 below). The hyperbolas are arbitrary; the set of roots can be represented as intersections of other curves in many ways. Calling a the constant on the right-hand side of (6.2.12) and b

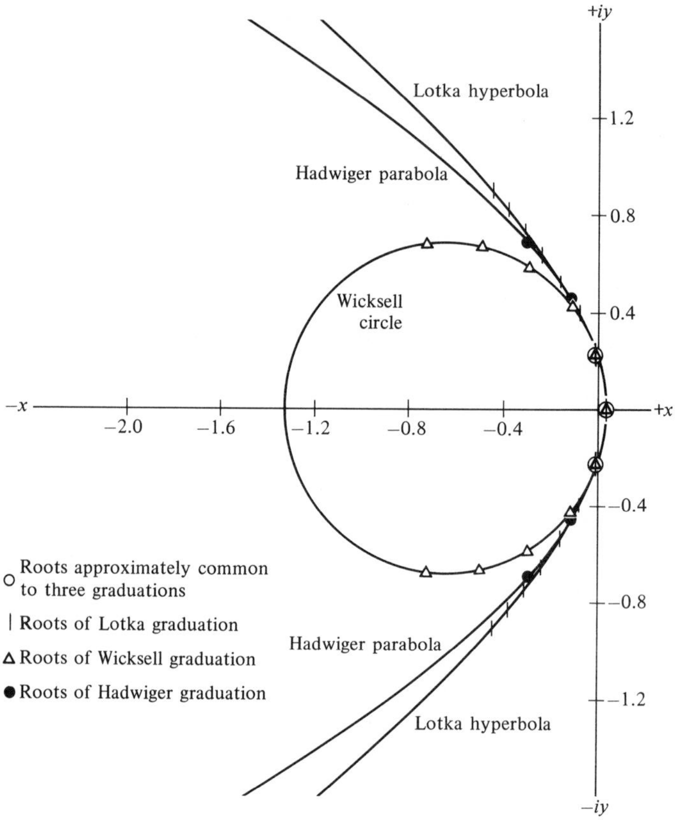

Fig. 6.1 Curves on which roots $r_1, r_2, \ldots$ fall on three graduations, Mexican females, 1960.

the constant on the right-hand side of (6.2.13), we can convert intersections of the set of hyperbolas

$$U^2 - v^2 = a\,, \qquad Uv = b \tag{6.2.14}$$

into intersections of circles and straight lines (see Lotka, 1945, pp. 355–385). For Eqs. (6.2.14) are the same as the pair

$$U^2 + v^2 = \sqrt{a^2 + 4b^2}\,, \qquad U + v = \sqrt{\sqrt{a^2 + 4b^2} + 2b}\,,$$

where b can take the values of the right-hand side of (6.2.13), i.e., 0, $\pm 2\pi/\sigma^2$, $\pm 4\pi/\sigma^2$, $\pm 6\pi/\sigma^2$, etc.

Where there is any departure from stability in the initial age distribution, one expects waves through time both in respect of the total population and the population of given ages. If $\sigma^2 = 0$, the quadratic (6.2.9) reduces to

$$-2r\mu + 2 \ln R_0 = \mp 4\pi i$$

for $m = \pm 1$. Then

$$r = \frac{\ln R_0 \pm 2\pi i}{\mu},$$

and the principal complex roots tend to a real part, $(\ln R_0)/\mu$, and an imaginary part, $\pm 2\pi i/\mu$. The corresponding terms in the solution for $B(t)$ are

$$Q_2 \exp[(\ln R_0 + 2\pi i)t/\mu] + Q_3 \exp[(\ln R_0 - 2\pi i)t/\mu] .$$

When R_0 is greater than one, $\ln R_0$ will be positive, and there will be no damping; instead, by virtue of the factor

$$\exp[(\ln R_0)t/\mu] = R_0^{t/\mu},$$

waves once present will grow to ever-increasing amplitude. This model applies exactly if all women have all their children at the same age.

In order to show damping, the model must include σ^2 of at least a certain value, which is to say, a minimum variation in the ages of women at childbearing. The minimum σ^2 to ensure damping is that which makes the principal complex roots have negative real parts. From (6.2.12), substituting back $u = U + \mu/\sigma^2$, we have

$$u = \mu/\sigma^2 - \sqrt{v^2 + (\mu^2/\sigma^4) - (2 \ln R_0/\sigma^2)} . \tag{6.2.15}$$

Evidently u will be negative if

$$v^2 - 2 \ln R_0/\sigma^2 > 0 ,$$

or

$$\sigma > \sqrt{2 \ln R_0}/v . \tag{6.2.16}$$

For an increasing population $\ln R_0 > 0$, and so long as the standard deviation of age at childbearing is greater than the quantity on the right of (6.2.16) (4.1 years in the case of the Netherlands 1964, whose $R_0 = 1.49$, $v = 0.2166$), damping will apply. If a population has R_0 as great as $e = 2.72$, and v as small as 0.2, damping will require $\sigma > \sqrt{2 \ln e}/v$, or $\sigma^2 > 2/v^2$. Since v is invariably close to 0.2, this requires that $\sigma^2 > 50$, a high value. However, the condition (6.2.16) seems always to be met by human populations.

The result (6.2.16) is exact if cumulants from the third onward are zero. A correction may be devised to allow for skewness and kurtosis.

For a given R_0 and μ, the variance in the ages at childbearing increases the real root or intrinsic rate of natural increase r. Differentiating (6.2.6) with respect to σ gives

$$\frac{dr}{d\sigma} = \frac{\sigma r^2}{\mu - \sigma^2 r}, \tag{6.2.17}$$

which is positive, though very small for values of μ, σ and r encountered in practice. The reader can evaluate and interpret (6.2.17) for Australian females, 1965, using the data of Table 5.5.

The value of Q for the initial condition of B_0 births (from Eq. 5.2.22) is B_0 divided by the derivative with sign reversed of the left-hand side of (5.2.2) with respect to r: $B_0/-\psi'(r)$. Equation (6.2.5) enables us to replace $\psi(r) = 1$ of (5.2.2) by

$$\psi(r) = R_0 e^{-r\mu+\sigma^2 r^2/2} = 1 \,,$$

and the derivative with respect to r of $\psi(r)$ is now

$$\psi'(r) = -R_0(\mu - \sigma^2 r)e^{-r\mu+\sigma^2 r^2/2} = -(\mu - \sigma^2 r)\,, \tag{6.2.18}$$

where r is any root of $\psi(r) = 1$. Hence

$$Q_s = \frac{B_0}{-\psi'(r_s)} = \frac{B_0}{\mu - \sigma^2 r_s}\,, \qquad s = 1, 2, \ldots \tag{6.2.19}$$

The average age of childbearing in the stable population may be calculated from (5.6.9) as the same derivative $-\psi'(r)$ evaluated at the real root:

$$A_r = \frac{-\psi'(r)}{\psi(r)} = \frac{-d \ln \psi(r)}{dr} = \mu - r\sigma^2 \tag{6.2.20}$$

Table 6.1 Mean age of childbearing in the stable population, as calculated on the normal graduation and on the histogram form of the net maternity function

	1000r	μ	σ^2	A_r CALCULATED ON NORMAL GRADUATION AS $\mu - r\sigma^2$	A_r ON HISTOGRAM
AUSTRALIA 1965	12.29	27.39	33.31	26.98	26.96
COLOMBIA 1964	28.35	29.60	50.90	28.16	28.17
DOMINICAN REPUBLIC 1960	26.50	29.64	49.65	28.32	28.31
FINLAND 1964	6.47	28.05	37.74	27.81	27.80
MEXICO 1959-61	32.95	29.06	46.26	27.54	27.52
UNITED STATES 1963	17.10	26.47	34.13	25.89	25.87
1964	15.70	26.53	34.26	25.99	25.97

VARIANCE σ^2 AS SHOWN IS CORRECTED FOR GROUPING BY SUBTRACTION OF 25/12 = 2.08.

on the normal graduation for a population of given R_0, μ and σ^2. Hence for an increasing population, $A_r < \mu$. The result $A_r = \mu - r\sigma^2$ is exact, given the normal graduation, but is an approximation for the original observations in five-year age groups. For six countries of quite different rates of increase, relevant data are shown in Table 6.1. Comment on the appropriateness of (6.2.20) for the four populations and estimate the order of magnitude of the discrepancy for Australia by $r^2\kappa_3/2$, the next term in (6.2.20) when the net maternity function cannot be assumed normal, using the κ_3 of Table 5.5.

The quantity T, the length of generation defined by $e^{rT} = R_0$, is readily expressed in terms of μ and A_r. From (6.2.5)

$$R_0 = e^{r\mu - \sigma^2 r^2/2} .$$

On equating this to e^{rT}, taking logarithms of both sides and dividing through by r, we have

$$T = \mu - \sigma^2 r/2 . \tag{6.2.21}$$

Comparison with (6.2.20) shows that

$$T = (A_r + \mu)/2$$

without approximation, once the normal graduation of the net maternity function is assumed. Relate this to (5.6.11), which showed that in general $(A_r + \mu)/2$ is larger than T by about $\kappa_3 r^2/12$.

6.3. GRADUATION BY THE INCOMPLETE GAMMA FUNCTION (WICKSELL)

Commenting on the work of Lotka summarized in the preceding section, Wicksell (1931, pp. 156–157) pointed out the superiority of the Pearson Type III curve which takes account of the nearly universal skewness of the maternity function, and mentioned the advantage of this fit for obtaining the complex roots. In the characteristic equation (5.2.2), he replaces $p(x)m(x)\,dx$ by

$$K \frac{c^k x^{k-1} e^{-cx}}{\Gamma(k)}\, dx , \tag{6.3.1}$$

where the three constants K, c and k are to be chosen once again by the method of moments, and $\Gamma(k) \doteq \sqrt{2\pi} k^{k-1/2} \exp(-k + 1/12k)$.

Equating the zeroth, first, and second moments of the formula to the corresponding moments of the observations gives the three equations

$$\int_0^\infty \frac{Kc^k x^{k-1} e^{-cx}}{\Gamma(k)}\, dx = \int_\alpha^\beta p(x)m(x)\, dx , \tag{6.3.2}$$

$$\int_0^\infty \frac{Kxc^k x^{k-1} e^{-cx}}{\Gamma(k)}\, dx = \int_\alpha^\beta xp(x)m(x)\, dx , \tag{6.3.3}$$

$$\int_0^\infty \frac{Kx^2 c^k x^{k-1} e^{-cx}}{\Gamma(k)}\, dx = \int_\alpha^\beta x^2 p(x)m(x)\, dx . \tag{6.3.4}$$

On evaluating the integrals in (6.3.2), we have

$$K = R_0\,, \tag{6.3.5}$$

the net reproduction rate. The left-hand side of (6.3.3) is

$$R_0\int_0^\infty \frac{c^k x^k e^{-cx}}{\Gamma(k)}\,dx = \frac{R_0 c^k}{c^{k+1}}\,\frac{\Gamma(k+1)}{\Gamma(k)}\int_0^\infty \frac{c^{k+1}x^k e^{-cx}}{\Gamma(k+1)}\,dx = \frac{R_0 k}{c}\,,$$

and the observations represented by the right-hand side of (6.3.3) are

$$\int_\alpha^\beta xp(x)m(x)\,dx = R_1\,;$$

equating these we obtain

$$\frac{k}{c} = \frac{R_1}{R_0} = \mu\,. \tag{6.3.6}$$

The left-hand side of (6.3.4) is

$$R_0\int_0^\infty \frac{c^k x^{k+1} e^{-cx}}{\Gamma(k)}\,dx = \frac{R_0\Gamma(k+2)}{\Gamma(k)}\,\frac{c^k}{c^{k+2}}\int_0^\infty \frac{c^{k+2}x^{k+1}e^{-cx}}{\Gamma(k+2)} = \frac{R_0(k+1)k}{c^2}\,,$$

and equating this to the observed $R_2 = R_0(\sigma^2 + \mu^2)$ on the right of (6.3.4) gives

$$\frac{R_0(k+1)k}{c^2} = R_0(\sigma^2 + \mu^2)\,. \tag{6.3.7}$$

Combining (6.3.6) and (6.3.7), we have

$$c = \frac{\mu}{\sigma^2} = \frac{R_1}{R_2 - R_1^2/R_0} \tag{6.3.8}$$

and

$$k = \frac{\mu^2}{\sigma^2} = \frac{R_1^2}{R_2R_0 - R_1^2}\,. \tag{6.3.9}$$

Equations (6.3.5), (6.3.8), and (6.3.9) constitute the fitting due to Wicksell.

In terms of the Type III curve the characteristic equation (5.2.2) is

$$\begin{aligned}\psi(r) &= \int_0^\infty e^{-rx}\,\frac{Kc^k x^{k-1}e^{-cx}}{\Gamma(k)}\,dx \\ &= \frac{Kc^k}{(r+c)^k}\int_0^\infty \frac{(r+c)^k x^{k-1}e^{-(r+c)x}}{\Gamma(k)}\,dx = 1\,,\end{aligned} \tag{6.3.10}$$

or

$$\psi(r) = Kc^k/(r+c)^k = 1\,, \tag{6.3.11}$$

since the second integral in (6.3.10) is unity by the definition of $\Gamma(k)$. Solving the much simplified characteristic equation (6.3.11):

$$r = c(K^{1/k} - 1)\,,$$

and substituting moments for the constants from (6.3.5), (6.3.8) and (6.3.9) gives

$$r = \frac{\mu}{\sigma^2}(R_0^{\sigma^2/\mu^2} - 1)\,. \qquad (6.3.12)$$

For the complex roots R_0 is replaced by $R_0e^{2\pi mi}$ with integral m. Show that for the Type III fitting all roots fall in a circle of center $-\mu/\sigma^2$ on the real axis and radius $r_1 + \mu/\sigma^2$ (Fig. 6.1).

The coefficient Q in the solution of the integral equation with B_0 births as initial condition is readily found. We need the derivative of $\psi(r)$, which may be shown from (6.3.11) to be

$$\psi'(r) = -\int_0^\infty xe^{-rx}p(x)m(x)\,dx = -\frac{Kc^kk}{(c+r)^{k+1}}$$

$$= -\left\{\frac{Kc^k}{(r+c)^k}\right\}\left\{\frac{k}{(c+r)}\right\} = -\frac{k}{(c+r)},$$

for all roots r which satisfy (6.3.11). Hence from (6.3.8) and (6.3.9),

$$Q_s = -\frac{1}{\psi'(r_s)} = \frac{B_0}{\mu} + \frac{B_0\sigma^2r_s}{\mu^2},$$

the second term on the right being $(100\sigma^2/\mu)r_1$ percent of the first for the real root or at most 5%. The reader can trace out the solution

$$B(t) \doteq \sum_{s=1}^{3} Q_se^{r_st}$$

for Portuguese females of 1965 from the data of Table 5.5.

6.4. GRADUATION BY A DISTRIBUTION THAT FITS THE SUCCESSIVE GENERATIONS (HADWIGER)

We have seen two analytic forms of the net maternity function, corresponding to graduation by a normal curve and by a Pearson Type III, and evidently many more are available which would provide some kind of fit to real data. Each of these would give rise to various geometrical configurations when its roots were portrayed on the complex plane. Among these functions one has a special claim to our attention. Hadwiger (1940) shows that if the probability of a girl child now born having a daughter at age x to $x + dx$ is (in our notation) represented by $n = 1$ in

$$\phi_n(x)\,dx = \frac{na}{\sqrt{\pi x^3}}\exp\left[nac - \left(\frac{n^2a^2}{x} + bx\right)\right]dx\,, \qquad (6.4.1)$$

then the probability of having a granddaughter through the female line when the original child is (or would be if she lived) x to $x + dx$ is represented by $n = 2$ in the same expression, and of having a great-granddaughter by $n = 3$, etc.

Table 6.2 Hadwiger exponential function $\phi_1(x)$ of (6.4.4) for $R_0 = 1$ and several values of μ and σ^2*

σ^2	μ	x = 15	x = 25	x = 35	x = 45
25	25	0.00612	0.07979	0.01154	0.00039
	27	0.00108	0.08214	0.02014	0.00076
	29	0.00011	0.06877	0.03314	0.00152
	31	0.00001	0.04512	0.05009	0.00306
35	25	0.01342	0.06743	0.01467	0.00117
	27	0.00401	0.07116	0.02257	0.00195
	29	0.00081	0.06643	0.03321	0.00330
	31	0.00010	0.04921	0.04591	0.00560
45	25	0.02008	0.05947	0.01623	0.00208
	27	0.00806	0.06362	0.02328	0.00319
	29	0.00237	0.06045	0.03220	0.00492
	31	0.00049	0.05001	0.04235	0.00759

* Programmed by Robert D. Retherford.

Note that the age of each descendant is measured not from her own birth date but from that of the original ancestor.

The reader may use the principle of Section 5.6 to derive an analogous result on the distribution of successive generations for the Lotka and Wicksell graduations, though these will be less convenient functions of n than is (6.4.1). Since the Hadwiger function (6.4.1) is not well known, a short table is shown (Table 6.2).

The standard definite integral

$$\int_0^\infty e^{-(\alpha^2\theta^2+(\beta^2/\theta^2))}\,d\theta = \frac{\sqrt{\pi}}{2\alpha}\,e^{-2\alpha\beta},$$

(Abramowitz and Stegun, 1965, p. 304; Chemical Rubber Publishing Co., 1963, p. 314) may be evaluated by writing $u = \alpha\theta - \beta/\theta$ and following through the substitution, which brings the problem down to finding the integral of e^{-u^2}. To apply the standard integral to (6.4.1), put $\theta = 1/\sqrt{x}$, $\alpha = na$, $\beta = \sqrt{b-r}$. One may show that the cumulant generating function of $\phi_n(x)$ is

$$\ln\int_0^\infty e^{rx}\phi_n(x)\,dx = \ln\psi_n(-r) = na(c - 2\sqrt{b-r})\,. \qquad (6.4.2)$$

By successive differentiation of $\ln \psi_n(-r)$, and putting $r = 0$, the zeroth, first, and second cumulants may be found. Following this the reader may match moments to obtain

$$a = \frac{\mu^{3/2}}{\sigma\sqrt{2}}, \qquad b = \frac{\mu}{2\sigma^2}, \qquad c = \frac{\sqrt{2}\mu}{\sigma} + \frac{\sqrt{2}\,\sigma \ln R_0}{\mu^{3/2}} \tag{6.4.3}$$

For $n = 1$, this turns (6.4.1) into

$$\phi_1(x) = \frac{R_0}{\sigma}\sqrt{\frac{\mu^3}{2\pi x^3}}\exp\left[-\frac{\mu}{2\sigma^2}\left(\sqrt{x} - \frac{\mu}{\sqrt{x}}\right)^2\right]. \tag{6.4.4}$$

We investigate now the characteristic equation of $\phi_1(x)$,

$$\psi(r) = \int_0^\infty e^{-rx}\frac{a}{\sqrt{\pi x^3}}\, e^{ac-(a^2/x+bx)}\, dx = 1\,,$$

which reduces to

$$e^{a(c-2\sqrt{b+r})} = 1\,. \tag{6.4.5}$$

Substituting from (6.4.3) in (6.4.5) gives, directly in terms of the moments,

$$\psi(r) = R_0 \exp\left(\frac{\mu^2}{\sigma^2} - \frac{\mu^{3/2}}{\sigma}\sqrt{\frac{\mu}{\sigma^2} + 2r}\right) = 1\,.$$

The roots will be obtained by taking logarithms,

$$\ln \psi(r) = a(c - 2\sqrt{b + r}) = \pm 2\pi m i\,,$$

and are

$$r = \left(\frac{c}{2}\right)^2 - b = \frac{\ln R_0}{\mu} + \frac{\sigma^2}{2\mu}\left(\frac{\ln R_0}{\mu}\right)^2 \tag{6.4.6}$$

for the real root, and

$$r = \left(\frac{c}{2} \pm \frac{\pi m i}{a}\right)^2 - b\,, \quad m = 1, 2, \ldots, \tag{6.4.7}$$

for the complex roots. From (6.4.7) we can set down equations for the curve on which the roots must lie by putting $r = x + iy$ and equating real and imaginary parts, to obtain

$$\left.\begin{aligned} x &= \frac{c^2}{4} - \frac{\pi^2 m^2}{a^2} - b\,, \\ y &= \frac{\pm\pi m c}{a}\,, \end{aligned}\right\} \quad m = 0, 1, 2, \ldots,$$

in terms of the parameter m. Eliminating m gives

$$y^2 = c^2(c^2/4 - b - x)\,,$$

a parabola whose main axis is the abscissa, which it crosses at $x = (c^2/4) - b$, the real root. The geometrically inclined reader may show that the focus of the parabola is at a distance $\mu/2\sigma^2$ left of the imaginary axis $x = 0$ (Fig. 6.1). The length of the generation T is given by entering the value of r from (6.4.6) in the definition of T:

$$T = \frac{\ln R_0}{r} = \frac{\mu}{1 + (\sigma^2 \ln R_0)/2\mu^2} \doteqdot \mu - \frac{\sigma^2 r}{2}. \tag{6.4.8}$$

The ridge in the plane of generations and age (or time from the initial ancestor) which was portrayed numerically in Table 5.6 may be studied on this graduation, now regarding n as a continuous rather than discrete variable. For a given x the maximum generation is found by solving $d\phi_n(x)/dn = 0$ as

$$n \doteqdot \frac{x}{\mu} + \frac{x\sigma^2 \ln R_0}{\mu^3},$$

which in an increasing population is slightly above x/μ. We write (6.4.1) in the form

$$\phi_n(x) = \frac{na}{\sqrt{\pi x^3}} \exp\left[na(c - 2\sqrt{b}) - (na/\sqrt{x} - \sqrt{bx})^2\right],$$

and other geometrical properties of the surface $\phi_n(x)$ over the (n, x)-plane may be worked out. Lotka (1939c, pp. 82–84) discusses these matters in terms of the normal graduation of the net maternity function.

In Chapters 3 and 5 it was asserted without proof that the damping of the waves in a population trajectory depends on the dispersion of the ages at which childbearing takes place, a dispersion which may be measured by the standard deviation σ of the net maternity function. In the discussion of the Lotka graduation in the present chapter, we found in (6.2.16) the minimum range required for damping. The Hadwiger graduation provides a very simple statement of the relation between the real part of the first complex root (which determines the rate of damping) and the range of ages of childbearing.

In (6.4.7) and Exhibit 6.1 the real part x is

$$x = \frac{c^2}{4} - b - \frac{\pi^2 m^2}{a^2}.$$

We make things easy by considering the relation between x and the variance σ^2 as among populations of *given intrinsic rate of increase* r_1 (since r_1 is not much affected by σ^2 this does not deprive the result of interest). Then we can replace $(c^2/4) - b$ by r_1 considered as a constant and have

$$x = r_1 - \frac{\pi^2 m^2}{a^2} = r_1 - \frac{2\sigma^2 \pi^2}{\mu^3}, \tag{6.4.9}$$

with $m = \pm 1$ for the first pair of complex roots. We proved in Section 5.2 that x is less than r_1; now (6.4.9) estimates the amount by which it is less: $2\sigma^2\pi^2/\mu^3$. For Netherlands females, 1964, $r_1 = 0.01375$, $\mu = 29.21$. Hence for damping to occur, the right-hand side of (6.4.9) must be negative, or $\sigma^2 > r_1\mu^3/2\pi^2$, which is $\sigma^2 > 17.36$ and $\sigma > 4.2$ years. On the Lotka graduation we derived (6.2.16) and found for the Netherlands $\sigma = 4.1$ years as the minimum spread of childbearing for damping. Show that the difference between the minima on (6.4.9) and on (6.2.16) is of the order of r^2 or less.

At the end of Chapter 3 it was also asserted that the imaginary part of the first complex root r_2 accounts for cycles in the trajectory of the population induced by an initial departure from stability, and that the wavelength of the cycles is approximately the length of the generation. This is conveniently exhibited in terms of the Hadwiger graduation. For on this graduation the roots r of $\phi(r) = 1$ have imaginary parts $y = \pi mc/a$, $m = 0, \pm 1, \pm 2, \ldots$ Putting $m = 1$, $y = \pi c/a$, and translating c and a back into terms of the moments, we have

$$y = \frac{2\pi}{\mu}\left(1 + \frac{\sigma^2 \ln R_0}{\mu^2}\right),$$

or a wavelength of

$$\frac{2\pi}{y} = \frac{\mu}{1 + (\sigma^2 \ln R_0/\mu^2)} \doteq \mu - \frac{\sigma^2 \ln R_0}{\mu}. \tag{6.4.10}$$

Using (6.4.8) and (6.4.10) the reader may show that $\mu > T > 2\pi/y$ if $R_0 > 1$, and

$$\mu - T = T - \frac{2\pi}{y} \doteq \left(\frac{\sigma^2 \ln R_0}{2\mu}\right).$$

He may also show that on this graduation $2\pi/y$ is exactly equal to A_r, the mean age of childbearing in the stable population.

Since $\ln R_0$ is usually less than unity in human populations (what annual rate of increase would make it unity?), and σ^2 is somewhat larger than μ but of the same order of magnitude, the second term in the denominator of (6.4.10) is usually less than 0.05; (6.4.10) says that the wavelength of the repetition of any disturbance in the population will be less than μ but within 5% of it for an increasing population.

Table 6.3 shows the quantities μ, T, and $2\pi/y$, along with A_r, the mean age of childbearing in the stable population. The difference $\mu - T$ is seen to be equal to $T - A_r$, as was proved to terms in r by the argument leading to (5.6.11), and if the Hadwiger graduation is appropriate, $2\pi/y$ ought to be equal to A_r. The differences in Table 6.3 suggest that $2\pi/y$ is very sensitive to departures of the net maternity function $\phi(x)$ from the Hadwiger graduation. The Pearson measure of skewness β_1 (Exhibit 6.1) is $9\sigma^2/\mu^2$ (Table 6.5) for a Hadwiger fit, and where $\beta_1\mu^2/\sigma^2$ departs considerably from 9, so usually does $2\pi/y$ from A_r. Find the relation between $2\pi/y - A_r$ on the one hand and β_1 on the other by means of a scatter diagram.

Table 6.3 Comparison of μ, the mean age of childbearing in the stationary population; T, the length of generation; A_r, the mean age of childbearing in the stable population; $2\pi/y$, the wavelength of the first complex component of age distribution; $\beta_1\mu^2/\sigma^2$, the criterion for agreement of A_r and $2\pi/y$

	μ	T	A_r	$2\pi/y$	CRITERION $\beta_1\mu^2/\sigma^2$
FEMALES					
AUSTRIA 1965	27.28	27.12	26.95	27.51	5
CANADA 1965	27.75	27.47	27.19	27.46	6
CZECHOSLOVAKIA 1962	25.87	25.87	25.75	25.07	19
ENGLAND AND WALES 1960-62	27.42	27.25	27.09	27.14	8
FINLAND 1964	28.05	27.92	27.80	27.96	7
GREECE 1965	28.09	28.07	28.05	28.43	5
MEXICO 1959-61	29.06	28.28	27.52	29.18	1
SCOTLAND 1963	27.63	27.42	27.22	27.31	7
UNITED STATES 1963	26.47	26.17	25.87	25.76	8
1964	26.53	26.25	25.97	25.94	8
MALES					
ENGLAND AND WALES 1960-62	30.52	30.31	30.11	29.65	14
UNITED STATES 1964	29.62	29.22	28.84	28.04	15

Roots beyond r_3 represent shorter wavelengths and are more rapidly damped. The wavelength is nearly inversely proportional to m on this graduation, since y in (6.4.10) takes on a factor m for the $2m$th and $(2m + 1)$th roots. These shorter waves, of period one-half, one-third, etc., the length of the generation, would be superimposed on the principal set embraced in r_2 and r_3. Compare them with the higher frequency waves of the ungraduated $\phi(x)$ in Chapter 5.

The hyperbola on which the roots of $\psi(r) = 0$ for the Lotka graduation fall, the circle for Wicksell, and the parabola for Hadwiger are shown in Fig. 6.1.

On any of these graduations a unique ordering of the roots exists, so that the sequence in ascending frequencies will be the same as the sequence in descending absolute values, except beyond a certain point in the Wicksell circle.

6.5. FIT OF THE SEVERAL GRADUATIONS OF THE NET MATERNITY FUNCTION

Exhibit 6.1 assembles the results of the three graduations for reference purposes, and Fig. 6.1 shows the roots. The three curves used are the best known of those fitted to the net maternity function. Pretorius (1930) and Lotka (1933a) have fitted the Type I, but the theory is more complicated for this.

To ascertain the quality of fit we may use various tests. We can draw histograms for a number of populations and examine graphically how satisfactorily each smooth curve fits the histogram. A second method is to compare the third and fourth moments of the fitted curves with the observed third and fourth moments. We may compare the function $\psi(r)$ on the graduation with the ungraduated $\psi(r)$, and compare real and complex roots of $\psi(r) = 1$ on graduated and ungraduated forms of the net maternity function. These four tests will be applied in summary fashion.

Fitted Curve and Histogram of Observations

To compare the several curves with the histogram of the observations, we must translate ordinates into areas over five-year intervals. The ordinates of the $\phi_1(x)$ of (6.4.4) at four ages for the R_0, μ, and σ^2 of Canadian females, 1965, are

$$\phi_1(20) = 0.0520\,,$$
$$\phi_1(25) = 0.1023\,,$$
$$\phi_1(30) = 0.0819\,,$$
$$\phi_1(35) = 0.0395\,.$$

These could be approximately integrated by a cubic, i.e., applying (1.1.11), with the result for the age interval 25–29 of

$$\int_{25}^{30} \phi_1(x)\,dx = 0.4798\,.$$

A more accurate result is computed with little more effort by working in strips one year wide, and within single years of age applying a Gauss formula with five ordinates, given in Chapter 10 as (10.4.6). Table 6.4 shows for four populations the areas under the curves obtained by this means. The curve which is closest at each age is underlined. Enough variation among countries exists that, pending the collection of a larger sample, it has not seemed worthwhile to apply a more elaborate statistical test.

Exhibit 6.1 Summary of properties of integral equation when net maternity function is graduated by normal (Lotka), Type III (Wicksell), and exponential (Hadwiger) curves

	Normal (Lotka)	Type III (Wicksell)	Exponential (Hadwiger)
Graduating function for $p(x)m(x)$	$\dfrac{R_0}{\sigma\sqrt{2\pi}} e^{-(x-\mu)^2/2\sigma^2}$	$R_0 \dfrac{c^k x^{k-1} e^{-cx}}{\Gamma(k)}$	$\dfrac{na}{\sqrt{\pi x^3}} e^{nac-[(n^2a^2/x)+bx]}$, $n = 1$ for first generation
Cumulant generating function $\ln \psi(-r)$ $= \ln \int_\alpha^\beta e^{rx} p(x)m(x)\,dx$	$r\mu + \dfrac{r^2\sigma^2}{2} + \ln R_0$	$-k \ln(c-r) + \ln R_0 + k \ln c$	$a(c - 2\sqrt{b-r})$
Constants in terms of observed moments	$\mu = R_1/R_0$; $\sigma = \sqrt{\dfrac{R_2}{R_0} - \left(\dfrac{R_1}{R_0}\right)^2}$	$k = \mu^2/\sigma^2$; $c = \mu/\sigma^2$	$a = \dfrac{\mu^{3/2}}{\sigma\sqrt{2}}$, $b = \dfrac{\mu}{2\sigma^2}$, $c = \dfrac{\sqrt{2\mu}}{\sigma} + \dfrac{\sqrt{2}\sigma \ln R_0}{\mu^{3/2}}$
Characteristic equation $\psi(r) = \int_\alpha^\beta e^{-rx} p(x)m(x)\,dx = 1$	$R_0 e^{(\sigma^2 r^2/2) - r\mu} = 1$	$\dfrac{R_0 c^k}{(r+c)^k} = 1$	$e^{a(c-2\sqrt{b+r})} = 1$
$\ln \psi(r)$	$\ln R_0 - \mu r + \dfrac{\sigma^2 r^2}{2}$	$\ln R_0 - \mu r + \dfrac{\sigma^2 r^2}{2} - \dfrac{\sigma^4 r^3}{3\mu} + \cdots$	$\ln R_0 - \mu r + \dfrac{\sigma^2 r^2}{2} - \dfrac{\sigma^4 r^3}{2\mu} + \cdots$
Solution for real root	$r_L = \dfrac{\mu - \sqrt{\mu^2 - 2\sigma^2 \ln R_0}}{\sigma^2}$	$r_W = c(R_0^{1/k} - 1)$	$r_H = \dfrac{c^2}{4} - b = \dfrac{\ln R_0}{\mu} + \dfrac{\sigma^2(\ln R_0)^2}{2\mu^3}$

Solution for complex roots	$r=\dfrac{\mu\pm\sqrt{\mu^2-2\sigma^2(\ln R_0\pm 2\pi mi)}}{\sigma^2}$	$r = c(R_0^{1/k}e^{2\pi mi/k} - 1)$	$r = \left(\dfrac{c}{2} \pm \dfrac{\pi mi}{a}\right)^2 - b$
Parametric equations of curve in which roots lie (integral values of m give the roots)	$\left(x - \dfrac{\mu}{\sigma^2}\right)y = \pm\dfrac{2\pi m}{\sigma^2}$ $\left(x - \dfrac{\mu}{\sigma^2}\right)^2 - y^2 = \dfrac{\mu^2}{\sigma^4} - \dfrac{2\ln R_0}{\sigma^2}$	$\cos\left(\dfrac{2m\pi}{k}\right) = \dfrac{x + c}{r_{\mathrm{W}} + c}$ $\sin\left(\dfrac{2m\pi}{k}\right) = \dfrac{y}{r_{\mathrm{W}} + c}$	$x = r_{\mathrm{H}} - \dfrac{\pi^2 m^2}{a^2}$ $y = \pm\dfrac{\pi mc}{a}$
Form of curve	Hyperbola	Circle	Parabola
Length of generation T_{L}, T_{W}, T_{H}	$\mu - \dfrac{\sigma^2 r}{2}$	$\mu - \dfrac{\sigma^2 r}{2} + \dfrac{\sigma^4 r^2}{3\mu} + \cdots$	$\mu - \dfrac{\sigma^2 r}{2} + \dfrac{\sigma^4 r^2}{2\mu} + \cdots$
Q_s, the coefficient of $e^{r_s t}$, for B_0 births as initial condition $Q_s = B_0/-\psi'(r_s)$	$Q_{s\mathrm{L}} = \dfrac{B_0}{\mu - \sigma^2 r_s}$	$Q_{s\mathrm{W}} = \dfrac{B_0(\mu + \sigma^2 r_s)}{\mu^2}$	$Q_{s\mathrm{H}} = \dfrac{B_0}{\mu}\sqrt{1 + \dfrac{2r_s\sigma^2}{\mu}}$
Pearson measures			
Skewness $\beta_1 = \dfrac{\kappa_3^2}{\sigma^6}$	0	$4(\sigma/\mu)^2$	$9\left(\dfrac{\sigma}{\mu}\right)^2$
Kurtosis $\beta_2 = \dfrac{\kappa_4}{\sigma^4} + 3$	3	$6(\sigma/\mu)^2 + 3$	$15\left(\dfrac{\sigma}{\mu}\right)^2 + 3$
$\kappa=\dfrac{\beta_1(\beta_2+3)^2}{4(2\beta_2-3\beta_1-6)(4\beta_2-3\beta_1)}$	0	∞	$\dfrac{(3(2 + 5(\sigma/\mu)^2))^2}{4(4 + 11(\sigma/\mu)^2)}$

Table 6.4 Net maternity function according to three graduations, and as observed, showing frequencies over five-year age intervals, females*

AGE	NORMAL (LOTKA) (6.2.1)	TYPE III (WICKSELL) (6.3.1)	EXPONENTIAL (HADWIGER) (6.4.1)	HISTOGRAM OBSERVED
CANADA, 1965**: $R_0 = 1.496$; $\mu = 27.753$; $\sigma^2 = 37.086$				
0-4	0.000140	0.000002		
5-9	0.002519	0.000072	0.000002	
10-14	0.024452	0.010113	0.004354	0.000480
15-19	0.124711	0.124468	0.116386	0.116108
20-24	0.335275	0.384074	0.411065	0.451853
25-29	0.476198	0.479394	0.484340	0.434967
30-34	0.357631	0.317326	0.300126	0.283489
35-39	0.141919	0.131866	0.125134	0.154216
40-44	0.029695	0.038446	0.040341	0.050293
45-49	0.003266	0.008489	0.010921	0.004523
50-54	0.000188	0.001499	0.002613	0.000071
55-59	0.000006	0.000220	0.000572	
60-64	0.000000	0.000028	0.000117	
65+	0.000000	0.000003	0.000029	
FRANCE, 1959-63: $R_0 = 1.321$; $\mu = 28.104$; $\sigma^2 = 33.509$				
5-9	0.0011	0.0000	0.0000	
10-14	0.0144	0.0047	0.0017	0.0000
15-19	0.0911	0.0848	0.0757	0.0571
20-24	0.2842	0.3236	0.3445	0.4013
25-29	0.4392	0.4472	0.4540	0.4249
30-34	0.3367	0.3017	0.2866	0.2571
35-39	0.1279	0.1199	0.1144	0.1290
40-44	0.0240	0.0318	0.0339	0.0488
45-49	0.0022	0.0062	0.0082	0.0030
50-54	0.0001	0.0009	0.0017	0.0001
55+	0.0000	0.0001	0.0004	

* Programmed by William Cummings and Wilhelm Flieger.

** Distribution for Canada, 1965, shown to six decimal places to permit verification of Table 6.6.

Table 6.4 (continued)

AGE	NORMAL (LOTKA) (6.2.1)	TYPE III (WICKSELL) (6.3.1)	EXPONENTIAL (HADWIGER) (6.4.1)	HISTOGRAM OBSERVED
SWEDEN, 1793-97: R_0 = 1.275; μ = 32.186; σ^2 = 41.786				
5-9	0.0004	0.0000	0.0000	
10-14	0.0046	0.0006	0.0001	0.0001
15-19	0.0329	0.0208	0.0134	0.0238
20-24	0.1319	0.1410	0.1412	0.1616
25-29	0.2990	0.3351	0.3557	0.3110
30-34	0.3834	0.3795	0.3797	0.3455
35-39	0.2783	0.2484	0.2354	0.2679
40-44	0.1143	0.1069	0.1020	0.1369
45-49	0.0265	0.0331	0.0345	0.0281
50-54	0.0035	0.0078	0.0098	0.0000
55+	0.0003	0.0017	0.0031	
VENEZUELA, 1963: R_0 = 2.753; μ = 28.502; σ^2 = 49.112				
5-9	0.0103	0.0005	0.0000	
10-14	0.0630	0.0311	0.0146	0.0037
15-19	0.2354	0.2462	0.2344	0.2803
20-24	0.5399	0.6316	0.6833	0.7124
25-29	0.7598	0.7830	0.8015	0.6893
30-34	0.6565	0.5864	0.5581	0.5107
35-39	0.3482	0.3041	0.2828	0.3866
40-44	0.1133	0.1194	0.1168	0.1346
45-49	0.0226	0.0377	0.0420	0.0315
50-54	0.0028	0.0100	0.0137	0.0044
55+	0.0002	0.0029	0.0057	

Agreement of Third and Fourth Moments

All three of the curves with which we have been concerned require from the data only the zeroth, first, and second moments. Hence for each of them we can calculate the third and fourth moments—or better, cumulants—in terms of the first and second. Exhibit 6.1 shows the cumulant generating function; by successive differentiation and then putting $r = 0$, we find the third and fourth cumulants as well as Pearson's β_1 and β_2 in terms of the first two. For the normal curve, $\kappa_3 = \kappa_4 = 0$. For the Type III,

$$\kappa_3 = \frac{2\sigma^4}{\mu}, \qquad \kappa_4 = \frac{6\sigma^6}{\mu^2};$$

for the Hadwiger exponential,

$$\kappa_3 = \frac{3\sigma^4}{\mu}, \qquad \kappa_4 = \frac{15\sigma^6}{\mu^2}.$$

From these the β_1 and β_2 shown in the headings of Table 6.5 are readily obtained. In the body of the table the graduation which falls closest to the observed is in each case underlined. The Hadwiger curve is preferable on β_1, the Lotka on β_2.

Figure 6.2 shows the β_1 and β_2 for the net maternity function of a number of countries; they all fall in the general Type I area, for which Pearson's κ is negative. The empirical straight line $\beta_2 = 2 + 2\beta_1$ would pass close to all points for ten populations, and it is worth examining how some other countries, for example those of Table 5.5, fall on Fig. 6.2 in relation to this empirical line.

Corresponding to the observed β_1, β_2 is a shadow β_1, β_2 for each of the three graduations, as given in Table 6.5. The reader may locate these on the β_1, β_2-plane.

Comparison of $\psi(r)$

A further way of presenting the comparison is by calculating the function $\psi(r)$ of (5.2.2) for the histogram of $\phi(a) = p(a)m(a)$,

$$\psi(r) = e^{-17.5r}\frac{{}_5L_{15}}{l_0}F_{15} + e^{-22.5r}\frac{{}_5L_{20}}{l_0}F_{20} + \cdots,$$

and comparing the graduations due to Lotka, Wicksell, and Hadwiger with this. The figures are shown in Table 6.6 for Canadian females, 1965, calculated from the corresponding columns of Table 6.4. The Wicksell function is closest to the histogram for $r \leq -0.02$ and seems on the whole best for this population. All of the curves agree for $r > -0.02$, and around the interval from $r = 0$ to the real root $r = r_1$ they are especially close. The reader may note that $\psi(0) = R_0$ for the three graduations. He may account for the differences among the $\psi(r)$ at $r = -0.10$, given the data of Table 5.5 and expressing the characteristic equation (5.2.2) in the form

$$\ln \psi(r) = \ln R_0 - \mu r + \frac{\sigma^2 r^2}{2!} - \frac{\kappa_3 r^3}{3!} + \frac{\kappa_4 r^4}{4!} - \cdots = 0 .$$

If the three approximations to $\psi(r)$ are designated $\psi_L(r)$, $\psi_W(r)$, and $\psi_H(r)$, show from Exhibit 6.1 that to terms in r^3

$$\ln \psi_W(r) = \ln \psi_L(r) - \sigma^4 r^3/3\mu ,$$
$$\ln \psi_H(r) = \ln \psi_L(r) - \sigma^4 r^3/2\mu ,$$

while

$$\ln \psi(r) = \ln \psi_L(r) - \kappa_3 r^3/6 .$$

The relation of κ_3 to σ^4/μ will generally determine which of $\psi_L(r)$, $\psi_W(r)$, and $\psi_H(r)$ is closest to $\psi(r)$ obtained directly in five-year age groups. The exception is when $\kappa_4 r/4$ outweighs κ_3, which is likely to happen only when $\psi(r)$ is evaluated for r equal to -0.1 or less—a part of the curve which is not relevant for human populations. Could the function $\psi(r)$ as shown in Table 5.1 or 6.6 be used conversely to ascertain the cumulants? With what accuracy?

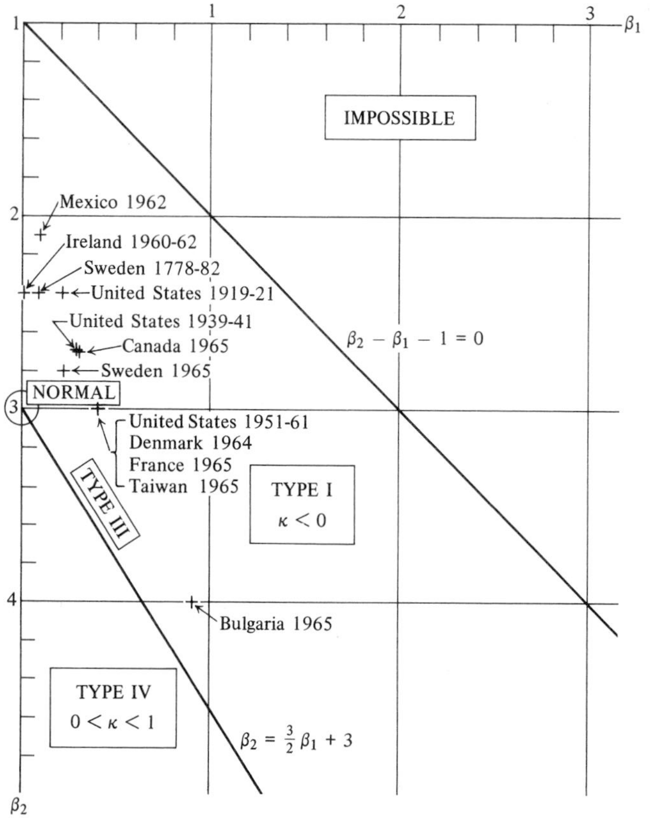

Fig. 6.2 Location of net maternity function on β_1, β_2 plane.

Table 6.5 Comparison of β_1 and β_2 as observed with β_1 and β_2 as expected for three graduations of the net maternity (paternity) function

	AS OBSERVED	AS CALCULATED FOR GRADUATIONS ON		
		NORMAL (LOTKA)	TYPE III (WICKSELL)	EXPONENTIAL (HADWIGER)
	$\beta_1 = \frac{\mu_3^2}{\sigma^6}$	$\beta_1 = 0$	$\beta_1 = 4\left(\frac{\sigma}{\mu}\right)^2$	$\beta_1 = 9\left(\frac{\sigma}{\mu}\right)^2$
FEMALES				
BULGARIA 1965	0.891	0	0.181	0.407
CANADA* 1965	0.277	0	0.193	0.433
DENMARK 1964	0.364	0	0.174	0.391
FRANCE 1959-63	0.388	0	0.169	0.380
MAURITIUS 1965	0.137	0	0.215	0.484
MEXICO 1959-61	0.051	0	0.219	0.493
SWEDEN 1788-92	0.008	0	0.164	0.370
TAIWAN 1965	0.408	0	0.171	0.384
TOGO 1961	0.222	0	0.273	0.615
U. S. 1962	0.417	0	0.196	0.441
1963	0.394	0	0.195	0.438
1964*	0.373	0	0.195	0.438
MALES				
NORWAY 1963	0.486	0	0.184	0.414
U. S.* 1964	0.777	0	0.205	0.462

* Verifiable from mean and variance as shown in Table 5.5.

Table 6.5 (continued)

	AS OBSERVED	AS CALCULATED FOR GRADUATIONS ON		
		NORMAL (LOTKA)	TYPE III (WICKSELL)	EXPONENTIAL (HADWIGER)
	$\beta_2 = \frac{\mu_4}{\sigma^4}$	$\beta_2 = 3$	$\beta_2=3+6\left(\frac{\sigma}{\mu}\right)^2$	$\beta_2=3+15\left(\frac{\sigma}{\mu}\right)^2$
FEMALES				
BULGARIA 1965	3.999	3.000	3.271	3.679
CANADA* 1965	2.710	3.000	3.289	3.722
DENMARK 1964	2.988	3.000	3.260	3.651
FRANCE 1959-63	2.849	3.000	3.253	3.633
MAURITIUS 1965	2.396	3.000	3.323	3.806
MEXICO 1959-61	2.116	3.000	3.329	3.822
SWEDEN 1788-92	2.402	3.000	3.247	3.616
TAIWAN 1965	3.003	3.000	3.256	3.639
TOGO 1961	2.433	3.000	3.410	4.025
U. S. 1962	2.943	3.000	3.294	3.735
1963	2.918	3.000	3.292	3.731
1964*	2.886	3.000	3.292	3.730
MALES				
NORWAY 1963	3.138	3.000	3.275	3.690
U. S.* 1964	3.605	3.000	3.308	3.770

Table 6.6 Comparison of $\psi(r) = \int_\alpha^\beta e^{-ra} p(a)m(a)\, da$ on four approximations from data of Table 6.4, Canadian females, 1965*

r	NORMAL (LOTKA)	TYPE III (WICKSELL)	EXPONENTIAL (HADWIGER)	HISTOGRAM OBSERVED
-0.100	29.193	29.734	30.076	29.692
-0.080	15.617	15.762	15.848	15.759
-0.060	8.487	8.519	8.537	8.520
-0.040	4.684	4.690	4.692	4.690
-0.020	2.627	2.627	2.627	2.627
0.000	1.496	1.496	1.496	1.496
0.002	1.41533	1.41533	1.41533	1.41533
0.004	1.33923	1.33923	1.33922	1.33923
0.006	1.26741	1.26741	1.26741	1.26741
0.008	1.19964	1.19963	1.19962	1.19963
0.010	1.13566	1.13565	1.13564	1.13564
0.012	1.07527	1.07524	1.07523	1.07524
0.014	1.01825	1.01821	1.01818	1.01820
0.016	0.96441	0.96434	0.96431	0.96433
0.018	0.91355	0.91346	0.91342	0.91344
0.020	0.86551	0.86540	0.86535	0.86537
0.040	0.50685	0.50813	0.50789	0.50799
0.060	0.30364	0.30263	0.30217	0.30231
0.080	0.18413	0.18269	0.18208	0.18221
0.100	0.11341	0.11173	0.11103	0.11112
0.200	0.01271	0.01139	0.01095	0.01086
R_0	1.496	1.496	1.496	1.496
μ	27.753	27.753	27.753	27.753
σ^2	37.086	37.086	37.087	37.086
κ_3	0.032	99.073	148.594	118.951
κ_4	-0.869	396.637	987.898	-403.623
β_1	0.000	0.192	0.433	0.277
β_2	3.000	3.288	3.718	2.707

* Function $\psi(r)$ and moments calculated from five-year integrals of net maternity function as shown in Table 6.4. They may be checked against $\psi(r)$ of Exhibit 6.1 with uncorrected $\sigma^2 = 39.169$, which gives for the three graduations at -0.100

$\psi_L(-0.100) = 29.193$ $\qquad \psi_W(-0.100) = 29.802$ $\qquad \psi_H(-0.100) = 30.195$

Note differences from Table 6.5 in β_1 and β_2.

Comparison of Latent Roots

To see the numerical differences among the approximations to the real root the reader may rewrite the characteristic equations of Exhibit 6.1 as $\ln \psi(r) = 0$, or

$$\begin{aligned} r_{\mathrm{L}} &= \frac{\ln R_0}{\mu} + \frac{r^2\sigma^2}{2\mu} && \text{(Lotka)},\\ r_{\mathrm{W}} &= \frac{\ln R_0}{\mu} + \frac{r^2\sigma^2}{2\mu} - \frac{r^3\sigma^4}{3\mu^2} + \cdots && \text{(Wicksell)},\\ r_{\mathrm{H}} &= \frac{\ln R_0}{\mu} + \frac{r^2\sigma^2}{2\mu} - \frac{r^3\sigma^4}{2\mu^2} + \cdots && \text{(Hadwiger)}, \end{aligned} \tag{6.5.1}$$

respectively, which would serve for iterative solution. If we think of the r on the right-hand side of (6.5.1) as the exact solution of (5.2.2), then it follows that the real roots fall in the order

$$r_{\mathrm{H}} < r_{\mathrm{W}} < r_{\mathrm{L}}$$

for $r > 0$, and whether or not $r > 0$,

$$2(r_{\mathrm{W}} - r_{\mathrm{H}}) = r_{\mathrm{L}} - r_{\mathrm{W}} = r^3\sigma^4/3\mu^2\,, \tag{6.5.2}$$

to terms in r^3. Show that the T's of Exhibit 6.1 are consistent with the r's of (6.5.1), in the sense that they satisfy (5.6.6); that is, to terms in r^2,

$$r_{\mathrm{L}}T_{\mathrm{L}} = r_{\mathrm{W}}T_{\mathrm{W}} = r_{\mathrm{H}}T_{\mathrm{H}} = \ln R_0\,,$$

where T_{L}, T_{W} and T_{H} are the length of generation on the three graduations.

An arithmetical verification of these approximations was sought for United States females, 1963. By direct calculation from the formulas of Exhibit 6.1, with $\ln R_0 = 0.447305$, $\mu = 26.4732$, $\sigma^2 = 34.13$, we find

$$1000r_{\mathrm{L}} = 17.0847\,, \qquad 1000r_{\mathrm{W}} = 17.0819\,, \qquad 1000r_{\mathrm{H}} = 17.0806\,,$$

and hence,

$$\begin{aligned} 2(1000r_{\mathrm{W}} - 1000r_{\mathrm{H}}) &= 0.0027\,,\\ 1000r_{\mathrm{L}} - 1000r_{\mathrm{W}} &= 0.0028\,,\\ 1000(r^3\sigma^4/3\mu^2) &= 1000(0.01708)^3(0.555) = 0.0028\,. \end{aligned}$$

Superfluous decimals are here given merely to test arithmetically the relation (6.5.2), which is thus confirmed. What are T_{L}, T_{W}, and T_{H} for United States females, 1963?

Comparing each of (6.5.1) with the corresponding rewriting of the logarithm of the characteristic equation (5.2.2) up to terms in r^3,

$$r = \frac{\ln R_0}{\mu} + \frac{r^2\sigma^2}{2\mu} - \frac{\kappa_3 r^3}{6\mu}\,, \tag{6.5.3}$$

then if r_0 is the solution of the histogram form (5.2.2) approximated by (6.5.3), we have, by entering r_L for the first two terms on the right of (6.5.3) and then transposing,

$$r_L \doteqdot r_0 + \kappa_3 r_0^3/6\mu \,, \tag{6.5.4}$$

disregarding fourth and higher cumulants. Thus r_L is high when skewness is positive, and depending on the amount of skewness, r_W and r_H will be high or low. We see without explicit solution for r that if

$\kappa_3\mu/\sigma^4$ is closest to 0, the Lotka form is best,

$\kappa_3\mu/\sigma^4$ is closest to 2, the Wicksell form is best,

$\kappa_3\mu/\sigma^4$ is closest to 3, the Hadwiger form is best.

The quantity $\kappa_3\mu/\sigma^4$ falls in the range 1 to 5 for 17 countries (Table 6.7). On this criterion the Wicksell formula has a slight advantage, being closest for seven countries, but our sample is small. Note the relation of what we are doing here to the comparison for β_1 in Table 6.5. Show that if κ_4 is of the same order of magnitude as κ_3, which is often the case (Table 5.5), the error $r_L - r_0$ calculated by (6.5.4) could only be modified by about one percent. Work out the actual amount of error of r_L, r_W, and r_H, for Costa Rica, 1963, and Mauritius, 1964, using data of Tables 5.5 and 6.7.

The graduations provide real roots which depart from the solution of the full integral equation by quantities less than 0.05 per thousand population. As Lotka pointed out (1939c, p. 74), the case is different for the complex roots. For the United States the principal complex roots r_2, r_3 are obtained from the full equation (5.3.2) as

$$\begin{aligned} 1962&: \quad -0.0259 \pm 0.2458i \,, \\ 1963&: \quad -0.0273 \pm 0.2439i \,, \\ 1964&: \quad -0.0287 \pm 0.2422i \,. \end{aligned}$$

The r_2, r_3 for the three graduations based on the same populations, births, and deaths are shown in Table 6.8. Variation among graduations is greater than among years, an unsatisfactory situation.

The reader may verify the real constants Q_L, Q_W, and Q_H of Exhibit 6.1 corresponding to the roots r_L, r_W, and r_H, where in each case

$$Q = -B_0/\psi'(r) \,.$$

The quantity in the denominator of Q is the mean age of childbearing in the stable population. For the United States females, 1964, this is 25.974 years on the full data in 5-year age groups; the reader may work out Q_L, Q_W, and Q_H from the information in Table 5.5. He may also use (6.5.1) to find relations among the principal complex roots analogous to (6.5.4). Note that the equality (6.5.2) applies separately to the real and imaginary parts of the complex roots given in Table 6.8.

Table 6.7 Third cumulant of net maternity function and criterion of which graduation gives the best estimate of the real root

	THIRD CUMULANT κ_3	CRITERION $\frac{\beta_1\mu^2}{\sigma^2} = \left(\frac{\kappa_3\mu}{\sigma^4}\right)^2$	REAL ROOT GIVEN MOST CLOSELY BY
FEMALES			
COSTA RICA 1963	105.0	2	r_W
GERMANY (EAST) 1964	126.2	10	r_H
ICELAND 1962	131.7	4	r_W
IRELAND 1960-62	32.9	1	r_L
MARTINIQUE 1965	50.4	1	r_L
MAURITIUS 1964	112.5	3	r_W
OHIO 1959-61	128.9	9	r_H
POLAND 1962	156.4	11	r_H
REUNION 1961	72.8	1	r_L
ROUMANIA 1965	160.7	12	r_H
SINGAPORE 1962	98.5	3	r_W
SOUTH AFRICA 1960 (COLORED)	179.6	4	r_W
MALES (NET PATERNITY FUNCTION)			
CHILE 1964	321.4	5	r_W
HUNGARY 1964	252.4	25	r_H
NORWAY 1963	213.8	11	r_H
TRINIDAD & TOBAGO 1956-58	263.9	5	r_W
UNITED STATES 1964	266.3	15	r_H

The several tests applied above all hinge substantially on the third moment, which may be expressed in the form of our criterion $(\kappa_3\mu/\sigma^4)^2 = \beta_1\mu^2/\sigma^2$. Tables 6.3, 6.5, and 6.7 seem to favor Hadwiger in as many cases as Wicksell and Lotka together. But the selection was arbitrary, and some countries were used for several dates.

Table 6.8 Principal complex roots r_2, r_3 on three graduations, United States females, 1962, 1963, and 1964

	NORMAL (LOTKA)	TYPE III (WICKSELL)	EXPONENTIAL (HADWIGER)
1962	-0.0182±0.2321i	-0.0207±0.2397i	-0.0219±0.2435i
1963	-0.0194±0.2312i	-0.0220±0.2386i	-0.0233±0.2423i
1964	-0.0205±0.2304i	-0.0232±0.2376i	-0.0245±0.2413i

In a complete survey of the 56 different countries for which we can obtain recent data on female mortality and fertility, the third moment criterion turned out to favor the Lotka graduation in 9, the Wicksell in 26, and the Hadwiger in 21. Countries of high fertility tend to be low on the criterion, and to be well fitted by the normal curve; those of low fertility tend to be high on the criterion. In the course of time the criterion has risen, for example over the English and Swedish historical series. The criterion is higher for males than for females—out of seven male populations five are fitted by the Hadwiger curve, two by the Wicksell.

Conclusions

The tests of the three graduations offer little room for satisfaction. While it looks as though on some criteria one graduation is especially bad, and on others, another, usually the third cumulant is decisive for all four of our tests.

Demographers have not turned up closer fitting curves than these that are equally easy to handle. Nor are the consequences of poor fit always serious; the real root r is given perfectly well on all three graduations, and most of the general inferences drawn from the graduations are valid.

Graduation is often required. Of immediate importance for the present exposition, graduations enable us to examine relationships, such as that between the variance σ^2 and the real part x of the main complex root in (6.2.6), which would be hard to study otherwise. They are also helpful when the trajectory $B(t)$ is to be calculated by hand.

A more contemporary interest is the classification of maternity patterns, with the filling in of data gaps in view. For an underdeveloped country where information is available on the net reproduction rate R_0, and where one can guess μ and σ^2, the average and variance of ages at childbearing, and where a model life table may be assumed, one seeks the age-specific fertility rates F_x. A way of proceeding is to find the values of the net maternity function by integrating over five-year intervals one of the curves of this chapter, for instance, the Pearson Type III proposed by Wicksell. The integrals are identified with

${}_5L_x F_x$. Then the value of F_x is estimated by

$$F_x = \frac{\int_0^5 l(x + t)m(x + t)\, dt}{{}_5L_x},$$

where the numerator comes from the five-year integrals of the curve assumed on the basis of R_0, μ, σ^2. The better the fit, the more satisfactory the imputation.

We turn now to applications of theory which fill data gaps of a different kind. These proceed mainly from the stable population analysis and make inferences on the intrinsic rate of natural increase, for example, working only from an observed census age distribution and a hypothetical life table.

CHAPTER 7

INTERRELATIONSHIPS OF DEMOGRAPHIC VARIABLES IN STABLE POPULATIONS

In Chapter 1 the relationships among the several columns of the life table were discussed, and the results may be thought of as properties of the stationary population—defined by equality of total births and deaths and constancy of age-specific death rates. Here we generalize to relations which exist in the less artificial stable model, still concerned with one sex only, and taking age-specific rates of birth and death as fixed, but no longer requiring total births to equal total deaths. The materials for this were introduced in Chapters 3 and 5. The exploration of the stable assumption is the subject of Sections 7.2 and 7.3. It is introduced in Section 7.1, which contains the few remarks that may be made on closed populations whose births and deaths vary without restriction.

7.1. RELATIONS IN ANY CLOSED POPULATION

Consider a closed population of K individuals of one sex, having B births and D deaths in a given short period, for which the crude birth rate $b = B/K$, the death rate $d = D/K$, and the rate of natural increase $r = (B - D)/K$ are calculated. The three rates are not independent, for $r = b - d$. This is an example of a relation which applies to real data, as well as to hypothetical cases such as stable populations, so long as migration may be supposed zero; such relations occasion no surprise and arise through our having introduced a variable which is redundant.

If births and deaths for all ages together are functions of time, $B(t)$ and $D(t)$, and population numbers are $K(t)$, then per unit time, where the unit is short, the increase of population is

$$R(t) = B(t) - D(t) = \frac{dK(t)}{dt}.$$

The corresponding rates, expressed as ratios to population, are

$$b(t) = \frac{B(t)}{K(t)}, \qquad d(t) = \frac{D(t)}{K(t)}, \qquad r(t) = b(t) - d(t) = \frac{B(t) - D(t)}{K(t)},$$

or, alternatively,

$$r(t) = \frac{1}{K(t)}\left(\frac{dK(t)}{dt}\right). \tag{7.1.1}$$

Suppose we know the birth and death rates over a period of time, or merely the difference $r(t)$ between them, along with the population at the outset. Then the population grows from an initial value $K(0)$ to

$$K(0)(1 + r(0)h) \doteq K(0)e^{r(0)h}$$

by the end of the interval h, assumed short enough that terms in second and higher powers of h may be neglected. By the end of a sequence of such intervals, it would be, in the limit as h tends to zero,

$$K(t) = K(0) \exp\left[\int_0^t r(\tau)\,d\tau\right] = K(0) \exp\left[\int_0^t (b(\tau) - d(\tau))\,d\tau\right].$$

This is the solution of the differential equation (7.1.1). As an example of its application, consider a chart showing the observed crude birth rate $b(t)$ and the crude death rate $d(t)$ of a closed population, between $t = t_0$ and $t = t_1$. The area between the two curves from t_0 to t_1 [i.e., the area of the surface bounded by $b(t)$, $d(t)$, and the vertical lines at t_0 and t_1] is A. Prove that the ratio of the population at time t_1 to that at time t_0 is e^A.

The theory of equation (7.1.1) is simpler if $r(t) = r$, a constant; the solution becomes

$$K(t) = K(0)e^{rt}.$$

The same applies to births: at a constant rate of increase equal to r, the number of births at time t is

$$B(t) = B(0)e^{rt}.$$

This curve may be integrated to find the total number of persons who lived during an interval. If at t_0 the number of births per year is B_0, and at t_1 the births are B_1, and the births may be supposed to increase in geometric proportion, show that the total number of births during the interval is

$$\frac{(B_1 - B_0)(t_1 - t_0)}{\ln B_1 - \ln B_0}.$$

Apply this to estimate the population that ever lived in the world, assuming that the births 1,000,000 years ago were 1 per year, and that now they are 100,000,000 per year. Why is the result, 5429×10^9, a gross overestimate? Show that it may be improved to 68.3×10^9 by supposing also that births 7000 years ago were 200,000, that 2000 years ago they were 10,000,000, and 300 years ago 20,000,000, still assuming geometric increase in all intervals.

The breakdown by age produces a variety of additional results. We defined $m(a)$ as the number of female children born to women between ages a and $a + da$ divided by the number of women between ages a and $a + da$ in the population, when da is small. Similarly for deaths, $\mu(a)$ (Chapter 1) is the death rate among women aged a to $a + da$.

The chance of surviving over the interval a to $a + da$ is $1 - \mu(a)\,da$, which equals $e^{-\mu(a)\,da}$ if $(da)^2$ may be neglected. The chance of surviving through a sequence of small intervals, $(a_0, a_1), (a_1, a_2), \ldots, (a_{n-1}, a_n)$, is approximately

$$\begin{aligned} &\exp[-\mu(a_0)(a_1 - a_0)]\exp[-\mu(a_1)(a_2 - a_1)] \cdots \exp[-\mu(a_{n-1})(a_n - a_{n-1})] \\ &\quad = \exp[-\mu(a_0)(a_1 - a_0) - \mu(a_1)(a_2 - a_1) - \cdots - \mu(a_{n-1})(a_n - a_{n-1})]\,. \end{aligned} \tag{7.1.2}$$

Since the intervals are small, it is permissible to replace the sum in the exponent of (7.1.2) by the integral, so that the probability of surviving from age a_0 to a_n is

$$\exp\left[-\int_{a_0}^{a_n} \mu(a)\,da\right] = \frac{\exp[-\int_0^{a_n} \mu(a)\,da]}{\exp[-\int_0^{a_0} \mu(a)\,da]}\,.$$

We may then define $l(x)$ as

$$l(x) = l_0 \exp\left[-\int_0^x \mu(a)\,da\right]. \tag{7.1.3}$$

This provides an alternative starting point for developing the life table formulas of Chapter 1.

As in Chapter 5, the number of persons between ages a and $a + da$ in the observed population is called $k(a)\,da$, corresponding to $l(a)\,da$, the number between a and $a + da$ in the stationary population. The proportion of the population between ages a and $a + da$ is $c(a)\,da$, where

$$c(a)\,da = \frac{k(a)\,da}{\int_0^\omega k(a)\,da}\,.$$

On the definition of the force of mortality $\mu(a)$, the number of deaths between a and $a + da$ in the observed population is $k(a)\mu(a)\,da$, and the total number of deaths D is

$$D = \int_0^\omega k(a)\mu(a)\,da\,, \tag{7.1.4}$$

so that the crude death rate is

$$d = \frac{D}{K} = \frac{\int_0^\omega k(a)\mu(a)\,da}{\int_0^\omega k(a)\,da} = \frac{\int_0^\omega c(a)\mu(a)\,da}{\int_0^\omega c(a)\,da}\,. \tag{7.1.5}$$

Since the integral of $c(a)$ over the whole of life is unity, the crude death rate may be expressed as

$$d = \int_0^\omega c(a)\mu(a)\,da = -\int_0^\omega c(a)\,d\big(\ln l(a)\big)\,. \tag{7.1.6}$$

[Prove (7.1.6) from (7.1.3).] The age-specific death rate in the age interval x to $x + n$ is

$$_nM_x = \frac{\int_x^{x+n} k(a)\mu(a)\,da}{\int_x^{x+n} k(a)\,da} = \frac{\int_x^{x+n} c(a)\mu(a)\,da}{\int_x^{x+n} c(a)\,da} . \tag{7.1.7}$$

Similar observations may be made in respect of $m(a)$, the probability of a woman bearing a child at age a, or more strictly the ratio of births to women for ages a to $a + da$. The crude birth rate is equal to

$$b = \frac{\int_\alpha^\beta k(a)m(a)\,da}{\int_0^\omega k(a)\,da} = \int_\alpha^\beta c(a)m(a)\,da , \tag{7.1.8}$$

where α and β are the beginning and the end of the childbearing period. Write down an expression for $_nF_x$, the age-specific birth rate, analogous to (7.1.7).

Further relations connect the age distribution (possibly changing in time) with the preceding births. From the fact that persons aged a at time t were born at time $t - a$, we may treat the density of persons aged a at time t, $k(a, t)$, as the expected value

$$k(a, t) = B(t - a)p(a) , \tag{7.1.9}$$

where $p(a) = l(a)/l_0$. The total population $K(t) = \int_0^\omega B(t - a)p(a)\,da$. Hence the proportion of the population which is of age a at time t is of density

$$c(a, t) = \frac{k(a, t)}{K(t)} = \frac{B(t - a)p(a)}{\int_0^\omega B(t - a)p(a)\,da} . \tag{7.1.10}$$

By putting $a = 0$ in (7.1.10) we obtain $c(0, t) = B(t)/K(t) = b(t)$; this means that if we know the age distribution $c(a)$, then we know $c(0) = b$, the birth rate. As an alternative expression to this or to (7.1.8), the number of births to women aged a being $m(a)$, the overall birth rate is

$$b(t) = \frac{B(t)}{K(t)} = \int_\alpha^\beta c(a, t)m(a)\,da = \frac{\int_\alpha^\beta B(t - a)p(a)m(a)\,da}{\int_0^\omega B(t - a)p(a)\,da} . \tag{7.1.11}$$

If the births are increasing geometrically at rate r, so that $B(t) = B(0)e^{rt}$, then from (7.1.10),

$$c(a, t) = \frac{e^{-ra}p(a)}{\int_0^\omega e^{-ra}p(a)\,da} , \tag{7.1.12}$$

an expression for $c(a, t)$ which does not contain t. With geometric increase, time t is likewise absent from the expression for $b(t) = c(0, t)$, obtained by putting $a = 0$ in the numerator of (7.1.12):

$$b(t) = c(0, t) = \frac{1}{\int_0^\omega e^{-ra}p(a)\,da} .$$

Table 7.1 Percentage distribution of observed and hypothetical stable populations based on life table for United States females, 1964*

AGE	r = 0.01	r = 0.0157 AS OBSERVED	r = 0.02	r = 0.03	r = 0.04
0-4	9.3	11.0	12.4	15.8	19.3
5-9	8.8	10.2	11.2	13.6	15.8
10-14	8.4	9.4	10.1	11.6	12.9
15-19	8.0	8.7	9.1	10.0	10.5
20-24	7.5	8.0	8.2	8.6	8.6
25-29	7.2	7.4	7.4	7.4	7.0
30-34	6.8	6.8	6.7	6.3	5.7
35-39	6.4	6.2	6.0	5.4	4.6
40-44	6.0	5.7	5.4	4.6	3.8
45-49	5.6	5.1	4.8	3.9	3.0
50-54	5.2	4.6	4.2	3.2	2.4
55+	20.8	17.0	14.4	9.6	6.3
TOTAL	100.0	100.0	100.0	100.0	100.0

* Programmed by Roger Avery and Ronald Lee.

The manner in which different stable age distributions $c(a)$ are determined by different intrinsic rates r with a given life table $p(a)$ is illustrated by Table 7.1.

The condition of exponentially increasing births was considered by Euler (1760, p. 156), who arrived at (7.1.12). [Euler used (a) for our $p(a)$, and his $1/n$ is our e^{-r}.] This is one way of proceeding to stable population theory, the subject of the next section.

7.2. RELATIONS UNDER STABILITY

A closed population is described by its rates of birth, death, and natural increase, b, d, and r, taken without regard to age, along with age-specific rates of birth and death, $m(a)$ and $\mu(a)$, and $c(a)\,da$, the proportion of the population at ages a to $a + da$. How many of these six quantities or sets have to be fixed and given for the remaining quantities to be calculable? One such quantity will not suffice for us to infer from it the others, but two will in certain combinations. In fact, of the 15 ways of selecting 2 objects out of 6, it turns out that 4, the combinations

1) $p(a), m(a)$; 2) $p(a), r$;

3) $p(a), b$; 4) $p(a), d$,

each determine the others [except $m(a)$] ultimately, after the effects of the initial age distribution have worn off, while 3,

$$5)\quad c(a), p(a); \qquad 6)\quad c(a), r\,;$$
$$7)\quad c(a), d\,,$$

each determine the population immediately, if present stability may be supposed. The discussion is in continuous terms, though translation into five-year age groups will be required at the point where numerical application is undertaken. The argument applies to either males or females. I am indebted to Leon Tabah for suggesting the arrangement of this section (see Tabah, 1965).

Fixed Rates in the Future

1) *Given $p(a)$ and $m(a)$.* We start with a given complete set of survival rates, $p(a)$, and birth rates for the several ages of mother, $m(a)$, and apply the homogeneous equation

$$B(t) = \int_{\alpha}^{\beta} B(t - a)p(a)m(a)\, da\,, \tag{7.2.1}$$

knowing from Chapter 5 that it may be solved in the form

$$B(t) = Q_1 e^{r_1 t} + Q_2 e^{r_2 t} + \cdots \tag{7.2.2}$$

If the age-specific rates of birth and death are fixed, then ultimately the rate of increase will be $r = r_1$, the dominant real root of the characteristic equation

$$\int_{\alpha}^{\beta} e^{-ra} p(a)m(a)\, da = 1\,, \tag{7.2.3}$$

and $B(t)$ will equal $Q_1 e^{r_1 t}$ where, as we saw in Chapter 5, Q_1 depends on initial conditions not specified by (7.2.1). Stability will be attained at rate r_1 irrespective of the initial age distribution, but Q_1, which determines the level of the curve of ultimate population, can be calculated only if the initial ages are known. Once $B(t)$ is at hand, then the assumption of fixed $p(a)$ permits the calculation of the expected number at any age at any subsequent time by (7.1.9).

Suppose that by time t_0 the terms of (7.2.2) beyond the first are negligible, so that

$$B(t - t_0) = B(t_0)e^{r(t-t_0)}\,, \quad t > t_0\,.$$

Let us take the distant future time t_0 as the origin in what follows, and write t for $t - t_0$. The number of women aged a to $a + da$ being $k(a, t)\, da$, where

$$k(a, t) = B(t - a)p(a) = B(0)e^{r(t-a)}p(a)\,, \qquad (7.2.4.)$$

integration gives for the total population at time t

$$K(t) = \int_0^{w} k(a, t)\, da = B(0)e^{rt}\int_0^{\omega} e^{-ra}p(a)\, da\,. \tag{7.2.5}$$

Since $B(0)e^{rt} = B(t)$, we may from (7.2.5) write the birth rate as

$$\frac{B(t)}{K(t)} = b = \frac{1}{\int_0^\omega e^{-ra}p(a)\,da}. \tag{7.2.6}$$

[Derive this directly from (7.1.11), remembering that r satisfies (7.2.3).] The fact that the expression on the right of (7.2.6) does not involve t shows again that the crude birth rate is ultimately constant for large t under fixed overall rate of increase r and fixed age-specific death rates.

Having r from (7.2.3) and b from (7.2.6), we find $d = b - r$. Finally, (7.2.4) gives, on division by $K(t)$,

$$c(a, t) = \frac{k(a, t)}{K(t)} = \frac{B(0)e^{r(t-a)}p(a)}{\int_0^\omega B(0)e^{r(t-a)}p(a)\,da}, \tag{7.2.7}$$

and applying (7.2.6) we obtain

$$c(a, t) = \frac{e^{-ra}p(a)}{\int_0^\omega e^{-ra}p(a)\,da} = be^{-ra}p(a), \tag{7.2.8}$$

which is also independent of time. This is the continuous expression for the stable age distribution (Lotka, 1907 and Section 5.2 above), whose discrete form we met as $\{\mathbf{K}_j\}$, $j = 1$, of (3.2.6).

Thus, given $p(a)$ and $m(a)$, one can calculate r, b, d, and $c(a)$, these applying not immediately but after the fixed life table and schedule of fertility rates have been in operation over a sufficient time. The population is said to be *asymptotically stable*.

The preceding relationships may be made the basis of an iterative method of simultaneously ascertaining r, b, d, and $c(a)$. The steps are

a) With arbitrary r and b and the given life table $p(a)$ construct $c(a) = be^{-ra}p(a)$ for the several ages;
b) From $c(a)$ and given $m(a)$, find improved b^* from (7.1.8);
c) With $c(a)$ and given $\mu(a)$, find improved d^* from (7.1.5);
d) Improve r to $r^* = b^* - d^*$, and repeat.

The sequence of quantities calculated for Nicaraguan females, 1962 (programmed by S. K. Sinha in five-year age groups), is given below:

$1000b$	$1000d$	$1000r$
50.000	—	20.000
40.219	8.737	31.482
39.834	7.523	32.312
39.733	7.467	32.266
39.738	7.470	32.268

Table 7.2 Female intrinsic rates of birth b, death d, and natural increase r

	BIRTH 1000b	DEATH 1000d	NATURAL INCREASE 1000r
AUSTRALIA 1965	20.94	8.64	12.29
ENGLAND AND WALES 1861	31.73	21.53	10.20
1891	29.71	19.70	10.01
1921	18.46	15.60	2.86
1941	10.32	20.51	-10.19
1950-52	14.10	13.88	0.22
1960-62	19.28	9.51	9.77
CHINA (TAIWAN) 1965	34.13	6.15	27.98
DENMARK 1964	17.73	10.12	7.61
FEDERAL REPUBLIC OF GERMANY 1965	16.74	11.21	5.54
HONDURAS 1965	42.49	8.43	34.06
HUNGARY 1965	10.51	17.59	-7.08
JAPAN 1963	12.38	15.15	-2.77
MAURITIUS 1965	39.22	8.07	31.15
NEW ZEALAND 1965	25.77	6.69	19.08
PORTUGAL 1965	20.64	10.86	9.77
PUERTO RICO 1965	28.99	6.60	22.40
ROUMANIA 1965	11.96	16.24	-4.28
SWITZERLAND 1964	17.81	10.10	7.71
VENEZUELA 1963	43.54	6.84	36.70

Four cycles provide five digits in r. This converges nearly as quickly as functional iteration (5.3.5), the best preceding method, and provides more information. Table 7.2 gives results for 15 countries; others are given for both males and females in Table 13.1.

2) *Given* $p(a)$ *and* r. To proceed to the next of the seven pairs of variables which permit inferences to be made, suppose that $p(a)$ and r are fixed and known. Then we can infer the birth rate from (7.2.6), and from this $d = b - r$. From (7.2.8) comes the proportion at age a, $c(a) = be^{-ra}p(a)$. This gives all the variables under consideration with one exception, $m(a)$.

The data $p(a)$ and r do not allow inference of the age-specific birth rates; these may vary considerably and still be consistent with the given r and $p(a)$. The reader may show the kind of variation possible in the age-specific birth rates which does not disturb the r and $p(a)$ by referring to the Lotka, Hadwiger, or Wicksell solution of (7.2.3) in terms of the zeroth, first, and second moments (Chapter 6). We previously (Section 4.4) noted that the age-specific birth rates are not identifiable in a set of equations based on successive censuses as observations. (They are identifiable if the age distributions depart sufficiently from the stable, but this does not help to make inferences from $p(a)$ and r.)

3) *Given $p(a)$ and b.* For $p(a)$ and b a similar argument applies to that for $p(a)$ and r given above. The only difference is that Eq. (7.2.6) must now be used in the other direction—to infer r. The reader may show from (7.2.6) that r is determinate, and that there must always be a unique real value of r, applying the method by which the same property was demonstrated for (5.2.2). He may also adapt the iterative processes that were used for (5.2.2) to the numerical solution of (7.2.6) for r.

With the definition

$$\bar{L}_i = \int_0^\omega a^i p(a)\, da\,, \quad i = 0, 1, \ldots, \tag{7.2.9}$$

dividing (7.2.6) by $\bar{L}_0$ and expanding under the integral and taking logs, Lotka (1939b) finds

$$\ln b = -\ln \bar{L}_0 + \frac{r\bar{L}_1}{\bar{L}_0} - \frac{r^2}{2!}\left[\frac{\bar{L}_2}{\bar{L}_0} - \left(\frac{\bar{L}_1}{\bar{L}_0}\right)^2\right] + \cdots \tag{7.2.10}$$

which may be solved either for b in terms of r or for r in terms of b.

The coefficients of r in (7.2.10) are cumulants of the life table, shown for four countries in Table 7.3, and will be applied in Chapter 9. The reader may use (7.2.10) to draw a curve of the way in which b varies with r, given the moments for the 1965 Austrian female life table of Table 7.3. On the same chart he may plot as a scatter diagram the observations on b and r for 20 countries reported in Table 7.2. In the degree in which the mortality of the several countries is similar the values of $\ln b$ will fall on the parabola in (7.2.10).

The cumulants of the life table may be written $\bar{\kappa}_i$, $i = 1, 2, \ldots$, and (7.2.10) is then

$$\ln b = -\ln \bar{L}_0 + \bar{\kappa}_1 r - \bar{\kappa}_2 r^2/2! + \cdots \tag{7.2.11}$$

Those of the net maternity function are written without bar as

$$\kappa_1 = \frac{R_1}{R_0}; \quad \kappa_2 = \frac{R_2}{R_0} - \left(\frac{R_1}{R_0}\right)^2; \quad \cdots$$

Table 7.3 Cumulants of life tables for four countries, 1965

	AUSTRIA	CANADA	HONDURAS	PORTUGAL
$\bar{L}_0 = \mathring{e}_0$				
MALES	66.58	68.75	59.13	63.12
FEMALES	72.99	75.00	61.53	68.95
$\bar{\kappa}_1 = \frac{\bar{L}_1}{\bar{L}_0}$				
MALES	36.12	37.10	35.12	36.40
FEMALES	38.77	39.63	35.86	38.69
$\bar{\kappa}_2 = \frac{\bar{L}_2}{\bar{L}_0} - \left(\frac{\bar{L}_1}{\bar{L}_0}\right)^2$				
MALES	484.9	513.3	484.6	495.4
FEMALES	541.0	566.4	497.1	540.7
$\bar{\kappa}_3$				
MALES	2,315	2,567	2,748	2,370
FEMALES	1,969	2,116	2,675	1,928
$\bar{\kappa}_4$				
MALES	-227,010	-254,744	-229,641	-240,960
FEMALES	-305,593	-337,408	-242,490	-308,282

By expanding $\psi(r)$ of (5.2.2) under the integral and taking its logarithm, we obtain an equation resembling (7.2.11):

$$0 = -\ln R_0 + \kappa_1 r - \kappa_2 r^2/2! + \cdots \tag{7.2.12}$$

Comment on the speed of convergence of (7.2.11) and (7.2.12) and their suitability for solving for r and b, using the data of Tables 5.5 and 7.3.

4) *Given $p(a)$ and d.* Here both items of data refer to mortality, but the relation between d and $p(a)$ can nonetheless tell us how fast the population is increasing. Entering $b = d + r$ in (7.2.6) gives the equation in r

$$d + r = \frac{1}{\int_0^\omega e^{-ra} p(a)\, da}, \tag{7.2.13}$$

also solvable by iteration. Hence $b = d + r$ and $c(a) = be^{-ra}p(a)$.

Roger Avery not only suggested the above equation but also programmed its solution, using the secant method of iteration. The results he inferred from $p(a)$ and d for two countries are as shown, along with the observed $1000b$ and $1000r$:

	England and Wales, 1961		Thailand, 1959	
	Inferred	Observed	Inferred	Observed
$1000b$	19.28	19.27	36.79	36.94
$1000r$	9.74	9.74	27.05	26.77

The inferred is closer to the observed for England and Wales than for Thailand, but both are close enough. The application of the procedure will be limited to instances in which we happen to know d and $p(a)$ but not the remaining quantities, which may not be often.

Beside the crude rates of birth and death, the average age of the population, $\bar{A}_r$, and the average age of childbearing, A_r of (5.6.8), vary with the intrinsic rate. It will be seen from Table 7.4 below, calculated by Ronald Lee and Roger Avery, in what degree b_r goes up and d_r goes down as r increases, the life table being fixed at the level shown by United States females, 1964. The overall death rate d_r goes down from 9.5 per thousand, if the population were increasing at rate $r = 0.01$, to 3.7 per thousand if the increase were at $r = 0.04$. The results given in the table are plotted in Fig. 7.1. The vertical line in the chart represents the actual r, b, d, and $\bar{A}_r$ of the United States 1964 female population, for which $1000r = 15.70$.

Table 7.4 Intrinsic rate of birth b and death d, along with mean age $\bar{A}_r$ and mean age of childbearing A_r, as functions of hypothetical values of r, based on life table for United States females, 1964*

1000r	$1000b_r$	$1000d_r$	$\bar{A}_r$	A_r
10	19.5	9.5	33.3	26.2
15	23.0	8.0	30.8	26.0
20	26.7	6.7	28.4	25.9
25	30.7	5.7	26.2	25.7
30	34.8	4.8	24.1	25.5
35	39.2	4.2	22.3	25.3
40	43.7	3.7	20.6	25.2

* Programmed by Roger Avery and Ronald Lee.

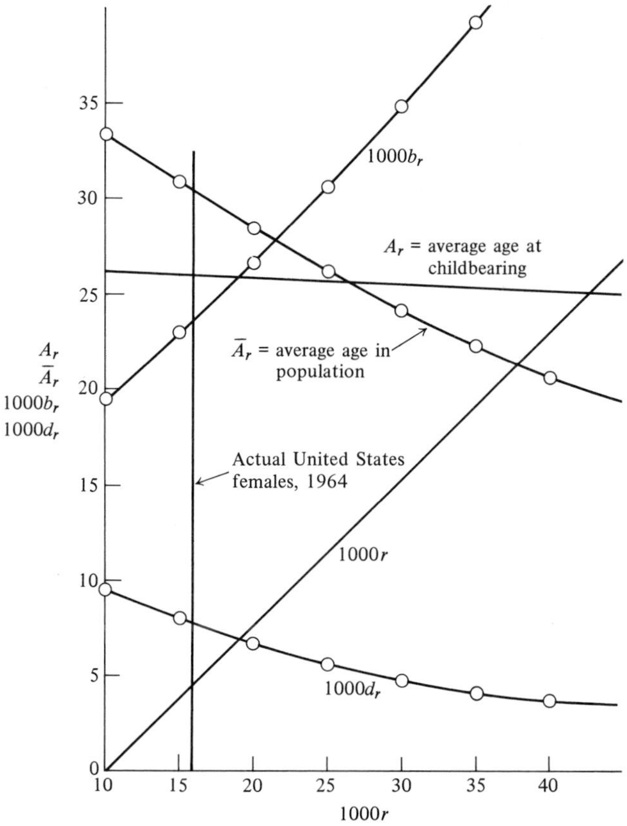

Fig. 7.1 Birth and death rates and average age as a function of r, taking as fixed the life table for United States females, 1964.

As r increases, the death rate d diminishes down to a certain point, and beyond this point rises again. Transposing r in (7.2.13), then differentiating with respect to r and equating the derivative of d to zero, we obtain for the minimum the equation,

$$\frac{d}{dr}\left(\frac{1}{\int_0^{\omega} e^{-ra}p(a)\,da} - r\right) = 0\,,$$

which reduces to

$$b\bar{A}_r - 1 = 0\,,$$

where $\bar{A}_r$ is the mean age in the stable population. Hence for a given life table the overall death rate is a minimum when the birth rate is the reciprocal of the mean age in the stable population, so that $d = 1/\bar{A}_r - r$ (Lotka, 1939c, p. 40).

In general $1/\bar{A}_r$ will be a birth rate higher than what actually prevails; one can convince himself of this by a study of Table 7.4.

Figure 7.1 illustrates how with a given life table we can ascertain the stable population by knowing any one of r, b, d, $\bar{A}_r$, but not A_r, the mean age at childbearing. The sensitivity of each of these five ways of entering the chart is proportional to the steepness of slope of its curve. Thus we would expect a horizontal line drawn from a given b to find the right point on the curve of b_r and hence to infer r with precision; after this comes $\bar{A}_r$, as also having a sufficient slope to enable us to locate r easily. This is followed at a considerable distance, so far as accuracy is concerned, by d, and A_r is nearly horizontal. Do these conclusions accord with your reading of the chart, and do they seem intuitively reasonable? Calculate the derivatives of the curves, and so express quantitatively the relative accuracy of their use to infer r.

This covers the four cases which are calculable asymptotically, which is to say, after the lapse of a sufficient time from the date the given regime was established. We pass to the other three cases, which Lotka refers to as *Malthusian* (1939c, p. 17).

Fixed Rates in the Past

In cases (5) through (7) the stable age distribution $c(a)$ is supposed to be presently existing.

5) *Given $c(a)$ and $p(a)$.* If $c(a)$ and $p(a)$ are fixed and known, then $c(0) = b$, and $d = -\int_0^\omega c(a)\, d(\ln p(a))$. Hence

$$r = b - d = b + \int_0^\omega c(a)\, d(\ln p(a)) \,.$$

Alternatively, r and b may be found simultaneously from the fact that $c(a) = be^{-ra}p(a)$ applies at any age. In practice one would have to give attention to matters of estimation in the face of error and of departure from stability in the data; one would not use a single pair of ages to infer r and b from $c(a)$ and $p(a)$, but a number of ages. (The procedure is exemplified in Section 7.3.) It is again not possible to infer $m(a)$. Except for $m(a)$ the facts regarding the population are determined, not asymptotically as before, but immediately.

6) *Given $c(a)$ and r.* This and the remaining case about which anything useful can be said are treated like (5). From $c(a)$ and r we have $b = c(0)$, $d = b - r$, from (7.2.8) $p(a) = c(a)e^{ra}/b$, which provides a way of obtaining a life table from a census (Arriaga, 1966).

7) *Given $c(a)$ and d.* From $c(a)$ and d we find $b = c(0)$, $r = b - d$, $p(a) = c(a)e^{ra}/b$. All variables except $m(a)$ are fixed and known immediately the two given ones are established, again on the assumption of stability.

The seven hypothetical situations and the inferences possible in each are summarized in Exhibit 7.1.

Exhibit 7.1 Six main demographic variables taken in pairs, showing which combinations determine the others

Given with	By age: $p(a)$	By age: $m(a)$	Intrinsic rates: r	Intrinsic rates: d	Intrinsic rates: b
$c(a)$	$b = c(0)$ $d = -\int c(a)\, d[\ln p(a)]$ $r = b - d$ Alternatively $\ln \frac{c(a)}{p(a)} = \ln b - ra$ $d = b - r$ I		$b = c(0)$ $d = b - r$ $p(a) = \frac{c(a)e^{ra}}{b}$ I	$b = c(0)$ $r = b - d$ $p(a) = \frac{c(a)e^{ra}}{b}$ I	
$p(a)$		$1 = \int_0^{\omega} e^{-ra} p(a) m(a)\, da$ gives r. $b = \frac{1}{\int e^{-ra} p(a)\, da}$ $d = b - r$ $c(a) = be^{-ra} p(a)$ A	$b = \frac{1}{\int_0^{\omega} e^{-ra} p(a)\, da}$ gives r. $d = b - r$ $c(a) = be^{-ra} p(a)$ A	$d + r = \frac{1}{\int_0^{\omega} e^{-ra} p(a)\, da}$ gives r. $b = r + d$ $c(a) = be^{-ra} p(a)$ A	$b = \frac{1}{\int_0^{\omega} e^{-ra} p(a)\, da}$ gives r. $d = b - r$ $c(a) = be^{-ra} p(a)$ A
$m(a)$					
r				$b = r + d$ $N(t) = N(0)e^{rt}$ T	$d = b - r$ $N(t) = N(0)e^{rt}$ T
d					$r = b - d$ $N(t) = N(0)e^{rt}$ T

$I \equiv$ stable immediately and calculable by age when the specified variables are fixed and given

$A \equiv$ stable asymptotically and calculable by age from the given variables, after the effects of the initial age distribution have worked themselves out

$T \equiv$ totals only, calculable when the specified variables are fixed and given

7.3. AN APPLICATION OF STABLE THEORY

The expression (7.1.12) for the proportion in the stable population between ages a and $a + da$, which reduces to $c(a)\,da = be^{-ra}p(a)\,da$, produces on division by $p(a)\,da$

$$\frac{c(a)}{p(a)} = be^{-ra}, \tag{7.3.1}$$

and this has been employed (Bourgeois-Pichat, 1957) to infer the birth rate and the intrinsic rate of increase using as data only a reliable census age distribution and a more or less appropriate life table. Taking natural logarithms of (7.3.1), Bourgeois-Pichat obtains

$$\ln \frac{c(a)}{p(a)} = \ln be^{-ra} = \ln b - ra\,. \tag{7.3.2}$$

Thinking of a as the x-ordinate and $\ln [c(a)/p(a)]$ as the y-ordinate, we need only put a straight line through the observed points $y = \ln [c(a)/p(a)]$, say $y = \alpha + \beta a$, and we can then identify the two parameters of the line with those of $\ln b - ra$ so that α would be $\ln b$ and β would be $-r$. Table 7.5 shows the data for Nicaraguan women, 1962, ages 30–64, where we approximate by assuming $c(a)$ and $p(a)$ constant within the five-year age group. First we use the given deaths and population to make a life table, and then approximate to $c(a)/p(a)$ with $l_0\,{}_5C_{a-2.5}/{}_5L_{a-2.5}$, where ${}_5C_x$ is the observed proportion of women between x and $x + 4$ at last birthday. We do not need the full range of ages; in fact, in a shorter range there is a better chance that the underlying rates have remained constant through the relevant period. The equations for the least squares fit of (7.3.2) are

$$\sum \ln \frac{c(a)}{p(a)} = n \ln b - r \sum a\,,$$

$$\sum a \ln \frac{c(a)}{p(a)} = \ln b \sum a - r \sum a^2\,,$$

where n age groups are used. Our numbers give $\alpha = -3.05$, $\beta = -0.0347$, and the line is $y = -3.05 - 0.0347x$.

Comparing this line with $\ln b - ra$, we have $\ln b = -3.05$ and $r = 0.0347$. The antilog of -3.05, that is, $e^{-3.05}$, is 0.0474. Thus we infer a rate of natural increase of 35 per thousand, and an intrinsic birth rate of 47 per thousand, at least as close to the truth as the registered 42 per thousand. However, in using a life table based on 1962 data we have undoubtedly underestimated deaths of earlier periods and hence exaggerated the rate of natural increase. Independent estimates for 1942 (United Nations, *Demographic Yearbook 1962*, p. 132, and *1963*, p. 186) show 863,000 persons, and for 1962 show 1,579,000, an increase of 83% in the 20 years, which implies an increase of 31 per thousand per year, confirming that our $1000r = 35$ is high, though our $1000b = 47$ could well be

Table 7.5 Estimate of births and natural increase from age distribution and life table, Nicaraguan females, 1962*

AGE = $a - 2.5$ (1)	${}_5C_{a-2.5}$ PROPORTION OF POPULATION IN AGE GROUP $\doteq 5c(a)$ (2)	${}_5L_{a-2.5}/\ell_0$ $\doteq 5p(a)$ (3)	(2)/(3) $\doteq \frac{c(a)}{p(a)}$ (4)	$\ln \frac{c(a)}{p(a)}$ (5)
30	0.0674	4.35	0.01550	-4.167
35	0.0579	4.27	0.01356	-4.301
40	0.0420	4.17	0.01007	-4.598
45	0.0367	4.05	0.00906	-4.704
50	0.0327	3.92	0.00834	-4.787
55	0.0210	3.78	0.00556	-5.192
60	0.0210	3.54	0.00593	-5.128

* Source for age distribution and deaths: United Nations *Demographic Yearbook*, 1963, pp. 186 and 566. Life table calculated by method of Section 1.2. From the above, the normal equations are

$$-32.877 = 7\alpha + 332.5\beta\,,$$
$$-1585.92 = 332.5\alpha + 16493.75\beta\,,$$

and hence

$$\alpha = -3.05\,,$$
$$\beta = -0.0347\,.$$

about right. [Make a chart for Table 7.5, comment on the closeness of fit, and estimate r and $\ln b$ from the chart. My graphical fitting gave $r = 0.036$ and $\ln b = -3.1$.]

Other ways of inferring birth rates from age distributions using weaker assumptions than the above example are given in Keyfitz, Nagnur, and Sharma (1967).

7.4. SOME EFFECTS OF FERTILITY AND MORTALITY CHANGE ON AGE DISTRIBUTION

Intrinsic Rate and Mean Age

We have seen that in the stable population the age distribution depends on the life table and on the intrinsic rate of increase, with the birth rate b a factor common to all ages:

$$c(a) = be^{-ra}p(a) = \frac{e^{-ra}p(a)}{\int_0^\omega e^{-ra}p(a)\,da}\,. \tag{7.4.1}$$

In order to study what happens when r changes, consider the proportion $c(a)$ at any particular age a as a function of r, and calculate the derivative of its logarithm (which is more convenient than calculating its derivative directly). From (7.4.1), using $d \ln u/dr = (1/u)(du/dr)$,

$$\frac{d(\ln c(a))}{dr} = \frac{d\left(-ra + \ln p(a) - \ln \int_0^\omega e^{-ra}p(a)\,da\right)}{dr}$$

$$= -a + \frac{\int_0^\omega ae^{-ra}p(a)\,da}{\int_0^\omega e^{-ra}p(a)\,da}, \qquad (7.4.2)$$

since $p(a)$ is not a function of r. The ratio of integrals in (7.4.2) being $\bar{A}_r$, the first moment or mean age of the stable population, we have (Lotka, 1939c, p. 24; 1938), if births change but not deaths:

$$\frac{d(\ln c(a))}{dr} = \bar{A}_r - a\,. \qquad (7.4.3)$$

The mean $\bar{A}_r$ is a function of r. For the "young" population of Nicaragua, it is 23.3 years of age; for the "old" population of England and Wales, 33.7 years.

The derivative (7.4.3) of the natural logarithm of $c(a)$ with respect to r shows in what direction $c(a)$ moves with a change in r. For a less than $\bar{A}_r$ the derivative is positive; that is to say, the proportion $c(a)$ increases with r. For a greater than $\bar{A}_r$ the derivative is negative, so that $c(a)$ decreases as r increases. Hence with an increase in r the curve of $c(a)$ swings around a short interval in its middle, the left end going up and the right, down. In fact, $\bar{A}_r$ is not quite a fixed point, and as r moves from a low value to a high one, the pivot about which the line swings, $(\bar{A}_r, c(\bar{A}_r))$, gradually moves along an interval from about 35 years to about 20 (Fig. 7.1).

The mean age $\bar{A}_r$ may be expressed in terms of the life-table constants (Lotka, 1939c, p. 22). From the definition of $\bar{A}_r$ it follows that

$$\bar{A}_r = \frac{\int_0^\omega ae^{-ra}p(a)\,da}{\int_0^\omega e^{-ra}p(a)\,da}$$

$$= \frac{\bar{L}_1 - r\bar{L}_2 + (r^2/2!)\bar{L}_3 - \cdots}{\bar{L}_0 - r\bar{L}_1 + (r^2/2!)\bar{L}_2 - \cdots},$$

where $\bar{L}_i = \int_0^\omega a^i p(a)\,da$. Then by long division,

$$\bar{A}_r = \frac{\bar{L}_1}{\bar{L}_0} - \left[\left(\frac{\bar{L}_2}{\bar{L}_0}\right) - \left(\frac{\bar{L}_1}{\bar{L}_0}\right)^2\right] r + \cdots \qquad (7.4.4)$$

[Derive this result in a way which shows that the coefficient of r^i is $(-1)^i/i!$ times the $(i+1)$-cumulant $\bar{\kappa}_{i+1}$ of the stationary population.] The first two or three terms of the right-hand side of (7.4.4) give a linear or quadratic approximation to the curve of $\bar{A}_r$ in Fig. 7.1. Note the resemblance of the expressions for $\bar{A}_r$ in (7.4.4) and for A_r, the mean age of childbearing, in (5.6.10).

If (7.4.4) applies to two points of time separately, we can find an equation for change between the two times by subtraction. Where the same life table applies to the two dates, we would have

$$\begin{aligned}\Delta\bar{A}_r &= -\bar{\kappa}_2\,\Delta r + \bar{\kappa}_3\frac{\Delta r^2}{2!} - \bar{\kappa}_4\frac{\Delta r^3}{3!} + \cdots \\ &= -\bar{\kappa}_2\,\Delta r + \bar{\kappa}_3 r\,\Delta r - \bar{\kappa}_4\frac{r^2\,\Delta r}{2} + \cdots \qquad (7.4.5)\end{aligned}$$

Between 1959–61 and 1965 the change of mortality in the United States was very small, and the drop in fertility was large. The cumulants of the 1959–61 female life table include $\bar{\kappa}_2 = 557$, $\bar{\kappa}_3 = 2330$, $\bar{\kappa}_4 = -320{,}384$; the intrinsic rate r was 0.02113 in 1959–61 and 0.01265 in 1965, an average of 0.01689 (all with adjusted births). Then from (7.4.5) $\Delta\bar{A}_r$ ought to be approximately

$$\begin{aligned}\Delta\bar{A}_r &\doteq -(557)(-0.00848) + (2330)(0.01689)(-0.00848) \\ &\quad -(-320{,}384/2)(0.01689)^2(-0.00848) \\ &= 4.723 - 0.334 - 0.388 \\ &= 4.001\,,\end{aligned}$$

as against the observed increase $\Delta\bar{A}_r = 4.152$ (Table 7.6). The higher life table cumulants are not negligible in the expansion (7.4.5). But the simple form $\Delta\bar{A}_r = -\bar{\kappa}_2\,\Delta r$ usually tells the direction and roughly the amount of shift in mean age due to fertility when mortality does not change much.

Neutral Change in Mortality

The effect on population increase of an across-the-board drop in mortality is often discussed. How does a decline in the force of mortality, say from $\mu(x)$ to $\mu(x) - k = \bar{\mu}(x)$, k being constant with respect to age, affect the intrinsic rate? We will see that the decline has the effect of raising the intrinsic rate by exactly k. For if the rate is r before the fall, then r satisfies

$$\int_\alpha^\beta e^{-rx}p(x)m(x)\,dx = 1\,, \qquad (7.4.6)$$

where

$$p(x) = \exp\left[-\int_0^x \mu(a)\,da\right].$$

Call the new survivorship $\bar{p}(x)$; then

$$\bar{p}(x) = \exp\left[-\int_0^x \bar{\mu}(a)\,da\right] = \exp\left[-\int_0^x (\mu(a) - k)\,da\right] = \exp(kx)p(x)\,.$$

The new $\bar{r}$ must satisfy

$$\int_\alpha^\beta e^{-\bar{r}x}\bar{p}(x)m(x)\,dx = 1\,, \qquad \text{or} \qquad \int_\alpha^\beta e^{-\bar{r}x}e^{kx}p(x)m(x)\,dx = 1\,,$$

or

$$\int_\alpha^\beta e^{-(\bar{r}-k)x}p(x)m(x)\,dx = 1\,.$$

Matching this last against (7.4.6) and recalling that the real root of (7.4.6) is unique proves that

$$r = \bar{r} - k\,,$$

so that

$$\bar{r} = r + k\,. \tag{7.4.7}$$

Hence the uniform drop in $\mu(x)$ results in a rise in r of exactly equal amount.

Does this have an effect on age distribution? No, since the number between ages a and $a + da$ in the new stable age distribution is proportional to

$$e^{-\bar{r}a}\bar{p}(a)\,da = e^{-(r+k)a}e^{ka}p(a)\,da = e^{-ra}p(a)\,da\,,$$

which is identical with the original stable age distribution.

The above argument suggests that a *neutral* change in mortality be defined as one which is either constant at all ages or, without being constant, has an incidence such that the age distribution of the population, or at least the mean age, is unaffected. If the incidence of improved mortality is on balance at younger ages, then the age distribution becomes younger, and vice versa. Our problem in assessing observed changes in mortality will be to find an index, or set of weights, that will tell us whether the change is neutral, and if not, whether it falls on the younger or the older side of neutrality.

A decrease in fertility rates cannot be neutral, but must make the population older, and an increase in fertility makes it younger. Let us investigate a new fertility function $\bar{m}(x)$,

$$\bar{m}(x) = e^{kx}m(x)\,.$$

Then the new characteristic equation is

$$\int_\alpha^\beta e^{-\bar{r}x}p(x)\bar{m}(x)\,dx = 1\,, \qquad \text{or} \qquad \int_\alpha^\beta e^{-(\bar{r}-k)x}p(x)m(x)\,dx = 1\,,$$

so $\bar{r} - k = r$, and $\bar{r} = k + r$, as before. But now, with the same life table, the stable age distribution is

$$\bar{c}(a)\,da = \bar{b}e^{-\bar{r}a}p(a)\,da = \bar{b}e^{-ka}e^{-ra}p(a)\,da\,.$$

The reader may complete the proof that with $k > 0$ the population is younger, with $k < 0$, older.

Decomposition of Observed Changes

Since in practice neither mortality nor fertility changes in a fashion uniform over all ages, we would like a measure of the effect on r of the changes which actually take place. The separate effects on the intrinsic rate may be exemplified in a comparison for Australia due to Beth Berkov. For 1957, $1000r$ was 16.947; if the death rates are unchanged but 1962 birth rates are entered, $1000r$ goes up to 17.505, an increase of 0.558. On the other hand, fertility held at the 1957 level but mortality altered to 1962 rates brings $1000r$ to 17.075, an increase over 1957 of 0.128. The actual $1000r$ for 1962 was 17.633, an increase over 1957 of 0.686.

It happens in this instance that the overall increase is equal to the sum of the increase due to fertility and that due to mortality, 0.558 plus 0.128. This justifies the statement that the increase in the intrinsic rate was 0.558/0.686 = 81% due to fertility change and 19% due to mortality. When the separate effects of mortality and fertility change add up to the combined change, we say that *interaction* is zero: the effect of changing from 1957 to 1962 mortality is the same in the presence of 1957 fertility as in that of 1962 fertility. Low interaction makes the interpretation of the results relatively clearcut.

The same analysis performed on $\bar{A}_r$, the mean age in the stable population, will show whether the change due to mortality alone is neutral, leaving the mean age unchanged, or whether on balance it is more an improvement in the older ages or in the younger ones.

The procedure for accomplishing this analysis starts with $\bar{A}_r$, the stable mean age, say for United States females in 1960 and then for 1965, both calculated in the normal fashion. Then fresh computations are made using the life table of 1960 and the birth rates of 1965, as well as the life table of 1965 and the birth rates of 1960. Suppose we refer to these, in the order mentioned, as $\bar{A}(p, m)$, $\bar{A}(\bar{p}, \bar{m})$, $\bar{A}(p, \bar{m})$, and $\bar{A}(\bar{p}, m)$, where, as before, p stands for the life table and m for fertility, the bar denotes 1965, and its absence denotes 1960. Then the difference due

$$\text{to mortality alone is } \bar{A}(\bar{p}, m) - \bar{A}(p, m)\,,$$

$$\text{to fertility alone is } \bar{A}(p, \bar{m}) - \bar{A}(p, m)\,,$$

$$\text{to interaction is } \{\bar{A}(\bar{p}, \bar{m}) - \bar{A}(p, \bar{m})\} - \{\bar{A}(\bar{p}, m) - \bar{A}(p, m)\}\,.$$

The mortality component in the decomposition of $\bar{A}_r$ will constitute the index of the age-incidence of improvement in mortality. If $\bar{A}(\bar{p}, m) - \bar{A}(p, m)$ is positive, we will say that the improvement in mortality is more at older ages, if negative, at younger ages, if zero, the mortality improvement is neutral. In dealing with the mean age in the stable population we are discussing tendencies as they are revealed in the stable model, rather than facts as shown by the census age distribution. The interest of the analysis depends on the tendency for the actual population to follow the stable.

Table 7.6 Decomposition of change in mean age of female stable population into effects of mortality and of fertility, United States, 1920–65*

THREE-YEAR INTERVAL CENTERED ON	$\mathring{e}_0$	INCREASE OF MEAN AGE		
		DUE TO MORTALITY CHANGE	DUE TO FERTILITY CHANGE	TOTAL INCLUDING INTERACTION
1920	56.41			
		-0.336	1.216	0.855
1925	59.01			
		0.142	3.309	3.519
1930	60.67			
		0.154	2.161	2.331
1935	62.58			
		0.216	-0.520	-0.314
1940	65.58			
		0.234	-2.590	-2.401
1945	68.11			
		0.344	-3.293	-3.035
1950	70.86			
		0.254	-2.401	-2.191
1955	72.61			
		0.085	-0.504	-0.423
1960	73.40			
		0.010	4.122	4.152
1965†	73.83			

* Births adjusted for underregistration; programmed by Wilhelm Flieger.
† One year only.

In all 5-year intervals from 1925 the effect of mortality change was to increase the mean age $\bar{A}_r$ for United States females, by an average of about 0.2 years per 5-year period (Table 7.6). The effect reached a peak of 0.344 years in 1945–50, at a time when mortality was falling rapidly, as indicated by the expectation at age zero. This result is in accord with the findings of Coale (1956, p. 114) and Hermalin (1966). Mortality up to the ages of reproduction had reached low levels by the time the table begins; we are not surprised that further improvements tend to be at older ages. Similar results (not quoted here) appear for Canada and Australia over the last generation.

A very different effect of mortality change on age distribution is shown for England and Wales from 1861 (Table 7.7). Fluctuations occur both in the general level of mortality and in its age-incidence. Apparently phases of the demographic transition occur in which mortality improvement affects older ages, then younger ages, then older ages again (W. Flieger, 1967). We can say in summary (of results not all shown here) that with the exception of the decade 1891–1901 in England and Wales and a similar period in Sweden, the

Table 7.7 Decomposition of change in mean age of female stable population into effects of mortality and of fertility, England and Wales, 1861–1961, and four high-fertility countries for recent periods

INTERVAL CENTERED ON	$\mathring{e}_0$	INCREASE OF MEAN AGE: DUE TO MORTALITY CHANGE	INCREASE OF MEAN AGE: DUE TO FERTILITY CHANGE	INCREASE OF MEAN AGE: TOTAL INCLUDING INTERACTION
		ENGLAND AND WALES		
1861	43.03	-0.223	-0.499	-0.714
1871	42.43	-0.799	0.370	-0.439
1881	47.38	-0.233	1.477	1.179
1891	45.64	0.609	2.257	2.995
1901	49.39	0.085	2.560	2.695
1911	53.33	-0.504	1.262	0.754
1921	59.94	-0.482	6.176	5.610
1931	62.34	0.723	-4.447	-3.959
1946	68.94	-0.411	2.112	1.668
1951	71.50	0.373	-1.500	-1.160
1956	73.29	0.115	-3.238	-3.144
1961	73.97			
		CHILE		
1960	59.19	-0.107	0.678	0.573
1964	61.29			
		HONDURAS		
1957	60.08	-0.790	-0.787	-1.520
1965	61.53			
		MARTINIQUE		
1961	68.21	-0.511	1.207	0.643
1963	67.89			
		MAURITIUS		
1955	56.58	-0.097	-0.338	-0.439
1964	63.72			

population tended to become younger because of the fall in mortality for the presently advanced countries in most periods up to World War II, and subsequently has become older. The four underdeveloped countries of Table 7.7 show a tendency in recent years for mean age to fall with the fall of mortality.

Table 7.8 Age-specific death rates ${}_nM_x$ for females of England and Wales, in three-year periods about the turning points of age-incidence of mortality revealed in Table 7.7, with percentage changes between given dates

	1000_nM_x FOR THREE-YEAR PERIOD CENTERED ON						
x	1861	(PERCENT CHANGE)	1891	(PERCENT CHANGE)	1911	(PERCENT CHANGE)	1931
0	157.0	-1	154.9	-15	131.2	-54	59.7
1	35.0	-25	26.1	-33	17.4	-59	7.1
5	6.8	-31	4.7	-28	3.4	-41	2.0
10	4.4	-34	2.9	-28	2.1	-29	1.5
15	7.0	-39	4.3	-37	2.7	-11	2.4
20	8.1	-36	5.2	-38	3.2	-9	2.9
25	8.9	-30	6.2	-40	3.7	-14	3.2
30	10.1	-21	8.0	-42	4.6	-26	3.4
35	11.1	-11	9.9	-40	5.9	-32	4.0
40	11.7	+5	12.3	-40	7.4	-31	5.1
45	13.4	+13	15.1	-35	9.8	-30	6.9
50	16.2	+20	19.4	-32	13.2	-27	9.7
55	24.4	+20	29.3	-35	19.0	-25	14.2
60	29.6	+28	38.0	-27	27.6	-21	21.9
65	50.0	+24	61.8	-36	39.4	-12	34.7
70	66.8	+24	82.5	-19	66.6	-14	57.4
75	109.3	+12	123.3	-20	99.0	-3	96.6
80	173.8	+15	200.7	-25	150.8	+2	154.3
85	274.4	+8	300.7	-23	231.9	+11	257.7

How can one be sure that the change in mean age $\bar{A}_r$ due to mortality, the second columns of Tables 7.6 and 7.7, really constitutes an index of the age-incidence of mortality change? Table 7.8 attempts to aid judgment on this question by showing the age-specific rates over a 70-year period in England and Wales. Since the effect of mortality improvement was to lower the mean age in the decades from 1861 to 1891, to raise it from 1891 to 1911, and then to lower it again from 1911 to 1931, all according to the second column of Table 7.7, the age-specific death rates ought to show a pattern in the first and third periods different from that in the second. Table 7.8 broadly accords with this—improvement was relatively greater in the ages under 40 from 1861 to 1891, in the older ages from 1891 to 1911, and again in the younger ages from 1911 to 1931. Definitive appraisal of the technique will require more extensive comparison.

Other variables than $\bar{A}_r$ may be subjected to a similar decomposition. The United States net reproduction rate fell by 0.338 from 1959–61 to 1965. This represented a total drop of 0.342 due to the fall of fertility, with a minute compensating rise of 0.004 due to the improvement of mortality. Surprisingly enough, the intrinsic death rate d, which rose by 2.126 per thousand, was more affected by fertility change (+2.257) than by mortality change (−0.133). The mortality and fertility effects on the population of school age, the dependency ratio, the total reproductive value, and other functions of age may likewise be partitioned out.

Consequence of Zero Mortality

What difference would it make if residual mortality were eliminated altogether, and people lived forever? It would affect individuals greatly, raising their $\mathring{e}_0$ to infinity, but it would affect a rapidly growing population surprisingly little. Suppose that $p(a)$ went to unity, and the former age-specific birth rate $m(a)$ was reduced to $m(a)p(a)$. The characteristic equation (5.2.2) would stand unaltered. For Honduras females, 1965, the R_0 is 2.613, and the gross reproduction rate, $\int_\alpha^\beta m(a)\,da$, is 3.036. The infinite extension of the individual life would be offset as far as population increase is concerned by a reduction of 14 percent in births. Suppose these two offsetting changes take place: that families forgo one child out of seven and mortality drops to zero. The intrinsic birth rate would fall from 42.49 per thousand to 34.06, and be the same as the rate of natural increase.

Since the intrinsic rate of natural increase for Honduras would continue to be 34.06 per thousand, the age distribution of the female stable population would be

$$c(a)\,da = \frac{e^{-ra}\,da}{\int_0^\infty e^{-ra}\,da} = re^{-ra}\,da\,, \tag{7.4.8}$$

evaluated at $r = 0.03406$. This results in 15.7% under 5 years of age, not a large reduction from the observed 19.9% or the 18.6% in the stable population with observed death rates. The mean age would be somewhat raised by the fact that people lived forever: it would go up from $\bar{A}_r = 21.6$ years to $\bar{A}_r = 1/r = 29.4$ years, as the reader can verify by integration in

$$\bar{A}_r = \frac{\int_0^\infty ae^{-ra}\,da}{\int_0^\infty e^{-ra}\,da} = \frac{1}{r}$$

with $r = 0.03406$.

The results seem astonishing, especially the moderateness of the fall in the percentage of children and of the rise in the mean age. But an increase of 3.4% per year is astonishing, whether people die or not.

The Interpretation of Age Distributions

The considerations of this chapter give rise to a number of ways of estimating birth rates from an observed age distribution and life table. One of these is worked out in Section 7.3, on a method due to Bourgeois-Pichat. A generalization has been devised which does not assume stability, but ascertains from the observed ages the linear and quadratic components of the change in the birth rate. An altogether different principle, known as Thompson's index (Thompson and Whelpton, 1933, p. 262), converts ratios of children to women into R_0 or intrinsic rates. An exposition of the mathematics underlying these is to be found in Keyfitz, Nagnur, and Sharma (1967) and will not be repeated here.

We now turn from application back to theory and compare the several versions of the age analysis for a single sex which have been proposed in Chapters 2 through 6, in order to find in what respects they are the same and in what respects they differ from one another.

CHAPTER 8

RECONCILIATION OF MATRIX AND INTEGRAL EQUATION

The starting point of our one-sex population analysis has been in either continuous form, as an integral equation (Chapter 5) or discrete, as a set of linear first-order difference equations (Chapter 2). The solution of the integral equation may proceed (either by elementary calculus or by use of the Laplace transform) to a sum of exponentials weighted by constants (Chapter 5). The discrete first-order set of difference equations may be expressed and solved in matrix terms (Chapter 3) or made to depend on a higher-order linear difference equation, the latter to be exhibited below. Determinants are a convenient way of writing the solution of either of these discrete formulations, and examples of this will be given below as well. This chapter is devoted to comparing the several one-sex models.

8.1. A HIGHER-ORDER DIFFERENCE EQUATION

A ninth-order difference equation, connecting

$$K_0^{(t)},\ K_0^{(t-1)},\ \ldots,\ K_0^{(t-9)}\,,$$

is derivable from the first nine members of the set of first-order relations (2.1.7). The argument will again be exemplified with 5-year age groups and a reproductive span ending at $\beta = 45$. Substituting in the first equation of (2.1.7) the variables $K_x^{(t)}$ of later equations, the variables corresponding to all ages but 0–4 can be eliminated, and the ninth-order equation is then in terms of $K_0^{(t)}$ alone. For example, $K_{15}^{(t)}$ by successive substitution becomes

$$K_{15}^{(t)} = K_{10}^{(t-1)}(L_{15}/L_{10}) = \cdots = K_0^{(t-3)}(L_{15}/L_0)\,. \tag{8.1.1}$$

After substituting for ${}_5K_x^{(t)}$, $x = 15, 20, \ldots, 40$, from expressions similar to (8.1.1) in the first equation of (2.1.7), we have

$$\tfrac{1}{2}\{K_0^{(t-2)} + K_0^{(t-3)}\}L_{15}F_{15} + \tfrac{1}{2}\{K_0^{(t-3)} + K_0^{(t-4)}\}L_{20}F_{20} + \cdots + \tfrac{1}{2}\{K_0^{(t-7)} + K_0^{(t-8)}\}L_{40}F_{40} = l_0K_0^{(t+1)}\,. \tag{8.1.2}$$

Rearranging the parentheses so as to collect terms in $K_0^{(t-3)}$, etc., yields

$$\tfrac{1}{2}L_{15}F_{15}K_0^{(t-2)} + \tfrac{1}{2}\{L_{15}F_{15} + L_{20}F_{20}\}K_0^{(t-3)} + \cdots + \tfrac{1}{2}\{L_{40}F_{40}\}K_0^{(t-8)} = l_0K_0^{(t+1)}\,. \tag{8.1.3}$$

This is a ninth-order homogeneous difference equation in the single variable $K_0^{(t)}$. To solve it we try $K_0^{(t)} = C\lambda^t$, and find a ninth-degree characteristic equation in λ,

$$f(\lambda) = 2l_0\lambda^9 - L_{15}F_{15}\lambda^6 - (L_{15}F_{15} + L_{20}F_{20})\lambda^5 - \cdots - L_{40}F_{40} = 0\,, \quad (8.1.4)$$

which, when $n = 9$, is identical with the characteristic equation $f(\lambda) = |\mathbf{M} - \lambda\mathbf{I}| = 0$ given as (3.2.4), and hence must have the same roots, $\lambda_1, \lambda_2, \ldots, \lambda_9$. Equation (8.1.3) being linear, its several solutions may be added and, assuming distinct roots, we have

$$K_0^{(t)} = C_1\lambda_1^t + C_2\lambda_2^t + \cdots + C_9\lambda_9^t\,. \quad (8.1.5)$$

The C's can be fitted to initial conditions. If we know the population at time zero, $K_0^{(0)}, K_5^{(0)}, \ldots$, we can infer (hypothetical) earlier K_0, $K_0^{(-1)}, K_0^{(-2)}, \ldots, K_0^{(-8)}$. On the assumption of fixed mortality, the preceding numbers would be

$$K_0^{(-1)} = K_5^{(0)}\frac{L_0}{L_5}\,, \quad K_0^{(-2)} = K_{10}^{(0)}\frac{L_0}{L_{10}}\,, \ldots, \quad K_0^{(-8)} = K_{40}^{(0)}\frac{L_0}{L_{40}}\,, \quad (8.1.6)$$

by a kind of reverse survivorship. Putting these on the left-hand side of (8.1.5) and entering $t = 0, -1, \ldots, -8$ on the right-hand side gives the nine equations

$$\begin{aligned}
K_0^{(0)} &= K_0^{(0)} &&= C_1 + C_2 + C_3 + \cdots + C_9\,,\\
K_0^{(-1)} &= K_5^{(0)}\frac{L_0}{L_5} &&= C_1\lambda_1^{-1} + C_2\lambda_2^{-1} + C_3\lambda_3^{-1} + \cdots + C_9\lambda_9^{-1}\,,\\
K_0^{(-2)} &= K_{10}^{(0)}\frac{L_0}{L_{10}} &&= C_1\lambda_1^{-2} + C_2\lambda_2^{-2} + C_3\lambda_3^{-2} + \cdots + C_9\lambda_9^{-2}\,,\\
&\vdots && \qquad\qquad\vdots\,,\\
K_0^{(-8)} &= K_{40}^{(0)}\frac{L_0}{L_{40}} &&= C_1\lambda_1^{-8} + C_2\lambda_2^{-8} + C_3\lambda_3^{-8} + \cdots + C_9\lambda_9^{-8}\,.
\end{aligned} \quad (8.1.7)$$

Taking (8.1.5) with the set (8.1.7) and eliminating the C's gives the condition for consistency of (8.1.5) and (8.1.7):

$$\begin{vmatrix}
K_0^{(t)}/L_0 & \lambda_1^t & \lambda_2^t & \cdots & \lambda_9^t\\
K_0^{(0)}/L_0 & 1 & 1 & \cdots & 1\\
K_5^{(0)}/L_5 & \lambda_1^{-1} & \lambda_2^{-1} & \cdots & \lambda_9^{-1}\\
K_{10}^{(0)}/L_{10} & \lambda_1^{-2} & \lambda_2^{-2} & \cdots & \lambda_9^{-2}\\
\vdots & & & & \vdots\\
K_{40}^{(0)}/L_{40} & \lambda_1^{-8} & \lambda_2^{-8} & \cdots & \lambda_9^{-8}
\end{vmatrix} = 0\,. \quad (8.1.8)$$

The left-hand side of this last equation, when expanded by its top row, provides an expression for $K_0^{(t)}$ in terms of $\lambda_1^t, \lambda_2^t, \ldots, \lambda_9^t$. In fact, (8.1.8) is merely a way of writing Cramer's rule for the solution of a set of simultaneous linear equations. If the determinant obtained from that in (8.1.8) by deleting the first column and first row be called $|\mathbf{B}|$, and the determinant obtained from $|\mathbf{B}|$ by deleting its ith row and jth column and multiplying by $(-1)^{i+j}$ be written $|\mathbf{B}_{ij}|$, then (8.1.8) is

$$K_0^{(t)} = L_0 \sum_{i=1}^{9} \left[\frac{K_0^{(0)}|\mathbf{B}_{1i}|}{L_0|\mathbf{B}|} + \frac{K_5^{(0)}|\mathbf{B}_{2i}|}{L_5|\mathbf{B}|} + \cdots + \frac{K_{40}^{(0)}|\mathbf{B}_{9i}|}{L_{40}|\mathbf{B}|} \right] \lambda_i^t \,. \tag{8.1.9}$$

Equation (8.1.9) expresses the trajectory of a population of given initial age distribution and regime of fertility and survivorship. The fertility and mortality pattern has been translated into the set of eigenvalues.

Reconciliation of Higher-Order Equation with First-Order Set

In the matrix analysis of Chapter 3, the first step was to find the eigenvalues of $\mathbf{M}$, which is to say the roots (nine in our case) of the polynomial equation $|\mathbf{M} - \lambda\mathbf{I}| = 0$; then for each λ_i solve the set of homogeneous linear equations

$$\mathbf{M}\{\mathbf{K}_i\} = \lambda_i\{\mathbf{K}_i\} \qquad \text{and} \qquad [\mathbf{H}_i]\mathbf{M} = \lambda_i[\mathbf{H}_i] \,.$$

The expansion of the arbitrary vector $\{\mathbf{K}^{(0)}\}$ projected to time t as $\mathbf{M}^t\{\mathbf{K}^{(0)}\}$ is

$$\{\mathbf{K}^{(t)}\} = c_1\lambda_1^t\{\mathbf{K}_1\} + c_2\lambda_2^t\{\mathbf{K}_2\} + \cdots + c_9\lambda_9^t\{\mathbf{K}_9\} \,, \tag{8.1.10}$$

where c_i is $[\mathbf{H}_i]\{\mathbf{K}^{(0)}\}$, obtained by multiplying (8.1.10) for $t = 0$ on the left by $[\mathbf{H}_i]$, since we can always make $[\mathbf{H}_i]\{\mathbf{K}_i\}$ equal unity.

For our purpose it will be convenient to consider the $c_i = [\mathbf{H}_i]\{\mathbf{K}^{(0)}\}$ as the elements of a vertical vector

$$\begin{Bmatrix} c_1 \\ c_2 \\ c_3 \\ \vdots \\ c_9 \end{Bmatrix} = \begin{Bmatrix} [\mathbf{H}_1] \\ [\mathbf{H}_2] \\ [\mathbf{H}_3] \\ \vdots \\ [\mathbf{H}_9] \end{Bmatrix} \{\mathbf{K}^{(0)}\} = \mathbf{H}\{\mathbf{K}^{(0)}\} \,, \tag{8.1.11}$$

where $\mathbf{H}$ is defined as the set of horizontal stable vectors. The corresponding set of vertical vectors is

$$\mathbf{K} = [\{\mathbf{K}_1\}\{\mathbf{K}_2\} \cdots \{\mathbf{K}_9\}] \,. \tag{8.1.12}$$

From the orthogonality of the vectors, that is, $[\mathbf{H}_i]\{\mathbf{K}_j\} = 0$, $i \neq j$, proved in Chapter 3, it follows that $\mathbf{H}$ and $\mathbf{K}$ are reciprocals, supposing we have normalized the vectors to make $[\mathbf{H}_i]\{\mathbf{K}_i\} = 1$. Since $\mathbf{H} = \mathbf{K}^{-1}$, we can replace $\mathbf{H}$ by $\mathbf{K}^{-1}$ in (8.1.11). This is convenient because $\mathbf{K}$ is merely the individual vertical stable vectors $\{\mathbf{K}_i\}$ set side by side, and each of the $\{\mathbf{K}_i\}$ may be expressed in the form [differing from (3.2.6), the stable population of radix l_0, only by a constant multiplier, $\sqrt{\lambda_i}$]:

$$\{\mathbf{K}_i\} = \begin{Bmatrix} L_0 \\ L_5/\lambda_i \\ \vdots \\ L_{40}/\lambda_i^8 \end{Bmatrix},$$

where the top element has now arbitrarily been taken as L_0.

Hence we may write $\mathbf{K}$ as

$$\mathbf{K} = \begin{bmatrix} L_0 & L_0 & L_0 & \cdots & L_0 \\ L_5\lambda_1^{-1} & L_5\lambda_2^{-1} & L_5\lambda_3^{-1} & \cdots & L_5\lambda_9^{-1} \\ L_{10}\lambda_1^{-2} & L_{10}\lambda_2^{-2} & L_{10}\lambda_3^{-2} & \cdots & L_{10}\lambda_9^{-2} \\ \vdots & & & & \vdots \\ L_{40}\lambda_1^{-8} & L_{40}\lambda_2^{-8} & L_{40}\lambda_3^{-8} & \cdots & L_{40}\lambda_9^{-8} \end{bmatrix}. \tag{8.1.13}$$

Factoring the right-hand side of (8.1.13), we obtain

$$\mathbf{K} = \begin{bmatrix} L_0 & 0 & 0 & \cdots & 0 \\ 0 & L_5 & 0 & \cdots & 0 \\ 0 & 0 & L_{10} & \cdots & 0 \\ \vdots & & & & \vdots \\ 0 & 0 & 0 & \cdots & L_{40} \end{bmatrix} \begin{bmatrix} 1 & 1 & 1 & \cdots & 1 \\ \lambda_1^{-1} & \lambda_2^{-1} & \lambda_3^{-1} & \cdots & \lambda_9^{-1} \\ \lambda_1^{-2} & \lambda_2^{-2} & \lambda_3^{-2} & \cdots & \lambda_9^{-2} \\ \vdots & & & & \vdots \\ \lambda_1^{-8} & \lambda_2^{-8} & \lambda_3^{-8} & \cdots & \lambda_9^{-8} \end{bmatrix} = \mathbf{AB}\,, \tag{8.1.14}$$

say. Of the two factors which together make up $\mathbf{K}$, the first, $\mathbf{A}$, is entirely obtained from the life table and depends in no way on fertility, while the second, $\mathbf{B}$, is assembled in a simple way from the reciprocals of the roots $\lambda_1, \lambda_2, \ldots, \lambda_9$.

It follows that $\mathbf{K}^{-1} = (\mathbf{AB})^{-1} = \mathbf{B}^{-1}\mathbf{A}^{-1}$, and entering this in (8.1.11) we have

$$\mathbf{H}\{\mathbf{K}^{(0)}\} = \mathbf{K}^{-1}\{\mathbf{K}^{(0)}\} = \mathbf{B}^{-1}\mathbf{A}^{-1}\{\mathbf{K}^{(0)}\}$$

$$= \begin{bmatrix} 1 & 1 & \cdots & 1 \\ \lambda_1^{-1} & \lambda_2^{-1} & \cdots & \lambda_9^{-1} \\ \vdots & & & \vdots \\ \lambda_1^{-8} & \lambda_2^{-8} & \cdots & \lambda_9^{-8} \end{bmatrix}^{-1} \begin{bmatrix} L_0 & 0 & \cdots & 0 \\ 0 & L_5 & \cdots & 0 \\ \vdots & & & \vdots \\ 0 & 0 & \cdots & L_{40} \end{bmatrix}^{-1} \begin{Bmatrix} K_0^{(0)} \\ K_5^{(0)} \\ \vdots \\ K_{40}^{(0)} \end{Bmatrix}$$

$$= \begin{bmatrix} 1 & 1 & \cdots & 1 \\ \lambda_1^{-1} & \lambda_2^{-1} & \cdots & \lambda_9^{-1} \\ \vdots & & & \vdots \\ \lambda_1^{-8} & \lambda_2^{-8} & \cdots & \lambda_9^{-8} \end{bmatrix}^{-1} \begin{Bmatrix} K_0^{(0)}/L_0 \\ K_5^{(0)}/L_5 \\ \vdots \\ K_{40}^{(0)}/L_{40} \end{Bmatrix} = \mathbf{B}^{-} \begin{Bmatrix} K_0^{(0)}/L_0 \\ K_5^{(0)}/L_5 \\ \vdots \\ K_{40}^{(0)}/L_{40} \end{Bmatrix}, \tag{8.1.15}$$

since the reciprocal of a diagonal matrix is the diagonal matrix of the reciprocals of its elements.

We recall that the product vector (8.1.15) is identical with (8.1.11), which was the start of the present series of manipulations. Hence the top element of

(8.1.15) regarded as a vertical vector must be the same as the top element of (8.1.11), that is, $[\mathbf{H}_1]\{\mathbf{K}^{(0)}\} = c_1$. Confining ourselves to this top element, we need only the top row of $\mathbf{B}^{-1}$, which is to say $1/|\mathbf{B}|$ times the set of cofactors of the first column of $\mathbf{B}$. The cofactor of the first element of the first column of $\mathbf{B}$ is

$$|\mathbf{B}_{11}| = \begin{vmatrix} \lambda_2^{-1} & \lambda_3^{-1} & \cdots & \lambda_9^{-1} \\ \lambda_2^{-2} & \lambda_3^{-2} & \cdots & \lambda_9^{-2} \\ \vdots & & & \vdots \\ \lambda_2^{-8} & \lambda_3^{-8} & \cdots & \lambda_9^{-8} \end{vmatrix}, \tag{8.1.16}$$

which omits the first row and first column of $|\mathbf{B}|$, and similarly $|\mathbf{B}_{i1}|$ omits the ith row and first column of $|\mathbf{B}|$. The value of c_1 being the first element of the vertical vector constituted by the product at the end of (8.1.15), we have

$$c_1 = \frac{|\mathbf{B}_{11}|}{|\mathbf{B}|}\left(\frac{K_0^{(0)}}{L_0}\right) + \frac{|\mathbf{B}_{21}|}{|\mathbf{B}|}\left(\frac{K_5^{(0)}}{L_5}\right) + \cdots + \frac{|\mathbf{B}_{91}|}{|\mathbf{B}|}\left(\frac{K_{40}^{(0)}}{L_{40}}\right). \tag{8.1.17}$$

The reader may compare this with (8.1.9) and fill out the proof for other c_i, $i = 2, 3, \ldots, 9$. He may use the fact that the right-hand side of (8.1.17) when assembled into a single determinant is

$$c_1 = \frac{\begin{vmatrix} K_0^{(0)}/L_0 & 1 & 1 & \cdots & 1 \\ K_5^{(0)}/L_5 & \lambda_2^{-1} & \lambda_3^{-1} & \cdots & \lambda_9^{-1} \\ \vdots & & & & \vdots \\ K_{40}^{(0)}/L_{40} & \lambda_2^{-8} & \lambda_3^{-8} & \cdots & \lambda_9^{-8} \end{vmatrix}}{|\mathbf{B}|}, \tag{8.1.18}$$

which is the same as the coefficient of λ_1^t in the expansion of (8.1.8) by its first row, except that the c_1 of (8.1.18) is $1/L_0$ of the coefficient of λ_1^t in (8.1.9). This is due to the fact that the top elements of the $\{\mathbf{K}_i\}$ in (8.1.13) were arbitrarily written as L_0, so providing symmetry in the subsequent equations; if we had written them as 1, then the c_1 would have come out L_0 times as large.

The argument shows that the trajectory of a population under a fixed regime of mortality and fertility is the same whether worked out by a single ninth-order difference equation (8.1.3) that leads to (8.1.8), or by successive premultiplications by a matrix after the fashion of the usual population projection that leads to (8.1.18). While the fact that these come out exactly the same is not surprising to the student of difference equations, the ninth-order equation, not often used in population study, gave us the result common to the two much more naturally. This was the reason for introducing it.

The proof so far applies only to the first age group. It may be extended to any other age group, say the $(i + 1)$th, $K_{5i}^{(t)}$, by noting that $K_{5i}^{(t)} = K_0^{(t-i)}L_{5i}/L_0$, as exemplified in (8.1.1). Writing out (8.1.8) with $t - i$ in place of t, and then substituting for $K_0^{(t-i)}$ the equivalent $K_{5i}^{(t)}L_0/L_{5i}$, gives

$$\begin{vmatrix} K_{5i}^{(t)}/L_{5i} & \lambda_1^{t-i} & \lambda_2^{t-i} & \cdots & \lambda_9^{t-i} \\ K_0^{(0)}/L_0 & 1 & 1 & \cdots & 1 \\ K_5^{(0)}/L_5 & \lambda_1^{-1} & \lambda_2^{-1} & \cdots & \lambda_9^{-1} \\ \vdots & & & & \vdots \\ K_{40}^{(0)}/L_{40} & \lambda_1^{-8} & \lambda_2^{-8} & \cdots & \lambda_9^{-8} \end{vmatrix} = 0\,, \tag{8.1.19}$$

from which we can obtain $K_{5i}^{(t)}/L_{5i}$ as a ratio of two determinants, one of tenth order with zero in the upper left divided by one of ninth order which we have called $|\mathbf{B}|$. This provides the required extension of (8.1.8) and (8.1.9).

8.2. MATRIX AND INTEGRAL EQUATION

The trajectory of births was established in Chapter 5 on a continuous model by the integral equation

$$B(t) = G(t) + \int_0^t B(t-x)p(x)m(x)\,dx\,, \tag{8.2.1}$$

whose solution is

$$B(t) = Q_1e^{r_1t} + Q_2e^{r_2t} + \cdots\,, \tag{8.2.2}$$

where the r's are the zeros of the characteristic equation

$$\psi(r) - 1 = \int_\alpha^\beta e^{-rx}p(x)m(x)\,dx - 1 = 0\,, \tag{8.2.3}$$

and the Q's are constants which for the particular initial age distribution of B_0 children aged 0 take the form

$$Q_i = \frac{B_0}{\int_\alpha^\beta xe^{-r_ix}p(x)m(x)\,dx} = \frac{B_0}{-\psi'(r_i)}\,. \tag{8.2.4}$$

An approximation to (8.2.3) was given as (5.3.2). If we write $\lambda = e^{5r}$ and multiply by λ^9, supposing 45 the upper limit of positive fertility for this argument, (5.3.2) becomes

$$l_0\lambda^9 - L_{10}F_{10}\lambda^{6.5} - L_{15}F_{15}\lambda^{5.5} - L_{20}F_{20}\lambda^{4.5} - \cdots - L_{40}F_{40}\lambda^{0.5} = 0\,. \tag{8.2.5}$$

Equation (8.2.5) is not identical with (8.1.4), but will be shown to converge to the same integral, as the grouping interval for age and time is diminished.

Asymptotic Equivalence of Characteristic Roots

To prove that the characteristic equation $|\mathbf{M} - \lambda\mathbf{I}| = 0$ of the projection matrix becomes equivalent to (8.2.5) as the interval of time and age is shortened, we think of doing the projection when the interval is s, a fraction of a year.

Then the projection matrix $\mathbf{M}_s$ would be a square array containing $45/s \times 45/s$ elements. Its subdiagonal would contain $(45/s) - 1$ elements, each a ratio of the form ${}_sL_{x+s}/{}_sL_x$, where x is a multiple of s, and

$$ {}_sL_x = \int_0^s l(x+t)\,dt\,. $$

Its top row would consist of such expressions as

$$ \frac{{}_sL_0}{2l_0}\left({}_sF_x + \frac{{}_sL_{x+s}}{{}_sL_x}\,{}_sF_{x+s}\right). $$

When the characteristic equation $|\mathbf{M}_s - \lambda\mathbf{I}| = 0$ is expanded, it is [by analogy to (8.1.4) and without the prefix s which here applies to all L and F]:

$$ l_0\lambda^{45/s} - \left(\frac{L_{15}F_{15}}{2}\right)\lambda^{30/s} - \left(\frac{L_{15}F_{15} + L_{15+s}F_{15+s}}{2}\right)\lambda^{(30-s)/s} - \cdots $$

$$ - \left(\frac{L_{x-s}F_{x-s} + L_xF_x}{2}\right)\lambda^{(45-x)/s} - \cdots = 0\,, \qquad (8.2.6) $$

15 and 45 being multiples of s. If s is 1/10 of a year, then the degree of (8.2.6) would be $45/s = 450$.

Dividing (8.2.6) by $\lambda^{45/s}$, and then replacing λ by its equivalent e^{rs}, yields the typical consecutive terms

$$ \tfrac{1}{2}(L_{x-s}F_{x-s} + L_xF_x)e^{-rx} + \tfrac{1}{2}(L_xF_x + L_{x+s}F_{x+s})e^{-r(x+s)}\,. $$

On reassembling by putting together the two elements involving L_xF_x, we have for (8.2.6)

$$ \sum_{15}^{45-s} L_xF_x(e^{-r(x+s/2)})\left(\frac{e^{rs/2} + e^{-rs/2}}{2}\right) = l_0\,, $$

or

$$ \left(1 + \frac{r^2s^2}{2!\,4} + \cdots\right)\sum_{15}^{45-s} L_xF_xe^{-r(x+s/2)} = l_0\,. $$

As s tends to zero, the term in parentheses (which is the hyperbolic cosine of $rs/2$) tends to 1. The summand contains L_xF_x, the number of girl children born in the stationary population to women between x and $x + s$ years of age, and a discount factor, $e^{-r(x+s/2)}$, from the middle of the interval $(x, x + s)$ back to birth. If as s diminishes L_xF_x tends to $l(x)m(x)\,dx$, then the characteristic equation (8.2.6) becomes

$$ \int_{15}^{45} e^{-rx}l(x)m(x)\,dx = l_0\,, $$

which is what it was for the integral equation, i.e., (8.2.3), with $l(x)/l_0$ in place of $p(x)$. From the equivalence of the characteristic equations $|\mathbf{M} - \lambda\mathbf{I}| = 0$ of Chapter 3 and $\psi(r) = 1$ of Chapter 5, it follows that the roots $\lambda_1, \lambda_2, \ldots,$ of the former, when transformed as $(\ln \lambda_1)/s$, $(\ln \lambda_2)/s$, ..., converge in number and value to the roots r_1, r_2, ..., of the latter as s tends to zero. We shall now see what happens to the pattern of the λ referring to $s = 5$, five-year age intervals, when transformed to $r = (\ln \lambda)/5$.

Mapping of the Roots λ and r

Mapping of λ on r hinges solely on the relation $\lambda = e^{5r}$, on which some general observations can be made (Kober, 1952, pp. 85–86; Pierpont, 1959, pp. 102–111). We will write $\lambda = u + iv$ and $r = x + iy$, where u, v, x, and y are real.

The λ-plane is shown in Fig. 8.1 as being divided into two parts by the unit circle, and the mapping carries the points λ of $|\lambda| > 1$, that is, outside the unit circle, to $x > 0$, that is, to the half-plane on the right of the ordinate $x = 0$ in r. Points inside the unit circle ($|\lambda| < 1$) map onto the left of the r-plane ($x < 0$). Moreover, the entire λ-plane maps into a horizontal strip on the r-plane of width $2\pi/5$, from $y = 0$ to $y = 0.4$. The strip is repeated from $y = 0.4(m + 1)\pi$ to $y = 0.4(m + 2)\pi$, $m = 0, \pm 1, \pm 2, \ldots$, and each point of the λ-plane therefore maps an infinite number of times into the r-plane. Uniqueness in the representation in both directions can be secured by cutting along the positive real axis of λ and never crossing the cut. In the 9×9 representation of the matrix there will be 9 roots in the λ-plane and 9 roots indefinitely repeated in successive strips in the r-plane. Any set of these in a band of width $2\pi/5$ constitutes a solution of the characteristic equation (Goodman, 1968a). The locations of the several roots may be matched between the λ-plane and the r-plane by dividing the latter into horizontal substrips, each mapping the quadrant of the circle marked with the corresponding letter.

We see in Fig. 8.1 the latent roots for the female population of the United States on 1963 data. The roots λ are on the right hand side, the three of importance being identified as λ_1, λ_2, and λ_3; corresponding to these are r_1, r_2, and r_3. For an increasing population, λ_1 is outside the unit circle and r_1 is to the right of the y-axis. The six roots after r_1, r_2, and r_3 are considerably to the left of the y-axis in the r-plane and correspond to roots within a circle measuring about $|\lambda| = \frac{1}{2}$ in the λ-plane. Note the striking difference between the pattern of r_1, r_2 here and that under any of the three graduations of Fig. 6.1. The sensitivity of the higher roots to the representation of the maternity function parallels their lesser demographic significance (Coale, 1967).

As the trajectory of the population is traced out under the supposed fixed regime of fertility and mortality, the several roots of λ are raised to powers, and this means that all but λ_1 follow spirals steadily down into the center of the circle. For complex $\lambda = |\lambda|e^{i\theta}$, we have $\lambda^t = |\lambda|^t(\cos t\theta + i \sin t\theta)$. By itself $\cos t\theta + i \sin t\theta$ would simply trace out an ever repeated circle; with the diminishing multiplier the circle becomes a spiral of diminishing radius. The corresponding movement in the r-plane will be outward toward the left. How would the three curves of Fig. 6.1 map on to the λ-plane, and how would they change in configuration with increase of t?

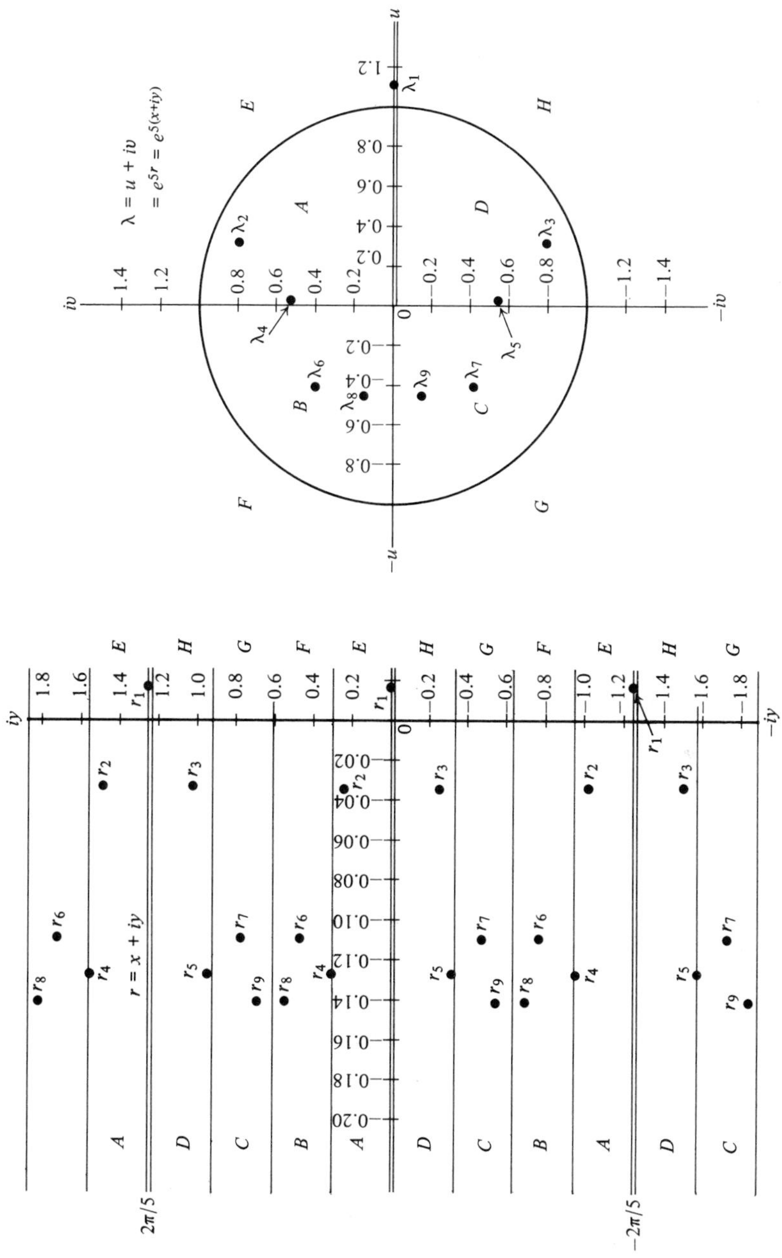

Fig. 8.1 Mapping of λ-plane on r-plane.

The Meeting of an Initial Condition on the Integral Equation and the Matrix

The reconciliation of Q_i of (8.2.2) and c_i of (8.1.17), where an arbitrary age distribution $\{\mathbf{K}^{(0)}\}$ is the start of the trajectory, is somewhat involved; our argument will be confined to an initial population of $K_0^{(0)}$ children 0–4 years of age, say of female sex. Then writing $K_5^{(0)} = K_{10}^{(0)} = \cdots = K_{40}^{(0)} = 0$ in (8.1.9), we find that the coefficient of λ_1^t appears as

$$c_1 = K_0^{(0)}|\mathbf{B}_{11}|/|\mathbf{B}|\,, \tag{8.2.7}$$

where $\mathbf{B}$ is the matrix of the latent roots given in (8.1.14). It is evident that $|\mathbf{B}|$ vanishes when $\lambda_i^{-1} = \lambda_j^{-1}$, $1 \le i \ne j \le 9$, and therefore $\lambda_i^{-1} - \lambda_j^{-1}$ must be a factor. Similarly, $|\mathbf{B}_{11}|$ vanishes for $\lambda_i^{-1} = \lambda_j^{-1}$, $2 \le i \ne j \le 9$, and hence $\lambda_i^{-1} - \lambda_j^{-1}$, $i, j \ne 1$, must be a factor; $|\mathbf{B}_{11}|$ also has the factors $\lambda_2^{-1}, \lambda_3^{-1}, \ldots, \lambda_9^{-1}$. Comparison of any term in $|\mathbf{B}|$ with the corresponding term in the product

$$|\mathbf{B}| = C(\lambda_1^{-1} - \lambda_2^{-1})(\lambda_1^{-1} - \lambda_3^{-1}) \cdots (\lambda_8^{-1} - \lambda_9^{-1})$$

will tell us what the constant C is. The principal diagonal of $|\mathbf{B}|$, which is $\lambda_2^{-1}\lambda_3^{-2} \cdots \lambda_9^{-8}$, corresponds to the product of all the right-hand terms in the several factors of

$$(\lambda_1^{-1} - \lambda_2^{-1})(\lambda_1^{-1} - \lambda_3^{-1}) \cdots (\lambda_8^{-1} - \lambda_9^{-1})\,,$$

or

$$(-\lambda_2)^{-1}(-\lambda_3)^{-2} \cdots (-\lambda_9)^{-8}\,.$$

Show this product to be positive and hence that $C = 1$. This argument takes advantage of the properties of *Vandermonde* or *simple alternant* determinants (Muir, 1960, p. 327; Householder, 1953, p. 91) of which $|\mathbf{B}|$ is typical.

A similar argument may be applied to the cofactor $|\mathbf{B}_{11}|$, with the result:

$$|\mathbf{B}_{11}| = \lambda_2^{-1}\lambda_3^{-1} \cdots \lambda_9^{-1}(\lambda_2^{-1} - \lambda_3^{-1})(\lambda_2^{-1} - \lambda_4^{-1}) \cdots (\lambda_8^{-1} - \lambda_9^{-1})\,. \tag{8.2.8}$$

After the factors common to numerator and denominator are removed from (8.2.7) there remains only

$$c_1 = \frac{K_0^{(0)}\lambda_2^{-1}\lambda_3^{-1} \cdots \lambda_9^{-1}}{(\lambda_1^{-1} - \lambda_2^{-1})(\lambda_1^{-1} - \lambda_3^{-1}) \cdots (\lambda_1^{-1} - \lambda_9^{-1})}\,, \tag{8.2.9}$$

and multiplying numerator and denominator of (8.2.9) by $\lambda_1^8\lambda_2\lambda_3 \cdots \lambda_9$, we have

$$c_1 = \frac{K_0^{(0)}\lambda_1^8}{(\lambda_1 - \lambda_2)(\lambda_1 - \lambda_3) \cdots (\lambda_1 - \lambda_9)}\,. \tag{8.2.10}$$

The denominator of the right-hand side of (8.2.10) is equivalent to

$$\lim_{\lambda \to \lambda_1} \frac{(\lambda - \lambda_1)(\lambda - \lambda_2) \cdots (\lambda - \lambda_9)}{\lambda - \lambda_1}\,, \tag{8.2.11}$$

where now the numerator under the limit must be the polynomial $f(\lambda)$ of the characteristic equation $f(\lambda) = |\mathbf{M} - \lambda\mathbf{I}| = 0$, given as (8.1.4) above. The limit in (8.2.11) is

$$\lim_{\lambda \to \lambda_1} \frac{f(\lambda) - f(\lambda_1)}{\lambda - \lambda_1} = f'(\lambda_1)\,, \tag{8.2.12}$$

since $f(\lambda_1) = 0$, and (8.2.12) is $f'(\lambda_1)$ by the usual definition of a derivative.

Substituting (8.2.12) for the denominator of (8.2.10) gives the coefficient of λ_1^t in the expansion (8.1.5) as c_1:

$$c_1 = K_0^{(0)}\lambda_1^8/f'(\lambda_1)\,. \tag{8.2.13}$$

This will be compared with Qi, $i = 1$, of (8.2.4). Demonstrating the equivalence to within a factor of 5 of the right-hand sides of (8.2.13) and (8.2.4) will complete the proof.

We have shown the resemblance of $\psi(r) - 1 = 0$ and $f(\lambda) = |\mathbf{M} - \lambda\mathbf{I}| = 0$, the characteristic equations of the integral equation and the matrix, respectively; they are not identical for any finite width of interval, but they are approximations to the same limiting expression as the interval of time and age tends to zero, when e^{5r} in $\psi(r) - 1$ is translated as λ and we multiply by $-\lambda^9$. If $e^{5r} = \lambda$, then $r = 0.2 \ln \lambda$. If

$$f(\lambda) = -\lambda^9(\psi(r) - 1)\,, \tag{8.2.14}$$

then, differentiating with respect to λ,

$$f'(\lambda) = -\lambda^9(\psi'(r))\frac{dr}{d\lambda} - 9\lambda^8(\psi(r) - 1) = -\lambda^9(\psi'(r))\frac{dr}{d\lambda}$$

at points which are roots of the characteristic equation $\psi(r) = 1$. Finally, since

$$\frac{dr}{d\lambda} = \frac{d(0.2 \ln \lambda)}{d\lambda} = \frac{0.2}{\lambda}\,,$$

the above expression for $f'(\lambda)$ becomes

$$f'(\lambda) = -0.2\lambda^8\psi'(r) \tag{8.2.15}$$

for any root $\lambda_i = e^{5r_i}$, $i = 1, 2, \ldots, 9$.

Replacing $f'(\lambda_1)$ in (8.2.13) by its equivalent in (8.2.15) yields

$$c_1 = \frac{K_0^{(0)}\lambda_1^8}{f'(\lambda_1)} = -\frac{K_0^{(0)}\lambda_1^8}{0.2\lambda_1^8\psi'(r_1)} = -\frac{5K_0^{(0)}}{\psi'(r_1)}\,, \tag{8.2.16}$$

which is five times the Q_1 of (8.2.4) except that the starting point in (8.2.4), the integral equation, is B_0 births and that in the present matrix representation it is $K_0^{(0)}$ children under five years of age. Since mortality under age five is fixed, we need not concern ourselves with the difference here. The c's are coefficients to be applied to the λ_i^t in order to produce the population under five years of age at time t, as inspection of (8.1.5) shows, and it is therefore necessary that the (arbitrary) $K_0^{(0)}$ somehow enter into each c. On the other hand, the Q's in (8.2.2) are coefficients to be applied to the $e^{r_i t}$ to produce $B(t)$ births at time t, and each Q must therefore contain the (arbitrary) B_0 initial births.

The 5 on the right of (8.2.16) enters because the unit for time counting in the matrix is five years, as can be seen by tracing the reasoning back through (8.2.15) to the expression $e^{5r} = \lambda$ just preceding (8.2.14). If we had used for the projection the (somewhat more cumbersome) 45×45 matrix, in whose characteristic equation λ would represent the ratio of increase for one year, and e^r would equal λ, then nothing would have been changed except that the 0.2 would not have appeared in (8.2.15) nor the 5 in (8.2.16). A factor of five was applied for this same reason to $B(t)$, $t > 0$, of the first column of Table 5.9 when it was compared with Tables 5.6 and 5.7.

This proof of the asymptotic equivalence of the real coefficients Q_1 and c_1 may be extended to the complex coefficients Q_i and c_i, $i = 2, 3, \ldots, 9$.

8.3. SUMMARY OF SOLUTIONS

The population projection can be analyzed by yet other means than first-order difference equations (Chapter 2), the ninth-order equation (8.1.3) and the integral equation (8.2.1). The argument of Section 5.6 led to a solution in partial fractions and gave rise to a further finite approximation to the characteristic roots. The reader who is interested may undertake algebraic manipulation similar to that of Section 8.2 and prove that the partial fraction method is equivalent to the other three as the interval of time and age becomes small. The proof, as before, will deal separately with (a) the characteristic roots and (b) the coefficients which make the result conform to given initial conditions.

One way of summing up the methods appearing in the literature, whose presentation and reconciliation have been the subject of this and the preceding chapters, is in the form of a tree (Table 8.1) whose two main branches are the discrete and continuous formulations.

The exposition started in Chapter 2 with the population projection at the points *b* and *d* in the tree of Table 8.1. In Chapter 8 we derived a ninth-order difference equation *f* and showed its solution in the form of a determinant *j*. This determinantal solution looks different from the Leslie matrix analysis *e* of Chapter 3, but the agreement of the two has been demonstrated.

Attention was given in Chapter 5 to the two forms of the continuous analysis, *g* and *h*, whose identical result was quoted from Lotka (1939c) and Feller (1941). The argument of Chapter 8 concentrated on the comparison of *j* and *e* on the one hand with *g* and *h* on the other, first in respect of eigenvalues, and then in respect of the constants used to fit to an initial condition consisting of a number of births occurring at a given moment.

Alternative Projection Matrices

So much for the asymptotic agreement of the several procedures for small intervals of age and time. On the side of computation, it is of interest to know how

Table 8.1 Models for deterministic analysis of the one-sex population with fixed age-specific rates of birth and death

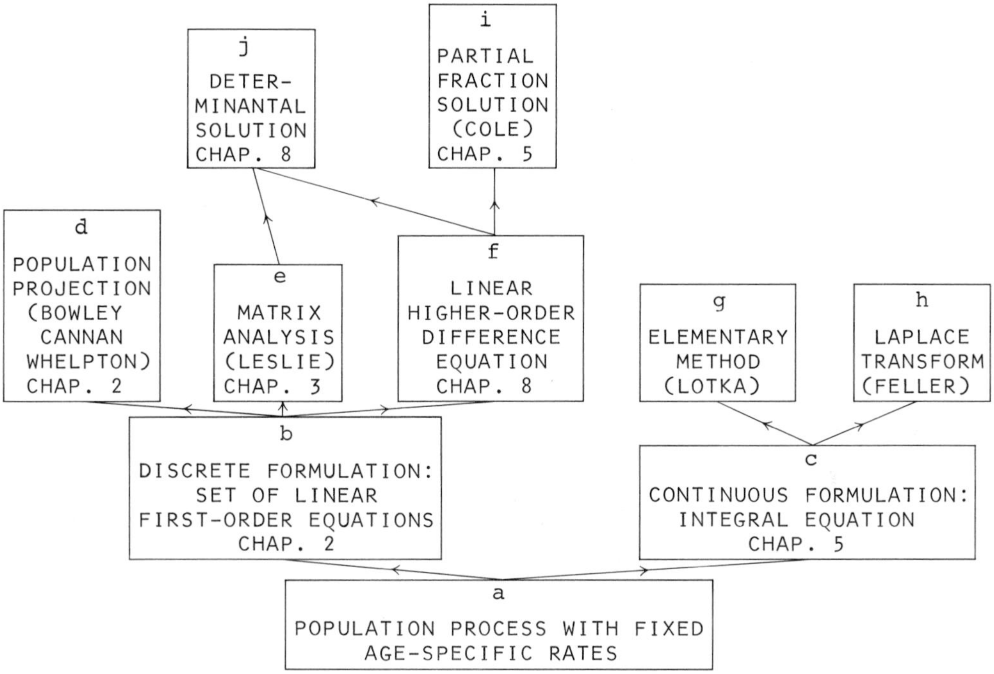

the several formulas differ when applied to data in five-year intervals of age and time. Each of the points of view here developed could be carried through the entire range of population analysis. For example, we could use the usual approximation to the integral equation, or the partial fraction solution of the recurrence equation, to project the population. To any equation of the form of (8.1.4) there is a corresponding matrix which will serve for projection. Instead of going from **M** to $f(\lambda) = |\mathbf{M} - \lambda\mathbf{I}| = 0$, we could choose $f(\lambda) = 0$ first, and then from it find **M**. The matrix which corresponds to a characteristic equation is not unique in principle, but it is virtually so in practice when we insist also that the matrix have fertility elements in its first row, survivorships in its subdiagonal, and zeros elsewhere.

A general characteristic equation may be written

$$f(\lambda) = \lambda^9 - u_0\lambda^8 - u_1\lambda^7 - u_2\lambda^6 - u_3\lambda^5 - \cdots - u_8 = 0\,, \qquad (8.3.1)$$

where for human populations, u_0 and u_1 are zero or negligible. Then the top row of a matrix **M** corresponding to it is

$$u_0 \qquad \frac{L_0}{L_5}u_1 \qquad \frac{L_0}{L_{10}}u_2 \qquad \frac{L_0}{L_{15}}u_3 \qquad \frac{L_0}{L_{20}}u_4 \cdots \frac{L_0}{L_{40}}u_8\,,$$

Table 8.2 Matrix (2.1.9) and the matrix whose first row is (8.3.5), United States females, 1960, showing also $r = 0.2 \ln \lambda$ for each root*

CHARACTERISTIC EQUATIONS $|\underset{\sim}{M} - \lambda \underset{\sim}{I}| = 0$:

PROJECTION MATRIX (3.2.4): $|\underset{\sim}{M} - \lambda \underset{\sim}{I}| = \lambda^{10} - 0.0010\lambda^{8}$
$- 0.1066\lambda^{7} - 0.4115\lambda^{6} - 0.5408\lambda^{5} - 0.3685\lambda^{4} - 0.1998\lambda^{3}$
$- 0.0842\lambda^{2} - 0.0191\lambda - 0.0011 = 0,$

MATRIX WHOSE FIRST ROW IS (8.3.4): $|\underset{\sim}{M} - \lambda \underset{\sim}{I}| = \lambda^{10}$
$- 0.0020\lambda^{7} - 0.2228\lambda^{6} - 0.6449\lambda^{5} - 0.4954\lambda^{4} - 0.2817\lambda^{3}$
$- 0.1396\lambda^{2} - 0.0379\lambda - 0.0023 = 0.$

	PROJECTION MATRIX (3.2.4)	MATRIX WHOSE FIRST ROW IS (8.3.4)
λ_1	1.11182	1.11151
λ_2, λ_3	0.3018 ± 0.7984i	0.4033 ± 0.8497i
λ_4, λ_5	0.0246 ± 0.5285i	0.0363 ± 0.5302i
λ_6, λ_7	-0.4314 ± 0.3645i	-0.5314 ± 0.4705i
λ_8, λ_9	-0.4096 ± 0.1283i	-0.4231 ± 0.1484i
λ_{10}	-0.0825	-0.0818
r_1	0.02120	0.02114
r_2, r_3	-0.0317 ± 0.2420i	-0.0123 ± 0.2255i
r_4, r_5	-0.1273 ± 0.3049i	-0.1264 ± 0.3005i
r_6, r_7	-0.1143 ± 0.4880i	-0.0686 ± 0.4834i
r_8, r_9	-0.1691 ± 0.5676i	-0.1604 ± 0.5608i
r_{10}	-0.4989	-0.5007

VALUES OF r OBTAINED AS 0.2 ln λ ARE SUBJECT TO AN ARBITRARY ADDITION OF (0.2)(2πn), n = 0, ±1, ±2, ... COMPLETE SETS OF r'S, WHICH SUFFICE TO GIVE ALL OF THE λ'S, MAY BE SELECTED IN VARIOUS WAYS; THE SELECTION HERE IS OF THOSE WHOSE IMAGINARY TERM IS IN A RISING SEQUENCE FROM ZERO TO π/5 = 0.628, AND THEIR CONJUGATES.

* Births adjusted.

the $(i+1)$th element of the top row being

$$\frac{L_0}{L_{5i}}u_i\,, \quad i = 0, 1, \ldots, 8\,, \tag{8.3.2}$$

and the subdiagonal

$$m_{i+1,i} = \frac{L_{5i}}{L_{5(i-1)}}\,, \quad i = 1, 2, \ldots, 8\,, \tag{8.3.3}$$

as may be shown by evaluating $|\mathbf{M} - \lambda\mathbf{I}|$ for this matrix and showing that its $|\mathbf{M} - \lambda\mathbf{I}|$ is the same as $f(\lambda)$ of (8.3.1).

For example, we may start with the characteristic equation (5.3.2) or (8.2.5) and set up a projection matrix which will be equivalent to it. Matching (8.2.5) with (8.3.1) shows that u_i is

$$u_i = \frac{L_{5i}F_{5i}}{l_0}\lambda^{1/2}\,, \quad i = 2, 3, \ldots, 8\,, \tag{8.3.4}$$

and $\lambda_1^{1/2}$, the square root of the positive eigenvalue, may be put in place of $\lambda^{1/2}$. Hence the top row of a matrix whose projection would be asymptotically identical with the solution of the integral equation $Q_1e^{r_1t}$ in the approximation (8.2.5) for $r = 0.2 \ln \sqrt{\lambda}$ is

$$0 \quad 0 \quad F_{10}\frac{L_0}{l_0}\sqrt{\lambda_1} \quad F_{15}\frac{L_0}{l_0}\sqrt{\lambda_1} \quad F_{20}\frac{L_0}{l_0}\sqrt{\lambda_1} \quad \ldots, \tag{8.3.5}$$

and the subdiagonal would be unchanged from (8.3.3). This form of the projection matrix was suggested to me by Norman Carrier.

The roots of the two forms are shown in Table 8.2, arranged in order of increasing frequency y. The complex parts y of $r = 0.2 \ln \lambda$ correspond to waves of period 26.0[$=2\pi/0.2420$], 20.6, 12.9, and 11.1 years in the projection matrix version, and to 27.8, 20.9, 13.0, and 11.0 years on the matrix with (8.3.5), which are not grossly different. The real parts for the first and third complex roots are, however, very different between the two approximations. For r_2, r_3, some of this may be traced back to the amount of variance in the net maternity function implied by (3.2.4), which is different from that implied by (8.3.5); to see how much is due to this, one may use the expression for the real part x from the Hadwiger fitting given in (6.4.9).

Alternatively to the two matrices of (3.2.4) and (8.3.5), whose roots appear in Table 8.2, we could use (8.3.1) and the argument following it to make projection matrices corresponding to the partial fraction form (5.8.7) and the Laplace transform method embodied in (5.7.5).

The three continuous versions of the net maternity function discussed in Chapter 6 might also be converted into projection matrices, as the reader may show. These, along with the four forms which use the data in five-year age groups, constitute seven methods altogether. Still others are potentially available, but the present volume will go no further with the one-sex model by age.

CHAPTER 9

POPULATION TIME SERIES

The preceding chapters work out the consequences of the assumption of fixed age-specific rates of mortality and fertility. They have said nothing about fitting particular analytical curves to changing population numbers. In the present chapter we investigate the curve of preceding births, $B(t)$, implied by a given set of changes in the numbers of people, $N(t)$, and will pay no attention to age distribution. Lotka (1939b) developed some of this theory in pursuing his interest in the logistic curve, (9.2.4) below; he showed in particular that when $N(t)$ follows a logistic, so does $B(t)$ to a close approximation. Since Lotka's time, the logistic has come to seem less useful in population analysis, and in our study it is used as a means of exemplifying some general procedures rather than for its own sake.

9.1. BIRTHS CORRESPONDING TO GIVEN TOTAL NUMBERS

When the births of a closed community have gone through a certain trajectory, described by $B(t)$, and a fixed life table gives the number surviving to age a on radix unity, $p(a)$, then the number of persons at each age a at time t is determinate and equal to $B(t - a)p(a)$, and by integration the total population at time t must be

$$N(t) = \int_0^\omega B(t - a)p(a)\, da\,, \tag{9.1.1}$$

as we have seen in Chapter 7 and elsewhere. Equation (9.1.1) is different from the integral equation (5.1.2) which had $B(t)$ rather than $N(t)$ on the left, and correspondingly, an additional factor of $m(a)$, the birth rate, in the integrand. We will first briefly consider $N(t)$ the unknown, and ascertain it from a given $B(t)$, and then deal with the converse problem of finding $B(t)$ corresponding to a given $N(t)$.

If we are told that the number of births is going up in arithmetic progression, say $B(t) = B(0) + ht$, then the number of persons in the population at time t must be

$$\begin{aligned} N(t) &= \int_0^\omega [B(0) + h(t - a)]p(a)\, da \\ &= [B(0) + ht]\int_0^\omega p(a)\, da - h\int_0^\omega ap(a)\, da\,. \end{aligned} \tag{9.1.2}$$

Suppose we know the constant h of the arithmetic increase of births as well as the zeroth and first cumulated sums of the number-living column of the life table, say $\quad \bar{L}_0 = \int_0^\omega p(a)\,da = \mathring{e}_0 \quad$ and $\quad \bar{L}_1 = \int_0^\omega ap(a)\,da$,

the first moment of $p(a)/\mathring{e}_0$ being $\bar{L}_1/\bar{L}_0$. Then from (9.1.2) the numbers of the population at subsequent times must be

$$N(t) = \big(B(0) + ht\big)\bar{L}_0 - h\bar{L}_1 = \big(B(0)\bar{L}_0 - h\bar{L}_1\big) + h\bar{L}_0 t\,. \qquad (9.1.3)$$

Apparently $N(t)$ is a straight line, and its slope is the slope of births h multiplied by $\bar{L}_0 = \mathring{e}_0$, the expectation of life. For Canadian females in 1965, whose life table moments including $\bar{L}_0 = \mathring{e}_0 = 75.00$ may be found in Table 7.3, we can say that if births were increasing by a uniform 5000 per year over a long period of time, population would increase by (5000)(75.00) = 375,000 per year.

If the births are a geometric progression, say $B(t) = B(0)e^{ht}$, then the population according to (9.1.1) will be

$$N(t) = \int_0^\omega B(0)e^{h(t-a)}p(a)\,da = B(0)e^{ht}\int_0^\omega e^{-ha}p(a)\,da = B(t)\int_0^\omega e^{-ha}p(a)\,da\,. \quad (9.1.4)$$

This proves that exponential births imply exponentially increasing total numbers. The number $N(t)$ at a given moment is $\int_0^\omega e^{-ha}p(a)\,da$ times the births $B(t)$; if h is r, the intrinsic rate of increase, this integral is the reciprocal of b, the intrinsic birth rate, as it ought to be from (7.2.6).

Inference in the other direction—finding the trajectory of births when the trajectory of the total number of the population is known—requires that instead of regarding (9.1.1) as a simple integral, we consider it as an integral equation whose unknown is the function $B(t)$ (Lotka, 1939b, pp. 144–161; Lotka, 1939c, pp. 44–48; Tabah, 1964, pp. 6–9). Its solution will require a somewhat different technique from the solution of (5.1.2) and will be our next task.

Still omitting age from consideration, suppose that $B(t)$ can be expressed in terms of $N(t)$ and its derivatives, say in the form

$$B(t) = c_0N(t) - c_1N'(t) + c_2\frac{N''(t)}{2!} - \cdots\,. \qquad (9.1.5)$$

Now suppose also that $B(t-a)$ can be expanded as a Taylor series around t,

$$B(t-a) = B(t) - aB'(t) + \frac{a^2}{2!}B''(t) - \cdots\,. \qquad (9.1.6)$$

The c's will turn out to be expressible as functions of the moments of the life table.

Each of the terms on the right-hand side of (9.1.6) can be represented by a series in $N(t)$ and its derivatives obtained by differentiating (9.1.5):

$$\begin{aligned} B'(t) &= c_0N'(t) - c_1N''(t) + c_2\frac{N'''(t)}{2!} - \cdots\,, \\ B''(t) &= c_0N''(t) - c_1N'''(t) + \cdots\,, \\ &\vdots \end{aligned} \qquad (9.1.7)$$

if (9.1.5) is differentiable. Substituting (9.1.5) and (9.1.7) in (9.1.6) gives

$$
\begin{aligned}
B(t-a) = c_0N(t) - {} & c_1N'(t) + c_2\frac{N''(t)}{2!} - c_3\frac{N'''(t)}{3!} + \cdots \\
& - a\left(c_0N'(t) - c_1N''(t) + c_2\frac{N'''(t)}{2!} - \cdots\right) \\
& + \frac{a^2}{2!}(c_0N''(t) - c_1N'''(t) + \cdots) \\
& - \frac{a^3}{3!}(c_0N'''(t) - \cdots) \\
& + \cdots \\
= c_0N(t) - {} & (c_1 + ac_0)N'(t) + \left(\frac{c_2}{2} + ac_1 + \frac{c_0a^2}{2}\right)N''(t) \\
& - \left(\frac{c_3}{6} + \frac{ac_2}{2} + \frac{a^2c_1}{2} + \frac{a^3c_0}{6}\right)N'''(t) + \cdots,
\end{aligned}
\tag{9.1.8}
$$

and entering this value of $B(t-a)$ in the integral equation (9.1.1) in order to solve for the c's, we have

$$
\begin{aligned}
N(t) &= \int_0^\omega \left[c_0N(t) - (c_1 + ac_0)N'(t) + (c_2 + 2ac_1 + a^2c_0)\frac{N''(t)}{2} + \cdots\right]p(a)\,da \\
&= N(t)c_0\bar{L}_0 - N'(t)(c_1\bar{L}_0 + c_0\bar{L}_1) + \frac{N''(t)}{2}(c_2\bar{L}_0 + 2c_1\bar{L}_1 + c_0\bar{L}_2) \\
&\quad - \frac{N'''(t)}{6}(c_3\bar{L}_0 + 3c_2\bar{L}_1 + 3c_1\bar{L}_2 + c_0\bar{L}_3) + \cdots
\end{aligned}
\tag{9.1.9}
$$

If (9.1.9) is an identity, then the coefficient of $N(t)$ on the right-hand side must be unity, and the coefficient of each derivative of $N(t)$ must be zero. [Prove this to be true, at least if $N(t)$ is a polynomial.] These conditions enable us to extract from (9.1.9) a set of equations in the c's and the $\bar{L}$'s:

$$
\begin{aligned}
c_0\bar{L}_0 &= 1\,, \\
c_1\bar{L}_0 + c_0\bar{L}_1 &= 0\,, \\
c_2\bar{L}_0 + 2c_1\bar{L}_1 + c_0\bar{L}_2 &= 0\,, \\
c_3\bar{L}_0 + 3c_2\bar{L}_1 + 3c_1\bar{L}_2 + c_0\bar{L}_3 &= 0\,, \\
c_4\bar{L}_0 + 4c_3\bar{L}_1 + 6c_2\bar{L}_2 + 4c_1\bar{L}_3 + c_0\bar{L}_4 &= 0\,, \\
c_5\bar{L}_0 + 5c_4\bar{L}_1 + 10c_3\bar{L}_2 + 10c_2\bar{L}_3 + 5c_1\bar{L}_4 + c_0\bar{L}_5 &= 0\,, \\
\vdots \qquad &
\end{aligned}
\tag{9.1.10}
$$

from which the c's can be successively obtained in terms of the $\bar{L}$'s:

$$
c_0 = 1/\bar{L}_0\,, \quad c_1 = -(\bar{L}_1/\bar{L}_0^2)\,, \quad c_2 = -(\bar{L}_2/\bar{L}_0^2) + 2\bar{L}_1^2/\bar{L}_0^3\,, \ldots \tag{9.1.11}
$$

Substituting the values of c from (9.1.11) in (9.1.5) gives the solution for $B(t)$:

$$B(t) = \frac{N(t)}{\bar{L}_0} + \frac{\bar{L}_1}{\bar{L}_0^2} N'(t) + \left(\frac{2\bar{L}_1^2}{\bar{L}_0^3} - \frac{\bar{L}_2}{\bar{L}_0^2}\right)\frac{N''(t)}{2} + \cdots \tag{9.1.12}$$

Equation (9.1.12) may be simplified by shifting the origin to the point $-(\bar{L}_1/\bar{L}_0)$. Writing $t = \theta - \bar{L}_1/\bar{L}_0$ and applying a Taylor expansion about θ in each term on the right of (9.1.12) results in

$$B\left(\theta - \frac{\bar{L}_1}{\bar{L}_0}\right) = \frac{N(\theta)}{\bar{L}_0} - \frac{1}{2\bar{L}_0}\left[\frac{\bar{L}_2}{\bar{L}_0} - \left(\frac{\bar{L}_1}{\bar{L}_0}\right)^2\right] N''(\theta) + \cdots, \tag{9.1.13}$$

and reverting to the original time scale t, we have

$$\mathring{e}_0 B(t) = N(t + \bar{\mu}) - \tfrac{1}{2}\bar{\sigma}^2 N''(t + \bar{\mu}) + \cdots, \tag{9.1.14}$$

where $\bar{\mu}$ is the mean and $\bar{\sigma}^2$ the variance of the life table number living, and $\mathring{e}_0 = \bar{L}_0$ is the total number living in a stationary population of radix $l_0 = 1$. For

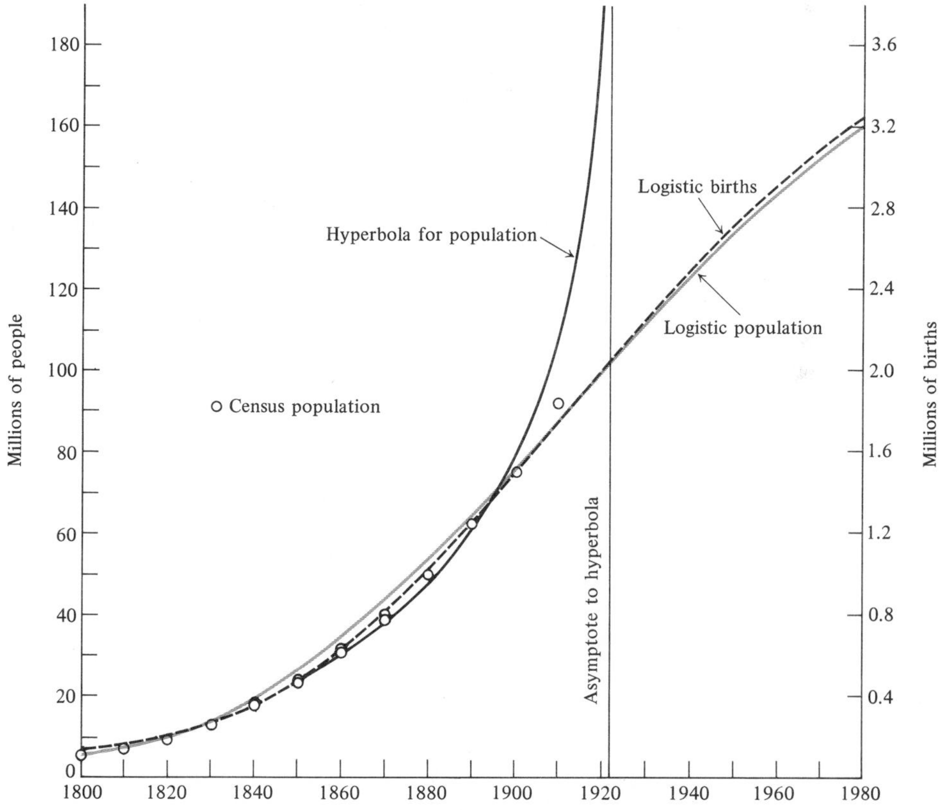

Fig. 9.1 Logistic and explosion (hyperbola) models fitted to United States census series ending 1910.

Canadian females, 1965, (9.1.13) is in thousands,

$$B(1965 - 39.63) = 0.01333N(1965) - 3.776N''(1965) + \cdots,$$

again referring to Table 7.3 for the necessary moments. The first term alone would give $(0.01333)(9{,}479) = 126$ thousands, slightly above the observed births of 1925. Note that $B(t)$ is not very sensitive to the constants of the life table, at least in the range of variation of Table 7.3, and moments of model tables might be applied. On the other hand it cannot cope with sudden changes in fertility.

The first approximation to the births is shown by (9.1.13) to be the total of the population at the given date divided by the expectation of life; the allowance for variance of the second term of (9.1.13) is a *subtraction* if the curve of total numbers is concave upward, otherwise an addition (Fig. 9.1). Note that a population where all deaths take place at the same age is implied by use of the first term only on the right-hand side of (9.1.14), and a positive variance of ages of dying is allowed for by the second term.

The application of (9.1.14) depends on an estimate of the second derivative. Such estimates are made by fitting an analytical curve to the series of observations of $N(t)$ and then differentiating on the curve. This is our next topic.

9.2. GRADUATION BY A CURVE IN WHICH THE CONSTANTS ENTER NONLINEARLY

If a curve $y = f(x)$ is to be fitted by least squares to a set of data, and if the fitting consists in finding the constants a, b, and c which enter in linear fashion, as in the function $y = a + bx + cx^2$, the set of normal equations obtained by differentiating $\sum(y - a - bx - cx^2)^2 = 0$ with respect to a, b, and c provides the complete result. If the constants do not enter linearly, as in the logistic $y = a/(1 + be^{-cx})$, a different procedure is required.

Let $s(a, b, c)$ be the sum of the squares of the departures of the fitted from the observed values, and a_0, b_0, and c_0 be approximations to a, b, and c; then by Taylor's expansion for three independent variables,

$$\begin{aligned} s(a, b, c) &= s(a_0, b_0, c_0) + (a - a_0)\left.\frac{\partial s(a, b, c)}{\partial a}\right|_{\substack{a=a_0\\ b=b_0\\ c=c_0}} + \cdots + \cdots \\ &\quad + \frac{(a - a_0)^2}{2!}\left.\frac{\partial^2 s(a, b, c)}{\partial a^2}\right|_{\substack{a=a_0\\ b=b_0\\ c=c_0}} + \cdots + \cdots \\ &\quad + (a - a_0)(b - b_0)\left.\frac{\partial^2 s(a, b, c)}{\partial a\, \partial b}\right|_{\substack{a=a_0\\ b=b_0\\ c=c_0}} + \cdots + \cdots, \end{aligned} \tag{9.2.1}$$

up to quadratic terms. For brevity the derivatives evaluated at a_0, b_0, and c_0 may be written $\partial s/\partial a_0$, $\partial s/\partial b_0$, and $\partial s/\partial c_0$. To minimize $s(a, b, c)$, differentiate with respect to a, b, and c and equate each derivative to zero, thus obtaining three linear equations, which may be expressed in matrix form as

$$\begin{bmatrix} \dfrac{\partial^2 s}{\partial a_0^2} & \dfrac{\partial^2 s}{\partial a_0\, \partial b_0} & \dfrac{\partial^2 s}{\partial a_0\, \partial c_0} \\ \dfrac{\partial^2 s}{\partial a_0\, \partial b_0} & \dfrac{\partial^2 s}{\partial b_0^2} & \dfrac{\partial^2 s}{\partial b_0\, \partial c_0} \\ \dfrac{\partial^2 s}{\partial a_0\, \partial c_0} & \dfrac{\partial^2 s}{\partial b_0\, \partial c_0} & \dfrac{\partial^2 s}{\partial c_0^2} \end{bmatrix} \begin{bmatrix} a - a_0 \\ b - b_0 \\ c - c_0 \end{bmatrix} = - \begin{bmatrix} \dfrac{\partial s}{\partial a_0} \\ \dfrac{\partial s}{\partial b_0} \\ \dfrac{\partial s}{\partial c_0} \end{bmatrix} \tag{9.2.2}$$

or, more compactly, as

$$\mathbf{HA} = -\mathbf{E}\,,$$

where $\mathbf{H}$ is the array of second derivatives of $s(a, b, c)$; $\mathbf{A}$, the departure of a from a_0, b from b_0, and c from c_0, may be called the adjustment or prediction vector; $\mathbf{E}$ is the vector of first derivatives of $s(a, b, c)$. Multiplying (9.2.2) on the left by $\mathbf{H}^{-1}$ gives the approximate solution for the adjustment vector:

$$\mathbf{A} = -\mathbf{H}^{-1}\mathbf{E}\,. \tag{9.2.3}$$

The process may be repeated with the new a taken as a_0, b as b_0, and c as c_0, until convergence is reached. More sophisticated forms of this descent method are found in Ralston (1965, p. 348) and Householder (1953, p. 132). The reader may compare (9.2.3) and generalizations of it with the Newton-Raphson procedure of (5.3.4), but with the caution that the larger the number of constants, the more serious are the problems of convergence.

The curve known as the *logistic*,

$$N(t) = \frac{a}{1 + be^{-ct}}\,, \tag{9.2.4}$$

will be fitted to the population of the United States as an example of the above procedure. Equation (9.2.4) may be verified to be the solution of the differential equation

$$N'(t) = \frac{c}{a}\{N(t)[a - N(t)]\}\,,$$

which specifies that the increase of $N(t)$ is proportional to the population already attained, $N(t)$, and also proportional to the difference between $N(t)$ and a, the asymptotic upper limit of $N(t)$. Our fitting of (9.2.4) is to the counts of the censuses from 1800 through 1910, reproduced in Table 9.1. We start with initial (guessed) trial values:

$$a = 210 \text{ millions}\,, \qquad b = 40\,, \qquad c = 0.03\,.$$

The first thing the program tells us is that the sum of the squares of deviations from the curve defined by the trial values is 176.56 (in millions as the population is in thousands). The adjustment on a for the first round was -18.77,

Table 9.1 Census and fitted population of the United States (thousands)

CONSTANTS FOR 1800-1910: a = 197.30; b = 35.60; c = 0.031186

YEAR	CENSUS COUNT*	FITTED VALUE FROM LEAST SQUARES LOGISTIC**	DIFFERENCE
1800	5,308	5,390	82
1810	7,240	7,290	50
1820	9,638	9,825	187
1830	12,866	13,180	314
1840	17,069	17,574	505
1850	23,912	23,248	-664
1860	31,443	30,443	-1000
1870	38,558	39,362	804
1880	50,156	50,109	-47
1890	62,948	62,626	-322
1900	75,995	76,642	647
1910	91,972	91,661	-311

VALUES OBTAINED ON FITTING TO 1800-1960†

CONSTANTS FOR 1800-1960: a = 256.41; b = 36.30; c = 0.02689

1800	6,874	1860	31,157	1920	105,092
1810	8,922	1870	39,298	1930	122,081
1820	11,551	1880	49,102	1940	139,288
1830	14,908	1890	60,669	1950	156,102
1840	19,164	1900	73,988	1960	171,966
1850	24,512	1910	88,902		

* Source: *Statistical Abstract of United States*, 1966, p. 5, except 1850 and 1870.
** Program provided through courtesy of Paul Meier, University of Chicago, using the method of steepest descent, which converges more rapidly than (9.2.3). The identical result was obtained by P. P. Talwar, who directly programmed (9.2.3).
† Programmed by P. P. Talwar.

for b it was -5.83, for c it was 0.001265. Hence the second cycle began with

$$a_0 = 210 - 18.77 = 191.23\,,$$
$$b_0 = 40.00 - 5.83 = 34.17\,,$$

and

$$c_0 = 0.030000 + 0.001265 = 0.031265\,.$$

The successive adjustments or predictions and the resultant values of the parameters are shown in Table 9.2. The sum of the squares of the deviations of the

Table 9.2 Successive approximations to parameters of logistic fitted to thousands of persons in United States censuses, 1800–1910

ARBITRARY INITIAL VALUES OF PARAMETERS:

$a_0 = 210.0$; $b_0 = 40.0$; $c_0 = 0.03$

INITIAL SUM OF SQUARES (ss) OF DEVIATIONS = 176.56×10^6

DESCENT METHOD FOR LEAST SQUARES, PROVIDED THROUGH COURTESY OF PAUL MEIER

ITERATION	0	1	2	3
a	210.0	191.23	197.02	197.30
b	40.0	34.17	35.55	35.60
c	0.03	0.031265	0.031190	0.031186
$ss \times 10^{-6}$	176.56	35.67	3.11	3.11

INDEPENDENT PROGRAMMING FOR LEAST SQUARES BY P.P. TALWAR, USING (9.2.3)

ITERATION	0	1	2	3
a	210.0	219.27	217.63	238.23
b	40.0	41.96	37.91	39.79
c	0.03	0.03136	0.03030	0.02925
$ss \times 10^{-6}$	176.56	12.8032	4.1227	6.2244
	4	5	6	
a	225.32	205.61	203.24	
b	38.34	36.29	36.17	
c	0.02978	0.03062	0.03086	
$ss \times 10^{-6}$	4.4300	3.8717	3.1779	
	7	8	9	
a	196.99	197.26	197.30	
b	35.56	35.60	35.60	
c	0.03119	0.03119	0.03119	
$ss \times 10^{-6}$	3.1171	3.1067	3.1067	

fitted values (at the end of the step or cycle) from the data decreases in the sequence 176.56, 35.67, 3.11, 3.11, again in millions if the data are thousands of persons. The remarkably close fit of the logistic to the United States population for 1800 to 1910 appears in Table 9.1, with the greatest departure only about 3 percent. This has been pointed out before, by Pearl and Reed (1920), and Lotka (1931a and 1939b), whose fitting was by selected points rather than least squares, but who nevertheless arrived at constants a, b, and c very similar to those of (9.3.1).

The first fitting of Table 9.2 is by an unspecified and evidently very efficient descent method; the second by (9.2.3) took nine iterations but is based on simpler theory. Results are identical.

We can continue the curve on the computer by the Taylor series

$$N(t + h) = N(t) + hN'(t) + \frac{h^2}{2!}N''(t) + \cdots,$$

proceeding step by step with $h = 0.1$ and $N'(t)$ and $N''(t)$ as given in (9.3.2) and (9.3.3) below, a technique that will be valuable for the differential equations of Chapter 13. Here we find, on starting at 1900 and applying Taylor's theorem 700 times, that $N(t)$ at 1970 has the value 167,570 thousands. This is satisfactorily checked by the direct calculation of (9.3.1) with $t = 170$, which gives 167,571 thousands. (Programming by Barbara Heyns, A. Okorafor, and K. L. Kohli.)

Agreement in relation to the real world after 1910 has been less satisfactory. By 1967 the population of the United States is already passing the 200 million mark, which is above the asymptote forecast by the logistic.

Show that the point of inflection of the logistic (9.2.4) occurs at time $t = (\ln b)/c$, making use of (9.3.3), and that in our case this is at 1914.5, thus checking the date at which the second derivative in the printout (not reproduced here) turns from positive to negative. If time t is measured from this point, the curve is described by $a/(1 + e^{-ct})$, where a and c have values identical to those in (9.2.4).

9.3. THE NEAR-LOGISTIC FORM OF BIRTHS IN A POPULATION GROWING LOGISTICALLY

The logistic for population numbers (9.2.4) as fitted by least squares in Section 9.2 to the United States census totals from 1800 to 1910 was

$$N(t) = \frac{197.30}{1 + 35.60e^{-0.031186t}} \text{ millions} \qquad (9.3.1)$$

of people, where t is in years counted from 1800. To apply now the theory of (9.1.4) relating $B(t)$ to $N(t)$, suppose that sections of $N(t)$ are representable by polynomials. We will need the derivatives:

$$N'(t) = cN(t)\left[1 - \frac{N(t)}{a}\right], \tag{9.3.2}$$

$$N''(t) = c^2N(t)\left[1 - \frac{N(t)}{a}\right]\left[1 - \frac{2N(t)}{a}\right]. \tag{9.3.3}$$

As an example consider 1900 when $N(t)$ was 76.642 millions (Table 9.1). Entering this along with $c = 0.031186$ and $a = 197.30$ in (9.3.3) gives $N''(t) = 0.01017$. If we guess for the United States, in the period prior to 1900, $\mathring{e}_0 = \bar{L}_0 = 50$ years, $\bar{\mu} = \bar{L}_1/\bar{L}_0 = 35$, and $\bar{\sigma}^2 = \bar{L}_2/\bar{L}_0 - (\bar{L}_1/\bar{L}_0)^2 = 450$, then according to (9.1.13), the births of $\bar{\mu} = 35$ years earlier (1865) would have been

$$\begin{aligned} B(1865) &= \frac{N(1900)}{50} - \frac{450}{(2)(50)} N''(1900) \\ &= 1.533 - 0.046 = 1.487 \text{ millions}. \end{aligned}$$

The first term, $N(1900)/50$ is the logistic component. At this point the births are just 0.046 million or 3 percent below a logistic curve with the same parameters as $N(t)$ except that $a = 197.30/50$ or 3.95 millions. Once the midpoint of the logistic is passed, at which $N(t) = a/2$, or about the year 1914.5 for our fitting to the United States, the births will be somewhat above the logistic (Lotka, 1933c, p. 52) (Fig. 9.1). Show that the greatest departure is where $N(t) = \left(1/2 \pm \sqrt{1/12}\right)a$.

9.4. THE POPULATION EXPLOSION

Extrapolation by indiscriminate curve fitting constitutes neither a reliable means of prediction nor an aid to scientific understanding. What is wanted is a form of curve which represents the mechanism actually operating, or some simplification of it. For a time it was thought that the logistic described such a mechanism, but students today are sceptical. The model of fruit flies growing in a jar has given way to the model of an explosion. Simplifying somewhat on von Foerster, Mora, and Amiot (1960), we fit the hyperbola

$$N(t) = \frac{a}{t_e - t}, \quad t < t_e, \tag{9.4.1}$$

to the world population figures (Durand, 1967b, p. 137),

$$N(1900) = 1650 \text{ millions}, \qquad N(1950) = 2515 \text{ millions},$$

and find for t_e, the date of the population explosion, the year 2045 A.D. (Derive a formula for making the calculation readily:

$$t_e = \frac{n_2 t_2 - n_1 t_1}{n_2 - n_1},$$

if the population is n_1 at time t_1 and n_2 at time t_2.) Hesitating, on so important a matter, to trust a single calculation, we try again with a longer-range perspective,

$$N(1750) = 791 \text{ millions}, \qquad N(1950) = 2515 \text{ millions}.$$

This time $t_e = 2042$. The value of t_e is not greatly affected by the years to which the fitting is made. The minimum conclusion to be drawn is that the world population will turn from its present trend during the next 75 years, if indeed the trend is the hyperbola (9.4.1).

The degree to which a prediction depends on the curve selected is suggested in Fig. 9.1, based on the United States population census totals to 1910 of Table 9.1. The least squares logistic moves toward an asymptote of 197 millions, while the hyperbola through 1850 and 1900 goes to infinity in 1923. We could hardly hope that either would serve as a concrete prediction, because neither has a form which takes adequate account of the mechanisms operating. Prediction is more difficult than curve fitting and, as we said in Chapter 4, involves elements of human behavior and social change far beyond the scope of this book.

The main purpose of introducing the hyperbola is to show that, as for the logistic fitting, births will nearly follow the curve if the population does. Entering (9.4.1) in (9.1.14) gives for the birth trajectory

$$B(t) \doteq \frac{1}{\bar{L}_0}\left(\frac{a}{t_e - \bar{\mu} - t}\right)\left[1 - \frac{\bar{\sigma}^2}{(t_e - \bar{\mu} - t)^2}\right], \tag{9.4.2}$$

where again $\bar{\mu}$ and $\bar{\sigma}^2$ are the mean and variance of the life table number living. The expression for $B(t)$ has no meaning for $t \geq t_e - \bar{\mu}$. At times considerably earlier than $t_e - \bar{\mu}$, the second term in the square brackets of (9.4.2) is small and positive, and $B(t)$ is below $[1/\bar{L}_0][a/(t_e - \bar{\mu} - t)]$ by an amount which increases until $t = t_e - \bar{\mu} - \bar{\sigma}\sqrt{3}$. Show that with $\bar{\mu} = 35$ and $\bar{\sigma}^2 = 400$, for $t < t_e - 3\bar{\mu}$ the birth curve will be less than 10 percent under the hyperbola

$$\frac{1}{\bar{L}_0}\left(\frac{a}{t_e - \bar{\mu} - t}\right) = \frac{N(t - \bar{\mu})}{\mathring{e}_0}.$$

Prove for the model (9.4.1) that with $t > t_e - 20$ the growth of the population exceeds the 5% per year to which the human species is physiologically limited.

To summarize the results for particular curves, we found that straight-line or exponential population growth implies a birth curve of identical form; a logistic or hyperbola for population implies a similar shape for birth except near where the hyperbola goes to infinity.

Use (9.1.14) to say what is the most general growth function for which births will have a shape similar to population.

Part IV

NUMERICAL TECHNIQUES

CHAPTER 10

INTERPOLATION AND GRADUATION

Interpolation and the other numerical methods to which it leads are necessary at many points in demographic work, and the literature on the subject is extensive and intricate (Wolfenden, 1954, pp. 134–166). This chapter is an attempt to compress as much of it as possible into a single general procedure expressed in determinantal form. Once a program has been devised for evaluating determinants, no further programming is required for the interpolation, graduation, and numerical differentiation and integration used in demography. A complete discussion is to be found in Nörlund (1924), whose approach is here followed.

10.1. STRAIGHT-LINE INTERPOLATION

A simple instance introduces the procedure that will be applied throughout. What is called the rule of false position is the method one intuitively applies in reading a table of logarithms; it corresponds to drawing a straight line on a chart between the two known points. Suppose that we know the values $y_1 = f(x_1)$ and $y_2 = f(x_2)$ for x_1 and x_2 respectively, and would like to have the value of the interpolatory function $f(x)$ for some intermediate or adjacent point x. Then if a straight line is appropriate, say $y = f(x) = Ax + B$, the conditions on the arbitrary point $(x, f(x))$ and the given points (x_1, y_1) and (x_2, y_2) are

$$Ax + B - f(x) = 0\,, \qquad Ax_1 + B - y_1 = 0\,, \qquad Ax_2 + B - y_2 = 0\,. \tag{10.1.1}$$

The three equations will be consistent with one another if

$$\begin{vmatrix} x & 1 & -f(x) \\ x_1 & 1 & -y_1 \\ x_2 & 1 & -y_2 \end{vmatrix} = 0\,, \tag{10.1.2}$$

where all the quantities in the second and third rows are known and A and B have been eliminated (Muir, 1960, p. 13). Solving (10.1.2) gives the value of $f(x)$ corresponding to an arbitrary x:

$$f(x) = \frac{\begin{vmatrix} x & 1 & 0 \\ x_1 & 1 & -y_1 \\ x_2 & 1 & -y_2 \end{vmatrix}}{\begin{vmatrix} x_1 & 1 \\ x_2 & 1 \end{vmatrix}} = \left(\frac{y_1 - y_2}{x_1 - x_2}\right)x + \frac{x_1y_2 - x_2y_1}{x_1 - x_2}\,. \tag{10.1.3}$$

To bring (10.1.2) or (10.1.3) into the form of divided differences, convenient when a desk calculator is used, change signs in the last column, subtract the second row from the third,

$$\begin{vmatrix} x & 1 & f(x) \\ x_1 & 1 & y_1 \\ x_2 - x_1 & 0 & y_2 - y_1 \end{vmatrix} = 0 ,$$

and divide the new third row by $x_2 - x_1$:

$$\begin{vmatrix} x & 1 & f(x) \\ x_1 & 1 & y_1 \\ 1 & 0 & \dfrac{y_2 - y_1}{x_2 - x_1} \end{vmatrix} = 0 .$$

The element in the lower right is

$$[y_1, y_2] = \frac{y_2 - y_1}{x_2 - x_1} ,$$

a divided difference, readily calculated either from observations or from other tabular values. Expanding the determinant by the third column gives

$$f(x) = y_1 + (x - x_1)[y_1, y_2] . \qquad (10.1.4)$$

The reader unfamiliar with divided differences is asked to use (10.1.4) to interpolate l_{40} from $l_{35} = 92{,}991$ and $l_{50} = 86{,}204$. He can then check his answer by writing and evaluating a determinant of the form of (10.1.2). The life table gives $l_{40} = 91{,}601$. Why is the interpolation inaccurate and in a downward direction? (Data for United States males, 1964, given in Table 1.3.)

10.2. DETERMINANTAL EXPRESSIONS FOR POLYNOMIAL INTERPOLATION

The advantage of determinants becomes apparent in the several directions of generalization of the straight-line rule. If we have three given points, not necessarily at equal intervals, and wish to interpolate with a quadratic, say $Ax^2 + Bx + C$, then the condition under which the four equations linear in the constants,

$$\begin{aligned} Ax^2 + Bx + C - f(x) &= 0 , \\ Ax_1^2 + Bx_1 + C - y_1 &= 0 , \\ Ax_2^2 + Bx_2 + C - y_2 &= 0 , \\ Ax_3^2 + Bx_3 + C - y_3 &= 0 , \end{aligned} \qquad (10.2.1)$$

are consistent is

$$\begin{vmatrix} x^2 & x & 1 & f(x) \\ x_1^2 & x_1 & 1 & y_1 \\ x_2^2 & x_2 & 1 & y_2 \\ x_3^2 & x_3 & 1 & y_3 \end{vmatrix} = 0 , \qquad (10.2.2)$$

from which

$$f(x) = \frac{\begin{vmatrix} x^2 & x & 1 & 0 \\ x_1^2 & x_1 & 1 & y_1 \\ x_2^2 & x_2 & 1 & y_2 \\ x_3^2 & x_3 & 1 & y_3 \end{vmatrix}}{\begin{vmatrix} x_1^2 & x_1 & 1 \\ x_2^2 & x_2 & 1 \\ x_3^2 & x_3 & 1 \end{vmatrix}}. \tag{10.2.3}$$

We verify that (10.2.2) and (10.2.3) pass through (x_1, y_1) by putting $x = x_1$ and expanding by the fourth column; nothing remains of (10.2.3) but $f(x_1) = y_1$. That the other conditions are met is verified in the same way. The extension to n given values takes the form of an $(n + 1) \times (n + 1)$ determinant, fitting a curve of degree $n - 1$.

To be satisfied that the determinantal equation (10.2.2) is the same as Newton's divided difference formula, we first subtract the third row from the fourth and divide the new fourth by $x_3 - x_2$; next we subtract the second row from the third and divide the new third by $x_2 - x_1$. Finally, we subtract the third, as it then stands, from the fourth and divide by $x_3 - x_1$, writing

$$[y_1, y_2, y_3] = \frac{[y_2, y_3] - [y_1, y_2]}{x_3 - x_1}.$$

The result is

$$\begin{vmatrix} x^2 & x & 1 & f(x) \\ x_1^2 & x_1 & 1 & y_1 \\ x_1 + x_2 & 1 & 0 & [y_1, y_2] \\ 1 & 0 & 0 & [y_1, y_2, y_3] \end{vmatrix} = 0, \tag{10.2.4}$$

which when expanded by its last column is

$$f(x) = y_1 + (x - x_1)[y_1, y_2] + (x - x_1)(x - x_2)[y_1, y_2, y_3].$$

The Waring-Lagrange formula for a polynomial passing through (x_1, y_1), (x_2, y_2), (x_3, y_3) is

$$f(x) = \frac{(x - x_2)(x - x_3)}{(x_1 - x_2)(x_1 - x_3)} y_1 + \frac{(x - x_3)(x - x_1)}{(x_2 - x_3)(x_2 - x_1)} y_2 + \frac{(x - x_1)(x - x_2)}{(x_3 - x_1)(x_3 - x_2)} y_3. \tag{10.2.5}$$

Prove that this is identical with (10.2.3), factoring the Vandermonde determinants of (10.2.3) as done for a quite different purpose in (8.2.8) for (8.1.16). The result may be extended to polynomial interpolation among n points (Hildebrand, 1956, p. 60).

The precision of quadratic interpolation may be exhibited by finding r for Netherlands females, 1965, using the computed values of $\psi(r)$ in Table 5.1. One might enter as y of (10.2.5) the function $\psi(r)$, and x would then be r, but this would require that a quadratic be solved for $\psi(r) = 1$. The quadratic is avoided by entering instead r for y in (10.2.5) and $\psi(r)$ for x. If $y_1 = 0.010$, $y_2 = 0.012$, $y_3 = 0.014$, and $x_1 = \psi(0.010)$, $x_2 = \psi(0.012)$, $x_3 = \psi(0.014)$, then the quantities needed are obtained from Table 5.1 as

$$\begin{aligned}
x - x_1 &= 1.00000 - 1.07474 = -0.07474\,, \\
x - x_2 &= 1.00000 - 1.01499 = -0.01499\,, \\
x - x_3 &= 1.00000 - 0.95870 = 0.04130\,, \\
x_1 - x_2 &= 1.07474 - 1.01499 = 0.05975\,, \\
x_2 - x_3 &= 1.01499 - 0.95870 = 0.05629\,, \\
x_3 - x_1 &= 0.95870 - 1.07474 = -0.11604\,,
\end{aligned}$$

and (10.2.5) is

$$\begin{aligned}
f(1) &= \frac{(-0.01499)(0.04130)}{(0.05975)(0.11604)}(0.010) + \frac{(0.04130)(-0.07474)}{(0.05629)(-0.05975)}(0.012) \\
&\quad + \frac{(-0.07474)(-0.01499)}{(-0.11604)(-0.05629)}(0.014) \\
&= (-0.089290)(0.010) + (0.917770)(0.012) + (0.171520)(0.014) \\
&= 0.0125216\,,
\end{aligned}$$

which agrees with the dominant root as calculated by the algebraic solution of $\psi(r) = 1$ to within unity in the seventh place. (The otherwise superfluous decimals help to evaluate the precision of the interpolation.) The linear (10.1.3) expressed in Lagrangian form is

$$\begin{aligned}
f(x) &= \left(\frac{x - x_3}{x_2 - x_3}\right) y_2 + \left(\frac{x - x_2}{x_3 - x_2}\right) y_3 \\
&= \left(\frac{0.04130}{0.05629}\right) 0.012 + \left(\frac{-0.01499}{-0.05629}\right) 0.014 \\
&= 0.0125325\,,
\end{aligned}$$

which is correct to only four decimal places.

Application to Differentiation

If we are interested not in evaluating a function at some point intermediate between tabulated values, but in finding its derivative, we need merely differentiate the top row, element by element, in a determinant such as that in (10.2.2). The result is

$$\begin{vmatrix} 2x & 1 & 0 & f'(x) \\ x_1^2 & x_1 & 1 & y_1 \\ x_2^2 & x_2 & 1 & y_2 \\ x_3^2 & x_3 & 1 & y_3 \end{vmatrix} = 0\,, \tag{10.2.6}$$

which may be readily solved for $f'(x)$ and the solution reduced to

$$f'(x) = [y_1, y_2] + (2x - x_1 - x_2)[y_1, y_2, y_3]\,, \tag{10.2.7}$$

in terms of divided differences. Check this by differentiating (10.2.4).

With the data from Table 5.1 for Netherlands females, 1965, the derivative by (10.2.7) at $\psi(r) = 1$ (i. e., at the real root $r = 0.01252$) is -28.54, in agreement to within one in the second decimal place with the negative of the mean age of childbearing in the stationary population as calculated directly. The equality of $-\psi'(r)$ and A_r was noted in connection with (5.2.23) and (5.6.8).

Numerical differentiation is needed to ascertain μ_x, the force of mortality at age x, defined as

$$\mu_x = -\frac{1}{l(x)}\left(\frac{dl(x)}{dx}\right).$$

If we are given successive quinquennial values of $l(x)$, say l_{a-5}, l_a, l_{a+5}, then by substituting these in (10.2.6) and multiplying by $1/l_x$, we have, after straightforward reduction,

$$\mu_x = \frac{1}{l_x}\left[\frac{{}_5d_{a-5}}{5} + \frac{2(x-a)+5}{50}\,({}_5d_a - {}_5d_{a-5})\right], \tag{10.2.8}$$

which, for the restricted case in which $a = x$, reduces to

$$\mu_a = \frac{0.1}{l_a}\,({}_5d_{a-5} + {}_5d_a)\,.$$

In this case four points give

$$\mu_a = \frac{1}{5l_a}\left(\frac{l_{a-5}}{3} + \frac{l_a}{2} - l_{a+5} + \frac{l_{a+10}}{6}\right). \tag{10.2.9}$$

With data of Table 1.3 verify that μ_{50} is 0.009685 on (10.2.8) and 0.009510 on (10.2.9). Intuitively μ_{50} ought to be close to the average of the death rates at 45–49 and 50–54, and this is $\mu_{50} = 0.5(m_{45} + m_{50}) = 0.009776$, or about 3% above (10.2.9), which is the preferred method.

Higher-order derivatives involve no new technique. If an nth-degree polynomial is fitted to $n+1$ points, then the nth derivative, which will be a constant, is estimated by the nth divided difference $f^{(n)}(x) = n!\,[y_1, y_2, \ldots, y_{n+1}]$, which is the same as

$$f^{(n)}(x) = n!\,[y_1, y_2, \ldots, y_{n+1}] = (-1)^n \frac{n!\begin{vmatrix} x_1^{n-1} & x_1^{n-2} & \cdots & 1 & y_1 \\ x_2^{n-1} & x_2^{n-2} & \cdots & 1 & y_2 \\ \vdots & & & & \vdots \\ x_{n+1}^{n-1} & x_{n+1}^{n-2} & \cdots & 1 & y_{n+1} \end{vmatrix}}{\begin{vmatrix} x_1^{n} & x_1^{n-1} & \cdots & 1 \\ x_2^{n} & x_2^{n-1} & \cdots & 1 \\ \vdots & & & \vdots \\ x_{n+1}^{n} & x_{n+1}^{n-1} & \cdots & 1 \end{vmatrix}}\,. \tag{10.2.10}$$

To see that the nth derivative is given by (10.2.10) consider the nth-degree curve $f(x)$ through $n + 1$ points, defined by

$$\begin{vmatrix} x^n & x^{n-1} \cdots 1 & f(x) \\ x_1^n & x_1^{n-1} \cdots 1 & y_1 \\ \vdots & & \vdots \\ x_{n+1}^n & x_{n+1}^{n-1} \cdots 1 & y_{n+1} \end{vmatrix} = 0 . \tag{10.2.11}$$

Differentiate (10.2.11) n times, and then solve for $f^{(n)}(x)$. The result (10.2.10) appears immediately.

Integration

Integration of some part of the function which passes through the given set of points follows the same principle. The integration of the determinant (10.2.2) requires only that the top row of (10.2.2) be replaced by integrals. This is true equally for indefinite and for definite integrals. In the latter the integral of the interpolating function between a and b, $\int_a^b f(x)\,dx$, is given by the equation

$$\begin{vmatrix} \dfrac{b^3 - a^3}{3} & \dfrac{b^2 - a^2}{2} & b - a & \displaystyle\int_a^b f(x)\,dx \\ x_1^2 & x_1 & 1 & y_1 \\ x_2^2 & x_2 & 1 & y_2 \\ x_3^2 & x_3 & 1 & y_3 \end{vmatrix} = 0 , \tag{10.2.12}$$

from which $\int_a^b f(x)\,dx$ emerges as the ratio of two determinants. If we put $a = x_1 = 0$, $x_2 = h$, $b = x_3 = 2h$, then (10.2.12), after simplification, becomes

$$\int_0^{2h} f(x)\,dx = \frac{h}{3}\,[y_1 + 4y_2 + y_3] , \tag{10.2.13}$$

which is Simpson's rule.

Integrals were required for filling out the values of Table 6.4. For instance, the Canadian 1965 integral of the fitting of a Hadwiger exponential curve from ages 25 through 29 at last birthday may be obtained by applying (10.2.13) in strips of 1-year width, which requires 11 values of the ordinate for each 5-year age interval. For ages 25–29 at last birthday the calculation in terms of $\phi_1(x)$ of (6.4.1) is

$$\begin{aligned} &\tfrac{1}{6}[\phi_1(25) + 4\phi_1(25.5) + 2\phi_1(26) + 4\phi_1(26.5) + \cdots + \phi_1(30)] \\ &\quad = \tfrac{1}{6}[0.10233 + 4(0.10328) + 2(0.10340) + 4(0.10273) \\ &\qquad + 2(0.10133) + 4(0.09927) + 2(0.09663) \\ &\qquad + 4(0.09348) + 2(0.08992) + 4(0.08603) \\ &\qquad + 0.08188] = 0.4843 , \end{aligned}$$

verifying the first four decimal places printed for this age group in the third column of Table 6.4. In fact, Table 6.4 was computed by the more precise Gaussian formula (10.4.6).

A further example is the obtaining of ${}_5L_x = \int_0^5 l(x+t)\,dt$ from four values of l_x at five-year intervals. The reader may write the determinantal equation and show that it reduces to

$$ {}_5L_x = \tfrac{5}{2}(l_x + l_{x+5}) + \tfrac{5}{24}({}_5d_{x+5} - {}_5d_{x-5}) \,, \qquad (10.2.14) $$

already used to ascertain ${}_5L_x$ in Table 1.3. For ${}_5L_{60}$ the first term of (10.2.14) is $\frac{5}{2}(l_{60} + l_{65}) = 344{,}895$, and the second term $\frac{5}{24}({}_5d_{65} - {}_5d_{55}) = 1052$, which add to within one in the last place of the ${}_5L_{60}$ shown.

Transcendental Functions

Determinants express equally well the fitting of expressions that are linear combinations of transcendental terms. Exponentials and other functions which cannot take negative values are often preferable to polynomials. Suppose that we wish to fit the interpolating function $y = Ae^x + Bx^2 + C = f(x)$ to three points. Then, eliminating the constants as before, we obtain the equation for $f(x)$,

$$ \begin{vmatrix} e^x & x^2 & 1 & f(x) \\ e^{x_1} & x_1^2 & 1 & y_1 \\ e^{x_2} & x_2^2 & 1 & y_2 \\ e^{x_3} & x_3^2 & 1 & y_3 \end{vmatrix} = 0 \,. \qquad (10.2.15) $$

The only condition is the nonvanishing of the determinant multiplying $f(x)$ in the expansion of (10.2.15).

Data Given as Areas Rather Than Points

So far the discussion has been of interpolation among points. The typical data of demography are not points but areas under a curve: the population over 45 and under 50 years of age, for example. Such data can be converted so that they represent points by cumulating them, which is to say, dealing with $F(x_1) = \int_0^{x_1} f(x)\,dx$, where $F(x_1)$ is the total of the frequency up to x_1. After the interpolation or graduation has produced $F(x)$, we can differentiate $F(x)$ to obtain $f(x) = F'(x)$. If, as is more likely, we need the total of the distribution lying between x and $x + 1$, $\int_x^{x+1} f(a)\,da$, we obtain it by subtraction, as

$$ \int_x^{x+1} f(a)\,da = F(x+1) - F(x) \,. \qquad (10.2.16) $$

Functions of Two Independent Variables

What has been set forth may be extended to functions of more than one variable, and so made useful in demographic work on births by age and parity (Section

13.5), or the surface of number living by time and age of the Lexis diagram (Fig. 5.1). To find $z = f(x, y)$, where we know that $z_1 = f(x_1, y_1)$, $z_2 = f(x_2, y_2)$, $z_3 = f(x_3, y_3)$ and linearity may be assumed, we put $z = Ay + Bx + C$, and have

$$\begin{aligned} f(x, y) &= Ay + Bx + C\,, \\ z_1 &= Ay_1 + Bx_1 + C\,, \\ z_2 &= Ay_2 + Bx_2 + C\,, \\ z_3 &= Ay_3 + Bx_3 + C\,, \end{aligned}$$

so that the equation for $f(x, y)$ is

$$\begin{vmatrix} f(x, y) & y & x & 1 \\ z_1 & y_1 & x_1 & 1 \\ z_2 & y_2 & x_2 & 1 \\ z_3 & y_3 & x_3 & 1 \end{vmatrix} = 0\,.$$

Nonlinear functions of x and y are treated similarly, provided as before that they are linear in the constants to be ascertained or eliminated.

Osculatory Interpolation

Formulas involving conditions on derivatives of a function as well as on its values are known as osculatory. The usual osculatory fitting is not a single expression which applies to the whole of a distribution, but the next best thing: a set of arcs which meet one another and are continuous because they have common tangents at their points of contact. Treatments by Miller (1949) and Greville (1944b) are recommended for a systematic approach to the subject.

In applying determinants to construct osculatory formulas, some rows will represent derivatives. Suppose that we wish the interpolating

$$y = f(x) = A + Bx + Cx^2 + Dx^3$$

to take given values $y_2 = f(x_2)$ and $y_3 = f(x_3)$, and to have the same derivative at x_2 as the quadratic passing through x_1, x_2, and x_3, and the same derivative at x_3 as the quadratic through x_2, x_3, and x_4. The four constants will meet the four conditions if five equations hold simultaneously:

$$\begin{aligned} f(x) &= A + Bx + Cx^2 + Dx^3\,, \\ y_2 = f(x_2) &= A + Bx_2 + Cx_2^2 + Dx_2^3\,, \\ y_3 = f(x_3) &= A + Bx_3 + Cx_3^2 + Dx_3^3\,, \\ y_2' = f'(x_2) &= B + 2Cx_2 + 3Dx_2^2\,, \\ y_3' = f'(x_3) &= B + 2Cx_3 + 3Dx_3^2\,, \end{aligned} \qquad (10.2.17)$$

where y_2' is the derivative at x_2 of the quadratic passing through x_1, x_2, and x_3, and similarly for y_3'. If the interpolating function $f_1(x)$, a quadratic, passes through x_1, x_2, and x_3, then

$$f_1(x) = f_1(x_1) + (x - x_1)[y_1, y_2] + (x - x_1)(x - x_2)[y_1, y_2, y_3] ,$$

and either from this or from (10.2.7),

$$f_1'(x_2) = [y_1, y_2] + (x_2 - x_1)[y_1, y_2, y_3] ,$$

which is used to replace $f'(x_2)$ in (10.2.17). Similarly the curve passing through x_2, x_3, and x_4 gives $f'(x_3)$. The condition for the set (10.2.17) to be solvable may thus be written

$$\begin{vmatrix} f(x) & 1 & x & x^2 & x^3 \\ y_2 & 1 & x_2 & x_2^2 & x_2^3 \\ y_3 & 1 & x_3 & x_3^2 & x_3^3 \\ [y_1, y_2] + (x_2 - x_1)[y_1, y_2, y_3] & 0 & 1 & 2x_2 & 3x_2^2 \\ [y_2, y_3] + (x_3 - x_2)[y_2, y_3, y_4] & 0 & 1 & 2x_3 & 3x_3^2 \end{vmatrix} = 0 , \qquad (10.2.18)$$

which gives $f(x)$ as the ratio of two determinants.

If the value of a function and its first three derivatives are given at a point (x_1, y_1), then we may ensure that the curve

$$f(x) = A + Bx + Cx^2 + Dx^3 ,$$

reproduces them by writing down a set of equations analogous to (10.2.17). The condition of consistency of the equations is

$$\begin{vmatrix} 1 & x & x^2 & x^3 & f(x) \\ 1 & x_1 & x_1^2 & x_1^3 & f(x_1) \\ 0 & 1 & 2x_1 & 3x_1^2 & f'(x_1) \\ 0 & 0 & 1 & 3x_1 & \dfrac{f''(x_1)}{2!} \\ 0 & 0 & 0 & 1 & \dfrac{f'''(x_1)}{3!} \end{vmatrix} = 0 , \qquad (10.2.19)$$

which, when expanded by the last column, is

$$f(x) = f(x_1) + (x - x_1)f'(x_1) + \frac{(x - x_1)^2}{2!} f''(x_1) + \frac{(x - x_1)^3}{3!} f'''(x_1) . \qquad (10.2.20)$$

This is because the 1×1 determinant on the upper left of (10.2.19) is 1, the 2×2 is $-(x - x_1)$, the 3×3 is $(x - x_1)^2$, the 4×4 is $-(x - x_1)^3$, and these are the coefficients in the expansion by the last column. Equation (10.2.20) is identical with the first four terms of the Taylor series.

The procedure is, however, more general than the usual form of the Taylor series in being easily extended to include as given other points and derivatives as well. If there are two points at each of which the function and its first derivative are available, at one of which the second is also known, then

$$\begin{vmatrix} 1 & x & x^2 & x^3 & x^4 & f(x) \\ 1 & x_1 & x_1^2 & x_1^3 & x_1^4 & f(x_1) \\ 0 & 1 & 2x_1 & 3x_1^2 & 4x_1^3 & f'(x_1) \\ 1 & x_2 & x_2^2 & x_2^3 & x_2^4 & f(x_2) \\ 0 & 1 & 2x_2 & 3x_2^2 & 4x_2^3 & f'(x_2) \\ 0 & 0 & 1 & 3x_2 & 6x_2^2 & \dfrac{f''(x_2)}{2!} \end{vmatrix} = 0. \tag{10.2.21}$$

The extension to further points and higher derivatives is immediate. Nor is it necessary that the derivatives be given explicitly. If, as is most common, they must be inferred from the observations, then all we need do is substitute an expression for the derivatives in terms of the observations. One such for $f'(x_1)$ is incorporated in (10.2.18), and similarly $f''(x_2)$, etc., may be substituted in (10.2.19) or (10.2.21). Determinants within determinants offer no special computing difficulty.

A more direct way of deriving results such as (10.2.21) is to start with arbitrary distinct points (x_i, y_i), as earlier, and then suppose certain of these to coincide. An equation $f(x) = A + Bx + Cx^2 + Dx^3 + Ex^4$ is fitted to distinct points $x_i, y_i, i = 1, \ldots, 5$, by solving for $f(x)$ in

$$\begin{vmatrix} 1 & x & x^2 & x^3 & x^4 & f(x) \\ 1 & x_1 & x_1^2 & x_1^3 & x_1^4 & y_1 \\ 1 & x_3 & x_3^2 & x_3^3 & x_3^4 & y_3 \\ 1 & x_2 & x_2^2 & x_2^3 & x_2^4 & y_2 \\ 1 & x_4 & x_4^2 & x_4^3 & x_4^4 & y_4 \\ 1 & x_5 & x_5^2 & x_5^3 & x_5^4 & y_5 \end{vmatrix} = 0\,. \tag{10.2.22}$$

The limiting value of (10.2.22) divided by $x_3 - x_1$ as x_3 tends to x_1, and then divided by $(x_5 - x_4)(x_5 - x_2)(x_4 - x_2)$ as x_4 and x_5 tend to x_2, will be found to be (10.2.21).

10.3. MATRIX EXPRESSIONS FOR POLYNOMIAL GRADUATION

Equation (10.2.22) or any of the other interpolation formulas of this chapter may be expanded by its last column in the form

$$\Delta_{1n} f(x) - \Delta_{2n} y_1 + \Delta_{3n} y_2 - \cdots + (-1)^{n-1} \Delta_{nn} y_{n-1} = 0\,,$$

or

$$f(x) = \frac{\Delta_{2n}}{\Delta_{1n}} y_1 - \frac{\Delta_{3n}}{\Delta_{1n}} y_2 + \cdots + \frac{(-1)^n \Delta_{nn}}{\Delta_{1n}} y_{n-1}\,,$$

where Δ_{1n} is the $(n-1) \times (n-1)$ minor determinant of (10.2.22) with first row and nth column deleted, and similarly for the other Δ_{in}. The Δ depend only on

Table 10.1 Midpanel Sprague, Greville, and Beers multipliers in form of matrix **A**, showing $\mathbf{A}\,{}_5\mathbf{V}_{20} = {}_1\mathbf{V}_{30}$

SPRAGUE

$$\begin{bmatrix} -0.0128 & +0.0848 & +0.1504 & -0.0240 & +0.0016 \\ -0.0016 & +0.0144 & +0.2224 & -0.0416 & +0.0064 \\ +0.0064 & -0.0336 & +0.2544 & -0.0336 & +0.0064 \\ +0.0064 & -0.0416 & +0.2224 & +0.0144 & -0.0016 \\ +0.0016 & -0.0240 & +0.1504 & +0.0848 & -0.0128 \end{bmatrix} \times \begin{Bmatrix} {}_5\underset{\sim}{K}_{20} \\ {}_5\underset{\sim}{K}_{25} \\ {}_5\underset{\sim}{K}_{30} \\ {}_5\underset{\sim}{K}_{35} \\ {}_5\underset{\sim}{K}_{40} \end{Bmatrix} = \begin{Bmatrix} {}_1\underset{\sim}{K}_{30} \\ {}_1\underset{\sim}{K}_{31} \\ {}_1\underset{\sim}{K}_{32} \\ {}_1\underset{\sim}{K}_{33} \\ {}_1\underset{\sim}{K}_{34} \end{Bmatrix}$$

GREVILLE

$$\begin{bmatrix} -0.0117 & +0.0804 & +0.1570 & -0.0284 & +0.0027 \\ -0.0019 & +0.0156 & +0.2206 & -0.0404 & +0.0061 \\ +0.0048 & -0.0272 & +0.2448 & -0.0272 & +0.0048 \\ +0.0061 & -0.0404 & +0.2206 & +0.0156 & -0.0019 \\ +0.0027 & -0.0284 & +0.1570 & +0.0804 & -0.0117 \end{bmatrix} \times \begin{Bmatrix} {}_5\underset{\sim}{K}_{20} \\ {}_5\underset{\sim}{K}_{25} \\ {}_5\underset{\sim}{K}_{30} \\ {}_5\underset{\sim}{K}_{35} \\ {}_5\underset{\sim}{K}_{40} \end{Bmatrix} = \begin{Bmatrix} {}_1\underset{\sim}{K}_{30} \\ {}_1\underset{\sim}{K}_{31} \\ {}_1\underset{\sim}{K}_{32} \\ {}_1\underset{\sim}{K}_{33} \\ {}_1\underset{\sim}{K}_{34} \end{Bmatrix}$$

BEERS

$$\begin{bmatrix} -0.0117 & +0.0804 & +0.1570 & -0.0284 & +0.0027 \\ -0.0020 & +0.0160 & +0.2200 & -0.0400 & +0.0060 \\ +0.0050 & -0.0280 & +0.2460 & -0.0280 & +0.0050 \\ +0.0060 & -0.0400 & +0.2200 & +0.0160 & -0.0020 \\ +0.0027 & -0.0284 & +0.1570 & +0.0804 & -0.0117 \end{bmatrix} \times \begin{Bmatrix} {}_5\underset{\sim}{K}_{20} \\ {}_5\underset{\sim}{K}_{25} \\ {}_5\underset{\sim}{K}_{30} \\ {}_5\underset{\sim}{K}_{35} \\ {}_5\underset{\sim}{K}_{40} \end{Bmatrix} = \begin{Bmatrix} {}_1\underset{\sim}{K}_{30} \\ {}_1\underset{\sim}{K}_{31} \\ {}_1\underset{\sim}{K}_{32} \\ {}_1\underset{\sim}{K}_{33} \\ {}_1\underset{\sim}{K}_{34} \end{Bmatrix}$$

the x and x_i, $i = 1, 2, \ldots, n - 1$. If these are equidistant the same Δ's will reappear in different problems, and their tabulation once and for all is worth undertaking. Such ratios Δ_{in}/Δ_{1n} taken with appropriate sign are called *multipliers.* In the most common application they would refer not to points but to areas, and be used on $F(x + 5) - F(x)$ to produce $F(x + 1) - F(x)$ of (10.2.16). Examples are the multipliers (Table 10.1) named after actuaries Sprague, Greville, and Beers, which meet variants of the conditions incorporated in (10.2.21) and each here considered as an array **A**.

The premultiplication of the vector of five consecutive five-year age groups, say $\{{}_5\mathbf{V}_{20}\}$, by **A** gives five consecutive single years of age, say $\{{}_1\mathbf{V}_{30}\}$. On the definitions of the five-element vectors,

$$\{{}_5\mathbf{V}_{20}\} = \begin{Bmatrix} {}_5K_{20} \\ {}_5K_{25} \\ {}_5K_{30} \\ {}_5K_{35} \\ {}_5K_{40} \end{Bmatrix}, \qquad \{{}_1\mathbf{V}_{30}\} = \begin{Bmatrix} {}_1K_{30} \\ {}_1K_{31} \\ {}_1K_{32} \\ {}_1K_{33} \\ {}_1K_{34} \end{Bmatrix}, \qquad \{{}_{0.2}\mathbf{V}_{32}\} = \begin{Bmatrix} {}_{0.2}K_{32.0} \\ {}_{0.2}K_{32.2} \\ {}_{0.2}K_{32.4} \\ {}_{0.2}K_{32.6} \\ {}_{0.2}K_{32.8} \end{Bmatrix}, \ldots \tag{10.3.1}$$

the successive application of **A** gives

$$\mathbf{A}\{{}_5\mathbf{V}_{20}\} = \{{}_1\mathbf{V}_{30}\}, \qquad \mathbf{A}^2\{{}_5\mathbf{V}_{20}\} = \{{}_{0.2}\mathbf{V}_{32}\}, \qquad \mathbf{A}^3\{{}_5\mathbf{V}_{20}\} = \{{}_{0.04}\mathbf{V}_{32.4}\}, \quad \text{etc.};$$

$\mathbf{A}^3\{\mathbf{V}\}$ gives numbers at intervals of twenty-fifths of a year. Table 10.2 shows the operation of the three sets of multipliers on males of ages 10–14, 15–19, ..., 30–34, to provide single years of age 20–24 and fifths of a year of age. The reader may verify some of the numbers on a desk calculator, given the following estimates for United States males,.1963, omitting armed forces abroad:

$$ {}_5K_{10} = 9170, \qquad {}_5K_{15} = 7892,$$
$$ {}_5K_{20} = 6331, \qquad {}_5K_{25} = 5453, \qquad {}_5K_{30} = 5625.$$

This approach to the use of matrix multipliers for graduation succesively applies a limited number of well-known formulas. Kimeldorf and Jones (1967), using a technique known as Bayesian graduation, provide ways of obtaining the graduating matrix which will meet more extensive sets of conditions.

10.4. TOPICS IN LIFE TABLE CONSTRUCTION

Repeated Application of Matrix

To make a life table, the multipliers may be applied once, twice, or three times in succession. Twice is recommended, to give intervals of one-fifth of a year for K_x and D_x. It may be assumed that ${}_{0.2}m_x$ is the same as ${}_{0.2}M_x = {}_{0.2}D_x/{}_{0.2}K_x$; then

$$\begin{aligned} {}_{0.2}q_x &= \frac{{}_{0.2}m_x}{5 + \frac{1}{2}({}_{0.2}m_x)}, & {}_{0.2}d_x &= (l_x)({}_{0.2}q_x); \\ l_{x+0.2} &= l_x - {}_{0.2}d_x, & {}_{0.2}L_x &= 0.1(l_x + l_{x+0.2}); \\ T_x &= T_{x+0.2} + {}_{0.2}L_x, & \mathring{e}_x &= T_x/l_x. \end{aligned} \tag{10.4.1}$$

Table 10.2 Graduation to years and to fifths of a year, estimated United States male population, 1963*

AGE	SPRAGUE MULTIPLIERS ONE YEAR	SPRAGUE MULTIPLIERS 1/5 YEAR	GREVILLE MULTIPLIERS ONE YEAR	GREVILLE MULTIPLIERS 1/5 YEAR	BEERS MULTIPLIERS ONE YEAR	BEERS MULTIPLIERS 1/5 YEAR	BEERS - SPRAGUE	BEERS - GREVILLE
20	1,382,176		1,381,517		1,381,517		-659	0
		281,811		281,804		281,803		
		279,138		279,008		279,005		
		276,456		276,253		276,250		
		273,743		273,551		273,552		
		271,028		270,902		270,907		
21	1,316,142		1,316,322		1,316,382		240	60
		268,360		268,294		268,307		
		265,737		265,727		265,745		
		263,166		263,210		263,228		
		260,660		260,748		260,759		
		258,220		258,343		258,343		
22	1,256,902		1,257,861		1,257,741		839	-120
		255,834		255,994		255,978		
		253,501		253,707		253,679		
		251,268		251,494		251,461		
		249,155		249,361		249,333		
		247,145		247,306		247,290		
23	1,207,918		1,208,098		1,208,158		240	60
		245,190		245,303		245,302		
		243,288		243,362		243,374		
		241,482		241,520		241,537		
		239,785		239,781		239,800		
		238,173		238,131		238,144		
24	1,167,861		1,167,202		1,167,202		-659	0
		236,607		236,550		236,557		
		235,094		235,002		235,003		
		233,586		233,452		233,451		
		232,055		231,886		231,882		
		230,519		230,313		230,309		

* Programmed by Nancy Wang.

Table 10.3 Comparison of $1000\,_5q_x$ on three graduated life tables and one iterative life table, Austrian females, 1963

	GRADUATION TO FIFTHS OF A YEAR			ITERATIVE LIFE TABLE OF CHAPTER 1
	SPRAGUE	GREVILLE	BEERS	
$1000\,_5q_0$	31.61	31.85	31.79	32.15
$1000\,_5q_{20}$	3.01	2.99	2.99	2.99
$1000\,_5q_{40}$	11.05	11.04	11.04	11.04
$1000\,_5q_{60}$	65.78	65.80	65.80	65.96
$1000\,_5q_{80}$	488.36	487.33	487.49	485.45

Consolidation back to 5-year age groups means *adding* 25 values for columns $_5d_x$ and $_5L_x$, etc., *selecting* the required values for columns l_x, T_x, $\mathring{e}_x$, and *recomputing* from these grouped values

$$_5q_x = {}_5d_x/l_x\,; \qquad {}_5m_x = {}_5d_x/{}_5L_x\,.$$

The variation which results from different sets of multipliers (as among Sprague, Greville, and Beers) can be ascertained without any change of program other than substituting alternative matrices. That the differences are trifling is seen in Table 10.3 where four variants of $1000q_x$ are shown for Austrian females, 1963. Sprague multipliers are somewhat further from the iterative life table than Greville and Beers. However, the graduations are all grossly wrong in the allocation of deaths as between ages 0 and 1–4. A hyperbola which does much better was used in Chapter 1 and is discussed below.

For the same Austrian females, 1963, the values of $\mathring{e}_0$ on double graduation to fifths of a year and application of (10.4.1) were:

Sprague 72.775, Greville 72.699, Beers 72.721,

as compared with $\mathring{e}_0 = 72.677$ for the iterative life table of Section 1.2. Observe again that Sprague multipliers stand somewhat away from the other graduations and from the iterative life table.

Ages under Five

So far we have confined ourselves to polynomial or exponential fitting. For the youngest ages these do not serve, since in the neighborhood of age zero the death rate is very high and descends rapidly. The fitting of a ratio of polynomials, for example $y = (A_1 + A_2x + A_3x^2)/(A_4 + A_5x)$, may be convenient in this circumstance, say to the four points (x_1, y_1), (x_2, y_2), (x_3, y_3), (x_4, y_4). Multiplying up by $A_4 + A_5x$ we have the five equations

$$\begin{aligned}
A_1 + A_2x + A_3x^2 &= A_4y + A_5xy\,, \\
A_1 + A_2x_1 + A_3x_1^2 &= A_4y_1 + A_5x_1y_1\,, \\
A_1 + A_2x_2 + A_3x_2^2 &= A_4y_2 + A_5x_2y_2\,, \\
A_1 + A_2x_3 + A_3x_3^2 &= A_4y_3 + A_5x_3y_3\,, \\
A_1 + A_2x_4 + A_3x_4^2 &= A_4y_4 + A_5x_4y_4\,,
\end{aligned}$$

and the condition for consistency is

$$\begin{vmatrix}
1 & x & x^2 & y & xy \\
1 & x_1 & x_1^2 & y_1 & x_1y_1 \\
1 & x_2 & x_2^2 & y_2 & x_2y_2 \\
1 & x_3 & x_3^2 & y_3 & x_3y_3 \\
1 & x_4 & x_4^2 & y_4 & x_4y_4
\end{vmatrix} = 0\,.$$

Call the cofactors of the elements in the first row of the determinant C_1, C_2, C_3, $-C_4$, $-C_5$, the cofactor of the jth element being $(-1)^{j-1}\Delta_{1j}$ if Δ_{1j} is the minor. In terms of these cofactors, the determinantal equation is

$$C_1 + C_2x + C_3x^2 = C_4y + C_5xy\,,$$

and dividing by $C_4 + C_5x$, we have

$$y = \frac{C_1 + C_2x + C_3x^2}{C_4 + C_5x}\,, \tag{10.4.2}$$

which is the required fitting, the C's being the A's sought above, one of which may be chosen arbitrarily. The life table of Chapter 1 uses this curve without the term in x^2, and we now test the procedure.

Consider the life table for the United States, both sexes together, for 1962 (as shown in *Vital Statistics for the United States, 1962*, Vol. II, Section 5, p. 8), from which the figures below were taken and expressed on radix 1.00000:

$$\begin{aligned}
l_0 &= 1.00000\,, & {}_1L_0 &= 0.98006\,, \\
l_1 &= 0.97772\,, & {}_4L_1 &= 3.90292\,, \\
l_5 &= 0.97439\,, & {}_5L_5 &= 4.86645\,. \\
l_{10} &= 0.97233\,,
\end{aligned}$$

These official calculations are based on detailed age data, and we will see how well various curves fit them. A straight line between l_0 and l_1 gives an integral for ${}_1L_0$ which is far too high: 0.98886. A parabola through l_0, l_1, and l_5 does not do much better: 0.98814. The parabola, moreover, is far out for l_{10}: 1.1632; not only is it insufficiently curved between zero and one, but it then turns upward in a way that cannot possibly represent any set of probabilities.

The problem is to find a function whose peculiarities will be similar to the peculiarities of the life table curve at these ages. A version of (10.4.2) is

$$l(x) = \frac{ax + b}{x + b}, \tag{10.4.3}$$

whose indefinite integral is

$$\int l(x)\,dx = ax + (b - ab)\ln(x + b) + C. \tag{10.4.4}$$

Fitting by equating the values of the curve and the life table at ages 1 and 5 gives the constants

$$b = \frac{5(l_1 - l_5)}{4 + l_5 - 5l_1}, \qquad \text{and} \qquad a = l_1(1 + b) - b.$$

For the l_1 and l_5 of the United States 1962, $b = 0.19408$ and $a = 0.97340$. The integral from 0 to 1 by (10.4.4) is ${}_1L_0 = 0.98277$ (against the published 0.98006), and from 1 to 4 is ${}_4L_1 = 3.90118$ (against 3.90292). The value of l_{10} as traced by the curve (10.4.3) is 0.97391 (against 0.97233). These results are of the right order of magnitude, but not so close as to discourage further search.

This permits the verification of the United States 1964 results in Table 1.3. From $l_1 = 97{,}285$ and $l_5 = 96{,}879$ of the final iterate shown, we find for the constants of (10.4.3) $a = 0.967578$ and $b = 0.194184$. Then from (10.4.4) the required integral is

$$\begin{aligned} {}_1L_0 &= a + b(1 - a)\ln[(1 + b)/b] \\ &= 0.967578 + (0.194184)(0.032422)(1.8164) \\ &= 0.97901. \end{aligned}$$

Similarly ${}_4L_1$ is 3.87956. The departures from the values of ${}_1L_0$ and ${}_4L_1$ shown in Table 1.3 are due to our starting here with l_1 and l_5 to five significant figures where the computer used eight.

To find the stable population for the first year of life we need the integral

$$\int_0^1 e^{-rx} l(x)\,dx = \int_0^1 e^{-rx}\left(\frac{ax + b}{x + b}\right)dx, \tag{10.4.5}$$

and similarly for ages one to four. Since rx is small in this range, we could expand e^{-rx}, say to $(rx)^3$, and obtain a rational function which may be integrated without approximation. In practice, it is simpler to apply Gaussian quadrature (Hildebrand, 1956, p. 319) directly to (10.4.5), say using

$$\int_0^1 f(x)\,dx = 0.32607(f_{0.33001} + f_{0.66999}) + 0.17393(f_{0.06943} + f_{0.93057}), \tag{10.4.6}$$

or, if the computer is fast enough, taking advantage of the easier programming for Simpson's rule (10.2.13), applied in strips 0.1 of a year wide.

In the construction of the male life table for Singapore on 1962 data, the values $l_1 = 96{,}907$, $l_5 = 95{,}953$, $r = 0.0093$ appeared in the last iteration. By applying either (10.4.6) or Simpson's rule with a suitable number of ordinates in the integral of (1.2.4), show that ${}_1M'_0 = 0.031832$ and ${}_4M'_1 = 0.002497$.

Makeham's Graduation

In actuarial work, sections of the $l(x)$ column of the life table are sometimes graduated by Makeham's curve,

$$l(x) = l_0 s^x g^{(c^x - 1)}, \qquad (10.4.7)$$

or the special case where $s = 1$ due to Gompertz (Morton D. Miller, 1949, p. 43; Wolfenden, 1954, p. 165). With the advent of computers and descent methods, a least squares fitting such as that of Chapter 9 is entirely feasible. I did not attempt this, but merely printed out (10.4.7) for a large number of values of s, g, and c, and observed that with $s = 0.998$, $g = 1.001$, and $c = 1.08$, the result is close to l_x of England and Wales, 1960–62, for ages from 20 to 35, in Table 10.4. Such a "fitting" to any table is feasible if one is willing to handle a sufficient bulk of computer printout, and devise means of finding his way through it. The "fit" in this table was obtained by inspection. A Makeham curve through l_x, l_{x+5}, l_{x+10}, l_{x+15}, of the form

$$l(x + t) = l_x s^t g^{c^t - 1},$$

may be found by taking logarithms and differencing twice. The constant c is

$$c = \left(\frac{\Delta^2 \ln l_{x+5}}{\Delta^2 \ln l_x} \right)^{1/5};$$

work out expressions for the other two constants, and test your formulas by inferring back the constants of the Makeham curve above from the values given at 20, 25, 30, and 35 in Column (2) of Table 10.4 (Spurgeon, 1932).

Table 10.4 Life table l_x column for males, England and Wales, 1960–62, and selected Makeham curve: $100{,}000(0.998)^x(1.001)^{1.08^x - 1}$

AGE x	ℓ_x BY ITERATIVE LIFE-TABLE METHOD (1)	SELECTED MAKEHAM CURVE TO CORRESPOND TO COLUMN (1) (2)
20	96,286	96,427
25	95,745	95,676
30	95,263	95,028
35	94,682	94,526

Table 10.5* Canadian 1965 male life table fitted by Gompertz curve $l_x = 100{,}000(1.42795)^{[0.993928]^x-1}$

AGE	ℓ_x AS CALCULATED BY ITERATIVE LIFE TABLE METHOD (1)	ℓ_x AS FITTED BY GOMPERTZ CURVE TO AGES 0, 20, AND 40 OF COLUMN (1) (2)
0	100,000	100,000
5	97,126	98,937
10	96,804	97,917
15	96,569	96,938
20	95,997	95,997
25	95,159	95,093
30	94,406	94,225
35	93,623	93,390
40	92,587	92,587
45	90,979	91,815
50	88,463	91,072

* Programmed by Effat Moussa.

What are the equations for passing a Gompertz curve through l_0, l_{20}, and l_{40}? Comment on the fitting of the Gompertz curve with $g = 1.42795$ and $c = 0.993928$ to the Canadian males, 1965, in Table 10.5. Compare it with a polynomial through l_0, l_{20}, l_{40}. If the Gompertz fit seems better, show how it may be used to find ${}_5L_x$ from the series of l_x at five-year intervals.

Alternative Exposure Data in the Form of Births

The principle of agreement with the data, on which the iterative life table of Section 1.2 and the present section depends, is applicable also to the youngest ages of the life table, when the births of the given and the preceding years provide estimates of the exposed population, often more precise than the census.

Births are usually given in calendar years, as are deaths. (The method is readily adapted and improved if they are given by month or other smaller time unit.) Let the deaths, in the calendar year to which the life table is to apply, be D_0 under one year of age and ${}_4D_1$ from ages one through four at last birthday; let the births of the given year be B_0, of the preceding year B_{-1}, of the years before that $B_{-2}, \ldots,$ up to B_{-5}. This is the whole of the information assumed in what follows.

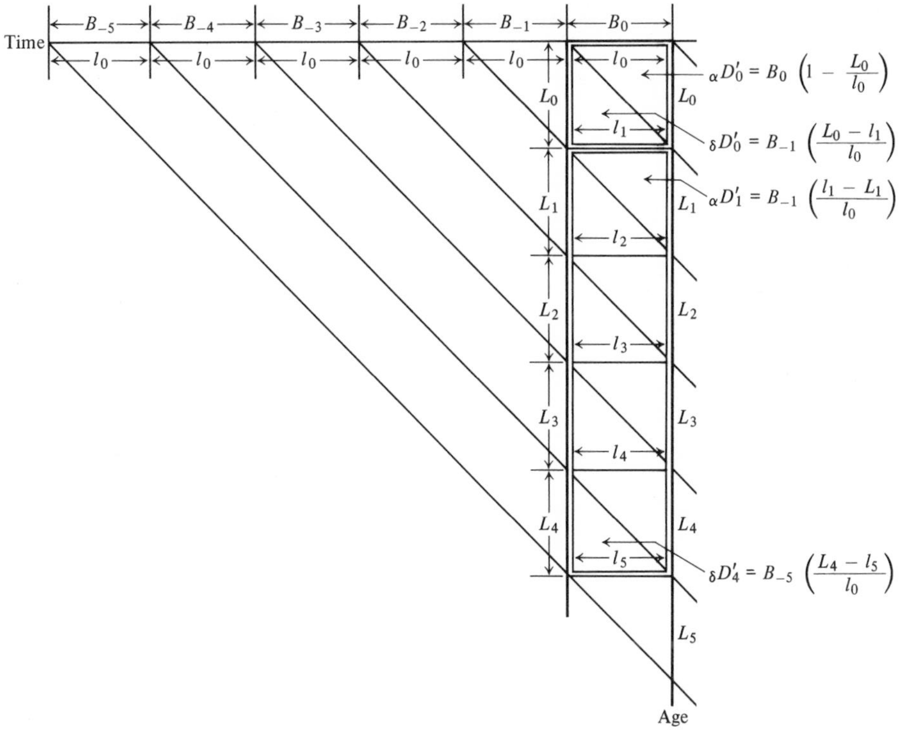

Fig. 10.1 Lexis diagram showing calculation of expected deaths at ages 0 and 1–4 at last birthday within given calendar year, based on preceding iteration of life table and births of six calendar years.

We conceive the deaths under one year as being divided into ${}_{\alpha}D_0$ from among B_0 and ${}_{\delta}D_0$ among B_{-1}. (One of the strengths of the method is that no data on this division are needed.) An arbitrary initial set of values for the life table l_0, l_1, and l_5 is chosen, and by the hyperbola (10.4.3) fitted through these three numbers the integrals ${}_1L_0$ and ${}_4L_1$ are worked out. If, as in Chapter 1, primes distinguish estimates made from the life table from the corresponding observations, then we have ${}_{\alpha}D'_0 = B_0(1 - L_0/l_0)$ and ${}_{\delta}D'_0 = B_{-1}(L_0 - l_1)/l_0$, and

$$D'_0 = {}_{\alpha}D'_0 + {}_{\delta}D'_0 = B_0\left(1 - \frac{L_0}{l_0}\right) + B_{-1}\left(\frac{L_0 - l_1}{l_0}\right), \tag{10.4.8}$$

is comparable with D_0, the observed number of deaths under one year. If D'_0 is greater (less) than D_0, then the arbitrary $q_0 = 1 - l_1/l_0$ is too high (low). Hence q_0 must be adjusted to q_0^* by

$$q_0^* = \left(1 - \frac{l_1}{l_0}\right)\left(\frac{D_0}{D'_0}\right), \tag{10.4.9}$$

for the next iteration (Fig. 10.1).

Table 10.6 Last iteration of life table for ages 0–4, showing agreement of expected with observed deaths, French males, 1965*

AGE x	YEAR y	OBSERVED BIRTHS $B_y = B_{-x}$	FROM PRECEDING ITERATION ℓ_x	$_1L_x$
0	1965	441,588	100,000	98,492.1
1	1964	449,511	97,973.9	97,836.3
2	1963	443,844		97,693.3
3	1962	425,919		97,628.6
4	1961	428,877		97,591.4
5	1960	419,775	97,577.9	

($_1L_x$ OBTAINED BY FITTING HYPERBOLA $\frac{ax+b}{x+b}$ TO ℓ_1 AND ℓ_5, FINDING $a = 0.974535$, $b = 0.256863$, THEN INTEGRATING.)

AGE x	EXPECTED DEATHS			OBSERVED DEATHS 1965
0	$B_0(1 - L_0/\ell_0)$	$_\alpha D_0'$	6658.7	
	$B_{-1}(L_0 - \ell_1)/\ell_0$	$_\delta D_0'$	2329.4	
		$D_0' =$	8988.1	$D_0 = 8988$
1	$B_{-1}(\ell_1 - L_1)/\ell_0$	$_\alpha D_1'$	618.5	
2	$B_{-2}(L_1 - L_2)/\ell_0$	$_\delta D_1' + {_\alpha D_2'}$	634.7	
3	$B_{-3}(L_2 - L_3)/\ell_0$	$_\delta D_2' + {_\alpha D_3'}$	275.6	
4	$B_{-4}(L_3 - L_4)/\ell_0$	$_\delta D_3' + {_\alpha D_4'}$	159.5	
5	$B_{-5}(L_4 - \ell_5)/\ell_0$	$_\delta D_4'$	56.7	
		$_4D_1' =$	1745.0	$_4D_1 = 1745$

* Source: United Nations *Demographic Yearbook*, 1965 and 1066, Tables 13 and 43. Uniform sex ratio assumed for births.

The corresponding estimate $_4D_1'$ of the deaths at one to four years of age is

$$_4D_1' = B_{-1}\left(\frac{l_1 - L_1}{l_0}\right) + B_{-2}\left(\frac{L_1 - L_2}{l_0}\right) + \cdots + B_{-5}\left(\frac{L_4 - l_5}{l_0}\right), \quad (10.4.10)$$

an expression which catches the deaths expected to occur in the given calendar year on the basis of the given B's and the l's and L's of the preceding iteration.

Table 10.7 Life table ${}_5d_0$ with birth registrations as the source on exposure, compared with ${}_5d_0$ on census count or population estimate as the source on exposure—nine countries for 1965*

	MALE		FEMALE	
	EXPOSURE MEASURED BY		EXPOSURE MEASURED BY	
COUNTRY	BIRTH REGISTRATION	CENSUS	BIRTH REGISTRATION	CENSUS
BULGARIA	3982	4031	3097	3291
FRANCE	2422	2419	1889	1884
GREECE	4139	4001	3683	3581
MAURITIUS	9547	9599	8258	8366
NETHERLANDS	2017	2021	1557	1556
NEW ZEALAND	2681	2488	2001	1860
PUERTO RICO	5405	5253	4500	4365
TAIWAN	4112	4280	3859	4007
UNITED STATES	3136	3049	2459	2388

* Life tables on birth registrations programmed by William Taylor; life tables on census by Wilhelm Flieger.

The improved ${}_4q_1^*$ is

$$ {}_4q_1^* = \left(1 - \frac{l_5}{l_1}\right)\left(\frac{{}_4D_1}{{}_4D_1'}\right). $$

With improved q_0^* and ${}_4q_1^*$ new l_1^* and l_5^* are available, and the process can be repeated until successive q's agree, say to one part in a million. Note that unlike the iteration of Section 1.2 the present one requires no use of a rate of increase r. This is the advantage of proceeding along cohort lines. A specimen worksheet appears in Table 10.6. The method could be improved to allow for changes within each year as these are inferred from a curve through B_0, B_{-1}, . . .

The separation factor $f_0^z = {}_\delta D_0^z / D_0^z$ of Section 1.1 is implicit in the process; show how it may be estimated between any pair of years which have sufficient differences in births. Show also how the method may be made to give a better life table when births of the six relevant years are available by month. Adapt the method to a three-year period of exposure.

Since the theory here given still offers no help in deciding which way of measuring exposure is superior, it is fortunate that the differences are often small, as the specimen ${}_5d_0$ of Table 10.7 show for nine countries varying in quality of statistical data.

10.5. THE ESTIMATE OF INTERPOLATION ERROR

The classical remainder terms for Taylor series and Newton interpolation have their uses, but in some circumstances a different procedure may provide more information on error and be better suited to machine computation.

When we are given n values of a function and wish to interpolate or graduate to find intermediate values, we can study the precision likely to be attained by using $n - 1$ of the points to interpolate the nth. The comparison of the interpolated with the given nth value will then constitute an estimate of error for any new point that is to be interpolated. If the interpolated nth value is written $f(x_n)$, and the given nth point y_n, then $f(x_n) - y_n$ is the error of $f(x_n)$.

Suppose $n = 4$. We know by solving Eq. (10.2.2) for $f(x)$ that the interpolated value for the fourth point is (10.2.3). Then $f(x) - y$ is the same as (10.2.3), with the sole difference that the zero in the upper right-hand corner of the numerator is replaced by y. When interpolated $f(x_4)$ is compared with observed y_4 the error is

$$f(x_4) - y_4 = \frac{\begin{vmatrix} x_4^2 & x_4 & 1 & y_4 \\ x_1^2 & x_1 & 1 & y_1 \\ x_2^2 & x_2 & 1 & y_2 \\ x_3^2 & x_3 & 1 & y_3 \end{vmatrix}}{\begin{vmatrix} x_1^2 & x_1 & 1 \\ x_2^2 & x_2 & 1 \\ x_3^2 & x_3 & 1 \end{vmatrix}} = -\frac{\begin{vmatrix} x_1^2 & x_1 & 1 & y_1 \\ x_2^2 & x_2 & 1 & y_2 \\ x_3^2 & x_3 & 1 & y_3 \\ x_4^2 & x_4 & 1 & y_4 \end{vmatrix}}{\begin{vmatrix} x_1^2 & x_1 & 1 \\ x_2^2 & x_2 & 1 \\ x_3^2 & x_3 & 1 \end{vmatrix}} = \frac{\Delta}{-\Delta_{44}}, \tag{10.5.1}$$

where Δ is the determinant in the numerator and Δ_{44} is Δ with the last column and last row deleted.

There being four points available, each of them in turn could be taken as x_4, y_4 in (10.5.1), and four indications of the error of the process obtained. With n points, n indications would be given, which in an extension of the above notation might be designated

$$f(x_i) - y_i = \frac{\Delta}{(-1)^{i+n+1}\Delta_{in}}, \quad i = 1, 2, \ldots, n. \tag{10.5.2}$$

The points may be far from equidistant; the interpolating formulas may involve derivatives as in Taylor's expansion or in osculatory interpolation; polynomial interpolating functions may be replaced by exponentials or other forms; these more general situations require at most obvious modifications of (10.5.2). Insofar as n points will give a better result than will $n - 1$, the application of (10.5.2) somewhat exaggerates the error to which the final interpolation will be subject.

The procedure may be exemplified with three points, say l_{25}, l_{30}, and l_{35}. If we interpolate single years, then the errors with straight lines through the known points are

$$-\frac{\Delta}{\Delta_{13}} = \frac{\begin{vmatrix} 25 & 1 & l_{25} \\ 30 & 1 & l_{30} \\ 35 & 1 & l_{35} \end{vmatrix}}{-\begin{vmatrix} 30 & 1 \\ 35 & 1 \end{vmatrix}},$$

and two other ratios which differ only by their denominators being

$$-\begin{vmatrix} 25 & 1 \\ 30 & 1 \end{vmatrix} \quad \text{and} \quad \begin{vmatrix} 25 & 1 \\ 35 & 1 \end{vmatrix},$$

respectively. The denominators are seen to equal 5, 5, and -10 respectively, and for United States males, 1964, in which $l_{25} = 94{,}854$, $l_{30} = 94{,}002$, and $l_{35} = 92{,}991$ (Table 1.3), the common numerator is 795. Hence the three estimates of error are $795/5 = 159$, $795/5 = 159$, and $795/(-10) = -79.5$, as may be verified without the use of determinants in this simple example. Given that l_{40} from the same table is 91,601, the reader may apply the technique to ascertain the error of a 4-point fitting, and comment on the improvement, referring to a chart. More broadly, he may compare the error obtained by (10.5.1) with the usual remainder term, for example in the form given by Freeman (1962, p. 57).

The technique may be applied to higher-order interpolation, including such instances as the Sprague and other multipliers of Table 10.1. The application requires that formulas be developed for unequal intervals, since if we are working with seven points, we will need to interpolate each separately from the other six and compare with the observed values. If a computer is available, one might avoid calculating coefficients such as those of Table 10.1 and, instead, use (10.5.2) directly.

CHAPTER 11

FINITE APPROXIMATIONS

Finite approximations are the business of everyone concerned with population analysis. One cannot make a life table, calculate survival rates, or establish an intrinsic rate without implicitly replacing integrals or derivatives by finite quantities which are approximations to them. The issues are by no means new, but with the advent of machine computation, they demand special attention. The more detailed results below are intended for reference rather than for general reading.

Five-Year and One-Year Intervals

Numerical integration is often facilitated, given five-year age groups in the original data, by an explicit graduation of these to single years of age with a fourth- or fifth-degree polynomial, using the methods of Chapter 10. The graduation is treated as though it were data, and any usual approximation such as the trapezoidal is applied to estimate integrals for the L_x column of the life table and similar derived numbers. The present chapter, however, does not introduce single years of age at all, but attempts to be more analytical. If the single years of age are merely divisions of a five-year age group, to be inferred from the relations of successive five-year groups (as they are in any graduation), so are the survivorships and other products of calculation. Why not go through to a conclusion that will directly give the five-year age groups required and avoid the intermediate single years? An example of the procedure appears in Chapter 1, where we are able to ensure that the life table agrees with the data, both final table and data being in five-year age groups. If we later want single years of age, we can graduate the final table.

11.1. THE PROJECTION MATRIX

The Corrected Survival Ratio

The issue goes beyond the construction of the life table; it extends also to its use, for instance in projection. If the population between ages x and $x + dx$ is $k(x)\,dx$, and if the life-table number living is $l(x)$, then the population between ages x and $x + dx$ surviving n years is

$$k(x)\,\frac{l(x+n)}{l(x)}\,dx\,, \qquad (11.1.1)$$

and that between ages x and $x + n$ surviving n years is

$$\int_0^n k(x + t) \frac{l(x + n + t)}{l(x + t)} dt . \tag{11.1.2}$$

In Chapter 2 and subsequently, we substituted for (11.1.2) the product of two integrals divided by a third; that is,

$$\frac{\int_0^n k(x + t)\, dt \int_0^n l(x + n + t)\, dt}{\int_0^n l(x + t)\, dt} = \frac{{}_nK_x\, {}_nL_{x+n}}{{}_nL_x} , \tag{11.1.3}$$

as is common practice in demography.

Nothing in logic gives us, in general, the right to decompose (11.1.2) in this way. Only in the special case where the distribution $k(x)$ within the age group x to $x + n$ is the same as that of $l(x)$ will a cancellation take place and make the simplification (11.1.3) valid.

But a rapidly growing population is shifted to lower ages within each age group, and the stable population is a much closer approximation to the actual than is the stationary. (Recall the application of this principle to make the iterative life table of Chapter 1.) Suppose that

$$k(x + t) = Ae^{-r(x+t)}l(x + t) ,$$

where both A and r need not be the same through all ages, but are assumed constant over intervals of $2n$ years, and substitute in (11.1.2):

$$\int_0^n k(x + t) \frac{l(x + n + t)}{l(x + t)} dt = \int_0^n Ae^{-r(x+t)}l(x + t) \frac{l(x + n + t)}{l(x + t)} dt .$$

We may multiply by unity in the form

$$\frac{{}_nK_x}{{}_nK_x} = \frac{{}_nK_x}{\int_0^n Ae^{-r(x+t)}l(x + t)\, dt} ,$$

and obtain for the projected population

$${}_nK_x \frac{\int_0^n Ae^{-r(x+t)}l(x + n + t)\, dt}{\int_0^n Ae^{-r(x+t)}l(x + t)\, dt} , \tag{11.1.4}$$

the ratio of the two integrals in (11.1.4) being the proper survivorship to apply to ${}_nK_x$. It is exact if the age distribution is stable in sections.

One way of tackling (11.1.4) is to expand e^{-rt} under the integral signs up to the term in r to obtain for the survivorship the ratio of integrals:

$$\frac{\int_0^n (1 - rt)l(x + n + t)\, dt}{\int_0^n (1 - rt)l(x + t)\, dt} . \tag{11.1.5}$$

Now

$$\int_0^n (1 - rt)l(x + t)\, dt = \int_0^n l(x + t)\, dt - r\int_0^n tl(x + t)\, dt ,$$

and we will evidently need approximations to $\int_0^n tl(x+t)\,dt$ as well as to $\int_0^n l(x+t)\,dt$. These will be obtained in the following section and inserted in (11.1.5) to produce the results (11.1.14) to (11.1.18).

Approximate Integration

Any analytical curve which is put through a succession of points on a plane will give rise to an integration formula over intervals of the independent variable. For fixed x the polynomial $l(x+t)$ defined by

$$\begin{vmatrix} t^2 & t & 1 & l(x+t) \\ 0 & 0 & 1 & l_x \\ 25 & 5 & 1 & l_{x+5} \\ 100 & 10 & 1 & l_{x+10} \end{vmatrix} = 0 \tag{11.1.6}$$

will pass through the points on l_x at x, $x+5$, and $x+10$, as a special case of (10.2.2). If

$$\Delta l_x = l_{x+5} - l_x ,$$
$$\Delta^2 l_x = \Delta l_{x+5} - \Delta l_x = l_{x+10} - 2l_{x+5} + l_x ,$$

then the reader may show that (11.1.6) is Newton's advancing difference formula with equal intervals

$$l(x+t) = l_x + \frac{t}{5}\Delta l_x + \frac{(t)(t-5)}{2!\,5^2}\Delta^2 l_x , \tag{11.1.7}$$

if third and higher differences vanish.

Integrating (11.1.6) or (11.1.7) from x to $x+5$ gives the approximation

$${}_5L_x = \int_0^5 l(x+t)\,dt = \tfrac{25}{12}l_x + \tfrac{10}{3}l_{x+5} - \tfrac{5}{12}l_{x+10} . \tag{11.1.8}$$

The same procedure applied to the cubic in t through values at $x-5$, x, $x+5$, $x+10$, would give a 5×5 determinant which after integration reduces to

$${}_5L_x = \int_0^5 l(x+t)\,dt = \tfrac{65}{24}(l_{x+5} + l_x) - \tfrac{5}{24}(l_{x+10} + l_{x-5}) . \tag{11.1.9}$$

It is customary (Greville, 1943, p. 40 and (1.1.11) above) to write this in the form

$$\int_0^5 l(x+t)\,dt = \tfrac{5}{2}(l_{x+5} + l_x) + \tfrac{5}{24}({}_5d_{x+5} - {}_5d_{x-5}) . \tag{11.1.10}$$

We also require $\int_0^5 tl(x+t)\,dt$. Integrating this last by parts and using

$$dT(x+t)/dt = -l(x+t) ,$$

we have

$$\int_0^5 tl(x+t)\,dt = -\int_0^5 t\,dT(x+t)$$
$$= -[tT_{x+t}]_0^5 + \int_0^5 T(x+t)\,dt = -5T_{x+5} + \int_0^5 T(x+t)\,dt\,. \tag{11.1.11}$$

Expanding $T(x+t)$ under the integral sign on the right-hand side of (11.1.11) by the same formula used for $l(x+t)$ in (11.1.7), and then integrating with respect to t we obtain

$$\int_0^5 tl(x+t)\,dt = -5T_{x+5} + (5T_x + \tfrac{5}{2}\,\Delta T_x - \tfrac{5}{12}\,\Delta^2 T_x)$$
$$= \tfrac{25}{12}\,{}_5L_x + \tfrac{5}{12}\,{}_5L_{x+5}\,, \tag{11.1.12}$$

and writing $x+5$ for x yields

$$\int_0^5 tl(x+5+t)\,dt = \tfrac{25}{12}\,{}_5L_{x+5} + \tfrac{5}{12}\,{}_5L_{x+10}\,. \tag{11.1.13}$$

Completion of Survivorship Correction

For the ratio of integrals in (11.1.4) we now write (11.1.5) and hence

$$\frac{\int_0^5 e^{-rt}l(x+5+t)\,dt}{\int_0^5 e^{-rt}l(x+t)\,dt} = \frac{{}_5L_{x+5} - r[\tfrac{25}{12}\,{}_5L_{x+5} + \tfrac{5}{12}\,{}_5L_{x+10}]}{{}_5L_x - r[\tfrac{25}{12}\,{}_5L_x + \tfrac{5}{12}\,{}_5L_{x+5}]}\,, \tag{11.1.14}$$

which the reader may show to be very nearly equal to

$$\frac{{}_5L_{x+5}}{{}_5L_x}\left[1 + \frac{5r}{12-25r}\left(\frac{{}_5L_{x+5}}{{}_5L_x} - \frac{{}_5L_{x+10}}{{}_5L_{x+5}}\right)\right]. \tag{11.1.15}$$

The argument includes substituting $1+\alpha$ for $1/(1-\alpha)$, where

$$\alpha = \frac{5r}{12-25r}\,\frac{{}_5L_{x+5}}{{}_5L_x}$$

is small enough that its square and higher powers may be disregarded.

Note that (11.1.15) uses ${}_5L_x$, ${}_5L_{x+5}$, and ${}_5L_{x+10}$, based on values l_x to l_{x+15} and therefore asymmetric with respect to the age interval x to $x+10$ with which the projection is concerned. If the correction factor is estimated from the preceding age groups [i.e., writing $x-5$ for x within the parentheses of (11.1.15)],

$$\frac{{}_5L_{x+5}}{{}_5L_x}\left[1 + \frac{5r}{12-25r}\left(\frac{{}_5L_x}{{}_5L_{x-5}} - \frac{{}_5L_{x+5}}{{}_5L_x}\right)\right], \tag{11.1.16}$$

and this is averaged with (11.1.15), the result is symmetrically located with respect to the age interval x to $x + 10$:

$$\frac{{}_5L_{x+5}}{{}_5L_x}\left[1 + \frac{5r}{24 - 50r}\left(\frac{{}_5L_x}{{}_5L_{x-5}} - \frac{{}_5L_{x+10}}{{}_5L_{x+5}}\right)\right]. \qquad (11.1.17)$$

The reader may show that when the quantity in the parentheses of (11.1.17) is expressed in terms of the ${}_5q_x$ and the term in r^2 disregarded, the survival factor is only slightly underestimated by

$$\frac{{}_5L_{x+5}}{{}_5L_x}\left[1 + \tfrac{5}{48}r({}_5q_{x+10} + {}_5q_{x+5} - {}_5q_x - {}_5q_{x-5})\right]. \qquad (11.1.18)$$

As in the analogous device incorporated in the life-table procedure at the end of Chapter 1, a choice may be made between a single r, the intrinsic rate, applied through the whole range of ages, and the "local r" of (1.2.7), separately inferred for each age group from the way in which the population is distributed by age. Besides being somewhat more appropriate, the "local r" has the convenience of being readily calculable.

The magnitude of the corrections clearly depends on the rate of increase with time of the population in question, and on the increase of death rates from age to age. For United States females, 1964, the value of ${}_5L_{45}/{}_5L_{40}$ is shown to five places at the lower right of the matrix of Table 2.2. The increase from one annual cohort to the next in this part of the age distribution suggests an r of 0.015. From Table 2.1, plus the fact that ${}_5L_{50}$ is 450,468, we have for the four corrected survival factors

(11.1.15)	$({}_5L_{45}/{}_5L_{40})1.0000573 = 0.983100$,
(11.1.16)	$({}_5L_{45}/{}_5L_{40})1.0000362 = 0.983080$,
(11.1.17)	$({}_5L_{45}/{}_5L_{40})1.0000468 = 0.983090$,
(11.1.18)	$({}_5L_{45}/{}_5L_{40})1.0000457 = 0.983089$,

against the uncorrected 0.983044. The preferred formula, (11.1.17), gives 6238 thousands on projection to 1969 instead of the 6237 thousands shown in Table 2.3. Evidently the point is one of principle rather than of numerical consequence.

Correction for Grouping

An entirely different aspect of approximation is Sheppard's correction for grouping, applicable to distributions with high-order contact with the x-axis at their extremes. The net maternity function $p(x)m(x)$ has such contact. In terms of the raw cumulants (Section 5.6) identified by a bar, the corrected cumulants are (Kendall and Stuart, 1958, Vol. I, p. 81)

$$\kappa_1 = \bar{\kappa}_1; \quad \kappa_2 = \bar{\kappa}_2 - \frac{d^2}{12}; \quad \kappa_3 = \bar{\kappa}_3; \quad \kappa_4 = \bar{\kappa}_4 + \frac{d^4}{120}, \ \ldots, \qquad (11.1.19)$$

where d is the grouping interval, taken here as 5. Our object in this section will be to go beyond the correction of cumulants to find the correction for grouping appropriate to the characteristic equation

$$\psi(r) = \int_0^\infty e^{-rx} p(x)m(x)\,dx = 1\,. \qquad (11.1.20)$$

We first alter the equation temporarily, as though we were about to work it out with cumulants as Lotka (1939c, p. 71) suggested, and as shown in Section 6.5. Dividing both sides of (11.1.20) by R_0, expanding the exponential, and integrating term by term, gives on the left the moment-generating function of $p(x)m(x)/R_0$ evaluated at $-r$. Then, taking logarithms to base e and remembering that the logarithm of the moment-generating function generates the cumulants

$$\ln \int_0^\infty e^{-ra} \frac{p(a)m(a)\,da}{R_0} = -\kappa_1 r + \frac{\kappa_2 r^2}{2!} - \cdots,$$

we have

$$-\kappa_1 r + \frac{\kappa_2 r^2}{2!} - \frac{\kappa_3 r^3}{3!} + \frac{\kappa_4 r^4}{4!} - \cdots = -\ln R_0\,, \qquad (11.1.21)$$

the cumulants κ being supposed exact, and, in particular, corrected for grouping. Substituting (11.1.19) with $d = 5$ in (11.1.21) gives

$$\left(-\bar{\kappa}_1 r + \frac{\bar{\kappa}_2 r^2}{2!} - \frac{\bar{\kappa}_3 r^3}{3!} + \frac{\bar{\kappa}_4 r^4}{4!} - \cdots\right) - \frac{5^2}{12}\frac{r^2}{2!} + \frac{5^4}{120}\frac{r^4}{4!} = -\ln R_0\,, \qquad (11.1.22)$$

on correcting up to the fourth cumulant only. The quantity in parentheses on the left of (11.1.22) is the logarithm of the left-hand side of (11.1.20) calculated without the correction for grouping. Hence, substituting back the uncorrected integral, distinguished by a bar, we find that (11.1.22) becomes

$$\ln\left(\overline{\int_0^\infty e^{-ra} \frac{p(a)m(a)\,da}{R_0}}\right) - \frac{25}{24}r^2 + \frac{125}{(24)^2}r^4 = -\ln R_0\,.$$

Taking antilogarithms, i.e., exponentials, and multiplying through by R_0, we are back to the original equation (11.1.20), except that in place of 1 on the right-hand side we have

$$\exp\left(\frac{25}{24}r^2 - \frac{125}{(24)^2}r^4\right) \doteq 1 + \frac{25}{24}r^2 + \frac{125}{384}r^4$$

to terms in r^4. That is to say, we have to solve

$$\bar{\psi}(r) = \overline{\int_0^\infty e^{-ra} p(a)m(a)\,da} = 1 + \tfrac{25}{24}r^2 + \tfrac{125}{384}r^4\,. \qquad (11.1.23)$$

The right-hand side departs little from unity for values of r in common use:

r	$1 + \frac{25}{24}r^2 + \frac{125}{384}r^4$
0.01	1.000104
0.02	1.000417
0.03	1.000938

In Table 5.3 the σ^2 was calculated in both columns without the correction for grouping. The resultant $1000r$ on (6.2.7) using this σ^2 was 0.003 higher than $1000r$ from (5.3.5). Given that κ_3 for United States females in 1964 was 122.4 and entering this value in the term containing r^3 of (6.5.4), we have $\kappa_3 r^3/6\mu = 2.98 \times 10^{-6}$. This explains the difference of 3 in the third decimal place between $1000r$ from (5.3.5) and $1000r_L$ from (6.2.7). A deduction from σ^2 for grouping of $5^2/12 = 2.083$ would have lowered $1000r_L$ to 15.696, out of line with $1000r$. The underlying fact is that both (5.3.5) and (6.2.7) with σ^2 uncorrected for grouping contain compensating errors, and by removing one of them (the grouping bias) we make the estimate of r slightly worse. On the other hand the correction for grouping was essential in Table 6.4 where we wanted the graduated distribution in five-year intervals to fit the observations as closely as possible.

The advanced reader may attempt to obtain the result (11.1.23) without the intermediacy of cumulants by a direct integration such as Kendall and Stuart use to find (11.1.19).

The First Row of the Projection Matrix

Three ways of drawing up the fertility element of the projection matrix suggest themselves, and these will be discussed in turn. That of Chapters 2 and 3 will be called method A.

METHOD A. *The projection starting with mean of initial and final populations.* In reexamining the claims of the projection method used in Chapters 2 and 3, we should recall that observed age-specific fertility rates were there applied to the arithmetic mean population presumed to exist over the time interval in question for the given age. With five-year age groups and an initial population aged x to $x + 4$ at last birthday equal to ${}_5K_x$, the projected population five years later of age x to $x + 4$ is ${}_5K_{x-5}({}_5L_x/{}_5L_{x-5})$, and the average exposed is taken as

$$\frac{1}{2}\left({}_5K_x + {}_5K_{x-5}\frac{{}_5L_x}{{}_5L_{x-5}}\right).$$

Reference to Fig. 11.1 shows method A of projection associated with mid-point A on the line RU. If ${}_5L_x/{}_5L_{x-5}$ may be thought of as applicable to each point of age from x to $x + 5$, then we may be said to have used the horizontal line passing through A (shown broken in Fig. 11.1) as though it represented the

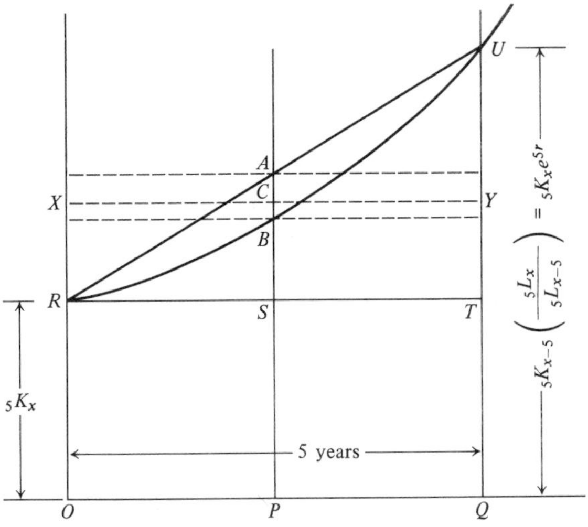

Fig. 11.1 Exponential curve of population growth *RBU* and three horizontal approximations.

population at each moment of the time interval OQ. The characteristic equation (3.2.4) will be written $\psi_A(r) = 1$ when $\lambda = e^{5r}$ and we multiply through by e^{-5nr}.

METHOD *B*. *The projection starting with geometric mean of initial and final populations.* If a population is increasing exponentially at the intrinsic rate, i.e., if it is behaving like a stable population, then at any intermediate time t during the five-year period of the first cycle of projection it will equal the initial population multiplied by e^{rt}, or ${}_5K_x e^{rt}$. At the midpoint, it will be equal to ${}_5K_x e^{5r/2}$. If the population were stable, with

$$\frac{B_0}{l_0}\,(e^{-(x+2.5)r}\,{}_5L_x)$$

individuals aged x to $x + 4$ at the start of the five-year period, as corresponds to the age distribution of a stable population whose births are B_0, then $2\frac{1}{2}$ years later it will have multiplied by $e^{2.5r}$. Using this midpoint population as the exposed over the five years, the births during the five years will be obtained by multiplying by the age-specific birth rate ${}_5F_x$:

$$\frac{B_0}{l_0}\left\{\sum_{x=0}^{\beta-5} e^{-(x+2.5)r}\,{}_5L_x\, e^{5r/2}\,{}_5F_x\right\}. \tag{11.1.24}$$

This is equivalent to treating the horizontal line through B as the average population from time O to Q on Fig. 11.1.

Again, if the population is stable, these births, occurring on the average at the middle of the period, ought to be $e^{5r/2}$ times the births B_0 which form the radix of the stable population at time zero. Hence, equating (11.1.24) to $B_0e^{5r/2}$ and canceling out $B_0e^{5r/2}$ gives

$$\bar{\psi}_B(r) = \frac{1}{l_0}\left\{\sum_{x=0}^{\beta-5} e^{-(x+2.5)r}\,{}_5L_x\,F_x\right\} = 1\,. \tag{11.1.25}$$

All subsequent equations will be related to (11.1.25) which we will write

$$\psi_B(r) = 1\,, \qquad \text{or} \qquad \bar{\psi}_B(r) = 1\,,$$

the latter when it is necessary to bear in mind that the correction for grouping is omitted. This is the approximation which is commonly used in demography (Coale, 1957b) and which has appeared earlier as (5.3.2). Is it obvious why $\bar{\psi}_B(r)$ should be the same as the denominator of (5.7.3), the result of applying the Laplace transform to a net maternity function concentrated at midpoints of intervals? What is its relation to the characteristic equation of the matrix whose first row is (8.3.5)?

METHOD C. *The projection assuming exponential increase and starting with mean of population over initial interval.* The introduction of the stable model suggests a further improvement; why should we not make the population during the first five-year cycle of projection equal to the *average* of the exponential trajectory which we are assuming? This we will call method C, in which, for each age group in the initial period, an average

$$\frac{K_x\int_0^5 e^{rt}\,dt}{5} = \frac{K_x e^{rt}\big|_0^5}{5r} = \frac{K_x(e^{5r}-1)}{5r} \tag{11.1.26}$$

is the base to which ${}_5F_x$ is applied. This is level C in Fig. 11.1, fixed to make area $OXCYQ$ equal to $ORBUQ$. The ratio of (11.1.26) to the $K_xe^{5r/2}$ of the preceding method B is

$$\begin{aligned}\frac{K_x(e^{5r}-1)/5r}{K_xe^{5r/2}} &= \frac{e^{5r/2}-e^{-5r/2}}{5r}\\ &= \frac{\sinh(5r/2)}{5r/2} = 1 + \frac{25}{24}r^2 + \frac{125}{384}r^4 + \cdots,\end{aligned} \tag{11.1.27}$$

where sinh is the hyperbolic sine.

If method B is our standard, then for method C the integral equation $\bar{\psi}_B(r) = 1$ is modified by multiplication by (11.1.27) on the left to give

$$\psi_C(r) = (1 + \tfrac{25}{24}r^2 + \tfrac{125}{384}r^4 + \cdots)\bar{\psi}_B(r) = 1\,. \tag{11.1.28}$$

Show that (11.1.28) is the same as (5.7.5) equated to unity.

Offsetting of Error in Method *B* by Correction for Grouping

The equation for the intrinsic rate when we correct for grouping is (11.1.23), and that for method *C* is (11.1.28). Applying both the correction for grouping and the improvement of *C* over *B* simultaneously gives, again to r^4,

$$\bar{\psi}_B(r)(1 + \tfrac{25}{24}r^2 + \tfrac{125}{384}r^4) = 1 + \tfrac{25}{24}r^2 + \tfrac{125}{384}r^4,$$

which on cancellation becomes $\bar{\psi}_B(r) = 1$ of (11.1.25). We have shown that up to r^4 *the correction for grouping offsets the improvement from the midpoint to the average of the exponential trajectory within projection intervals*, and leaves us with the characteristic equation $\bar{\psi}_B(r) = 1$.

Comparison of Methods *A* and *B*

Let us see what the usual population projection, which we called method *A*, amounts to in terms of *B*. If applied to an initial population which is stable, then any group which starts at K_x ends the five-year period at $e^{5r}K_x$. Since the arithmetic mean of the initial and final populations is used in *A*, the implicit average of method *A* in the first period is $K_x(1 + e^{5r})/2$. The ratio of this to the midpoint of the exponential curve, which is *B*, our standard, is

$$\begin{aligned}\frac{K_x(1 + e^{5r})/2}{K_x e^{5r/2}} &= \frac{e^{5r/2} + e^{-5r/2}}{2}\\ &= \cosh\frac{5}{2}r = 1 + \frac{25}{8}r^2 + \frac{625}{384}r^4 + \cdots \qquad (11.1.29)\end{aligned}$$

Translated into the geometry of Fig. 11.1, Eq. (11.1.29) says that $AC \doteq 2CB$, where we recall that *C* is on the horizontal line *XY*, drawn so that the area of *XYQO* equals that of *RBUQO*, and compare the term in r^2 with (11.1.27).

Having found the ratio of the level of method *A* to the level of method *B*, we are in a position to show how the intrinsic rate calculated by *A* compares with that calculated by *B*. Since the level of *A* relative to *B* is given by (11.1.29), then the characteristic equation for *A* must be

$$\begin{aligned}\psi_A(r) &= \cosh\left(\frac{5}{2}r\right)\psi_B(r) = \frac{e^{5r/2} + e^{-5r/2}}{2}\psi_B(r)\\ &= \left(1 + \frac{25}{8}r^2 + \frac{625}{384}r^4\right)\psi_B(r) = 1,\end{aligned}$$

if terms beyond that in r^4 are negligible. Raising $\psi_B(r)$ raises the real root in an amount which may be found from geometrical considerations on Fig. 5.2. The reader may show that to r^2 the intrinsic rate derived from the matrix method *A* exceeds that of the integral-equation method *B* by $25r^2/8A_r$, where A_r is the average age of childbearing in the stable population.

Summary of Corrections

Our work to this point is summarized in Exhibit 11.1, whose rows show the principal options of computational procedure. The usual projection matrix A implies too high an intrinsic rate, an overstatement due to use of the arithmetic mean of the extremities where the population is increasing geometrically. The integral equation $\psi_B(r) = 1$ seems slightly low because it starts with the mid-point rather than a mean population, but this is compensated by the absence of the correction for grouping. The difference between the roots of the matrix A and of the integral equation B is about three times that between the roots of B and C. The last line of the table combines the improved method C with the correction for grouping and brings us back to B.

Table 11.1 shows for five countries how the discrepancy between the two ways of calculating the intrinsic rate increases with the square of the rate. The discrepancy in $1000r$ between methods A and B for Mauritius, 1965, is $31.261 - 31.149 = 0.112$, against 0.119 in the last column. Elsewhere the last column is practically identical with the difference between the two methods to the places shown.

Insofar as the integral equation (method B) provides a better approximation to the intrinsic rate than does the usual projection matrix, there is a case for forming our projection matrix by means of it, using elements (8.3.5) in the top row. The convenience of a matrix using (8.3.5) is that the ultimate population, increasing according to the dominant root alone, would agree exactly with the projected population. Unfortunately, the recurrence equations (2.1.7) by which the matrix was developed lose their linearity when this change is made,

Table 11.1 Value of $1000r$ by matrix [method A of (11.5.3)] and integral equation [method B of (11.1.25)], accounting for difference by $1000(25r^2/8A_r)$, females of five countries, 1965

	METHOD				
	A	B			
	MATRIX $1000r$	INTEGRAL EQUATION $1000r_0$	A − B	A_r	$1000 \times 25r^2/8A_r$
CANADA	14.691	14.667	0.024	27.2	0.025
FINLAND	4.550	4.548	0.002	27.9	0.002
MAURITIUS	31.261	31.149	0.112	27.3	0.119
NETHERLANDS	12.539	12.522	0.017	28.5	0.017
UNITED STATES*	12.670	12.650	0.020	26.1	0.019

* Births adjusted.

Exhibit 11.1 Summary of methods of projection and resultant values of r

(1)	(2)	(3)	(4)	(5)	(6)
Method	Assumed average of first interval as ratio to population at beginning of projection	Column (2) relative to method B	Characteristic equation	r given r_0 from $\bar{\psi}_B(r_0) = 1$ of Method B (A_r is evaluated at r_0)	$1000r$ for Mauritius 1964 females
A. Standard projection applying fertility rates to arithmetic mean of initial and final population in age groups	$\dfrac{1 + e^{5r}}{2}$	$\dfrac{e^{5r/2} + e^{-5r/2}}{2} = \cosh\left(\dfrac{5r}{2}\right) = 1 + \dfrac{25}{8}r^2 + \dfrac{625}{384}r^4$	$\psi_A(r) = \cosh\left(\dfrac{5r}{2}\right)\bar{\psi}_B(r) = 1$	$r_A \doteqdot r_B + \dfrac{25r_0^2}{8A_r}$	34.418
B. Applying fertility rates to midpoint exponential population; this corresponds to integral equation	$e^{5r/2}$	1	$\bar{\psi}_B(r) = 1$	$r = r_B = r_0$	34.283
C. Applying fertility rates to average exponential population	$\dfrac{e^{5r} - 1}{5r}$	$\dfrac{e^{5r/2} - e^{-5r/2}}{5r} = \dfrac{\sinh(5r/2)}{5r/2} = 1 + \dfrac{25}{24}r^2 + \dfrac{125}{384}r^4$	$\psi_C(r) = \dfrac{\sinh(5r/2)\bar{\psi}_B(r)}{5r/2} = 1$	$r_C \doteqdot r_B + \dfrac{25r_0^2}{24A_r}$	34.328
Integral equation (method *B*) corrected for grouping			$\psi_B(r) = \dfrac{(5r/2)\bar{\psi}_B(r)}{\sinh(5r/2)} = 1$	$r \doteqdot r_B - \dfrac{25r_0^2}{24A_r}$	34.238
Method *C* corrected for grouping			$\psi_C(r) = \bar{\psi}_B(r) = 1$	$r = r_B$	34.283

and their explicit solution would be awkward. In practice they could be solved by iterative methods if necessary. In (8.3.5) and Table 8.2, linearity was restored by replacing $\sqrt{\lambda}$ by $\sqrt{\lambda_1}$.

The reader who wishes to push this further may consider various combinations of the corrections for survivorship, Eqs. (11.1.15) through (11.1.18), and those for the fertility elements given in Exhibit 11.1.

Extension to a General Interval

The above discussion has been conducted in terms of a five-year interval of age, for concreteness and because this is the most familiar case in practice. The reader may derive the formulas for a general interval, say d years, and show that the allowance for grouping gives the equation

$$\bar{\psi}(r) = 1 + \frac{(rd)^2}{24} + \frac{(rd)^4}{1920} + \cdots,$$

in place of (11.1.23), where the uncorrected equation would be $\bar{\psi}(r) = 1$. The ratio of the uncorrected characteristic function $\bar{\psi}(r)$ to the corrected $\psi(r)$ is

$$\frac{\bar{\psi}(r)}{\psi(r)} = 1 + \frac{(rd)^2}{24} + \frac{(rd)^4}{1920}, \tag{11.1.30}$$

to terms in r^4.

If the projection gives rise to the equation $\psi_A(r) = 1$, and the integral equation to $\bar{\psi}_B(r) = 1$, disregarding the correction for grouping, then the reader may generalize Exhibit 11.1 to show that the ratio of the characteristic function on method A to that on method B is

$$\frac{\psi_A(r)}{\bar{\psi}_B(r)} = \frac{e^{rd/2} + e^{-rd/2}}{2} = 1 + \frac{1}{2!}\left(\frac{rd}{2}\right)^2 + \frac{1}{4!}\left(\frac{rd}{2}\right)^4 + \cdots. \tag{11.1.31}$$

The ratio of $\psi_C(r)$ to $\bar{\psi}_B(r)$ is

$$\frac{\psi_C(r)}{\bar{\psi}_B(r)} = \frac{e^{rd/2} - e^{-rd/2}}{rd} = 1 + \frac{1}{3!}\left(\frac{rd}{2}\right)^2 + \frac{1}{5!}\left(\frac{rd}{2}\right)^4 + \cdots. \tag{11.1.32}$$

We now superimpose two of these modifications on one another. In going from method B to method C we increase the characteristic function by the ratio $\psi_C(r)/\bar{\psi}_B(r)$, given as (11.1.32) above. In correcting for grouping we multiply by $\psi(r)/\bar{\psi}(r)$, the reciprocal of the right-hand side of (11.1.30). In going from method B to method C *and* correcting for grouping, we multiply by the quotient of (11.1.32) divided by (11.1.30), which is unity on the right-hand side to r^4.

The above argument shows how the curve $\psi(r)$ is moved up and down by changing the conditions under which the calculation is made. The reader is again invited to interpret the argument by reference to Fig. 5.2.

The Terminal Open-Ended Age Interval

The application of the life table to find survivorship at the terminal age of a projection is somewhat different from that at younger ages. We can of course take the last age interval to be five years in width, say 85 to 89 at last birthday; if it is supposed that no one lives beyond this, the element in the lower right-hand corner of the projection matrix would be zero, and the subdiagonal elements would all be five-year survivorships ${}_5L_{x+5}/{}_5L_x$. But if we regard the last interval of the age distribution as open-ended, we need a nonzero element in the lower right-hand corner of the matrix; this will carry over some survivors into the same open interval in the next period. Call the unknown required element m_{nn} and the last population group k_n. Then the condition of stability is $\mathbf{MK} = \lambda\mathbf{K}$, a set of n linear equations, of which the last is

$$m_{n,n-1}k_{n-1} + m_{nn}k_n = \lambda k_n ,$$

so that

$$m_{nn} = \lambda - \frac{m_{n,n-1}k_{n-1}}{k_n} .$$

The reader may write $n = 18$ to put this in terms of the 85+ group and verify that

$$m_{18,18} = \lambda - \frac{({}_5L_{85}/{}_5L_{80})({}_5L_{80}\lambda^{-16.5})}{{}_5L_{85}\lambda^{-17.5} + {}_5L_{90}\lambda^{-18.5} + \cdots} = \frac{{}_5L_{90} + {}_5L_{95}\lambda^{-1} + \cdots}{{}_5L_{85} + {}_5L_{90}\lambda^{-1} + \cdots} ,$$

which is λ times the ratio of the stable population 90 years and over to that 85 years and over.

11.2. THE STABLE AGE DISTRIBUTION OBTAINED FROM THE l_x COLUMN OF THE LIFE TABLE

The number of the population between ages x and $x + 5$ in the stable age distribution, say ${}_5K_x$, is on radix l_0,

$${}_5K_x = \int_x^{x+5} e^{-ra}l(a)\,da , \qquad (11.2.1)$$

as follows from the argument of Chapter 7. Expanding the exponential under the integral as $e^{-r(x+2.5)}[1 - (a - x - 2\frac{1}{2})r + \cdots]$ and then integrating by applying (11.1.12) gives the approximations

$$\begin{aligned} {}_5K_x &\doteq e^{-r(x+2.5)}[{}_5L_x + \tfrac{5}{12}r({}_5L_x - {}_5L_{x+5})] , \\ {}_5K_x &\doteq e^{-r(x+2.5)}[{}_5L_x + \tfrac{5}{24}r({}_5L_{x-5} - {}_5L_{x+5})] , \end{aligned} \qquad (11.2.2)$$

the second being symmetrically located and obtained by averaging the first with a similar expression having $({}_5L_{x-5} - {}_5L_x)$ within the parentheses.

An alternative is to consider $e^{-ra}l(a)$ as a single function whose values at discrete points five years apart are known; put a third-degree curve through

Table 11.2 Excerpt from official United States male life table for 1959–61, together with exponentials for stable population

FIVE-YEAR AGE INTERVALS

x	ℓ_x	$e^{-0.02x}$	${}_5L_x$	$e^{-0.02(x+2.5)}$
60	73,887	0.301194	346,168	0.286505
65	64,177	0.272532	291,793	0.259240
70	52,244	0.246597	228,353	0.234570
75	38,950	0.223130	160,542	0.212248

SINGLE-YEAR AGE INTERVALS

x	ℓ_x	$e^{-0.02x}$	${}_1L_x$	$e^{-0.02(x+0.5)}$
65	64,177	0.272532	63,062	0.269820
66	61,947	0.267135	60,789	0.264477
67	59,631	0.261846	58,433	0.259240
68	57,235	0.256661	56,002	0.254107
69	54,770	0.251579	53,507	0.249075

four consecutive values, and integrate by (11.1.9):

$$\begin{aligned} {}_5K_x &= \int_0^5 e^{-r(x+t)} l(x+t)\,dt \\ &= \tfrac{65}{24}(e^{-r(x+5)}l_{x+5} + e^{-rx}l_x) - \tfrac{5}{24}(e^{-r(x+10)}l_{x+10} + e^{-r(x-5)}l_{x-5})\,. \end{aligned} \quad (11.2.3)$$

As a numerical example of the differences which result from different formulas, consider the official United States life table for 1959–61 males, age group 65–69, with an arbitrary r of 0.02. Using the data given in Table 11.2, the reader can verify that simply using $e^{-67.5r}{}_5L_{65}$ for ${}_5K_{65}$ results in 75,644; that the correction (11.2.2) by expansion of e^{-ra} up to r within the integral results in $e^{-67.5r}[{}_5L_{65} + \frac{5}{24}r({}_5L_{60} - {}_5L_{70})] = 75{,}772$; that (11.2.3), the third-degree curve through $e^{-rx}l(x)$, $x = 60, 65, 70, 75$, results in 75,815.

We now have three results and would like to choose the best. If the graduation into single years carried out officially is correct, we may multiply each ${}_1L_x$ by $e^{-r(x+2.5)}$ and add. The official figures being given in Table 11.2, the reader may verify that the result is ${}_5K_{65} = 75{,}799$. [By how much would this be raised if we allow for the term in r in the expansion for a one-year interval analogous to (11.2.2)?] This evidence suggests that our third method (11.2.3) is superior, although one wishes a better test were available.

The intrinsic birth rate is the birth rate in the stable population. Weighting the age-specific birth rates by the numbers in the stable population gives

$$b = \frac{\int_0^\omega e^{-ra}p(a)m(a)\,da}{\int_0^\omega e^{-ra}p(a)\,da}\,.$$

If r satisfies the characteristic equation $\psi(r) = 1$, the numerator is 1, and hence

$$b = \frac{1}{\int_0^\omega e^{-ra}p(a)\,da}$$

is readily calculated from the stationary age distribution and the intrinsic rate r. The first two age groups cannot be fitted satisfactorily by a polynomial, so we write

$$b = \frac{1}{\int_0^{10} e^{-ra}p(a)\,da + \int_{10}^\omega e^{-ra}p(a)\,da}\,,$$

or, from (11.2.3),

$$\frac{l_0}{b} = \int_0^{10} e^{-rx}l(x)\,dx - \frac{5}{24}e^{-5r}l_5 + \frac{5}{2}e^{-10r}l_{10}$$
$$+ \frac{125}{24}e^{-15r}l_{15} + 5e^{-20r}l_{20} + 5e^{-25r}l_{25} + \cdots\,, \qquad (11.2.4)$$

where $\int_0^{10} e^{-rx}l(x)\,dx$ would have to be handled by the hyperbola of (10.4.5) or other means.

Alternatives to (11.1.15) through (11.1.18) for survivorship are suggested by the relatively high accuracy of (11.2.3). Still writing $k(x)$ for $e^{-rx}l(x)$, the ratio of integrals in (11.1.14) is

$$\frac{e^{5r}\int_0^5 k(x+5+t)\,dt}{\int_0^5 k(x+t)\,dt}\,.$$

Evaluating each integral by (11.2.3) gives for the survival ratio

$$\frac{e^{5r}[13(k_{x+10}+k_{x+5}) - (k_{x+15}+k_x)]}{13(k_{x+5}+k_x) - (k_{x+10}+k_{x-5})}\,. \qquad (11.2.5)$$

In order to apply this to the ${}_5L_{45}/{}_5L_{40}$ of United States females, 1964, we need the five values of l_x:

$$l_{35} = 95{,}573\,,$$
$$l_{40} = 94{,}685\,,$$
$$l_{45} = 93{,}385\,,$$
$$l_{50} = 91{,}450\,,$$
$$l_{55} = 88{,}566\,,$$

along with the corresponding $e^{-0.015x}$. Then (11.2.5) works out to 0.983085, as against the uncorrected ${}_5L_{45}/{}_5L_{40}$ of 0.983044 and the several corrected values ranging from 0.983080 to 0.983100 of (11.1.15) through (11.1.18) exhibited earlier.

Numerical differences between the commonly used survival factor ${}_5L_{x+5}/{}_5L_x$ and the improvements (11.1.15) through (11.1.18), or the somewhat different improvement (11.2.5) are evidently small. Nonetheless, the principle of allowing for the fact that an increasing population tends to make the distribution within each age group somewhat younger than that of a stationary population is worth retaining. Of the several ways in which this principle may be applied, that embodied in (11.2.5) seems the most precise.

11.3. STABLE POPULATIONS CHANGED FROM ONE FINITE APPROXIMATION TO ANOTHER

The matrix **M** permits easy computation of many population parameters. We know from (3.2.30), for example, that

$$\mathbf{M}^t \doteq \lambda_1^t \mathbf{Z}_1 = \lambda_1^t \{\mathbf{K}_1\}[\mathbf{H}_1]\,,$$

and for t greater than 64 or 128 the approximation is very close. Hence the stable age distribution $\{\mathbf{K}_1\}$ is readily obtained as the first (or any other) column of $\mathbf{M}^t/\lambda_1^t$. But we saw above that working from the matrix (method A) results in a λ_1, and hence an $r_1 = 0.2 \ln \lambda_1$, that is slightly high.

In the stable age distribution the improved ${}_5K_x^*$ based on the integral equation r^* of the preferred method B may be obtained by correcting ${}_5K_x$, a column of $\mathbf{M}^t/\lambda_1^t$:

$$\begin{aligned}{}_5K_x^* &= {}_5K_x \frac{\exp[-r^*(x+2.5)]}{\lambda^{-(x+2.5)/5}} = {}_5K_x \exp[-(r^* - r)(x+2.5)] \\ &\doteq {}_5K_x\big(1 + (r - r^*)(x+2.5)\big)\,. \end{aligned} \tag{11.3.1}$$

if both the original and the improved distributions are on the same radix l_0. Since $r - r^* = 25r^2/8A_r$, where A_r is the mean age of childbearing in the stable population ($r - r^*$ is the same as $r_A - r_B$ of the first row of Exhibit 11.1), we have

$$ {}_5K_x^* \doteq {}_5K_x\left[1 + \frac{25r^2}{8A_r}\left(x + \frac{5}{2}\right)\right] \doteq {}_5K_x\left[1 + \frac{r^2}{8}\left(x + \frac{5}{2}\right)\right],$$

using the fact that A_r is not far from 25 in human populations. The values of ${}_5K_x^*$ will be sensibly larger than those of ${}_5K_x$ at higher ages in rapidly increasing populations.

The corresponding improved intrinsic birth rate is

$$b^* = \frac{l_0}{\Sigma\, {}_5K_x^*}\,, \tag{11.3.2}$$

if the radix of ${}_5K_x^*$, which may be thought of as the limiting value ${}_0K_0^*$, is equal to l_0. Entering (11.3.1) in (11.3.2), and dividing numerator and denominator by $\Sigma\,{}_5K_x$, gives

$$b^* = \frac{l_0}{\Sigma\,{}_5K_x + (r - r^*)[\Sigma\,{}_5K_x(x + \frac{5}{2})]} = \frac{b}{1 + (r - r^*)\bar{A}_r}$$

$$\doteqdot b\left(1 - \frac{\bar{A}_r r^2}{8}\right), \qquad (11.3.3)$$

where $\bar{A}_r$ is the average age in the stable population. The improved b^*, like r^*, is smaller than the quantity based on the matrix. [Find d^*.]

By similar manipulation the reader may show that the improved mean age in the stable population, $\bar{A}_r^*$, is

$$\bar{A}_r^* = \frac{b^*}{b}[\bar{A}_r + (r - r^*)(\bar{\sigma}_r^2 + \bar{A}_r^2)] \doteqdot \bar{A}_r + \frac{\bar{\sigma}_r^2 r^2}{8},$$

where $\bar{\sigma}_r^2$ is the variance of the stable population. The improved length of generation, T^*, is

$$T^* = \frac{\ln R_0}{r^*} \doteqdot \frac{T}{1 - 25r/8A_r} \doteqdot T\left(1 + \frac{r}{8}\right).$$

Table 11.3 Approximations by matrix (method *A*) and by integral equation (method *B*) to seven parameters of the stable population for two countries

	ENGLAND AND WALES, 1960-62, MALES		TOGO, 1961, FEMALES	
	A STANDARD PROJECTION OR MATRIX (3.2.4)	B * INTEGRAL EQUATION (11.1.25)	A STANDARD PROJECTION OR MATRIX (3.2.4)	B * INTEGRAL EQUATION (11.1.25)
1000r	9.56	9.55	27.29	27.21
1000b	20.35	20.34	50.39	50.30
${}_5K_0$	4.7571	4.7572	3.8521	3.8529
${}_5K_{20}$	3.8717	3.8725	1.7416	1.7449
${}_5K_{40}$	3.1028	3.1040	0.7952	0.7981
$\bar{A}_r$	31.89	31.89	21.03	21.06
T	30.30	30.31	27.89	27.97

The preceding paragraphs have shown how the estimates from the matrix, method A unstarred, may be changed into estimates agreeing with the integral equation, method B here written with star. The results for males, England and Wales, 1960–62, and for females, Togo, 1961, based on the matrix and the integral equation, will show the magnitude of the differences in countries of low and of high fertility (Table 11.3). All the results on method B for Togo may be reproduced from those on method A, given $\bar{\sigma}_r^2 = 307$.

The above results for changing from B to A are readily adapted to shifting between any other pair of methods among those shown in Exhibit 11.1.

11.4. THE CONSTANTS Q OF THE INTEGRAL EQUATION

In Chapter 5 we found an expression Qe^{rt} as the typical term of the solution to the integral equation, where Q is defined as

$$Q = \frac{\int_0^\beta e^{-rt}G(t)\,dt}{-\psi'(r)} = \frac{V}{A_r},$$

and we need some finite form by which this can be numerically evaluated from the data ordinarily available, say population, life table, and fertility rates, all in five-year age groups. Remembering the definition of $G(t)$ as the number of children born at time t to those women already alive at time 0, that is,

$$G(t) = \int_0^\beta k(x)\frac{p(x+t)}{p(x)}m(x+t)\,dx\,, \quad t < \beta\,,$$

we see that V, the numerator of Q, is in effect a double integral, to be evaluated over the area on the upper right-hand side of the diagonal in the Lexis diagram (Fig. 5.1). For the real root V is total reproductive value and A_r is the mean age in the stable population; other roots require complex analogs of these.

For each t that is a multiple of 5, that is, along each horizontal line, we will require the single integral multiplied by e^{-rt},

$$e^{-rt}G(t) \doteq e^{-rt}\sum_{x=0}^{x=\beta-5} {}_5K_x \frac{{}_5L_{x+t}}{{}_5L_x} F_{x+t}\,,$$

where, as usual, x takes values at five-year intervals, 0, 5, 10, ..., $\beta - 5$. To go from this estimate of the integrand of Q over any single horizontal line to an estimate of it over the strip between two values of t, we need the average between t and $t + 5$ multiplied by 5:

$$\frac{5e^{-r(t+5)}G(t+5) + 5e^{-rt}G(t)}{2}\,,$$

and adding over t gives

$$\begin{aligned} V &= \tfrac{5}{2}G(0) + 5e^{-5r}G(5) + \cdots \\ &= \tfrac{5}{2}\sum_{x=0}^{\beta-5} {}_5K_xF_x + 5\sum_{x=0}^{\beta-5}\sum_{t=5}^{\beta-x-5} e^{-rt}{}_5K_x\frac{{}_5L_{x+t}}{{}_5L_x}F_{x+t} \end{aligned} \qquad (11.4.1)$$

as the numerator of Q. This quantity divided by $A_r = -\psi'(r)$ provides the required estimate of Q.

The data of Table 2.1 will serve again for a numerical example. For Q_1 we first calculate ${}_5K_x/{}_5L_x$, $x = 0, 5, 10, \ldots$, and then multiply this by ${}_5L_x\,F_x$ and add through the ages x that are multiples of 5; then we multiply by ${}_5L_{x+5}\,F_{x+5}$ and add again, and so forth. The result on (11.4.1) for United States females, 1964, is

$$Q_1 = \frac{V}{A_r} = \frac{55{,}696}{25.974} = 2144.3$$

in thousands of births. Hence the first term of (5.1.3) for an initial condition consisting of the age distribution of United States females, 1964, is

$$\begin{aligned} B(t) &= 2144.3e^{(0.01570)t} \\ &= 2144.3(1.08168)^{t/5} \text{ thousands.} \end{aligned}$$

At $t = 100$ this is 10,310.1 thousands. As a rough check, we note that the matrix projection of the 1964 female population would give 10,382.8 thousand births in the year 2064. The check is approximate because other roots than the dominant one are still acting at 100 years, and because the projection is a different finite approximation from the equation for $B(t)$.

The numerator of Q_1 given in (11.4.1) and applied to the real root is an approximation to the same V, total female reproductive value, defined for a woman of age x in (3.2.15), and shown in the aggregate of all ages in Table 3.5. Its estimate in (11.4.1) is appropriate to the integral equation, while $[\mathbf{H}_1]\{\mathbf{K}^{(0)}\}$ of Section 3.2 corresponds to the matrix formulation. For United States females, 1964, the value from (11.4.1) shown above is $V = 55{,}696{,}000$, against that given in Table 3.5, which is $V = 55{,}728{,}000$, a difference of 1 part in 2000.

For the real root r_1, the solid figure whose volume we aim to measure as V is a rather asymmetric bell shape over the x-axis at time 0; it slopes downward as it comes forward in time. If r is 33 per thousand, then at the end of 30 years it will be about 1/2.7 of the initial height. The part of it which constitutes the integral V is only that to the right of the diagonal line on the Lexis diagram (Fig. 5.1): one-half of a loaf sliced diagonally. [Lotka (1942) shows a somewhat different form of chart.]

11.5. SUMMARY AND NUMERICAL COMPUTATION ON FOUR FORMULATIONS OF THE RENEWAL PROCESS

Following is a summary of the four finite approximations to the integral equation introduced above as A (Chapters 2 and 3), B (Sections 5.2 and 5.3), C (Section 5.7), and D (Section 5.8). They will here be arranged in ascending order of the real root to which they give rise: B, C, A, D.

The renewal equation as solved by the Hertz-Lotka method gives the commonly used approximation (11.1.25) to the characteristic equation (5.2.2):

$$l_0\psi_B(r) = e^{-17.5r}L_{15}F_{15} + e^{-22.5r}L_{20}F_{20} + \cdots + e^{-52.5r}L_{50}F_{50} = l_0\,, \quad (11.5.1)$$

where fertility goes from age 15 to 55 and we omit correction for grouping.

The second formulation of the renewal equation in ascending order of the real root made use of the Laplace transform. The histogram form gives as (5.7.5) the characteristic equation

$$l_0\psi_C(r) = \frac{L_{15}F_{15}}{5r}(e^{-15r} - e^{-20r}) + \frac{L_{20}F_{20}}{5r}(e^{-20r} - e^{-25r}) + \cdots$$
$$+ \frac{L_{50}F_{50}}{5r}(e^{-50r} - e^{-55r}) = l_0\,. \quad (11.5.2)$$

By directly comparing terms in $L_{15}F_{15}$, etc., the reader may show that

$$\psi_C(r) = \psi_B(r)\sinh(5r/2)/(5r/2)\,,$$

where again sinh is the hyperbolic sine.

The method of Chapter 3 is the ordinary population projection translated into matrix form. If in (3.2.4) we consider the characteristic roots λ of the projection matrix as $\lambda = e^{5r}$ or $r = 0.2\ln\lambda$, then we obtain an equation in r comparable with the preceding:

$$2l_0\psi_A(r) = L_{15}F_{15}e^{-15r} + (L_{15}F_{15} + L_{20}F_{20})e^{-20r}$$
$$+ (L_{20}F_{20} + L_{25}F_{25})e^{-25r} + \cdots + L_{50}F_{50}e^{-55r} = 2l_0\,. \quad (11.5.3)$$

Show that

$$\psi_A(r) = \psi_B(r)\cosh(5r/2) = \psi_C(r)\coth(5r/2)5r/2\,,$$

coth being the hyperbolic cotangent.

The fourth formulation is through partial fractions, in Section 5.8. The equation resulting when s is replaced by e^{-5r} in (5.8.7) is

$$l_0\psi_D(r) = 5l_{15}F_{12.5}e^{-15r} + 5l_{20}F_{17.5}e^{-20r} + \cdots + 5l_{55}F_{52.5}e^{-55r} = l_0\,, \quad (11.5.4)$$

where $F_{12.5}$, etc. is the age-specific fertility for the five years centered on age 15, etc. We cannot apply this to data without an approximation to $F_{x+2.5}$ from F_x; the simplest is the arithmetic mean:

$$F_{x+2.5} = \frac{F_x + F_{x+5}}{2}\,, \quad x = 15, 20, \ldots, 50\,,$$

and we will suppose $\psi_D(r)$ to be based on this.

[Prove that the approximation

$$F_{x+2.5} = 0.1\left(\frac{L_xF_x}{l_{x+5}} + \frac{L_{x+5}F_{x+5}}{l_{x+5}}\right), \quad x = 15, 20, \ldots, 50\,,$$

in (11.5.4) makes $\psi_D(r)$ identical with $\psi_A(r)$.]

Table 11.4 shows in four columns the solutions for the real root of the four equations summarized in this section. Not only do the real roots rise from left to right—the integral equation gives the lowest r and the partial fractions give the highest—but the differences increase as we go from left to right; the excess of the projection (11.5.3) over the Laplace transform (11.5.2) is about twice that of the Laplace transform (11.5.2) over the integral equation (11.5.1); the partial fraction solution (11.5.4) is irregular and up to two percent greater than the others.

The variation among the complex roots shown in Table 11.4 is greater yet. The partial fraction result is close to the projection, although somewhat erratic,

Table 11.4 First three roots of characteristic equation in four formulations, females

	INTEGRAL EQUATION (11.5.1) $\psi_B(r) = 1$	LAPLACE TRANSFORM OF HISTOGRAM (11.5.2) $\psi_C(r) = 1$	PROJECTION (11.5.3) $\psi_A(r) = 1$	PARTIAL FRACTION (11.5.4) $\psi_D(r) = 1$
	REAL ROOT r_1			
FRANCE 1962	0.01015	0.01016	0.01016	0.01016
MEXICO 1960	0.03325	0.03329	0.03338	0.03398
NETHERLANDS 1962	0.01375	0.01376	0.01377	0.01387
TAIWAN 1961	0.03141	0.03145	0.03152	0.03185
	PRINCIPAL COMPLEX ROOTS r_2, r_3			
FRANCE 1962	−0.0245 ±0.2278i	−0.0263 ±0.2266i	−0.0298 ±0.2240i	−0.0297 ±0.2240i
MEXICO 1960	−0.0164 ±0.2158i	−0.0176 ±0.2147i	−0.0198 ±0.2125i	−0.0192 ±0.2126i
NETHERLANDS 1962	−0.0163 ±0.2139i	−0.0177 ±0.2132i	−0.0207 ±0.2114i	−0.0206 ±0.2114i
TAIWAN 1961	−0.0066 ±0.2194i	−0.0082 ±0.2185i	−0.0115 ±0.2165i	−0.0112 ±0.2166i

while the Laplace transform is comfortably intermediate and again about half as far from the integral equation as from the projection. [Prove that the three points representing the principal complex roots of the three equations (11.5.1), (11.5.2), and (11.5.3) lie on a straight line.]

A General Criterion

Where different finite methods are available for estimating an integral or other quantity, we would like to use the one which comes closest to the "true" answer. But suppose no true answer is to be had? A general criterion for comparing proposed finite approximations is obtained by calculating them from data with different widths of age interval, say ten years and five years. If we do not know what the true answer is, we can observe which of the (otherwise reasonable) methods alters least in the answer it gives between the ten-year and the five-year interval. Lacking other knowledge we may assume that this method will also vary least from five years to one year, etc. Develop a theory to show in what circumstances the error of a linear approximation is proportional to the square of the width of the interval, and in what circumstances to the cube.

This terminates a somewhat lengthy account of the various necessarily approximate ways in which numbers may be obtained from the formulas developed in the theory of earlier chapters, and particularly of Chapter 5. One should apologize for it as consisting of details of small numerical effect, and yet machine computation does make small differences conspicuous where earlier they would have been lost among the errors to which handwork is inevitably subject.

Part V

MULTIPLE POPULATIONS IN INTERACTION

CHAPTER 12

QUALITATIVE ASPECTS OF INTERACTION AMONG POPULATIONS

Independence and Association

So far our discussion has been of isolated, one-sex, one-species populations within which no subdivisions other than age are recognized. The models of Chapters 1 to 8 are too simple to describe the relations of categories additional to age in a single species or sex, and they have made no attempt to deal with several species or the two sexes simultaneously.

In *biological association* (Volterra, 1926, pp. 33–37) the numbers of one species affect, favorably or not, the growth of other species. Association takes various forms, to be discussed in this and the two succeeding chapters: the relations of predator and prey, the two sexes in a human or animal population, migration between the populations of two communicating territories, the married and single of a human group, women of different parities, persons at school or in the labor force.

12.1. THE LINEAR MODEL

Some of these situations may be analyzed in preliminary fashion (Lotka, 1956, pp. 78, 146) by means of a pair of linear differential equations

$$\begin{aligned} dN_1(t)/dt &= a_{11}N_1(t) + a_{12}N_2(t)\,, \\ dN_2(t)/dt &= a_{21}N_1(t) + a_{22}N_2(t)\,, \end{aligned} \qquad (12.1.1)$$

expressed in matrix terms as $\{\mathbf{N}'(t)\} = \mathbf{A}\{\mathbf{N}(t)\}$, where

$$\mathbf{A} = \begin{bmatrix} a_{11} & a_{12} \\ a_{21} & a_{22} \end{bmatrix}, \qquad \text{and} \qquad \mathbf{N}(t) = \begin{Bmatrix} N_1(t) \\ N_2(t) \end{Bmatrix}.$$

If a_{11} is positive, the more there are of the first species, the more it will increase, and in the absence of the second at rate a_{11}, which we call its *autonomous* rate. If a_{22} is also positive and $a_{12} = a_{21} = 0$, the species are independent and no new issues arise. This configuration will be symbolized by

$$\boxed{\begin{matrix} + & 0 \\ 0 & + \end{matrix}}\,,$$

and implies absence of association in the sense of this chapter.

The associations of principal interest are four in number.

a) *Competition.* Suppose the two species impede one another. Both of the autonomous rates, a_{11} and a_{22}, will have to be positive if each species is to survive in the absence of the other, and *a fortiori* if they are to survive together. Because the growth of the first diminishes the sustenance of the second and hence the rate of increase of the second, $dN_2(t)/dt$, we have

$$\frac{\partial(dN_2(t)/dt)}{\partial N_1(t)} = a_{21} < 0\,, \tag{12.1.2}$$

which may be called the *dependency* (negative in this case) of the second on the first, and this relation is reciprocal between the two species. Hence the description of competition, insofar as it can be given in the linear model, is

$$a_{11} > 0\,; \qquad a_{22} > 0\,; \qquad a_{12} < 0\,; \qquad a_{21} < 0\,,$$

which we may write

$$\boxed{\begin{matrix} + & - \\ - & + \end{matrix}}\,.$$

b) *Predation.* If the second species lives by eating the first, or as a parasite on the first, then greater numbers of the second species adversely affect the increase of the first, and

$$\frac{\partial(dN_1(t)/dt)}{\partial N_2(t)} = a_{12} \tag{12.1.3}$$

must be negative. Conversely, greater numbers of the prey will permit an increase in the predator, and a_{21} must be positive. For pure predation the second has no other support than the first, and its autonomous rate a_{22} is negative. Hence we have

$$a_{11} > 0\,; \qquad a_{22} < 0\,; \qquad a_{12} < 0\,; \qquad a_{21} > 0\,,$$

or, in brief,

$$\boxed{\begin{matrix} + & - \\ + & - \end{matrix}}$$

for the prey-predator, the host-parasite, and intermediate situations (Elton, 1933, p. 27).

c) *Scavenging or Saprophytism.* If the second lives on the waste product or the cadaver of the first, doing it neither good nor harm, and could not live without it, then

$$a_{11} > 0\,; \qquad a_{22} < 0\,; \qquad a_{12} = 0\,; \qquad a_{21} > 0\,;$$

that is,

$$\boxed{\begin{matrix} + & 0 \\ + & - \end{matrix}}\,.$$

d) *Symbiosis.* If the second lives on the first, but cultivates it, the relation is symbiotic, where each aids the growth of the other; if each is also necessary to the other, we have

$$a_{11} < 0 \,; \qquad a_{22} < 0 \,; \qquad a_{12} > 0 \,; \qquad a_{21} > 0 \,,$$

or

$$\begin{array}{|cc|} - & + \\ + & - \end{array}\,.$$

The human and the cattle population of an area exist in symbiotic relation where milk and meat are human food and people grow pasture for the cows. If the pasture grows naturally, the humans who eat meat are predators on the cows; those who drink milk are parasites.

The larger set out of which these four instances are selected may be made up by writing in a square array the possible signs of the four constants, a_{ij}, $i = 1, 2$, $j = 1, 2$. The number of combinations is evidently $2^4 = 16$ if $a_{ij} \neq 0$, and $3^4 = 81$ if zero values are permitted. Some of these are best seen as combinations of others—for example,

$$\begin{array}{|cc|} + & + \\ + & + \end{array}$$

means that the two species have positive autonomous rates of increase and support each other symbiotically as well.

Those who do not care for the technicalities of explicit solution of differential equations can study the properties of (12.1.1) with the help of a computer. The equations provide derivatives at the starting time from a knowledge of $N_1(0)$ and $N_2(0)$, the initial numbers of the two species. Given these and the a's, the derivatives permit a step h ahead:

$$N_1(h) = N_1(0) + hN_1'(0) = N_1(0) + h[a_{11}N_1(0) + a_{12}N_2(0)] \,,$$
$$N_2(h) = N_2(0) + hN_2'(0) = N_2(0) + h[a_{21}N_1(0) + a_{22}N_2(0)] \,.$$

Now $N_1(h)$ and $N_2(h)$ can be printed out, and then put in place of $N_1(0)$ and $N_2(0)$ and the cycle repeated. This *marching process* gives a more precise solution when h is small, and can be greatly improved by using higher-order derivatives, as in Chapter 13, but refinement is not necessary for the present purpose, which is to ascertain the general character of the trajectory. [Express the marching conditions as a matrix equation, and outline an analysis in terms of eigenvalues. What happens to this solution as h becomes small?]

As a numerical example we try the equations (Table 12.1, Section I)

$$N_1'(t) = 0.01N_1(t) - 0.04N_2(t) \,,$$
$$N_2'(t) = 0.02N_1(t) - 0.05N_2(t) \,,$$

which correspond to predation, and start with $N_1(0) = 90$, $N_2(0) = 80$; at the end of 500 cycles (years), numbers have fallen to the order of 0.1. On the other

Table 12.1 Approximate numerical solution for eight cases of predation using first derivatives only and intervals of one year*

	I		II	
	$N_1'(t) = 0.01N_1(t) - 0.04N_2(t)$ $N_2'(t) = 0.02N_1(t) - 0.05N_2(t)$		$N_1'(t) = 0.05N_1(t) - 0.04N_2(t)$ $N_2'(t) = 0.02N_1(t) - 0.01N_2(t)$	
t	$N_1(t)$	$N_2(t)$	$N_1(t)$	$N_2(t)$
0	90	80	90	80
50	27.36	21.31	203	159
100	10.65	6.99	574	382
200	2.84	1.50	7.90×10^3	4.21×10^3
300	0.99	0.50	1.43×10^5	7.24×10^4
400	0.36	0.18	2.73×10^6	1.37×10^6
500	0.13	0.07	5.24×10^7	2.62×10^7

	III		IV	
	$N_1'(t) = 0.1N_1(t) - 0.1N_2(t)$ $N_2'(t) = 0.1N_1(t) - 0.2N_2(t)$		$N_1'(t) = 0.01N_1(t) - 0.04N_2(t)$ $N_2'(t) = 0.03N_1(t) - 0.05N_2(t)$	
t	$N_1(t)$	$N_2(t)$	$N_1(t)$	$N_2(t)$
0	80	90	80	90
50	1.07×10^3	409	-1.03	16.04
100	2.15×10^4	8.21×10^3	-11.26	-4.65
200	8.64×10^6	3.30×10^6	-0.86	-1.39
300	3.47×10^9	1.33×10^9	0.25	0.16
400	1.39×10^{12}	5.34×10^{11}	0.00	0.02
500	5.62×10^{14}	2.15×10^{14}	0.00	0.00

* Programmed by William Cummings and William Taylor.

hand, the equations (Table 12.1, Section II)

$$N_1'(t) = 0.05N_1(t) - 0.04N_2(t)\,,$$
$$N_2'(t) = 0.02N_1(t) - 0.01N_2(t)\,,$$

also representing predation and with coefficients that do not look very different from the preceding ones, produce numbers of the order of 10^7 at the end of 500 years. The two pairs of equations have very different outcomes: in the first the species have both almost disappeared, while in the second they have grown

Table 12.1 (continued)

	V		VI	
	$N_1'(t) = 0.05N_1(t) - 0.04N_2(t)$ $N_2'(t) = 0.03N_1(t) - 0.01N_2(t)$		$N_1'(t) = 0.03N_1(t) - 0.04N_2(t)$ $N_2'(t) = 0.03N_1(t) - 0.03N_2(t)$	
t	$N_1(t)$	$N_2(t)$	$N_1(t)$	$N_2(t)$
0	80	90	80	90
50	2.33	126	-0.95	45.5
100	-580	-210	-82.4	-32
200	-3.24×10^3	-4.47×10^3	-55.6	-82
300	3.74×10^4	1.97×10^4	103	60
400	1.05×10^5	2.05×10^5	23.7	65
500	-2.21×10^6	-1.44×10^6	-114	-83

	VII		VIII	
	$N_1'(t) = 0.01N_1(t) - 0.03N_2(t)$ $N_2'(t) = 0.03N_1(t) - 0.05N_2(t)$		$N_1'(t) = 0.05N_1(t) - 0.03N_2(t)$ $N_2'(t) = 0.03N_1(t) - 0.01N_2(t)$	
t	$N_1(t)$	$N_2(t)$	$N_1(t)$	$N_2(t)$
0	80	90	80	90
50	23.6	27.2	175	202
100	6.55	7.88	367	439
200	0.33	0.51	1.11×10^3	1.64×10^3
300	-0.03	0.00	-3.13×10^3	6.71×10^2
400	-0.01	-0.01	-1.04×10^5	-7.62×10^4
500	0.00	0.00	-1.34×10^6	-1.14×10^6

astronomically. Carrying out such a process for equations with the eight sets of coefficients appearing in Table 12.1 results in the highly varied trajectories of which values are excerpted. The explanation of the large differences lies in the roots of a characteristic equation, to whose formulation we now proceed.

We differentiate the first member of (12.1.1) and in the derivative substitute the value of $dN_2(t)/dt$ from the second member; after some further simplification, left to the reader, a second-order linear equation in $N_1(t)$ emerges:

$$N_1''(t) - (a_{11} + a_{22})N_1'(t) + (a_{11}a_{22} - a_{12}a_{21})N_1(t) = 0 . \qquad (12.1.4)$$

Evidently $e^{\lambda t}$ is a solution if λ satisfies the characteristic equation

$$\lambda^2 - (a_{11} + a_{22})\lambda + a_{11}a_{22} - a_{12}a_{21} = 0 ,$$

whose roots are

$$\lambda_1, \lambda_2 = \tfrac{1}{2}\{(a_{11} + a_{22}) \pm \sqrt{(a_{11} - a_{22})^2 + 4a_{12}a_{21}}\} , \qquad (12.1.5)$$

and solutions being additive, the trajectory of the first species is

$$N_1(t) = n_{11}e^{\lambda_1 t} + n_{12}e^{\lambda_2 t} , \qquad (12.1.6)$$

where n_{11} and n_{12} are constants. (They are determined from the initial conditions with a technique exemplified below.) Since we would secure the same characteristic roots for the corresponding second-order differential equation in $N_2(t)$ alone [this follows from the symmetry of (12.1.5)], the other part of the solution must be

$$N_2(t) = n_{21}e^{\lambda_1 t} + n_{22}e^{\lambda_2 t} . \qquad (12.1.7)$$

The array of the n's as a matrix will be written $\mathbf{N}$.

Study of the Phase Trajectory

However, the detailed quantitative solution is less often required than a qualitative statement; we want to know, for instance, whether the trajectories of the two species will ultimately be stationary at a finite level or explode to infinity, and, if they are finite, whether cycles will be present. For such conclusions, it helps to know how the numbers of the two species will be related to one another, irrespective of time. The relation of N_1 to N_2 with time eliminated is called the *phase trajectory* of the system. The various possible outcomes in the solution of (12.1.1) through the phase trajectory are discussed by Davis (1960, p. 311), Kaplan (1958, p. 412), and Coddington and Levinson (1955, p. 371), and will be briefly summarized below.

To eliminate the time variable between (12.1.6) and (12.1.7), we solve these as though they were a pair of linear equations in the unknowns $e^{\lambda_1 t}$ and $e^{\lambda_2 t}$,

$$e^{\lambda_1 t} = \frac{n_{22}N_1(t) - n_{12}N_2(t)}{n_{11}n_{22} - n_{12}n_{21}} ,$$
$$e^{\lambda_2 t} = \frac{n_{11}N_2(t) - n_{21}N_1(t)}{n_{11}n_{22} - n_{12}n_{21}} , \qquad (12.1.8)$$

assuming that the common denominator, $|\mathbf{N}| = n_{11}n_{22} - n_{12}n_{21}$, is not zero. Then we take the first to the power λ_2/λ_1, and equate the two values of $e^{\lambda_2 t}$. Now by a rotation of axes without shifting the origin, (12.1.8) gives rise to the phase trajectory

$$w = z^{\lambda_2/\lambda_1} , \qquad (12.1.9)$$

where $w = (n_{11}N_2 - n_{21}N_1)/|\mathbf{N}|$ and $z = (n_{22}N_1 - n_{12}N_2)/|\mathbf{N}|$ are the new coordinates.

Table 12.2 Possible stationary points in interaction of two species, on four selected conditions in signs of coefficients of linear differential equations, showing eight conditions in the roots of the characteristic equation of (12.1.4) (see Fig. 12.1)

CONDITIONS IN THE ROOTS	SIGNS OF COEFFICIENTS			
	(a) COMPE-TITION	(b) PRE-DATION	(c) SCAV-ENGING	(d) SYM-BIOSIS
	$+\ -$ $-\ +$	$+\ -$ $+\ -$	$+\ 0$ $+\ -$	$-\ +$ $+\ -$
REAL AND UNEQUAL $(a_{11} - a_{22})^2 + 4a_{12}a_{21} > 0$				
I. BOTH NEGATIVE--STABLE $a_{11}a_{22} > a_{12}a_{21};\ a_{11} + a_{22} < 0$		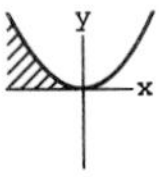		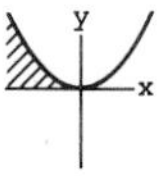
II. BOTH POSITIVE--UNSTABLE $a_{11}a_{22} > a_{12}a_{21};\ a_{11} + a_{22} > 0$	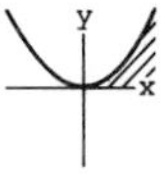	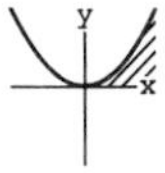		
III. OF OPPOSITE SIGN--UNSTABLE $a_{11}a_{22} < a_{12}a_{21}$	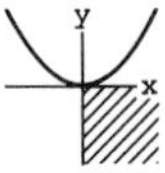	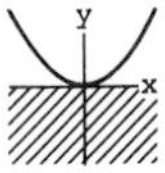	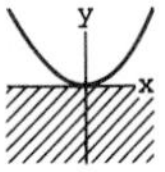	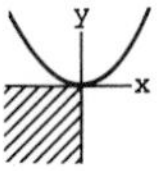
COMPLEX $(a_{11} - a_{22})^2 + 4a_{12}a_{21} < 0$				
IV. NEGATIVE REAL PART--DAMPED CYCLES $a_{11} + a_{22} < 0$		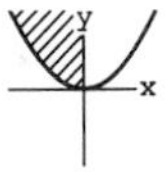		
V. POSITIVE REAL PART--INCREASING CYCLES $a_{11} + a_{22} > 0$		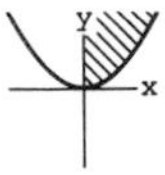		
VI. PURE IMAGINARIES--UNCHANGING CYCLES $a_{11} + a_{22} = 0$		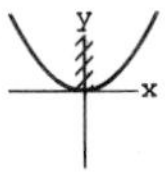		
REAL AND EQUAL $(a_{11} - a_{22})^2 + 4a_{12}a_{21} = 0$				
VII. NEGATIVE--STABLE $a_{11} + a_{22} < 0$		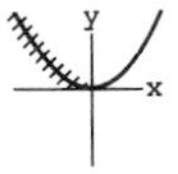		
VIII. POSITIVE--UNSTABLE $a_{11} + a_{22} > 0$		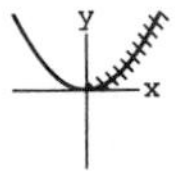		

IN THE xy-PLANE, $x = a_{11} + a_{22};\ y = a_{11}a_{22} - a_{12}a_{21}$.

The new axes will not be rectangular unless it happens that $n_{11}n_{12} + n_{21}n_{22} = 0$, but this is of secondary importance for the present purpose, and the drawings of the phase trajectory will be distorted into a rectangular reference system. The formal solution of (12.1.1) may now be applied to the four forms of association. Curves of w against z are shown in Fig. 12.1, each in the area of the x, y-plane in which it can occur.

a) *Competition.* Two species in competition are designated

$$\begin{array}{|cc|} + & - \\ - & + \end{array}\,.$$

Since the off-diagonal terms a_{12} and a_{21} are negative, the roots must be real, as can be proved by (12.1.5). Being real, if they are nonzero they must be (I) negative, (II) positive, or (III) one negative and one positive (see Table 12.2).

I) Both roots negative requires that the sum of a_{11} and a_{22} be negative [why?], and this is inconsistent with their being separately positive as required by the condition of competition. Model I therefore cannot represent competition, a fact which is important in that only negative roots (or complex roots with negative real parts) permit stability, in a sense to be discussed below.

II) Both roots will be positive if $a_{11}a_{22} > a_{12}a_{21}$ [prove this], which is to say if the (geometric) mean of the autonomous rates is greater than the mean of the interdependencies. Reference to (12.1.6) and (12.1.7) shows that with positive roots the numbers $N_1(t)$ and $N_2(t)$ will go off to plus or minus infinity, depending on the coefficient n_{ij} of the term with the bigger λ. The situation is one in which no upper bound can be set to the absolute values of the numbers.

III) The roots will be of opposite sign if $a_{11}a_{22} < a_{12}a_{21}$, i.e., if the autonomous rates are less (on geometric average) than the absolute value of the effects of competition. This is more genuine competition than the preceding case, where the competitive effects modified the autonomous effects but could not reverse them. With one positive root and one negative, (12.1.9) will be a hyperbola of saddle shape, resembling Condition III of Fig. 12.1 [Prove this.] Evidently one of w and z drops to zero, and the other goes to plus or minus infinity along the axes as asymptotes. To get to $N_1(t)$ and $N_2(t)$ from w and z the axes must be rotated back again, and evidently the movement is towards an asymptote which still passes through the origin. This implies a fixed ratio of the numbers $N_1(t)$ to $N_2(t)$ as t becomes large. Eqs. (12.1.1) assume indefinite supply of the common food, and hence indefinite growth of the two species at a rate determined by the positive root, despite the fact that they hamper one another.

Evidently (II) and (III) above constitute the exhaustive set of possibilities for competition in the linear case, with the unimportant exception $a_{11}a_{22} = a_{12}a_{21}$. The reader may show that here $\lambda_1 = a_{11} + a_{22}$, $\lambda_2 = 0$, and describe the trajectories. There being no other cases under competition, we turn to predation.

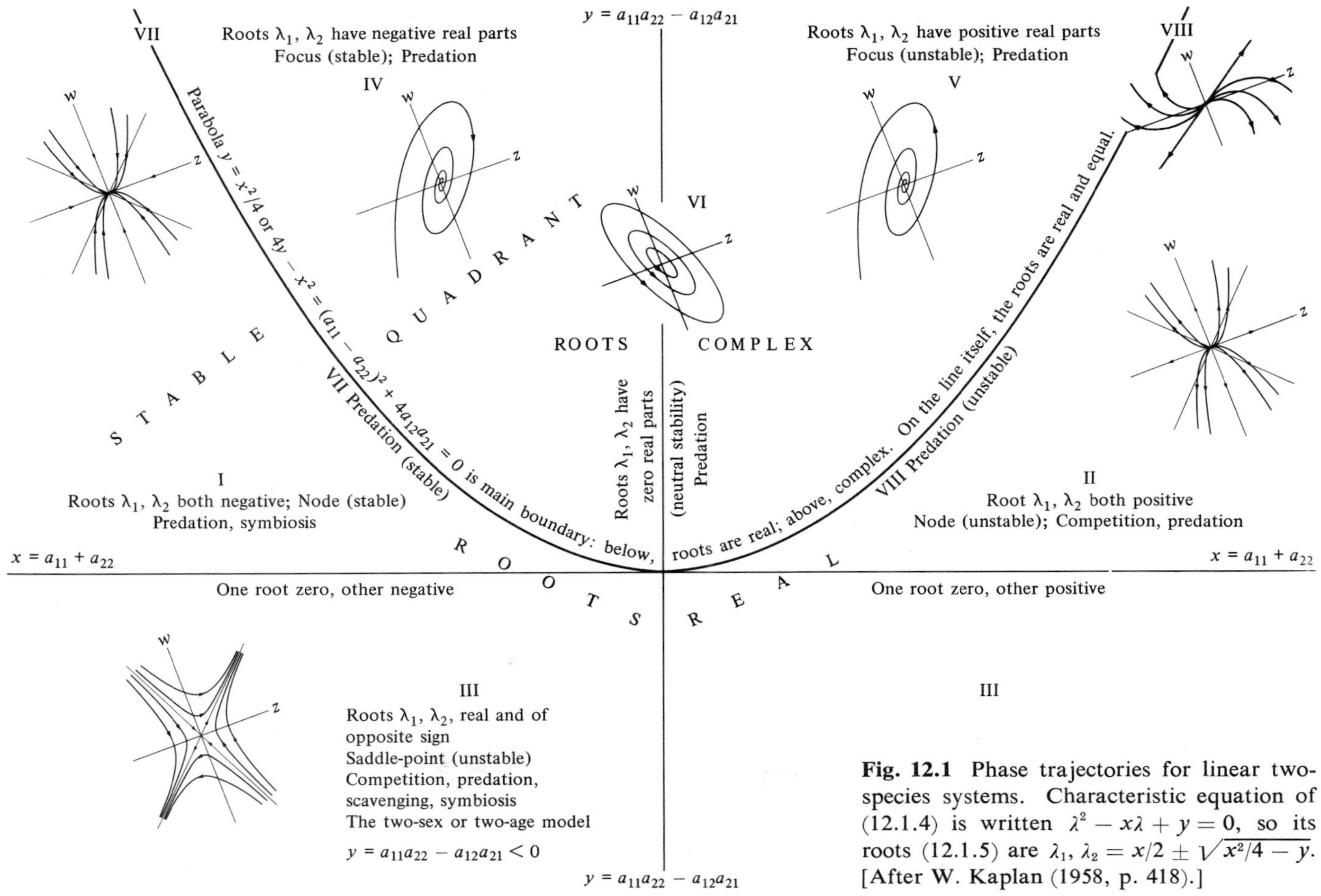

Fig. 12.1 Phase trajectories for linear two-species systems. Characteristic equation of (12.1.4) is written $\lambda^2 - x\lambda + y = 0$, so its roots (12.1.5) are $\lambda_1, \lambda_2 = x/2 \pm \sqrt{x^2/4 - y}$. [After W. Kaplan (1958, p. 418).]

Table 12.3 Location of coefficients and magnitude of roots for eight cases of predation from Table 12.1

	LOCATION IN FIG. 12.1			ROOTS		
CASE	x	y	Δ	λ_1		λ_2
I	−	+	+	−0.01		−0.03
II	+	+	+	0.03		0.01
III	−	−	+	0.0618		−0.1618
IV	−	+	−	−0.02	±	0.0173i
V	+	+	−	0.02	±	0.0173i
VI	0	+	−		±	0.0173i
VII	−	+	0	−0.02		−0.02
VIII	+	+	0	0.02		0.02

$x = a_{11} + a_{22}$; $y = a_{11}a_{22} - a_{12}a_{21}$; $\Delta = (a_{11} - a_{22})^2 + 4a_{12}a_{21}$.

b) *Predation.* For predation, designated

$$\begin{bmatrix} + & - \\ + & - \end{bmatrix}$$

in reference to the matrix of coefficients of (12.1.1), the product $4a_{12}a_{21}$ under the radical in (12.1.5) is necessarily negative. The roots will be real if the expression under the radical in (12.1.5) is positive. It is positive if

$$(a_{11} + |a_{22}|)/2 > \sqrt{|a_{12}|a_{21}}\,, \tag{12.1.10}$$

or in words, the (arithmetic) mean of the absolute values of the autonomous rates a_{11} and $|a_{22}|$ is greater than the (geometric) mean of the interdependencies $|a_{12}|$ and a_{21}. Such a relation could readily hold if the second species has some alternative prey in addition to the first species.

Conditions for Oscillation

Quite different is the outcome of genuine predation among two species only, in the situation where the (geometric) mean of the interdependencies is greater than the (arithmetic) mean of the autonomous rates. Then the roots are complex and may be written $\lambda_1, \lambda_2 = x \pm iy$. The first trajectory will be

$$N_1(t) = n_{11}e^{(x+iy)t} + n_{12}e^{(x-iy)t}\,,$$

or if $n_{11} + n_{12} = m_{11}$, $n_{11} - n_{12} = m_{12}$,

$$N_1(t) = e^{xt}(m_{11} \cos yt + im_{12} \sin yt) , \tag{12.1.11}$$

a real expression, since m_{12} is a pure imaginary for the same reason that $Q_2 - Q_3$ in (5.8.9) is a pure imaginary.

The term in parentheses in (12.1.11) is a pair of sine curves differing in phase by 90°, of wavelength $2\pi/y$. Their amplitude increases or diminishes with time according as x is positive or negative. But x is $\frac{1}{2}(a_{11} + a_{22})$; the waves are damped if the average of the autonomous rates is negative; increasing if the average is positive; unchanging if the average is zero.

Equation (12.1.11) and its analog for $N_2(t)$ may be regarded as a pair of simultaneous equations in the unknowns $e^{xt} \cos yt$ and $e^{xt} \sin yt$. Their solution is the same as the right-hand sides of (12.1.8) if m is written for n. Rotating the axes by calling the right-hand sides z and w respectively gives

$$e^{xt} \cos yt = z , \qquad e^{xt} \sin yt = w ,$$

or

$$\sqrt{z^2 + w^2} = e^{xt} , \qquad w/z = \tan yt .$$

If $x = 0$, the roots are pure imaginaries and constitute Case VI of Tables 12.1, 12.2, and 12.3; the phase trajectory is a circle in the units of w and z selected. With $x > 0$, eliminating t produces the equation of a spiral with motion outward as t increases, and we have Case V. With $x < 0$, the same curve applies but motion is inward, indicating stability (IV). If $x = 0$, the system could continue indefinitely with oscillations about a fixed mean (VI). It could also continue indefinitely about a fixed mean if the prey had a partial shelter and the predator increased only up to what an annual cropping of the prey could feed (Sauvy, 1959, Vol. I, p. 19). This latter cannot be described by the linear model (12.1.1), but is covered by (12.3.1) below.

Waves were produced by the one-sex populations of Chapters 3 and 5 in which age was recognized, and by the two populations in predator-prey relation. What the otherwise unlike situations have in common is a delay effect, similar to a thermostat which responds to change in temperature not immediately but after a finite period. Feedback mechanisms have some analogies with population.

Moran (1950) discusses a single species whose numbers in the tth year are generated by a relation $N_t = aN_{t-1} + bN_{t-2}$, where a and b are constants. The usual approach to such equations (Goldberg, 1961, p. 141; Miller, 1960, p. 133) is to try $N_t = x^t$ and obtain a characteristic equation in x whose roots are x_1 and x_2. The solution is then $N_t = Ax_1^t + Bx_2^t$, A and B being arbitrary constants. Waves will be present when the roots of the characteristic equation are complex, which the reader may show occurs if and only if $b < -a^2/4$; they will be of diminishing amplitude after an initial disturbance if b is also less than $1 - a^2/2$. Identify the areas of the a, b-plane corresponding to the several solutions. Relate this result to a finite difference version of Eq. (12.1.4) and also to the model of Section 5.8 if two age groups are recognized.

The predation association seems to be the only one of the linear two-species processes represented by the configuration of signs (a), (b), (c), and (d) in Table 12.2 which can spontaneously generate cycles. While the matter is by no means settled, such spontaneous cycles may well exist in nature (Gause, 1935a, pp. 44–48; Kostitzin, 1934; Neyman, Park, and Scott, 1956). Unfortunately, imposed cycles, including the seasons of the year, are also present, and it is not easy to discriminate observationally between the effects of imposed and of spontaneous cycles.

Numerical Examples of Predation

The one set of signs among the four combinations (a), (b), (c), and (d) of Table 12.2 on which all eight conditions in the roots are possible is (b) Predation,

+	−
+	−

and this has been chosen for the arithmetical exercise of Tables 12.1 and 12.3. A set of coefficients has been arbitrarily selected to correspond to each of the eight conditions in the roots, numbered I to VIII. The matrix of the column headed I, corresponding to row I of Table 12.2,

$$\mathbf{A} = \begin{bmatrix} a_{11} & a_{12} \\ a_{21} & a_{22} \end{bmatrix} = \begin{bmatrix} 0.01 & -0.04 \\ 0.02 & -0.05 \end{bmatrix},$$

may be cited as an example, **A** being the matrix of coefficients in (12.1.1). The three conditions in the coefficients such that both the roots will be negative,

$$\Delta = (a_{11} - a_{22})^2 + 4a_{12}a_{21} = 0.0004 > 0\,,$$
$$x = a_{11} + a_{22} = -0.04 < 0\,,$$
$$y = a_{11}a_{22} - a_{12}a_{21} = 0.0003 > 0\,,$$

are all satisfied. From Solution (12.1.5) to the quadratic characteristic equation, the roots are $\lambda_1 = -0.01$ and $\lambda_2 = -0.03$.

The starting values $N_1(0) = 90$, $N_2(0) = 80$ provide the conditions

$$N_1(0) = 90 = n_{11}e^{-0.01(0)} + n_{12}e^{-0.03(0)}\,,$$
$$N_2(0) = 80 = n_{21}e^{-0.01(0)} + n_{22}e^{-0.03(0)}\,, \qquad (12.1.12)$$

or

$$90 = n_{11} + n_{12}\,,$$
$$80 = n_{21} + n_{22}\,. \qquad (12.1.13)$$

The derivatives at $t = 0$ are

$$dN_1(0)/dt = 0.01N_1(0) - 0.04N_2(0) = (0.01)(90) - (0.04)(80) = -2.3\,,$$
$$dN_2(0)/dt = 0.02N_1(0) - 0.05N_2(0) = (0.02)(90) - (0.05)(80) = -2.2\,,$$

and equating these respectively to the derivatives of (12.1.6) and (12.1.7) we have

$$-2.3 = -0.01n_{11} - 0.03n_{12}\,,$$
$$-2.2 = -0.01n_{21} - 0.03n_{22}\,. \qquad (12.1.14)$$

Solving the four Eqs. (12.1.13) and (12.1.14) in four unknowns gives $n_{11} = 20$, $n_{12} = 70$, $n_{21} = 10$, $n_{22} = 70$, so that the expansion path is

$$N_1(t) = 20e^{-0.01t} + 70e^{-0.03t}\,,$$
$$N_2(t) = 10e^{-0.01t} + 70e^{-0.03t}\,. \qquad (12.1.15)$$

This exact result works out to $N_1(50) = 27.75$, as against $N_1(50) = 27.36$ in Table 12.1; the marching process similar to Table 12.1 but with second derivatives as well produces $N_1(50) = 27.67$; third derivatives bring agreement between (12.1.15) and the marching process of Table 12.1 to one part in 1000.

The same pair of equations, (12.1.15), may be regarded as the phase trajectory, since any given t provides a point on the curve relating N_1 and N_2. By solving (12.1.15) as linear equations in $e^{-0.01t}$ and $e^{-0.03t}$ and then eliminating t, the phase curve is obtained explicitly as

$$\frac{2N_2 - N_1}{70} = \left(\frac{N_1 - N_2}{10}\right)^3,$$

or by changing to coordinates w and z,

$$w = z^3\,.$$

Figure 12.1 includes sketches of this and the other curves drawn on the z, w-plane, giving their shapes in terms of w and z which are specifiable linear functions of N_1 and N_2. The material of Table 12.1 may be used to find six points on each phase trajectory and so verify its shape, just as one joins dots to reveal the hidden object in a picture puzzle.

Other Configurations

c) *Scavenging.* Scavenging is represented by the configuration of signs

+	0
+	−

,

and since a_{12} is zero, inspection of (12.1.5) shows that the roots will be real and equal to a_{11} and a_{22}; there will be no oscillation. Since a_{22} is negative, its exponential will have declining importance, and the scavenging species will ultimately increase in proportion to $e^{a_{11}t}$, which is to say at the autonomous rate of the species on which it depends.

d) *Symbiosis.* In symbiosis,

$$\boxed{\begin{matrix} - & + \\ + & - \end{matrix}}\,,$$

where a_{21} and a_{12} are both positive, the roots will be real in all circumstances; again the equation indicates no tendency for the numbers of the two species to oscillate. Note that both roots cannot be positive, and analyze the two cases which are possible (Table 12.2).

We have not yet discussed the case of the roots being equal (and therefore real). If $\lambda_1 = \lambda_2 = \lambda$, the solution given as (12.1.6) and (12.1.7) is replaced by

$$N_1(t) = n_{11}e^{\lambda t} + n_{12}te^{\lambda t}\,,$$
$$N_2(t) = n_{21}e^{\lambda t} + n_{22}te^{\lambda t}\,. \qquad (12.1.16)$$

Prove this by substitution back into (12.1.1), and show that one form of the phase trajectory is $w = z \ln z$. In our problem the equal roots can only be $(a_{11} + a_{22})/2$, and if this quantity is negative, the system is stable and finite; if it is positive, the system becomes infinite. We call these VII and VIII respectively, and the relation of z and w may be a straight line, a parabola, or a logarithmic curve, the last being implied in Table 12.3. The reader may prove that they can apply only to predation, and can go on to distinguish the conditions in the a's that produce the various types of solution within VII and VIII (Davis, 1962, p. 42).

Our exposition is, so far, in terms of the highly simplified linear Eqs. (12.1.1). We move slightly closer to actuality with a nonlinear model for predation devised by Volterra (1926, p. 38).

12.2. A NONLINEAR CASE

Consider two populations, one of predators (say wolves) and the other of their prey (say goats), whose numbers at time t are $N_2(t)$ and $N_1(t)$ respectively. Suppose that in the absence of the wolves, the goats will increase at rate a, and in the absence of the goats, the wolves would diminish at rate c. Suppose also that the frequency of encounters is k times the product of the numbers in the two populations, and that each encounter between a wolf and a goat subtracts b/k of a goat and adds d/k of a wolf to their respective numbers, where k is a constant that relates encounters to density and need not be explicitly mentioned in the equations. Then we may write for the rates of change, where now a, b, c, and d are all greater than zero:

$$dN_1(t)/dt = aN_1(t) - bN_1(t)N_2(t)\,,$$
$$dN_2(t)/dt = -cN_2(t) + dN_1(t)N_2(t)\,. \qquad (12.2.1)$$

Equations (12.2.1) cannot be solved for $N_1(t)$ and $N_2(t)$ in terms of elementary functions, but some of the properties of the solution are obtainable from

Table 12.4 Abridged table of x^a/e^{ax} used for calculating Volterra's predator-prey cycles*

	a			a	
x	1/2	1	x	1/2	1
0.10	0.3008	0.0905	1.60	0.5684	0.3230
0.20	0.4047	0.1638	1.70	0.5573	0.3106
0.30	0.4714	0.2222	1.80	0.5455	0.2975
0.40	0.5178	0.2681	1.90	0.5331	0.2842
0.50	0.5507	0.3033	2.00	0.5203	0.2707
0.60	0.5738	0.3293	2.10	0.5071	0.2572
0.70	0.5896	0.3476	2.20	0.4937	0.2438
0.80	0.5996	0.3595	2.30	0.4802	0.2306
0.90	0.6049	0.3659	2.40	0.4666	0.2177
1.00	0.6065	0.3679	2.50	0.4530	0.2052
1.10	0.6051	0.3662	2.60	0.4394	0.1931
1.20	0.6012	0.3614	2.70	0.4260	0.1815
1.30	0.5952	0.3543	2.80	0.4126	0.1703
1.40	0.5876	0.3452	2.90	0.3995	0.1596
1.50	0.5785	0.3347	3.00	0.3865	0.1494

* Programmed by Andrea Tyree.

the relation between N_1 and N_2 when time is eliminated (the phase trajectory described above). We first change the scales by substituting cx/d for N_1 and ay/b for N_2. Equations (12.2.1) then become

$$\begin{aligned} x' &= ax - axy\,, \\ y' &= -cy + cxy\,, \end{aligned} \tag{12.2.2}$$

and, by division,

$$\frac{y'}{x'} = \frac{-cy + cxy}{ax - axy}\,,$$

or, on multiplying up and dividing by xy,

$$ay'/y - ay' + cx'/x - cx' = 0\,. \tag{12.2.3}$$

Integrating (12.2.3) and taking antilogs gives

$$\left(\frac{x}{e^x}\right)^c\left(\frac{y}{e^y}\right)^a = e^A\,, \tag{12.2.4}$$

where A is a constant of integration. Now substituting back $x = dN_1/c$, $y = bN_2/a$, we find Volterra's result

$$\left(\frac{N_1^c}{e^{dN_1}}\right)\left(\frac{N_2^a}{e^{bN_2}}\right) = K\,, \tag{12.2.5}$$

where K is a constant. A brief excerpt from the printout of x^a/e^{ax} is shown as Table 12.4.

If the left-hand side of (12.2.4) is equal to z, a function of x and y represented by height above the x, y-plane, then the values of z fall on a gently sloping hill with rounded crest, the top of the hill being located at $x = 1$, $y = 1$, or $N_1 = c/d$, $N_2 = a/b$. This proves that for given K, N_2 as a function of N_1 consists of a contour line of the hill, and hence a closed curve, rather like a distorted ellipse. For any two functions $f_1(N_1)$ and $f_2(N_2)$ having unique modes, a simple way of drawing contour lines $f_1(N_1)f_2(N_2) = K$ is to tabulate $f_1(N)$ and $f_2(N)$ for values of N at small intervals; enter the table of $f_1(N)$ with $N = N_1$ to find $f_1(N_1)$; divide this into K to obtain $K/f_1(N_1)$; then enter the body of the table of $f_2(N_2)$ with $K/f_1(N_1)$ to find to what (two) arguments N_2 this corresponds. The result of this sequence of two searches is the values of N_2 corresponding to N_1.

This principle was applied to drawing the curve (12.2.5), the result being shown as Fig. 12.2 for $a = b = 1/2$, $c = d = 3$, and $K = 0.02$. [What is the shape of $(x^a/e^{ax})(y^b/e^{by}) = K$ when K assumes a value such that x and y are both small? Ascertain its center, orientation, and the lengths of its axes.]

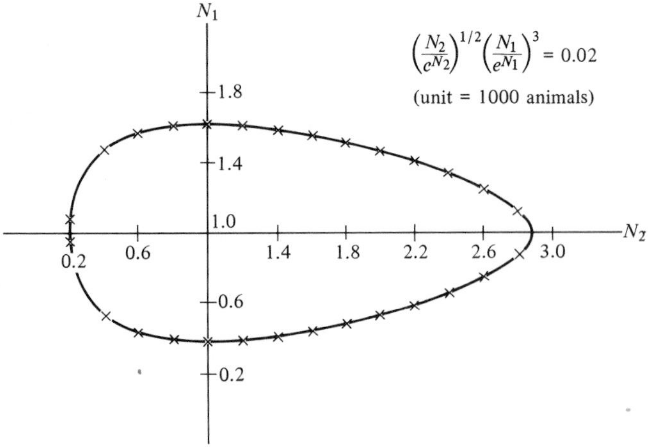

Fig. 12.2 Phase trajectory for predator-prey cycles in nonlinear system (hypothetical).

The closed figure around which a point in the phase trajectory moves as long as our suppositions apply corresponds to an endless series of waves in the separate trajectories $N_1(t)$ and $N_2(t)$ (see Fig. 12.2). Again predation produces oscillations, though here not of simple trigonometric form.

The numerical solution of (12.2.1) offers no difficulty for the usual approximate methods, once we have the constants a, b, c, and d, and a set of initial conditions. Further progress in this field requires ways of establishing the constants to reflect the physical and biological properties of the organisms and their environment.

A next stage in making the two-species model realistic is the subtraction of terms in $[N_1(t)]^2$ and $[N_2(t)]^2$ from the right-hand side of the first and second members respectively of (12.1.1) or of (12.2.1). This allows for the diminution of the rate of increase caused by encounters among members of the same species (Gause, 1935a, p. 5). The square terms suppose limits on the environment and imply genuine competition among the members of each species. They can be expected to impose on the two-species situation the kind of ceiling which the upper asymptote of the logistic (9.2.4) constitutes for a single species. This will be more easily taken up after a discussion of the general nonlinear model.

12.3. THE GENERAL NONLINEAR MODEL

Two Species

The most general two-species scheme which appears in the literature (Lotka, 1934, pp. 40–41; Davis, 1962, p. 317; Gause, 1935a, p. 9; Kostitzin, 1934, p. 41) is

$$\begin{aligned} dN_1(t)/dt &= P\big(N_1(t), N_2(t)\big) , \\ dN_2(t)/dt &= Q\big(N_1(t), N_2(t)\big) , \end{aligned} \tag{12.3.1}$$

where P and Q are polynomial or other functions of the numbers of both species; their derivatives in the domain of interest must be finite or zero. The *critical* or *stationary points* of the system are defined as the values of N_1 and N_2 for which the two derivatives (12.3.1) vanish; that is, they are the solutions in N_1 and N_2 of

$$P(N_1, N_2) = 0 \,; \qquad Q(N_1, N_2) = 0 \,. \tag{12.3.2}$$

Referring back to (12.2.1) for illustration, the stationary points in the example of wolves and goats are obtained by solving

$$aN_1 - bN_2N_1 = 0 \,, \qquad -cN_2 + dN_2N_1 = 0 \,. \tag{12.3.3}$$

Evidently $N_1 = 0$, $N_2 = 0$ satisfy the equations, and here the stationary point is where both species are extinguished. A more interesting point is where the goats are $N_1 = c/d$ and the wolves $N_2 = a/b$, and it is around this that the cycles revolve: in Fig. 12.2 for example the point c/d, a/b is 1, 1.

Since the derivatives vanish at the stationary points, the numbers of the two species must be constant there, at least momentarily, which is to say that the stationary points are also points of *equilibrium*. Slight deviations from equilibrium may set in motion forces which restore equilibrium, in which case we speak of *strict stability*, or may take the system indefinitely far away, a case of *instability*; alternatively, departure from equilibrium may result in cycles about the stationary point. (Contrast this meaning of stability with that of Chapters 3 and 5. The two usages come from different fields of study.) All these are exemplified in Table 12.1 for the linear model of predation.

The behavior of the equations around the stationary points permits us to classify their behavior elsewhere. For in the neighborhood of a stationary point, the stability characteristics of the solution are the same as those of the linear terms obtained by a Taylor expansion, a proposition known as the stability theorem of nonlinear mechanics (Davis, 1962, p. 318). If a solution in N_1 and N_2 of (12.3.2) is N_{10}, N_{20}, then

$$\begin{aligned} P(N_1, N_2) &= P(N_{10}, N_{20}) + (N_1 - N_{10})P_1'(N_{10}, N_{20}) \\ &\quad + (N_2 - N_{20})P_2'(N_{10}, N_{20}) + \cdots , \\ Q(N_1, N_2) &= Q(N_{10}, N_{20}) + (N_1 - N_{10})Q_1'(N_{10}, N_{20}) \\ &\quad + (N_2 - N_{20})Q_2'(N_{10}, N_{20}) + \cdots , \end{aligned} \tag{12.3.4}$$

where $P_1'(N_1, N_2) = \partial P(N_1, N_2)/\partial N_1$, etc. The first term on the right of each of Eqs. (12.3.4) disappears by the definition of stationary points, (12.3.2); terms of higher order than those listed we are entitled to neglect in the neighborhood of the stationary points, where the powers of the small quantities $N_1 - N_{10}$ and $N_2 - N_{20}$ are small, the derivatives of P and Q being assumed finite. With several stationary points, the condition of stability is not the same everywhere, and our observations apply only to the neighborhood of each point. The linear case, on the other hand, had only one stationary point, so all statements about stability applied *in the large*. The main interest of the conditions on the coefficients discussed in the first part of this chapter is in their application as first approximations to various nonlinear configurations.

Competition in a Limited Environment

This nonlinear approach allows us to make a substantial improvement on the model of competition of Section 12.1. We now suppose that each species is affected both by its own density and by the density of the other species:

$$\begin{aligned} N_1'(t) &= r_1N_1(t) - r_{11}N_1^2(t) - r_{12}N_1(t)N_2(t) , \\ N_2'(t) &= r_2N_2(t) - r_{21}N_1(t)N_2(t) - r_{22}N_2^2(t) . \end{aligned} \tag{12.3.5}$$

That the square terms are subtracted expresses the limited character of the environment. For competition the autonomous rates r_1 and r_2 are both positive, and the interdependencies or cross-product terms would be negative. This configuration may be written

$$\boxed{\begin{matrix} + & - & - \\ + & - & - \end{matrix}}\,,$$

and we suppose all r's in (12.3.5) positive.

To see what sorts of stationary points will be possible, the derivatives on the left-hand sides of the two Eqs. (12.3.5) are made zero:

$$0 = r_1N_1 - r_{11}N_1^2 - r_{12}N_1N_2\,, \qquad 0 = r_2N_2 - r_{21}N_1N_2 - r_{22}N_2^2\,. \qquad (12.3.6)$$

A pair of quadratic equations in two variables will in general have four solutions—corresponding to the four points at which two conic sections intersect. Inspection shows that the equations are satisfied by $N_1(t) = N_2(t) = 0$, and a stationary point is clearly arrived at when both species are extinct. Another solution corresponds to $N_1(t) = 0$ and $N_2(t) = r_2/r_{22}$, which would be positive. A third solution is constituted by $N_2(t) = 0$ and $N_1 = r_1/r_{11}$, also positive. At these last two stationary points, one species is extinct and the other has the field (Lotka, 1932).

The fourth solution of the pair of quadratics (12.3.6) is the interesting one, possibly corresponding to a stationary point in which positive numbers of the two species exist in equilibrium. We will find under what conditions such a stationary point can exist under competition. The root in N_1 and N_2 for which we are searching is obtained by dividing the members of (12.3.6) by N_1 and N_2 respectively, to obtain

$$r_1 - r_{11}N_1 - r_{12}N_2 = 0\,, \qquad r_2 - r_{21}N_1 - r_{22}N_2 = 0\,. \qquad (12.3.7)$$

Given that the r's are small positive numbers and the N's are generally large numbers, it is easier to think of sets of r's in (12.3.7) such that at least one of N_1 and N_2 is negative, but nonetheless, for some values of the r's, both N_1 and N_2 could be positive. Suppose that there is such a solution $N_1 = N_{10}$, $N_2 = N_{20}$, where $N_{10} > 0$, $N_{20} > 0$, and write $n_1 = N_1 - N_{10}$, $n_2 = N_2 - N_{20}$. Then we seek the expansion of (12.3.5) corresponding to (12.3.4), around the stationary point N_{10}, N_{20}. If $P(N_1, N_2)$ of (12.3.1) is $r_1N_1 - r_{11}N_1^2 - r_{12}N_1N_2$ as in the first equation of (12.3.5), then expansion in a two-dimensional Taylor series about N_{10}, N_{20} gives

$$\begin{aligned} P(N_1, N_2) &= P(N_{10}, N_{20}) + n_1P_1'(N_{10}, N_{20}) + n_2P_2'(N_{10}, N_{20}) \\ &= r_1N_{10} - r_{11}N_{10}^2 - r_{12}N_{10}N_{20} \\ &\qquad + n_1(r_1 - 2r_{11}N_{10} - r_{12}N_{20}) + n_2(-r_{12}N_{10})\,, \end{aligned} \qquad (12.3.8)$$

and similarly for $Q(N_1, N_2)$, stopping at terms linear in n_1 and n_2.

But using the fact that N_{10}, N_{20} satisfies (12.3.7) permits a simplification of (12.3.8) down to

$$P(N_1, N_2) = (-r_{11}N_{10})n_1 + (-r_{12}N_{10})n_2\,,$$

and similarly,

$$Q(N_1, N_2) = (-r_{21}N_{20})n_1 + (-r_{22}N_{20})n_2 .$$

Entering these linear approximations in (12.3.5) gives

$$n_1'(t) = -r_{11}N_{10}n_1 - r_{12}N_{10}n_2 , \qquad n_2'(t) = -r_{21}N_{20}n_1 - r_{22}N_{20}n_2 , \qquad (12.3.9)$$

whose coefficients may be identified with the a's of (12.1.1).

In order to study the stability properties around the point N_{10}, N_{20}, which we are supposing to lie in the positive quadrant, we refer to the criteria summarized in Table 12.2. The roots will be complex only if $(a_{11} - a_{22})^2 + 4a_{12}a_{21} < 0$, which in this case is if

$$(-r_{11}N_{10} + r_{22}N_{20})^2 + 4(-r_{12}N_{10})(-r_{21}N_{20}) < 0 . \qquad (12.3.10)$$

Since the expression on the left of (12.3.10) consists of two positive terms, it cannot as a whole be negative, so the roots must be real; once again, spontaneous cycles cannot arise in competition.

If the roots are real, the first condition for stability is that $a_{11} + a_{22} < 0$, which requires $-r_{11}N_{10} - r_{22}N_{20} < 0$, and is evidently satisfied. But the second condition is $a_{11}a_{22} > a_{12}a_{21}$ or $r_{11}N_{10}r_{22}N_{20} > r_{12}N_{10}r_{21}N_{20}$; that is,

$$r_{11}r_{22} > r_{12}r_{21} ,$$

and this is only satisfied in restricted circumstances. Stability requires that the (geometric mean of the) resistance offered by the environment be greater than the (geometric mean of the) interference of the species with one another.

If we think of genuine competition as the situation where the competitive forces are more severe than the environmental ones, $r_{12}r_{21} > r_{11}r_{22}$, then genuine competition is inherently unstable in the limited environment. In summary, most configurations of the r's in (12.3.5) will show no stationary point in the positive quadrant; if one does exist, the trajectory will move away from it if $r_{12}r_{21} > r_{11}r_{22}$; i.e., if the competitive forces are greater than the resistance of the environment, movement will in general be towards a point in which one of the species is extinct and the other has the field.

This theory appears to correspond with the results of experiment. Thomas Park (1964, p. 138) summarizes some of his own work as follows: "If we measure what X does and what Y does when both are *alone*, we thereby are able to detect and evaluate what is *new*, or competitive, when both are together... It is this. One species is always eliminated and the other survives!" But he goes on to say that under one set of external conditions it need not be the same species that survives as under a different set. In nature two species rarely live and compete in the same environment. For other features of competition the reader is referred to Park's article and the biological literature which he cites.

Predation in a limited environment,

$$\begin{array}{|ccc|} + & - & - \\ - & + & - \end{array} ,$$

can have stable points at positive numbers for both species, as the reader may demonstrate from the analogs to (12.3.9) and (12.3.10), and can have cycles, as appears from the analog to (12.3.8) obtained for this case.

Many Species

The multispecies generalization was considered by Lotka (1956, p. 158), Rashevsky (1960, Chap. 36), and Volterra (1937). Lotka said that study of the evolution of individual species does not bear promise of success; "The physical object before us is an undivided system." If this undivided system consists of k species, there being $N_i(t)$ individuals (or $N_i(t)$ units of weight or biomass) of the ith species, and the change in the numbers of any species is a function P of the numbers of all species in the system, then we have

$$\begin{aligned} dN_1(t)/dt &= P_1(N_1(t), N_2(t), \ldots, N_k(t)), \\ dN_2(t)/dt &= P_2(N_1(t), N_2(t), \ldots, N_k(t)), \\ &\vdots \\ dN_k(t)/dt &= P_k(N_1(t), N_2(t), \ldots, N_k(t)). \end{aligned} \tag{12.3.11}$$

As before, the stationary points are found by replacing the derivatives on the left-hand side of Eqs. (12.3.11) by zero and solving the k simultaneous equations. Around any chosen stationary point each equation in (12.3.11) can be expanded as a Taylor series whose absolute term will necessarily vanish. Truncating after the first derivatives gives k linear equations for the k species, which, like (12.1.1), may be written

$$\{\mathbf{N}'(t)\} = \mathbf{A}\{\mathbf{N}(t)\},$$

with the understanding that $\mathbf{A}$ is now a $k \times k$ rather than a 2×2 matrix, and that $\{\mathbf{N}(t)\}$ is $k \times 1$, with numbers $N_i(t)$ measured from a stationary point rather than from zero. The solution of the set in the neighborhood of the singular point is of the form

$$\begin{aligned} N_1(t) &= n_{11}e^{\lambda_1 t} + n_{12}e^{\lambda_2 t} + \cdots + n_{1k}e^{\lambda_k t}, \\ N_2(t) &= n_{21}e^{\lambda_1 t} + n_{22}e^{\lambda_2 t} + \cdots + n_{2k}e^{\lambda_k t}, \\ &\vdots \\ N_k(t) &= n_{k1}e^{\lambda_1 t} + n_{k2}e^{\lambda_2 t} + \cdots + n_{kk}e^{\lambda_k t}, \end{aligned} \tag{12.3.12}$$

where the λ_i are the k solutions of the characteristic equation $|\mathbf{A} - \lambda\mathbf{I}| = 0$, and the n_{ij} depend on the initial numbers $N_i(0)$.

The λ_i may be positive or negative, real or complex, and the pattern of these will determine the nature of the trajectory at the stationary point under study. If the equilibrium is to be stable, so that a small displacement of the numbers $N_i(t)$ from the stationary point will bring into play forces which return the system to the same singular point, *all* the real roots must be negative (illustrated for two species by Cases I and VII in Tables 12.1, 12.2 and 12.3), *and* the real parts of all the complex roots must also be negative (illustrated for two species by Case IV) (Lotka, 1934, pp. 38–42; Kostitzin, 1934, pp. 39–40).

The nonlinear many-species model permits examination of what happens when competing species have, in addition to their common and limited source of food, some supplementary source which is private to each (Gause and Witt, 1964, p. 112). As was surmised above, this attenuates the competition, and both species, even if not equally efficient, can continue to exist, whereas competition for a single source of food eliminates the less efficient species. The oscillations in the predator-prey situation are also modified by presence of further species. An alternative source of food for the predator might seem likely to divert attention from the original prey, but by modifying a parameter of the linear model it may be shown that this can result in the latter's extinction. The reader may wish to examine the equations for the three-species case and show how the alternative source of food (now an explicit third species) changes the interrelationships among the original two species (Kerner, 1961).

Out of information consisting of hypothetical rates of increase and interdependency, the methods outlined infer oscillations in the predator-prey situation, and demonstrate the extinction of the weaker of unequal competitors. The purpose of this chapter is not to teach biology, but to show how some qualitative conclusions can be drawn from simple equations. The biology of the matter is subtle and intricate, and the reader is referred to Wynne-Edwards (1962), L. C. Cole (1951 and 1965), and Slobodkin (1961) for discussion of the issues. Bartlett (1960) has provided a concise summary of stochastic models for association of species, whose properties are by no means the same as those of the deterministic version to which this chapter is confined. Kenneth Boulding's skillful transformation of the theory into graphical form (1962, Chap. 1) contains numerous suggestions of its relevance to social interaction. The limited biological application of the theory is partly due to lack of data. The best to be had on animals in nature are rough total numbers for a few points in time.

The individuals of human populations, on the other hand, are carefully counted and classified into categories such as sex, marital status, and age. The rules governing their interaction are no less complex, and we need not confine ourselves to the one-sex model of Chapters 1 through 8. Chapter 13 will revert to human populations and take up interaction among subpopulations categorized by sex and marital status. In Chapter 14 some of the same problems will be considered with a matrix technique that permits more convenient computation where age distributions are concerned.

CHAPTER 13

THE PROBLEM OF THE SEXES AND OTHER USES OF SIMULTANEOUS DIFFERENTIAL EQUATIONS

The intermeshing of changes in two groups which Volterra elaborated applies also among humans if, by analogy with his work, we regard males and females within a given territory as two populations in interaction. The eating and being eaten of Volterra's model now become the processes of marriage and procreation, and some of the resulting equations are linear and readily solved. The earliest reference to this which I have been able to find is David G. Kendall (1949), who shows how the consideration of the two sexes together enriches the discussion of population and leads to a more realistic result.

13.1. INCONSISTENCY IN TREATING THE SEXES SEPARATELY

Kendall starts from the simple equation describing population change,

$$N'(t) = (b - d)N(t)\,, \tag{13.1.1}$$

where $N(t)$ is the number of individuals in the population at time t and $N'(t)$ its derivative, b the birth rate, and d the death rate. If the difference $(b - d)$ is constant, the solution to (13.1.1) is

$$N(t) = N(0)e^{(b-d)t}\,, \tag{13.1.2}$$

$N(0)$ being the initial population. A value that might be entered for $(b - d)$ is the intrinsic rate of natural increase for either sex, for instance as shown in Table 13.1 and computed by (5.3.2). When the values for males and females in the United States for 1964 are inserted in (13.1.2) we have

$$M(t) = M(0)e^{0.01748t}\,,$$
$$F(t) = F(0)e^{0.01570t}\,,$$

where the number of males at time t is $M(t)$ and of females $F(t)$.

These results are inconsistent in the sense that the sex ratio,

$$\frac{M(t)}{F(t)} = \frac{M(0)}{F(0)}\,e^{0.00178t}\,,$$

increases steadily with time. By the end of 100 years males will outnumber females by over 19%, by the end of 200 years by 43%. The model can throw no light on the trend in the sex ratio. To use it to derive such a trend would

Table 13.1 Intrinsic rates of birth, death, and natural increase, comparing calculations on male and female data†

	MALE		
	$1000b_m^*$	$1000d_m^*$	$1000r_m^*$
CHILE 1964	36.02	12.47	23.55
CYPRUS 1956-58	28.33	7.51	20.82
ENGLAND AND WALES 1960-62	20.34	10.79	9.55
HUNGARY 1964	13.35	16.31	-2.96
NORWAY 1963	20.35	9.93	10.42
TRINIDAD AND TOBAGO 1956-58	39.34	8.79	30.55
UNITED STATES 1959-61	28.89	7.97	20.92
1962	27.98	8.17	19.81
1963	27.17	8.49	18.68
1964	26.23	8.75	17.48
	FEMALE		
	$1000b_f$	$1000d_f$	$1000r_f$
CHILE 1964	31.99	10.94	21.05
CYPRUS 1956-58	24.45	7.62	16.83
ENGLAND AND WALES 1960-62	19.28	9.51	9.77
HUNGARY 1964	10.36	17.64	-7.28
NORWAY 1963	20.27	8.53	11.74
TRINIDAD AND TOBAGO 1956-58	39.98	7.63	32.35
UNITED STATES 1959-61	27.31	6.61	20.70
1962	25.84	7.01	18.83
1963	24.56	7.46	17.10
1964	23.48	7.78	15.70

† Programming by Wilhelm Flieger on the integral-equation approximation *B* of Eq. (11.5.1). Note that values of r_m^* and r_f are lower by 0.00003 for the United States in 1964 than the corresponding figures in Table 14.2, obtained from the projection matrix, method *A* of (11.5.3).

be as wrong as to forecast the wolves and goats of the preceding chapter by separate projections, which could only lead to such absurdities as the wolves increasing to infinity while their sole food, the goats, diminishes to zero.

Karmel (1948a, pp. 243–44) developed a method of accounting for the difference in the male and female intrinsic rates r_m and r_f in terms of the difference in age distributions of the male and female populations, initially supposing fathers to be of the same ages as mothers. His function ${}_5H_x$ may be expressed in five-year age intervals as

$$ {}_5H_x = \frac{{}_5K_x^*/{}_5K_x}{s\,{}_5L_x^*/{}_5L_x}\,, $$

where s is the masculinity or sex ratio at birth (the ratio of male to female babies born in the period under observation), ${}_5K_x^*$ and ${}_5K_x$ are the male and female observed numbers at ages x to $x + 4$ at last birthday, and ${}_5L_x^*$ and ${}_5L_x$ the survivors to age x to $x + 4$ in the male and female life tables. Then H is defined as the harmonic mean of the ${}_5H_x$ weighted at each age by the net maternity function:

$$ \frac{1}{H} = \frac{1}{R_0}\sum \frac{{}_5L_x\,{}_5F_x}{{}_5H_x}\,, \qquad x = 10, 15, \ldots, 50\,. $$

By straightforward algebra, it turns out that the difference between the male and female net reproduction rates, $(r_m - r_f)$, is estimated by

$$ (r_m - r_f) \doteq -\frac{\ln H}{T}\,, \tag{13.1.3} $$

T being again the length of generation.

Since this takes no account of the statistics of births by age of father, it can be calculated for any population for which life tables, age-sex distribution of the population, and age-specific fertility rates of women are available. It cannot therefore give the same results as those on the full data of Table 13.1, but seems in general to go in the right direction. For the United States, 1964, Eq. (13.1.13) shows a difference, $1000(r_m - r_f)$, of 2.25 in favor of males, against the observed 1.78 of Table 13.1, also in favor of males. For six other populations the differences $1000(r_m - r_f)$ compare as follows:

	Observed (from Table 13.1 as calculated from births by age of mother and by age of father)	Estimated (by Karmel method (13.1.3) from births by age of mother only)
Chile 1964	2.50	2.47
Cyprus 1956–58	3.99	5.19
England and Wales 1960–62	−0.22	1.19
Hungary 1964	4.32	2.90
Norway 1963	−1.32	0.33
Trinidad and Tobago 1956–58	−1.80	1.46

Draw a diagram and show the regression to be only approximately a straight line, and not one which passes through the origin. The relation between the two estimates of $r_m - r_f$ would be altered if we supposed fathers to be five years older than mothers, rather than the same age, or interpolated between estimates based on zero and five years difference in H of (13.1.3).

Karmel's tabulation (1948a, pp. 254–55) of (13.1.3) for a number of places and dates shows r_m to be higher than r_f four times out of five. The preceding migration, misstatement of age, and other factors all have a bearing on this apparently greater male rate of increase (Myers, 1941). Without going into these here, we proceed to the two-sex model.

Kendall (1949, p. 247) and Goodman (1953b) escape from the contradiction implicit in the separate treatment of the sexes by setting down a pair of equations, each of which allows for interaction:

$$\begin{aligned} M'(t) &= -d_m M(t) + b_m L[M(t), F(t)]\,, \\ F'(t) &= -d_f F(t) + b_f L[M(t), F(t)]\,, \end{aligned} \tag{13.1.4}$$

where the function L of the numbers of the two sexes at time t is yet to be specified. The first member of (13.1.4) expresses the fact that the rate of increase of the number of males, $M'(t)$, consists in the negative effect of the death rate and the positive effect of the birth rate, the latter being applied to some function L of the male and female populations; the second is similar for females. Like (13.1.1), Eqs. (13.1.4) take no account of age. They could be studied by the methods used for the nonlinear set (12.3.1), but the treatment here will be confined to special cases which are linear.

13.2. DOMINANCE

Female—the Goodman Solution

Goodman (1953b) gave explicit solutions of (13.1.4) for various possibilities in L, and provided most of the results of the present chapter. (He then went on to stochastic models, where we will follow him in Chapter 16.) His first line of attack was to tie the births for each sex to the number of women, applying the assumption known as *female dominance*, that the births for both boy and girl children depend only on the number of females. This is to say that in place of the function L he wrote $F(t)$, the number of females at time t, so that (13.1.4) became

$$\begin{aligned} M'(t) &= -d_m M(t) + b_m F(t)\,, \\ F'(t) &= -d_f F(t) + b_f F(t)\,. \end{aligned} \tag{13.2.1}$$

[Identify these equations with those for the scavenging case in Table 12.2. Does the resemblance have any demographic meaning? Use the argument centered on (12.1.5) to prove that the roots of (13.2.1) are real and of opposite sign for an increasing population.]

The simultaneous linear differential Eqs. (13.2.1) are solvable by a simple device which will not be available in the cases which follow, for we can here make use of the fact that the second member contains only $F(t)$ and not $M(t)$. The second member of (13.2.1) alone gives

$$F(t) = F(0)e^{(b_f - d_f)t}, \tag{13.2.2}$$

identical with (13.1.2). This expression for $F(t)$ may then be substituted in the first member of (13.2.1), which becomes

$$M'(t) + d_m M(t) = b_m F(0)e^{(b_f - d_f)t}.$$

If we multiply both sides by $e^{d_m t}$, the left-hand side becomes the derivative of $e^{d_m t}M(t)$. The solution obtained on integrating is thus

$$e^{d_m t}M(t) = \frac{b_m F(0) \exp[(b_f - d_f + d_m)t]}{b_f - d_f + d_m} + K, \tag{13.2.3}$$

where K is a constant. To fit the boundary condition that the number of males at time $t = 0$ is $M(0)$, we put $t = 0$ in (13.2.3) and find

$$K = M(0) - \frac{b_m F(0)}{b_f - d_f + d_m}. \tag{13.2.4}$$

Dividing (13.2.3) by $e^{d_m t}$ gives

$$M(t) = \frac{F(0)b_m e^{(b_f - d_f)t}}{b_f - d_f + d_m} + Ke^{-d_m t}, \tag{13.2.5}$$

which, along with (13.2.4) and (13.2.2), constitutes the solution to (13.2.1). [Check this result by applying the method used to solve (12.1.1).]

Comparing with the earlier calculation based on (13.1.2), we find the trajectory for females unchanged, but that for males now has two exponential terms, with exponents of opposite signs in increasing populations. The sex ratio may be traced through time and seen to reach a finite level. For on dividing (13.2.5) by (13.2.2), noting that the b's, d's, and $b_f - d_f + d_m$ are all positive, we see that the exponentials in the ratio disappear in the limit, and we are left with

$$\frac{M(\infty)}{F(\infty)} = \lim_{t\to\infty} \frac{M(t)}{F(t)} = \frac{b_m}{b_f - d_f + d_m}. \tag{13.2.6}$$

This simple and basic theoretical result permits a variety of numerical answers, depending on how its four parameters are selected. The principal options are as between

a) intrinsic and crude rates,

b) retention of the observed sex ratio at birth or of b_m and b_f obtained for the two sexes separately,

c) use of the female or male intrinsic rate of natural increase for ascertaining the male intrinsic death rate.

The initial application will be with the first of the two options under each of (a), (b), and (c). The parameters will be intrinsic, which is to say based on the assumption of fixed age-sex-specific rates in the future. The sex ratio at birth will be retained; b_f being the female intrinsic birth rate of Chapter 7, the value used for b_m will be $b_f s$, where s is the observed sex ratio at birth. Finally, the male intrinsic death rate d_m will be obtained from the male life table, but with a rate of increase imposed on it equal to the female intrinsic rate. This makes d_m in general different from the male intrinsic death rate designated d_m^* in Table 13.1. For the United States in 1964, $1000d_m^* = 8.75$ of Table 13.1 is lower than $1000d_m = 9.23$ obtained from the male life table and the female intrinsic rate of increase, because the male r_m^* is greater than the female r_m, and hence produces a younger stable population.

On this basis, with the data for United States females in 1964 from Table 13.1, plus the fact that the sex ratio of the births was $s = 1.0472$, we obtain from (13.2.6) an ultimate sex ratio of

$$\frac{M(\infty)}{F(\infty)} = \frac{(23.48)(1.0472)}{23.48 - 7.78 + 9.23} = 0.986 .$$

If $S(t) = M(t)/F(t)$ is the path of the sex ratio, derive from (13.2.1) the equation

$$S'(t) = b_m - S(t)(b_f - d_f + d_m) .$$

How does the theory of Section 12.3 on stationary points make it obvious that this differential equation in $S(t)$ gives (13.2.6) as the limiting value of $S(t)$? Note that although the Eqs. (13.2.1) have no stationary point other than the uninteresting one at which $M(t) = F(t) = 0$, the single equation in $S(t)$ derived from them has a finite stationary point of stable equilibrium.

Unlike the separate projections of males and females, the use of dominance makes for identically equal rates of increase of the two sexes after the effects of the initial distributions have worn off. Table 13.2 is based on a projection at fixed age-sex-specific rates with female dominance by (14.1.5), an extension of matrix **L** of (2.1.9). It shows for four countries that the ratios of increase over the five-year period from $t = 95$ to $t = 100$ are the same for males as for females to nearly four decimal places. Slight departures from equality disappear with further projection; an experiment with Czechoslovakian data for 1962 showed a ratio of increase $M(100)/M(95) = 1.0190$, against $F(100)/F(95) = 1.0192$, but by 500 years we had agreement to five decimal places:

$$M(500)/M(495) = F(500)/F(495) = 1.01918 .$$

This is equal to $e^{5(b_f - d_f)} = e^{5(0.01583 - 0.01203)}$ from the same data (not shown in the table). Dominance is discussed in relation to projection in Section 14.1.

The results of the actual population projection also verify (13.2.6) arithmetically. Projection with the fixed rates of 1963 and female dominance (again

Table 13.2 Projection by age and sex with female dominance for 100 years, showing convergence of male and female ratios of increase

	AUSTRIA 1963	FINLAND 1964	JAPAN 1960	THAILAND 1959
RATIO OF TOTAL MALES TO TOTAL MALES FIVE YEARS EARLIER:				
M(5)/M(0)	1.0332	1.0479	1.0489	1.1627
M(50)/M(45)	1.0508	1.0361	0.9968	1.1496
M(100)/M(95)	1.0521	1.0329	0.9855	1.1451
RATIO OF TOTAL FEMALES TO TOTAL FEMALES FIVE YEARS EARLIER:				
F(5)/F(0)	1.0255	1.0450	1.0479	1.1496
F(50)/F(45)	1.0473	1.0372	0.9972	1.1465
F(100)/F(95)	1.0522	1.0327	0.9851	1.1451

by the 36 $\times$ 36 matrix in (14.1.5)) brings Austrian males, by the year 2063, to 8,426,000 and Austrian females to 8,662,000, so that the sex ratio for Austria at time 100 is

$$\frac{M(100)}{F(100)} = \frac{8{,}426{,}000}{8{,}662{,}000} = 0.9728 \,,$$

as shown in the bottom line of Table 13.3, while (13.2.6) gives

$$\frac{M(\infty)}{F(\infty)} = \frac{b_m}{b_f - d_f + d_m} = \frac{20.64}{19.83 - 9.69 + 11.08} = 0.9727 \,,$$

which appears in the second-to-last line of Table 13.3. Though the result (13.2.6) has not taken explicit account of age, yet when intrinsic rates are entered for the constants, it gives the same ultimate sex ratio as the full projection by age and sex.

The model includes the Karmel assumption that the ultimate increase of males is the same as the ultimate increase of females, $r_m = r_f$, so that, if b'_m is the ultimate male birth rate, we have $r_m = b'_m - d_m$ and $r_f = b_f - d_f$, and hence

$$b'_m - d_m = b_f - d_f \,,$$

enabling us to calculate b'_m as

$$b'_m = b_f - d_f + d_m \,.$$

Table 13.3 Comparison of Goodman ultimate sex ratio (13.2.6) with result of projection by age and sex for 100 years*

	AUSTRIA 1963	FINLAND 1964	JAPAN 1960	THAILAND 1959
INTRINSIC RATES:				
$1000b_f$	19.83	17.38	12.68	36.78
$1000d_f$	9.69	10.91	15.66	9.74
$1000d_m$	11.08	12.49	16.68	10.86
GOODMAN FEMALE-DOMINANT BIRTH RATE FOR MALES:				
$1000b_m = 1000sb_f$	20.64	18.26	13.39	41.86
KARMEL BIRTH RATE FOR MALES $(r_m = r_f)$:				
$1000b'_m = 1000(b_f - d_f + d_m)$	21.22	18.96	13.70	37.90
INITIAL SEX RATIO	0.8752	0.9329	0.9650	1.0277
ULTIMATE SEX RATIO (13.2.6) FROM DIFFERENTIAL EQUATION:†				
$\frac{M}{F} = \frac{b_m}{b_f - d_f + d_m} = \frac{b_m}{b'_m}$	0.9727	0.9631	0.9773	1.1045
SEX RATIO AT 100 YEARS FROM FEMALE-DOMINANT PROJECTION BY AGE AND SEX:				
M(100)/F(100)	0.9728	0.9628	0.9768	1.1043

* Programmed by Nancy Wang.
† See further discussion in Goodman (1967e).

We will call b'_m the Karmel intrinsic birth rate, while the b_m obtained by multiplying the female intrinsic birth rate by the sex ratio at birth may be called the Goodman intrinsic rate. Neither depends on a knowledge of births by age of father. The ultimate sex ratio under female-dominant projection found as (13.2.6) is from this point of view equal to

$$\frac{M(\infty)}{F(\infty)} = \frac{b_m}{b_f - d_f + d_m} = \frac{b_m}{b'_m},$$

or the ratio of the Goodman to the Karmel intrinsic male birth rate.

We have thus referred to three different ultimate or intrinsic male birth rates; for the United States in 1964 they are, per thousand population,

Female-dominant

$$\left.\begin{array}{rl}\text{Goodman:} & 1000b_m = 1000sb_f = 24.59 \\ \text{Karmel:} & 1000b'_m = 1000(b_f - d_f + d_m) = 24.93\end{array}\right\}\text{From data on births by age of mother}$$

Male-dominant

$$1000b^*_m = 26.23\} \text{ From data on births by age of father.}$$

To each corresponds a sex ratio at birth which only for the first, $1000b_m$ above, is necessarily the same as the observed sex ratio at birth. (Observe how these numbers arise in Table 13.4 below.)

Where b_m is b_f multiplied by the sex ratio s, we can see how (13.2.6) is affected by the difference in death rates by dividing numerator and denominator by b_f to obtain

$$\frac{M(\infty)}{F(\infty)} = \frac{s}{1 + (d_m - d_f)/b_f}.$$

Aside from s which is substantially fixed in human populations, the operative element in the ultimate sex ratio is the difference between the male and female death rates, as a ratio to the female birth rate.

Application to Intrinsic and Crude Rates

The application of (13.2.6) up to this point has enabled us to say that the limiting sex ratio is the one which would evolve if the age-specific death rates in the given period were to continue indefinitely, along with the age-specific female birth rates and the sex ratio at birth. The female-dominant *intrinsic sex ratio*, as $M(\infty)/F(\infty)$ of (13.2.6) may be called under these conditions, has somewhat the title to our attention that the intrinsic rate of natural increase has in the model recognizing age for a single sex, but it is logically one remove further off. The equations assume not only that the present age distribution will approach stability, but that the stable or intrinsic rates for each sex will then operate to make Eq. (13.2.6) true. These two logically distinguishable steps take place at the same time, and the approach to stability is rapid. Show from (13.2.2) and (13.2.5) that the departure from the stable sex ratio at time t is of the order of $e^{-b_f t}$.

A different interpretation is to set the b's and d's equal to the current crude rates rather than to the intrinsic rates. This should tell in what direction the sex ratio is more proximately heading. Equation (13.2.6) then becomes

$$\begin{aligned}\frac{M(\infty)}{F(\infty)} &= \frac{b_m}{b_f + d_m - d_f} \\ &= \frac{B_M/K_F}{B_F/K_F + D_M/K_M - D_F/K_F} = \frac{B_M}{B_F + D_M(K_F/K_M) - D_F},\end{aligned}$$

where K_M, B_M, and D_M are the absolute numbers of male population, births, and deaths and K_F, B_F, and D_F the corresponding female numbers. For the United States in 1964 we have the statistics shown in Table 13.4, which give $M(\infty)/F(\infty) = 0.919$.

The ultimate sex ratio applying the intrinsic rates of 1964 is 0.986; the ultimate ratio on the crude rates of 1964 is 0.919. What is the meaning of this gross difference? Apparently, if the crude rates were to be maintained in the future, the proportion of males would continue to decline, as in fact it has been declining over the past few censuses. The sex ratio observed for the resident population of the United States in 1940 was 1.008; the 1950 ratio was 0.987; the 1960 ratio was 0.971 (U. S. *Statistical Abstract*, 1967, p. 24). The continuance of the crude rates of birth and death will be possible, however, only if the age-specific rates change. If the age-specific death rates for men and women (which favor women at the present time by up to 100 percent in some age groups) continue, a relatively older female population will result; 10.27% of women, against 8.36% of men, are 65 years of age and older, a difference of 1.91%; this difference increases with time to an ultimate 2.74%, and correspondingly the excess of the male death rate falls from 2.82 to 1.45 per thousand population. This diminishes the quantity $(d_m - d_f)/b_f$ to a degree which suffices to bring the ultimate sex ratio (as calculated by (13.2.6) using crude rates at each stage on the female-dominant projection) up from 0.919 to 0.986, by steps which are especially large in the first ten years of the projection (Table 13.4).

Male Dominance

Equations (13.2.1) are unnecessarily restricted in tying births for children of both sexes to the number of women. The same births can equally well be tied to men. By solving a new set of equations similar to (13.2.1), in which the male birth rate (boys to fathers) is b_m^* and female rate b_f^* is defined as b_m^*/s, and, as is appropriate to male dominance, b_m^* and b_f^* are multiplied by the number of males at time t, a new ultimate sex ratio is obtained:

$$\frac{M(\infty)}{F(\infty)} = \frac{b_m^* - d_m^* + d_f^*}{b_f^*}. \tag{13.2.7}$$

(Derive this from $M(\infty)/F(\infty)$ of Eq. (13.2.6) by interchanging males and females and then taking the reciprocal.) If the death rates for males and females are equal, Eqs. (13.2.6) and (13.2.7) both make the ultimate sex ratio in the population equal to $b_m/b_f = b_m^*/b_f^*$, which is the sex ratio at birth. We may interpret $M(\infty)/F(\infty)$ by breaking the expression on the right of (13.2.7) into two portions, of which the first is the sex ratio at birth, the second, the excess of male deaths referred to the female birth rate b_f^*:

$$\frac{M(\infty)}{F(\infty)} = s - \frac{d_m^* - d_f^*}{b_f^*}.$$

The ultimate sex ratio is equal to the advantage of males in respect to the number of births, less their excess of deaths taken relative to b_f^*.

Table 13.4 Population, births, and deaths, by sex, United States, 1964; ultimate sex ratios based on crude rates at 5, 10, 15, and ∞ years of projection

	ABSOLUTE NUMBERS		
	MALES	FEMALES	TOTAL
POPULATION	93,990,000	97,379,000	191,369,000
BIRTHS	2,060,162	1,967,328	4,027,490
DEATHS	1,017,778	780,273	1,798,051

	ON FEMALE-DOMINANT PROJECTION				
	MALES		FEMALES		ULTIMATE SEX RATIO
	$1000b_m$	$1000d_m$	$1000b_f$	$1000d_f$	$\frac{b_f s}{b_f + d_m - d_f}$
OBSERVED 1964	21.92	10.83	20.20	8.01	0.919
PROJECTED					
1969	23.34	10.96	21.42	8.56	0.942
1974	24.89	10.88	22.80	8.87	0.962
1979	25.74	10.61	23.61	8.96	0.979
STABLE	24.93	9.23	23.48	7.78	0.986

	ON MALE-DOMINANT PROJECTION				
	MALES		FEMALES		ULTIMATE SEX RATIO
	$1000b_m^*$	$1000d_m^*$	$1000b_f^*$	$1000d_f^*$	$\frac{b_m^* - d_m^* + d_f^*}{b_m^*/s}$
OBSERVED 1964	21.92	10.83	20.20	8.01	0.912
PROJECTED					
1969	23.01	10.96	21.11	8.57	0.938
1974	24.90	10.90	22.82	8.88	0.962
1979	26.35	10.62	24.17	8.96	0.981
STABLE	26.23	8.75	24.78	7.31	0.990

Sex ratio at birth preserved by defining b_m as sb_f in the female-dominant projection, and b_f^* as b_m^*/s in the male-dominant; $s = 2{,}060{,}162/1{,}967{,}328 = 1.04719$.

A satisfactory feature of this model is that it gives about the same ultimate sex ratio for male and for female dominance. For the United States in 1964, now using the male intrinsic rates of Tables 13.1 and 13.4, we find the ultimate sex ratio to be

$$\frac{M(\infty)}{F(\infty)} = \frac{26.23 - 8.75 + 7.31}{26.23/1.0472} = 0.990\,,$$

against 0.986 obtained from (13.2.6). What makes the male- and female-dominant versions similar is their both depending in much the same way on the difference between male and female death rates, and this difference is $1000(d_m^* - d_f^*) = 1.44$ on the male-dominant model, and $1000(d_m - d_f) = 1.45$ on the female-dominant.

Intermediate Dominance

More realistic than either male or female dominance is some intermediate form in which births are determined by the average number of men and women. The solution when the L function of (13.1.4) is the arithmetic mean $\frac{1}{2}(M(t) + F(t))$ is left as an exercise for the reader.

A geometric mean seems slightly more logical, at least in that a zero number of either sex would result in zero births. Moreover, if of N individuals the fraction f are female, the number of couples is fN, $0 \le f \le \frac{1}{2}$, and $(1 - f)N$, $\frac{1}{2} \le f \le 1$. The arithmetic mean of males and females is $N/2$, the geometric mean $N\sqrt{f(1 - f)}$; with a diagram the reader may ascertain over what part of the range $0 \le f \le 1$ the geometric mean is a better approximation to the number of couples.

Equations (13.1.4) now become (Kendall, 1949, p. 248; Goodman, 1953b, p. 215)

$$\begin{aligned} M'(t) &= -d_m M(t) + b_m\sqrt{M(t)F(t)}\,, \\ F'(t) &= -d_f F(t) + b_f\sqrt{M(t)F(t)}\,. \end{aligned} \tag{13.2.8}$$

A change of variables makes these linear. Write $R^2(t) = M(t)$ and $S^2(t) = F(t)$, so that $M'(t) = 2R(t)R'(t)$ and $F'(t) = 2S(t)S'(t)$. Substituting and dividing the first equation by $R(t)$ and the second by $S(t)$ gives

$$\begin{aligned} 2R' &= -d_m R + b_m S\,, \\ 2S' &= b_f R - d_f S\,, \end{aligned} \tag{13.2.9}$$

a pair of linear first-order homogeneous differential equations. These can be solved explicitly by standard methods, exemplified in Section 12.1 and below in the solutions of (13.3.1) and (13.4.1), and here left to the reader. [Note that (13.2.9) has the same pattern of signs as symbiosis in Table 12.2. Are cycles possible in the trajectory? Can both roots of the characteristic equation be negative? Show that for an increasing population, on the theory of Chapter 12, (13.2.9) will have one negative and one positive root, and because the roots are real and unequal a limiting value of the sex ratio must exist.]

Suppose that only the limiting or stable sex ratio is of interest. The condition for stability in the sex ratio

$$\frac{M(t)}{F(t)} = \left[\frac{R(t)}{S(t)}\right]^2 \tag{13.2.10}$$

is that its derivative,

$$\frac{d}{dt}\left[\frac{R(t)}{S(t)}\right]^2 = 2\left[\frac{R(t)}{S(t)}\right]\left[\frac{S(t)R'(t) - R(t)S'(t)}{S^2(t)}\right], \tag{13.2.11}$$

be equal to zero. The numerator of the second factor of the right-hand side of (13.2.11) will provide the only relevant root, and equating it to zero gives

$$R(t)/S(t) = R'(t)/S'(t)\,. \tag{13.2.12}$$

Substituting for the derivatives in this last expression their equivalents from (13.2.9) and rearranging, we obtain

$$b_f(R/S)^2 + (d_m - d_f)(R/S) - b_m = 0\,, \tag{13.2.13}$$

a quadratic in R/S whose solution provides the ultimate or intrinsic $M/F = (R/S)^2$. Evaluate (13.2.13) for the United States, 1964 of Table 13.1, using as data (a) the arithmetic mean and (b) the geometric mean of the male-dominant and female-dominant constants. The following discussion of mixed dominance leaves open the definitions of the constants.

This simple device for ascertaining the ultimate sex ratio without explicit evaluation of the trajectories for the two sexes is applicable to other forms of intermediate dominance. Suppose the births depend on males in the fraction D, where $0 \le D \le 1$, and on females in the fraction $1 - D$, so that the function L of (13.1.4) is

$$L\big(M(t), F(t)\big) = DM(t) + (1 - D)F(t)\,. \tag{13.2.14}$$

Again we could show, as in (13.2.12), that at stability the ratio of the derivatives is equal to the ratio itself:

$$M(t)/F(t) = M'(t)/F'(t)\,, \tag{13.2.15}$$

and entering for the derivatives (13.1.4) with the function L of (13.2.14) inserted reduces (13.2.15) to the quadratic in M/F:

$$(M/F)^2Db_f + (M/F)[b_f + d_m - d_f - D(b_m + b_f)] - (1 - D)b_m = 0\,. \tag{13.2.16}$$

Derive this and then check it by putting $D = 0$ to obtain (13.2.6) and $D = 1$ to obtain (13.2.7). Show that for a population in which $M/F < 1$ the ultimate M/F is a monotonically decreasing function of the D selected.

In what precedes, the degree of male dominance D is *exogenous*, which is to say arbitrary, or at least determined by considerations outside the system. If the model could itself determine D in a realistic fashion, it would be improved.

We may write

$$\begin{aligned} M'(t) &= -d_m M(t) + b_m[M(t)D(t) + F(t)(1 - D(t))]\,, \\ F'(t) &= -d_f F(t) + b_f[M(t)D(t) + F(t)(1 - D(t))]\,, \\ D(t) &= \frac{F(t-\lambda)}{M(t-\lambda) + F(t-\lambda)}\,, \end{aligned} \tag{13.2.17}$$

for example. The last member expresses the fact that male dominance is appropriate when men are scarce, and that there is a lag λ in the effect of male scarcity on actual births. The first two equations are not highly sensitive to the value of D. While Set (13.2.17) is nonlinear and its explicit solution would be a formidable task, numerical tracing of the trajectory as a marching problem with the help of a computer presents no difficulty.

One way of following out the set of equations is with the help of Taylor's theorem. We have, by going one term further than in the similar work of Section 12.1,

$$M(t+h) = M(t) + hM'(t) + \frac{h^2}{2!}M''(t)\,,$$

up to second derivatives, and similarly for $F(t)$. If $h = 1$ year and $\lambda = 5$ years, and the starting values are $M(0) = F(0) = 500$ and $D(t) = 0.5$, $t \leq 5$, then $M'(0)$ and $F'(0)$ are calculable from (13.2.17), and, by differentiation of (13.2.17), so are $M''(0)$ and $F''(0)$. The quantity $D(0)$ is treated as constant in small intervals. Then Taylor's theorem gives $M(1)$ and $F(1)$; $D(1)$ is taken as 0.5, and the process continues.

Table 13.5 shows excerpts from two paths following out Eqs. (13.2.17), both having the compromise constants referring to Norway, 1963, shown on the last line of Table 13.6, and with lag λ equal to five years. The first of the two paths starts with equal numbers of the two sexes, and since this is close to the ultimate sex ratio, no changes other than a nearly geometric increase are to be expected. The other path starts with 1000 females and 0 males, far from the ultimate distribution, and changes are great. In order to start the process, $D(t)$ was set equal to 0.5 for the first five years, since with zero males and strictly following (13.2.7), births would be zero throughout. (In effect, this present system on Eq. (13.2.17) starts at time 5 with 52 males and 1008 females.) Following this, $F(t)$ declines as the fewness of males causes a heavy male dominance; relatively few births appear until the number of males builds up. The loss of births through this cause results in a population less than one-half as great at three hundred years on this one-sided initial condition as the population resulting when we start with 500 of each sex. By $t = 300$ both groups are increasing at the same rate, and the sex ratio is close to the value 0.9986 to which the constants conform on (13.2.6).

One major difficulty remains: the determination of the constants b_m and b_f. A possibility is the observed male b_m^* and female b_f, separate intrinsic birth rates.

Table 13.5 Path of male and female populations with endogenous dominance, based on (13.2.17), constants for Norway, 1963*

	INITIAL POPULATION M(0) = F(0) = 500			INITIAL POPULATION M(0) = 0; F(0) = 1000		
YEAR t	M(t)	F(t)	D(t)	M(t)	F(t)	D(t)
0	500	500	0.500	0	1000	0.500
5	529	529	0.500	52	1008	1.000
10	560	560	0.500	60	976	0.951
15	592	592	0.500	70	947	0.942
20	627	627	0.500	81	921	0.931
25	663	663	0.500	93	898	0.919
30	701	702	0.500	107	878	0.906
35	742	743	0.500	122	861	0.892
40	785	786	0.500	140	847	0.876
45	831	832	0.500	159	836	0.859
50	879	880	0.500	180	828	0.840
100	1546	1548	0.500	506	924	0.660
150	2719	2723	0.500	1081	1350	0.561
200	4783	4790	0.500	2043	2217	0.523
250	8413	8426	0.500	3689	3803	0.508
299	14632	14654	0.500	6476	6555	0.503
300	14799	14821	0.500	6550	6629	0.503

* Equation (13.2.17) with constants $b_m^\dagger = 0.02077$; $b_f^\dagger = 0.01984$; $d_m = 0.00949$; $d_f = 0.00853$; lag $\lambda = 5$ years, shown in Table 13.6. Programmed by William Taylor.

But the ratio b_m^*/b_f for Norway, 1963, for example, is $0.02035/0.02027 = 1.0039$, and this is very different from the actual 1963 sex ratio at birth of 1.0468.

The three observed values,

b_m^* male intrinsic birth rate,

b_f female intrinsic birth rate, and

s sex ratio at birth,

Table 13.6 Intrisic or ultimate sex ratio, using various selections of data, Norway, 1963

DATA USED				INTRINSIC SEX RATIO	
$d_m - d_f$	b^*_m	b_f	s	FEMALE-DOMINANT (13.2.6)	MALE-DOMINANT (13.2.7)
0.00096	0.02035		1.0468	0.9975	0.9974
0.00096		0.02027	1.0468	0.9995	0.9995
0.00096	0.02035	0.02027		0.9585	0.9566
	COMPROMISE $b^\dagger_m$, $b^\dagger_f$, SATISFYING (13.2.18)				
	$b^\dagger_m$	$b^\dagger_f$	s		
0.00096	0.02077	0.01984	1.0468	0.9986	0.9985

will in general be inconsistent with one another. Since s is known to be more constant through time than either the male or female birth rate, it ought to be retained. If we preserve s, we are tempted to take account of both b^*_m and b_f in such fashion that the average of b^*_m and b_f is unchanged; i.e., they would become $b^*_m + \varepsilon = b^\dagger_m$ and $b_f - \varepsilon = b^\dagger_f$. This corresponds to the condition

$$\frac{b^\dagger_m}{b^\dagger_f} = \frac{b^*_m + \varepsilon}{b_f - \varepsilon} = s\,, \tag{13.2.18}$$

and hence we have

$$\varepsilon = \frac{sb_f - b^*_m}{1 + s}\,. \tag{13.2.19}$$

Use of $b^\dagger_m = b^*_m + \varepsilon$, $b^\dagger_f = b_f - \varepsilon$, and s seems to constitute the minimum violation of the data. For Norway, 1963, with $s = 1.0468$, this compromise would produce $\varepsilon = 0.00043$ and the modified $b^\dagger_m = 0.02077$ and $b^\dagger_f = 0.01984$. Hence (13.2.6) for female dominance would give as the ultimate sex ratio

$$b^\dagger_m/(b^\dagger_f - d_f + d_m) = 0.9986\,;$$

(13.2.7) for male dominance would give 0.9985.

Table 13.6 shows by way of summary the options in selecting among the three values b^*_m, b_f, and s from the data for Norway, 1963, disregarding the variants of $d_m - d_f$ due to differing male and female rates of increase. The three lines preserving s, the observed ratio of male to female births, are seen to agree fairly well, while that using the observed b_m^* and b_f is grossly different. The compromise $b_m^\dagger$, $b_f^\dagger$ at the bottom seems to make the best use of all the data.

Other formulations of the problem of the sexes have been proposed. Pollard (1948, p. 313) related sons to mothers and daughters to fathers, which over a number of generations corresponds to dominance of somewhat over 0.5; his joint intrinsic rate r is

$$r = \frac{T^*\rho^* + T\rho}{T^* + T}, \tag{13.2.20}$$

where T^* and T are the male and female length of generation and ρ^* and ρ the male and female intrinsic rates. His ingenious model can never become self-contradictory. Yntema (1952) took it that out of k generations there will be Ck in which the ratios are attached to fathers and $(1 - C)k$ in which they are attached to mothers. This generalization of Pollard's method gives the characteristic equation

$$(\psi^*(r))^C(\psi(r))^{1-C} = \left(\int_0^\beta e^{-rx}\phi^*(x)\,dx\right)^C \left(\int_0^\beta e^{-rx}\phi(x)\,dx\right)^{(1-C)} = 1\,, \tag{13.2.21}$$

where $\phi^*(x)$ is the net paternity function, i.e., the male analog of $\phi(x)$. The dominant root of (13.2.21) will divide the distance between the male and female roots into two intervals whose lengths are in the ratio CT^* to $(1 - C)T$. The proof of this statement requires the approximation $\psi(r) = R_0e^{-rT}$, which is equivalent to (6.2.5) when T replaces $\mu - (\sigma^2r/2)$. Then (13.2.21) becomes

$$(R_0^*e^{-rT^*})^C(R_0e^{-rT})^{(1-C)} = 1\,,$$

and taking logarithms and solving for r gives, if $\rho = (\ln R_0)/T$, etc.,

$$r = \frac{CT^*\rho^* + (1 - C)T\rho}{CT^* + (1 - C)T}, \tag{13.2.22}$$

of which (13.2.20) is the special case where $C = 1 - C = 1/2$. The degree of male dominance D used earlier may be shown by (14.1.7) and the argument following to have an effect similar to the present C.

13.3. SIMULTANEOUS TREATMENT OF AGES AND SEXES

The application of differential equations to the simultaneous treatment of age and sex may be illustrated with one sex and two age groups. Call the number of those under 15 years of age at time t $A(t)$, and those over 15, $B(t)$. Suppose for those under 15 a fixed death rate d_a and zero rate of bearing children, and for those 15 and over a death rate d_b and rate of childbearing b. Suppose also that the proportion of $A(t)$ which reach age 15 and exit from the group is e

per year. The rules of interaction are embodied in the pair of equations

$$\begin{aligned} A'(t) &= -(d_a + e)A(t) + bB(t)\,, \\ B'(t) &= eA(t) - d_b B(t)\,. \end{aligned} \tag{13.3.1}$$

The first of these is justified by saying that change in the younger age group depends negatively on deaths and aging out of the group, and positively on births to members of the older group; change in the latter depends positively on entrants by aging and negatively on deaths. The Eqs. (13.3.1) fall under symbiosis in the scheme of Table 12.2. Show that their roots are both negative if $b < (1 + d_a/e)d_b$.

For United States women for 1960 the data [arranged in the same order as the symbols of (13.3.1)] are

$$\begin{aligned} A'(t) &= -\frac{61{,}297 + 1{,}483{,}000}{27{,}427{,}000}A(t) + \frac{2{,}078{,}142}{63{,}565{,}000}B(t)\,, \\ B'(t) &= \frac{1{,}483{,}000}{27{,}427{,}000}A(t) - \frac{675{,}037}{63{,}565{,}000}B(t)\,, \end{aligned} \tag{13.3.2}$$

which simplify to

$$\begin{aligned} A'(t) &= -0.056306A(t) + 0.032693B(t)\,, \\ B'(t) &= 0.054071A(t) - 0.010620B(t)\,. \end{aligned} \tag{13.3.3}$$

On substituting the trial value e^{rt}, we obtain the characteristic equation in r,

$$\begin{vmatrix} -r - 0.056306 & 0.032693 \\ 0.054071 & -r - 0.010620 \end{vmatrix} = 0\,, \tag{13.3.4}$$

and

$$\begin{aligned} r_1 &= 0.01439\,, \\ r_2 &= -0.08131\,, \end{aligned}$$

as the two possible r's. Hence the solution to (13.3.2) is

$$\begin{aligned} A(t) &= a_1 e^{0.01439t} + a_2 e^{-0.08131t}\,, \\ B(t) &= b_1 e^{0.01439t} + b_2 e^{-0.08131t}\,. \end{aligned} \tag{13.3.5}$$

We seek the ultimate age ratio $A/(A + B)$, and as it does not depend on the initial conditions [how do we know?] we can take these arbitrarily as

$$\begin{aligned} A(0) &= 1{,}000{,}000\,, \\ B(0) &= 0\,, \end{aligned}$$

and setting $t = 0$ in (13.3.3) gives

$$\begin{aligned} A'(0) &= -56{,}306\,, \\ B'(0) &= 54{,}071\,. \end{aligned}$$

Now four equations for the constants can be derived from (13.3.5) by setting $t = 0$, and also taking the derivatives and setting $t = 0$:

$$1{,}000{,}000 = a_1 + a_2\,,$$
$$0 = b_1 + b_2\,,$$
$$-56{,}306 = 0.01439a_1 - 0.08131a_2\,,$$
$$54{,}071 = 0.01439b_1 - 0.08131b_2\,.$$

Of the four constants only a_1 and b_1 affect the ultimate population, since r_2 is negative. Hence we arrive at

$$A/(A + B) = a_1/(a_1 + b_1) = 0.3162\,,$$

which is an estimate of the proportion of the stable population under fifteen years of age, based on only two age groups and correspondingly rough. A more precise figure is 0.3430, calculated in five-year age groups on the method of Chapter 3.

An alternative way of arranging the argument, analogous to (13.2.11) above, is to set down the condition for stability in the proportion under 15:

$$\frac{d[A(t)]/[A(t) + B(t)]}{dt} = 0\,,$$

which reduces to

$$A(t)/B(t) = A'(t)/B'(t)\,.$$

Substitute the values of $A'(t)$ and $B'(t)$ from (13.3.3) and solve the resulting quadratic to verify $A/(A + B) = 0.3162$.

An even simpler approach, when a computer is available, is the marching process (used above to construct Table 13.5), now operating directly on Eqs. (13.3.1) and with arbitrary starting values. With the coefficients of (13.3.3), and starting with 1000 individuals under 15 years of age and none over, at 250 years we find 9530 under age 15; starting with 500 under 15 and 500 over, we have at 250 years 10,995 under 15; starting with 1000 aged 15 and over, 12,460 under age 15. In all three the fraction under 15 is the same 0.3162 obtained by the full solution above, but the absolute numbers vary considerably (Table 13.7).

Given only the fact that with 1000 in the second category initially, the number at 150 years is 6392, and at 250 years the number is 26,941, we see that the intrinsic rate r is the solution of $e^{100r} = 26{,}941/6392 = 4.215$; hence $r = 0.01439$, in agreement with (13.3.4).

By the same reasoning that justified the notion of a stable equivalent in Section 3.2, we here ask what initial population having the stable 0.3162 of its members under age 15 would have projected the same population for large t as was obtained for each of the three initial conditions of Table 13.7. This must be the total at 250 years, which is $10{,}995 + 23{,}774 = 34{,}769$ in the case where we started with 500 in each category, taken backwards in time at the rate $r = 0.01439$:

$$(34{,}769)[e^{(-0.01439)(250)}] = 953\,.$$

Table 13.7 Trajectory of numbers in two age groups $A(t)$ and $B(t)$, based on (13.3.3), comparing outcomes on three initial age distributions, constants for United States females, 1960*

YEAR t	$A(t)$	$B(t)$	$\frac{100A(t)}{A(t)+B(t)}$	$A(t)$	$B(t)$	$\frac{100A(t)}{A(t)+B(t)}$	$A(t)$	$B(t)$	$\frac{100A(t)}{A(t)+B(t)}$
0	1000	0	100.00	500	500	0.5	0	1000	0.00
5	773	231	76.99	456	599	43.22	140	968	12.61
10	629	402	61.03	436	686	38.89	243	969	20.05
15	542	534	50.38	432	764	36.16	323	994	24.53
20	494	642	43.46	441	835	34.45	388	1036	27.26
25	471	736	39.04	458	914	33.38	445	1093	28.93
30	467	821	36.25	481	990	32.71	496	1160	29.96
35	475	902	34.51	510	1069	32.30	545	1237	30.59
40	493	983	33.41	543	1153	32.04	594	1323	30.98
45	518	1065	32.73	581	1241	31.88	644	1418	31.23
50	549	1150	32.31	622	1335	31.78	696	1521	31.38
100	1102	2381	31.63	1270	2747	31.62	1440	3114	31.62
150	2261	4889	31.62	2608	5640	31.62	2956	6392	31.62
200	4642	10037	31.62	5355	11580	31.62	6069	13123	31.62
250	9530	20607	31.62	10995	23774	31.62	12460	26941	31.62

* Programmed by William Taylor.

The three initial age distributions of Table 13.7 have stable equivalents of 826, 953, and 1080, respectively. Convince yourself that the stable equivalents for the two ages are the coefficients a_1 and b_1 of (13.3.5) which correspond to given $A(0)$ and $B(0)$, and that in terms of the roots and coefficients they may be written

$$a_1 = \frac{-(d_a + e + r_2)A(0) + bB(0)}{r_1 - r_2},$$

$$b_1 = \frac{eA(0) - (d_b + r_2)B(0)}{r_1 - r_2}.$$

For our problem the total stable equivalent of a distribution $A(0)$ and $B(0)$ is

$$a_1 + b_1 = 0.826A(0) + 1.080B(0).$$

The interaction of the sexes in two age groups each may be expressed with four equations. If $M_a(t)$ and $M_b(t)$ represent younger and older males respectively, $F_a(t)$ and $F_b(t)$ younger and older females, and if the cutting point between young and old is below the age of reproduction, then

$$\begin{aligned}
M_a'(t) &= -(d_{ma} + e_m)M_a(t) && + b_m F_b(t), \\
M_b'(t) &= e_m M_a(t) - d_{mb}M_b(t), && \\
F_a'(t) &= && -(d_{fa} + e_f)F_a(t) + b_f F_b(t), \\
F_b'(t) &= && e_f F_a(t) - d_{fb}F_b(t),
\end{aligned} \tag{13.3.6}$$

where d_{ma} is the death rate for young males, d_{mb} the death rate for old males, e_m the proportion of young males who reach the end of the young age group, b_m the ratio of male births to the older female population. Rates for females are shown by the same symbols except that f appears in place of m. All rates, here as previously, are instantaneous and expressed on an annual basis. The reader should express the first two equations of (13.3.6) in words. He may also write out the differential equations for a two-sex model recognizing $M(t)$, total males; $F_a(t)$, girls under 15; $F_b(t)$, women 15–44; $F_c(t)$, women 45 and over.

This and formulations (13.3.1) and (13.3.6) have the disadvantage that the quantities e, representing the exits from the younger to the older age group, are taken from the data, along with the birth and death rates. The matrix models of Chapters 3 and 14 require only the rates from the data.

13.4. A MARRIAGE MODEL

In a monogamous society, those who are married constitute a subpopulation whose sex ratio is unity—say $N(t)$ males and $N(t)$ females. The subpopulation consisting of married persons cannot be taken as closed since, aside from entrants by marriage, procreation generates (unmarried) children, and mortality among married people drops out widows and widowers, here treated as single.

The relevant facts are expressed (again by Kendall, 1949, p. 248, and Goodman, 1953a, p. 216) in the equations

$$\begin{aligned} M'(t) &= -d_m M(t) \qquad -mF(t) + (b_m^\circ + d_f^\circ)N(t)\,, \\ F'(t) &= \qquad -(d_f + m)F(t) + (b_f^\circ + d_m^\circ)N(t)\,, \\ N'(t) &= \qquad mF(t) - (d_f^\circ + d_m^\circ)N(t)\,, \end{aligned} \tag{13.4.1}$$

where $M(t)$ is the number of single males, $F(t)$ of single females, and $N(t)$ of married couples; m is the (assumed fixed) proportion of single females marrying. Ratios which refer to the married population are distinguished by $^\circ$. The first member of (13.4.1), for example, says that the change in the number of unmarried males, $M'(t)$, is equal to

a) minus the male deaths $\quad -d_m M(t)\,,$
b) minus the number of females marrying, each of whom takes one male out of $M(t)$ $\quad -mF(t)\,,$
c) plus new male babies born $\quad b_m^\circ N(t)\,,$
d) plus married women dying, each of whom releases one male into the ranks of the unmarried $\quad d_f^\circ N(t)\,.$

Similarly for the other two equations of (13.4.1).

Now the dominance of marriages, not births, must be specified; the female marriage-dominance of (13.4.1) may be modified as desired. The reader may write out a modification of Eqs. (13.4.1) corresponding to intermediate dominance for marriage similar to (13.2.17) for birth dominance. [What further modification would be required if three ages of females are to be recognized: under 15, 15–44, and 45 and over?]

If in (13.4.1) the trial function e^{rt} is entered for each of the unknowns $M(t)$, $F(t)$, and $N(t)$, then the condition for consistency provides a determinantal equation in r:

$$\begin{vmatrix} -r - d_m & -m & b_m^\circ + d_f^\circ \\ 0 & -r - d_f - m & b_f^\circ + d_m^\circ \\ 0 & m & -r - d_f^\circ - d_m^\circ \end{vmatrix} = 0\,. \tag{13.4.2}$$

The form of analysis applied to (12.1.1) will show that (13.4.1) can have only real roots, of which at most one is positive.

We replace the symbols of (13.4.2) by their values for the United States in 1960, based on data which are partly hypothetical. For instance, the first marriages which occurred during 1960 were calculated by taking the total marriages, 1,527,000, and allocating them according to the distribution by previous marital condition for the 33 states which show such information. Moreover, a compromise had to be made with respect to married couples, since the numbers of married men and married women are different in the census and the equations make no allowance for this. The round figure of 42,750,000 was taken—intermediate between the two. Since age-specific information was lacking, all rates are crude rather than intrinsic.

With data constructed in this fashion the determinantal equation, arranged in the same order as (13.4.2), becomes

$$\begin{vmatrix} -r-0.009260 & -0.02412 & 0.05099+0.00557 \\ 0 & -r-0.01037-0.02412 & 0.04861+0.01294 \\ 0 & 0.02412 & -r-0.00557-0.01294 \end{vmatrix} = 0\,. \tag{13.4.3}$$

Expanding and changing signs in (13.4.3) gives

$$(r+0.009260)(r^2+0.05297r-0.0008467)=0\,,$$

of which the roots are

$$r_1 = 0.01286$$
$$r_2 = -0.06584$$
$$r_3 = -0.00926\,,$$

and the solution to (13.4.1) in terms of these roots is

$$\begin{aligned} M(t) &= m_1e^{r_1t}+m_2e^{r_2t}+m_3e^{r_3t}\,,\\ F(t) &= f_1e^{r_1t}+f_2e^{r_2t}+f_3e^{r_3t}\,,\\ N(t) &= n_1e^{r_1t}+n_2e^{r_2t}+n_3e^{r_3t}\,, \end{aligned} \tag{13.4.4}$$

where again the coefficients are to be fitted to initial conditions.

The dominant root, $r_1 = 12.86$ per thousand, represents the rate at which the population would increase after adjustment to the marriage, birth, and death rates which we fed into (13.4.1), and may be called the *sex-marriage-intrinsic* rate. It compares with the crude rate obtained as female births less deaths divided by female population of 14.69 per thousand; apparently the continuance of the crude marriage, birth, and death rates of 1960 implies an ultimate rate of increase less by 1.83 per thousand than the continuance of the crude birth and death rates.

We have now reached several values for the United States increase per thousand female population in 1960:

crude rate of increase	14.69,
age-intrinsic rate	20.71,
sex-marriage-intrinsic rate	12.86.

The age-intrinsic rate is higher than the crude because of the hollow in the age distribution corresponding to children born in the 1930's; the mere smoothing out of these by continuance of the age-specific rates of 1960 would cause a rise in the (crude) birth rate by over 6 per thousand. The sex-marriage-intrinsic rate is lower than the crude because of an opposite phenomenon: the high marriage rates up to 1956 and the decline thereafter. The marriages per thousand women were over 80 in most years from 1940 to 1956, being 82.4 in 1956, and they had dropped to 73.5 by 1960 (U. S. *Statistical Abstract*, 1966, p. 61). The continuance of 1960 marriage rates and married birth rates would result in a fall of the overall birth rate by about 1.34 per thousand.

In what way has the separation of the category of married couples in the Eqs. (13.4.1) affected the ultimate sex ratio? In order to find this we solve (13.4.1), starting from arbitrary boundary conditions as was done for (13.3.1) above. By straightforward differentiating of (13.4.4) twice, putting $t = 0$, and solving the nine simultaneous equations to provide the nine unknowns, we find numbers proportional to the male, female, and married-couple population in the stable condition:

$$M/m_1 = F/f_1 = N/n_1 ,$$

or

$$M/1193 = F/1362 = N/1047 . \tag{13.4.5}$$

The sex ratio of the total population is

$$\frac{M+N}{F+N} = \frac{1193+1047}{1362+1047} = \frac{2240}{2409} = 0.930 .$$

This is comparable with the calculation through Eqs. (13.2.1) and (13.2.6), which did not distinguish the married population and came out to 0.919 when 1960 crude rates were inserted. The recognition of marriage in (13.4.1) gives in this instance the slightly higher ultimate sex ratio.

As before, we trace out the trajectory defined by (13.4.1) numerically, and this will both check the part of the solution of the differential equation given as (13.4.5) and tell us about the other properties of the solution. With the initial values $M(0) = 0$, $F(0) = 0$, and $N(0) = 100$ (deliberately chosen to be far from equilibrium), $M'(0)$, $F'(0)$, $N'(0)$ are calculable from (13.4.1), and by differentiation of (13.4.1) so are $M''(0)$, $F''(0)$, $N''(0)$. These in the first two terms of Taylor's expansion with $h = 0.1$ give $M(0.1)$, $F(0.1)$, $N(0.1)$, and the process continues.

Table 13.8 shows the trajectory. We note:

a) The ratio $M(200) : F(200) : N(200) = 898 : 1025 : 788$ is the same as (13.4.5) obtained by solving the equations.
b) The total population at the end of 200 years is $898 + 1025 + 2(788) = 3499$, and at the end of 199 years, 3454, a ratio of 1.0130, which is approximately equal to the exponential of the dominant root $r = 0.01286$ of (13.4.3).
c) The sex ratio at the end of 200 years is $(898 + 788)/(1025 + 788) = 0.930$, against 0.930 in the solution to Eqs. (13.4.1).
d) The stable sex and marital status distribution with which the table ends enables us to calculate what stable initial number of individuals would have been equivalent to the 100 married couples used. It is $3499e^{(-0.01286)(200)} = 267.3$, from a table of exponentials. Without such a table the calculation is easily

Table 13.8 Trajectory on female-dominant marriage model (13.4.1), constants partly hypothetical, partly for United States, 1960*

YEAR t	SINGLE MALES M(t)	SINGLE FEMALES F(t)	MARRIED COUPLES N(t)	SEX RATIO
0	0	0	100	1.0000
1	6	6	98	0.9953
2	11	12	97	0.9912
3	16	17	95	0.9874
4	20	22	94	0.9841
5	25	27	93	0.9811
6	29	32	92	0.9784
7	33	36	91	0.9759
8	37	40	90	0.9737
9	41	45	90	0.9716
10	44	48	89	0.9697
20	73	80	88	0.9567
30	94	104	94	0.9494
40	113	125	104	0.9448
50	131	146	116	0.9415
60	150	168	131	0.9391
70	170	192	148	0.9372
80	194	218	169	0.9358
90	220	249	192	0.9346
100	250	283	218	0.9337
150	473	539	414	0.9312
199	887	1011	778	0.9304
200	898	1025	788	0.9304

* Programmed by Peter Smith.

made from the fact that the population at $t = 100$ years is 969 as $(969)^2/3499 = 268.4$. If we are not sure that stability has been attained by 100 years, we could use the total at 150 years, which is 1840, in the form $(1840)^4/(3499)^3 = 267.6$.

By varying the parameters in the model and recomputing, we can answer numerically such questions as the effect of the initial conditions on the population at 200 years, or of the marriage rate on the stable rate of increase. Dropping the marriage rate from 0.02412 to 0.01 gives only 1011 persons at the end of 200 years and a rate of increase $r_1 = 0.00545$, much below the r_1 of 0.01286 found above.

More surprising is the fact that the sex ratio is affected by the marriage rate. With $m = 0.02412$ we have a sex ratio of 0.930 at the end of 200 years; with $m = 0.010$ we have 0.952. How could you ascertain these effects of changing m directly from the equations (13.4.1) and (13.4.2) without any use of the computer?

An alternative procedure is to revert to (13.4.1), again consider ratios, say $M(t)/F(t)$ and $N(t)/F(t)$, and equate each of these ratios to the corresponding ratio of derivatives, the condition for stability as we saw before. The reader may show that (13.4.1) gives for stable ratios $N/F = N'/F'$ and $M/F = M'/F'$ the equations

$$(N/F)^2(b_f^\circ + d_m^\circ) + (N/F)(d_f^\circ + d_m^\circ - d_f - m) - m = 0\,,$$
$$(M/F)[(N/F)(b_f^\circ + d_m^\circ) + d_m - d_f - m] = (N/F)(b_m^\circ + d_f^\circ) - m\,,$$

written in this fashion because we would ordinarily solve the first for N/F and then treat the second as linear in M/F.

The preceding is no more than a short step, leaning on the work of Goodman and Kendall, in the application of linear homogeneous differential equations with constant coefficients to human populations. Differential equations are particularly helpful when one wishes to take account of a number of directions of change. This is exemplified in the set (13.4.1): a woman may get married, have a child, and then die, all in the same year, but the equations do not need to take explicit account of such a multiple contingency because, in effect, they reduce the process to elements of infinitesimally short time span.

13.5. PARITY AND BIRTH ORDER BY AGE

As a direction for further work, consider the female population classified according to *parity* (the number of children a woman has had) and age, and whether married or single. Let the number of women at time t of age a and parity p be $F_{a:p}(t)$. Those married without children are parity 0, and those unmarried are parity -1. Age could be in five-year groups, though any other grouping would fit and there is no requirement that the same width of age group be used throughout. Parities could likewise be grouped.

Whatever the groups decided on, the following relation would hold for all ages except the youngest, and for all parities, $F'_{a:p}(t)$ being the derivative of $F_{a:p}(t)$ with respect to t:

$$F'_{a:p}(t) = -(d_{a:p} + e_{a:p} + b_{a:p})F_{a:p}(t) + b_{a:p-1}F_{a:p-1}(t) + e_{a-1:p}F_{a-1:p}(t)\,. \qquad (13.5.1)$$

The coefficients with minus sign of $F_{a:p}(t)$ on the right-hand side are the rate of death $d_{a:p}$, of exit through aging $e_{a:p}$, and of having a child $b_{a:p}$, all for women at the ath age group and pth parity; the positive terms represent the entry into the group through earlier groups attaining the given age or parity. In practice not all the distinctions provided for in Eq. (13.5.1) are necessary or feasible; for instance, death rates in a given age group would usually be taken as the same for all parities.

The set (13.5.1) needs to be supplemented by an equation of different form for the very youngest group, to take account of the births as entrants into the population. If the youngest group is labelled $F_{0:-1}(t)$, then

$$F'_{0:-1}(t) = \sum_{a,p} b_{a:p}F_{a:p}(t) - (d_{0:-1} + e_{0:-1})F_{0:-1}(t) \,. \tag{13.5.2}$$

Equations (13.5.1) and (13.5.2) could be a large or a small set according as one did or did not wish to recognize fine groupings of age and parity. It could be readily modified to include both sexes. Computers are capable of handling hundreds of simultaneous equations, but it is not to be taken for granted that the larger the number of equations, the better. The opposite is rather the case: the smaller the set which is capable of representing given data, the clearer the understanding provided by the model.

An alternative means of handling some of the problems of interaction of populations is through a matrix formulation. This is especially convenient for machine computation where a number of age groups are to be recognized, as will be exemplified in the following chapter.

CHAPTER 14

INTERACTING POPULATIONS ANALYZED BY AGE

The discussion of interacting populations by means of differential equations in the preceding pages largely omits the all-important variable of age. Age is more conveniently incorporated with the two methods developed earlier—matrices (Chapter 2) and integral equations (Chapter 5). These will be used to deal with questions relating to the sexes, parity, participation in the labor force, and relations among other subdivisions of the population. The populations of Chapters 1 to 8 are collections of individuals of one sex differentiated only by age; Chapters 12 through 14 deal with total numbers of individuals in interacting populations; Chapter 14 itself introduces interacting populations by age.

14.1. THE GENERALIZED MATRIX

Generalization of the matrix of Chapters 2 and 3, due to Leslie and applying to a single sex, seems to take four different directions whose discussion constitutes Section 14.1: (a) noncommunicating populations, (b) interactions such as those of migration and the sexes, (c) multiple classification of each individual at any one moment, and (d) each individual moving through a succession of states.

a) *Noncommunicating populations.* If migration is zero among the several regions in a country, or among several countries, represented by projection matrices **R**, **S**, and **T**, and initial age vectors $\{\mathbf{J}\}$, $\{\mathbf{K}\}$, and $\{\mathbf{L}\}$, then separate projection would give $\mathbf{R}\{\mathbf{J}\}$, $\mathbf{S}\{\mathbf{K}\}$, and $\mathbf{T}\{\mathbf{L}\}$ as the age vectors after one time unit. We could alternatively put the three together in a larger matrix (filled out with zero sub-matrices written as 0) and a larger vector and multiply:

$$\begin{bmatrix} \mathbf{R} & 0 & 0 \\ 0 & \mathbf{S} & 0 \\ 0 & 0 & \mathbf{T} \end{bmatrix} \begin{Bmatrix} \mathbf{J} \\ \mathbf{K} \\ \mathbf{L} \end{Bmatrix} = \begin{Bmatrix} \mathbf{RJ} \\ \mathbf{SK} \\ \mathbf{TL} \end{Bmatrix}, \qquad (14.1.1)$$

using the rules for partitioned matrices. The latent roots of the square matrix in (14.1.1) are all the latent roots of **R**, **S**, and **T**, and only these. By the decomposition of the projection process worked out in Chapter 3, the projected population at time t depends on $\sum_i c_i\lambda_i^t$, where i ranges up to the order of the large matrix in (14.1.1). Any migration will introduce elements into the positions occupied by zeros in (14.1.1) and modify the diagonal elements, so changing at least some of the latent roots λ_i, and this brings us to the next case.

b) *Migration and the sexes.* To provide for movement from the second to the first region, which will diminish $\mathbf{S}\{\mathbf{K}\}$ and increase $\mathbf{R}\{\mathbf{J}\}$, a further matrix, say $\mathbf{M}$, is required in the second positions of the first and second rows of the operator in (14.1.1). Then, if the migration is to take place at the end of the interval of projection, we will have

$$\begin{bmatrix} \mathbf{R} & \mathbf{MS} & 0 \\ 0 & (\mathbf{I}-\mathbf{M})\mathbf{S} & 0 \\ 0 & 0 & \mathbf{T} \end{bmatrix} \begin{Bmatrix} \mathbf{J} \\ \mathbf{K} \\ \mathbf{L} \end{Bmatrix} = \begin{Bmatrix} \mathbf{RJ}+\mathbf{MSK} \\ (\mathbf{I}-\mathbf{M})\mathbf{SK} \\ \mathbf{TL} \end{Bmatrix}, \tag{14.1.2}$$

where $\mathbf{M}$ is a diagonal matrix whose elements are the fraction moving at each age. If the migration takes place at the beginning of the interval but we suppose that the migrants retain during one interval the mortality and fertility of the group they leave, then the projection is

$$\begin{bmatrix} \mathbf{R} & \mathbf{SM} & 0 \\ 0 & \mathbf{S}(\mathbf{I}-\mathbf{M}) & 0 \\ 0 & 0 & \mathbf{T} \end{bmatrix} \begin{Bmatrix} \mathbf{J} \\ \mathbf{K} \\ \mathbf{L} \end{Bmatrix} = \begin{Bmatrix} \mathbf{RJ}+\mathbf{SMK} \\ \mathbf{S}(\mathbf{I}-\mathbf{M})\mathbf{K} \\ \mathbf{TL} \end{Bmatrix}.$$

If the migration occurs at the beginning of the interval and the migrants immediately assume the mortality and fertility of the group to which they go, we have

$$\begin{bmatrix} \mathbf{R} & \mathbf{RM} & 0 \\ 0 & \mathbf{S}(\mathbf{I}-\mathbf{M}) & 0 \\ 0 & 0 & \mathbf{T} \end{bmatrix} \begin{Bmatrix} \mathbf{J} \\ \mathbf{K} \\ \mathbf{L} \end{Bmatrix} = \begin{Bmatrix} \mathbf{RJ}+\mathbf{RMK} \\ \mathbf{S}(\mathbf{I}-\mathbf{M})\mathbf{K} \\ \mathbf{TL} \end{Bmatrix}.$$

In the last case, the $\mathbf{SMK}$ subtracted from the second group is not in general equal to the $\mathbf{RMK}$ added to the first group. Under what conditions will the cases be the same?

Andrei Rogers (1967) has used matrix algebra in the study of migration along different lines. He investigates the problem of inferring the migration exchanges among a number of regions from a knowledge of their several populations on several occasions; this is the problem of inferring the matrix $\mathbf{M}$ from the vectors $\{\mathbf{K}^{(0)}\}$, $\{\mathbf{K}^{(1)}\}$, $\{\mathbf{K}^{(2)}\}, \ldots$, which are population counts by age at successive annual or quinquennial points of time. Assuming that the same matrix $\mathbf{M}$ applies through all intervals between these, we have for any one region the equations in $\mathbf{M}$, which here includes migration, birth, and death,

$$\begin{aligned} \mathbf{M}\{\mathbf{K}^{(0)}\} &= \{\mathbf{K}^{(1)}\}, \\ \mathbf{M}\{\mathbf{K}^{(1)}\} &= \{\mathbf{K}^{(2)}\}, \\ &\vdots \end{aligned}$$

Unfortunately, the process as it occurs is sufficiently unstable that the $\mathbf{M}$ which results from the equations with real data entered for the $\{\mathbf{K}^{(t)}\}$ varies beyond reasonable bounds. Rogers found, at least in initial experiments, that we cannot assume that the same $\mathbf{M}$ continues to operate over the successive periods.

The approach is mentioned here because a simpler version, the survivorship method of measuring migration, has been extensively and successfully used by demographers. Given numerically the projection matrix **R** of (14.1.2) representing mortality and fertility for one region, the observed initial age vector $\{\mathbf{J}^{(0)}\}$, and the observed age vector after one cycle $\{\mathbf{J}^{(1)}\}$, then the absolute amount of migration by age is estimated by $\{\mathbf{J}^{(1)}\} - \mathbf{R}\{\mathbf{J}^{(0)}\}$ in absolute numbers. In the system (14.1.2), two estimates of the migration vector $\mathbf{M}\,\mathbf{S}\{\mathbf{K}\}$ may be obtained if everything else is known.

J. H. Pollard (1966) considers a constant, known, immigration vector $\{\mathbf{b}\}$ added to the population in each time period, again for a population classified by age. Then

$$\begin{aligned}\{\mathbf{K}^{(t)}\} &= \mathbf{M}\{\mathbf{K}^{(t-1)}\} + \{\mathbf{b}\}\\ &= \mathbf{M}(\mathbf{M}\{\mathbf{K}^{(t-2)}\} + \{\mathbf{b}\}) + \{\mathbf{b}\}\\ &\ \ \vdots\\ &= \mathbf{M}^t\{\mathbf{K}^{(0)}\} + \mathbf{M}^{t-1}\{\mathbf{b}\} + \mathbf{M}^{t-2}\{\mathbf{b}\} + \cdots + \{\mathbf{b}\}\,.\end{aligned}$$

To find the sum, say $\{\mathbf{G}\}$, of the matrix geometric progression on the right, we premultiply by **M**,

$$\mathbf{M}\{\mathbf{G}\} = \mathbf{M}^t\{\mathbf{b}\} + \mathbf{M}^{t-1}\{\mathbf{b}\} + \cdots + \mathbf{M}\{\mathbf{b}\}\,,$$

subtract both sides from $\{\mathbf{G}\}$,

$$\{\mathbf{G}\} - \mathbf{M}\{\mathbf{G}\} = (\mathbf{I} - \mathbf{M}^t)\{\mathbf{b}\}\,,$$

and finally premultiply by $(\mathbf{I} - \mathbf{M})^{-1}$,

$$\{\mathbf{G}\} = (\mathbf{I} - \mathbf{M})^{-1}(\mathbf{I} - \mathbf{M}^t)\{\mathbf{b}\}\,.$$

The population at the end of t cycles of projection is thus

$$\{\mathbf{K}^{(t)}\} = \mathbf{M}^t\{\mathbf{K}^{(0)}\} + (\mathbf{I} - \mathbf{M})^{-1}(\mathbf{I} - \mathbf{M}^t)\{\mathbf{b}\}\,.$$

The behavior of the population as t becomes large may be studied as a generalization of the stable population of Section 3.2.

The two sexes in a closed region may also be considered communicating populations, and a combined operator may be devised for describing their relation. If we go through the procedure of Chapter 2, setting up a series of difference equations relating the population in successive periods of time, using as the interval of time and age 1 year, 5 years, or 15 years, we end up with a set of equations that again can be put into matrix form. On the female side the square matrix for fertility whose nonzero elements are all in the first row will be designated **B** (as in Chapter 4), and the one for survivorship whose nonzero elements are in the subdiagonal will be **S**. The matrices $\mathbf{B}^*$ and $\mathbf{S}^*$ have the corresponding meanings for the male part of the population.

If the model is female dominant, which is to say that the births of both sexes are related to the number of women of reproductive age (Section 13.2), then the set of linear equations may be written

$$\begin{Bmatrix}\mathbf{K}^{(1)*}\\ \mathbf{K}^{(1)}\end{Bmatrix} = \begin{bmatrix}\mathbf{S}^* & s\mathbf{B}\\ 0 & \mathbf{B}+\mathbf{S}\end{bmatrix}\begin{Bmatrix}\mathbf{K}^{(0)*}\\ \mathbf{K}^{(0)}\end{Bmatrix}, \tag{14.1.3}$$

where

$$\begin{Bmatrix}\mathbf{K}^{(t)*}\\ \mathbf{K}^{(t)}\end{Bmatrix}$$

is the column vector of numbers of persons at the several ages at time t, with males listed first. For convenience, s is now defined not as the sex ratio at birth, but rather as the ratio of male to female survivors to the end of the projection cycle. Thus s is ${}_5L_0^*/{}_5L_0$ times the ratio of male to female births. The square matrix in (14.1.3) is of the kind called reducible in Section 3.2. The reader may show that its nonzero roots are those of $|\mathbf{B}+\mathbf{S}-\lambda\mathbf{I}| = 0$.

We may write (14.1.3) as a pair of simultaneous equations in the smaller vectors describing the age distribution of each sex, and change the origin from 0 to $t-1$:

$$\{\mathbf{K}^{(t)*}\} = \mathbf{S}^*\{\mathbf{K}^{(t-1)*}\} + s\mathbf{B}\{\mathbf{K}^{(t-1)}\},$$
$$\{\mathbf{K}^{(t)}\} = (\mathbf{B}+\mathbf{S})\{\mathbf{K}^{(t-1)}\}. \tag{14.1.4}$$

Equation (14.1.4) relates the population at time t to that at $t-1$, and may be solved for time t in terms of the initial $\{\mathbf{K}^{(0)*}\}$ and $\{\mathbf{K}^{(0)}\}$. The reader may show by successive substitution of the second member of (14.1.4) into the first that the solution of the pair of simultaneous matrix equations is (Goodman, 1967a)

$$\{\mathbf{K}^{(t)}\} = (\mathbf{B}+\mathbf{S})^t\{\mathbf{K}^{(0)}\},$$
$$\{\mathbf{K}^{(t)*}\} = (\mathbf{S}^*)^t\{\mathbf{K}^{(0)*}\} + s\left[\sum_{i=0}^{t-1}(\mathbf{S}^*)^{t-i-1}\mathbf{B}(\mathbf{B}+\mathbf{S})^i\right]\{\mathbf{K}^{(0)}\}.$$

Reading from right to left, the factors in each term of the summation in the square bracket may be interpreted in words: $(\mathbf{B}+\mathbf{S})^i$ projects the female population through i periods; $\mathbf{B}$ generates the children in the $(i+1)$th period; $(\mathbf{S}^*)^{t-i-1}$ is the survivorship ratio for those children age by age through the remaining $t-i-1$ periods to time t.

Escape from the restriction to female dominance is possible, though at the cost of greater complexity of the results. Suppose that a fraction D of the males produce births, and $1-D$ of the females, as in Chapter 13. Then, corresponding to (14.1.3), we have

$$\begin{Bmatrix}\mathbf{K}^{(1)*}\\ \mathbf{K}^{(1)}\end{Bmatrix} = \begin{bmatrix}D\mathbf{B}^* + \mathbf{S}^* & s(1-D)\mathbf{B}\\ D\mathbf{B}^*/s & (1-D)\mathbf{B}+\mathbf{S}\end{bmatrix}\begin{Bmatrix}\mathbf{K}^{(0)*}\\ \mathbf{K}^{(0)}\end{Bmatrix}, \tag{14.1.5}$$

or, in the form of a pair of simultaneous linear equations relating the separate age vectors at time t to those at time $t-1$,

$$\{\mathbf{K}^{(t)*}\} = (D\mathbf{B}^* + \mathbf{S}^*)\{\mathbf{K}^{(t-1)*}\} + s(1-D)\mathbf{B}\{\mathbf{K}^{(t-1)}\},$$
$$\{\mathbf{K}^{(t)}\} = (D\mathbf{B}^*/s)\{\mathbf{K}^{(t-1)*}\} + \big((1-D)\mathbf{B}+\mathbf{S}\big)\{\mathbf{K}^{(t-1)}\}. \tag{14.1.6}$$

The solution of (14.1.6) for $\{\mathbf{K}^{(t)*}\}$ and $\{\mathbf{K}^{(t)}\}$ in terms of $\{\mathbf{K}^{(0)*}\}$ and $\{\mathbf{K}^{(0)}\}$ is straightforward but cumbersome. Instead of pursuing it, the reader may consider the nature of the solution from the square matrix in (14.1.5). He can show, by setting the matrix out explicitly, subtracting $\lambda\mathbf{I}$, and expanding the determinant of the resulting matrix by its first row, that the characteristic equation is

$$\lambda^n(D|\mathbf{B}^* + \mathbf{S}^* - \lambda\mathbf{I}| + (1 - D)|\mathbf{B} + \mathbf{S} - \lambda\mathbf{I}|) = 0\,, \qquad (14.1.7)$$

if the matrices for the sexes separately are $n \times n$. With $n \times n$ matrices (14.1.7) has n zero roots, and its positive root may be given as a weighted average of those of the male projection matrix $\mathbf{B}^* + \mathbf{S}^*$ and the female $\mathbf{B} + \mathbf{S}$. If the positive male root be λ_1^* and the positive female root λ_1, then by an argument similar to that leading to (13.2.22) but this time using the Newton-Raphson method (5.3.4), the positive root of (14.1.7) turns out to be nearly

$$\frac{DT^*\lambda_1^* + (1 - D)T\lambda_1}{DT^* + (1 - D)T}\,.$$

Prove that this agrees with (13.2.22) to terms of first degree in $\rho = 0.2 \ln \lambda_1$ and that $C = D$. Compare it numerically with the exact result of Table 14.2.

The projection of United States females on 1964 rates of birth and death was shown in Table 2.3 as carried out with the matrix of Table 2.2. The separate matrix for United States males, also on 1964 rates, is shown in Table 3.6. A summary of their application for separate projections appears in the first part of Table 14.1. The contradiction between the results for the two sexes which was to be expected from the argument at the start of Chapter 13 is here visible in the increasing disproportion between the numbers of males and females.

A self-consistent projection is possible by the single matrix of (14.1.5), which in five-year age groups contains 36×36 elements. The reproduction of such a matrix in this book would not be convenient, but any element for the ages of positive fertility is readily obtained from Tables 2.3 and 3.6. Other ages require the survivorships ${}_5L_{x+5}/{}_5L_x$ for ages from the end of reproduction onwards; for males these are calculable from Table 1.3; for females they are provided under the matrix of Table 2.2. If the large matrix of (14.1.5) be called $\mathbf{A}$, then some of its elements for the United States in 1964 may be verified to be

$$\begin{aligned} a_{1,1} &= 0.0 & a_{15,14} &= 0.77638 \\ a_{1,6} &= 0.44940D & a_{19,7} &= (0.28323)D/s \\ a_{1,23} &= s(1 - D)(0.47607) & a_{19,23} &= (1 - D)(0.47607) \\ a_{5,4} &= 0.99190 & a_{24,5} &= 0.0 \\ a_{5,22} &= 0.0 & a_{28,27} &= 0.98304 \end{aligned}$$

where

$$s = 1.04719(485{,}860/488{,}970) = 1.04053.$$

This is the matrix which provides the joint projections of Table 14.1.

Table 14.1 Summary of projections by age for the sexes separately, and of joint projections by (14.1.5), United States, 1964 (thousands)*

	MALES	FEMALES	TOTAL	SEX RATIO
SEPARATE PROJECTIONS				
1964	93,990	97,379	191,369	0.9652
1984	124,103	128,284	252,387	0.9674
2004	172,247	171,659	343,906	1.0034
2024	245,290	235,347	480,637	1.0422
2044	348,218	322,685	670,903	1.0791
JOINT PROJECTION				
WITH MALE DOMINANCE (D = 1)				
1964	93,990	97,379	191,369	0.9652
1984	124,103	128,610	252,713	0.9649
2004	172,247	175,297	347,544	0.9826
2024	245,290	247,376	492,666	0.9916
2044	348,218	350,589	698,807	0.9932
WITH INTERMEDIATE DOMINANCE (D = 0.5)				
1964	93,990	97,379	191,369	0.9652
1984	123,821	128,444	252,265	0.9640
2004	170,108	173,467	343,575	0.9806
2024	238,597	241,312	479,909	0.9887
2044	333,123	336,529	669,652	0.9899
WITH FEMALE DOMINANCE (D = 0)				
1964	93,990	97,379	191,369	0.9652
1984	123,545	128,284	251,829	0.9631
2004	167,993	171,659	339,652	0.9786
2024	232,005	235,347	467,352	0.9858
2044	318,259	322,685	640,944	0.9863

* Programmed by Diego Salazar.

Table 14.2 Nonzero solutions of two-sex equation (14.1.7) with male, female, and intermediate dominance, United States, 1964

$$|\underset{\sim}{A} - \lambda \underset{\sim}{I}| = D(\lambda^{11} - 0.0212\lambda^8 - 0.2321\lambda^7 - 0.4711\lambda^6 - 0.4367\lambda^5 - 0.2726\lambda^4 - 0.1399\lambda^3 - 0.0598\lambda^2 - 0.0245\lambda - 0.0085) + (1 - D)(\lambda^{11} - 0.0010\lambda^9 - 0.0874\lambda^8 - 0.3462\lambda^7 - 0.4712\lambda^6 - 0.3329\lambda^5 - 0.1798\lambda^4 - 0.0740\lambda^3 - 0.0168\lambda^2 - 0.0009\lambda) = 0.$$

	MALE DOMINANCE	INTERMEDIATE DOMINANCE†			FEMALE DOMINANCE
	D = 1	D = 0.7	D = 0.5	D = 0.3	D = 0
λ_1	1.09149	1.08884	1.08697	1.08500	1.08185
λ_2, λ_3	.3975 ± .7890i	.3742 ± .7844i	.3582 ± .7820i	.3419 ± .7801i	.3167 ± .7782i
λ_4, λ_5	−.4434 ± .4422i	−.4371 ± .4278i	−.4317 ± .4163i	−.4248 ± .4023i	−.4068 ± .3690i
λ_6, λ_7	−.5553 ± .1464i	−.5392 ± .1455i	−.5245 ± .1444i	−.5036 + .1427i	−.4213 ± .1373i§
λ_8, λ_9	−.1591 ± .5456i	−.1357 ± .5299i	−.1135 ± .5151i	−.0774 ± .4969i	.0074 ± .5192i§
$\lambda_{10}, \lambda_{11}$	.2146 ± .4391i	.1934 ± .4122i	.1681 ± .3875i	.1214 ± .3491i	−.0738; 0

FOLLOWING ARE THE ROOTS OF THE SAME EQUATION $|\underset{\sim}{A} - \lambda \underset{\sim}{I}| = 0$, EXPRESSED AS $r = 0.2 \ln \lambda$:

	D = 1	D = 0.7	D = 0.5	D = 0.3	D = 0
r_1	0.01751	0.01702	0.01668	0.01632	0.01573
r_2, r_3	−.0248 ± .2208i	−.0281 ± .2251i	−.0301 ± .2283i	−.0321 ± .2316i	−.0348 ± .2369i
r_4, r_5	−.0936 ± .1568i	−.0983 ± .1549i	−.1023 ± .1534i	−.1072 ± .1516i	−.1198 ± .1473i
r_6, r_7	−.1109 ± .0516i	−.1165 ± .0527i	−.1217 ± .0537i	−.1295 ± .0552i	−.1628 ± .0630i§
r_8, r_9	−.1130 ± .2574i	−.1207 ± .2640i	−.1279 ± .2708i	−.1375 ± .2833i	−.1311 ± .3113i§
r_{10}, r_{11}	−.1432 ± .2232i	−.1573 ± .2264i	−.1724 ± .2323i	−.1991 ± .2472i	−.5213; −∞

† Note departure from weighting by DT^* and $(1 - D)T$, especially for roots of smaller absolute value; $T^* = 29.222$, $T = 26.250$.
§ Exception to arrangement by decreasing absolute value.

The latent roots of the projection system (14.1.5) for the United States age-specific rates of birth and death in 1964 are obtained from (14.1.7) and appear in Table 14.2.

c) *Multiple classification of each individual.* An individual may be both at school and in the labor force at the same time; he can have a certain family status and a certain job status at the same time, neither of which need depend on the other. The proportions of individuals with the status in question in the several age intervals are spoken of as participation rates. The labor force participation of the male and of the female population, i.e., the proportion in the labor force of each age group, is shown for the United States in Table 14.3. Convenience of application in five-year age intervals would require splitting the given ten-year intervals in two.

Suppose that we recognize n five-year age groups, in which the proportions for males are $p_1, p_2, \ldots, p_n$, where $p_1 = p_2 = 0$, and that we arrange these in a horizontal vector $[\mathbf{P}]$. Suppose also that we project the male population in n age groups, shown as a vertical vector $\{\mathbf{K}\}$, by premultiplication by an $n \times n$ matrix $\mathbf{L}$ containing probabilities of survivorship in the subdiagonal and probabilities of fatherhood in the first row. Then the labor force at the initial moment is given by $[\mathbf{P}]\{\mathbf{K}\}$, 5 years later by $[\mathbf{P}]\mathbf{L}\{\mathbf{K}\}$, 10 years later by $[\mathbf{P}]\mathbf{L}^2\{\mathbf{K}\}$, $5t$ years after the start by $[\mathbf{P}]\mathbf{L}^t\{\mathbf{K}\}$. If one is interested in participation as a voter for the Republican Party insofar as this is a function of age, represented by rates q_i in the

Table 14.3 Labor-force participation rates, United States, 1960 and 1965*

	PERCENT IN LABOR FORCE 100[P]′			
	MALE		FEMALE	
	1960	1965	1960	1965
14-19	46.3	43.8	30.1	28.9
20-24	88.9	86.2	46.1	49.7
25-34	96.4	96.0	35.8	38.5
35-44	96.4	96.2	43.1	45.9
45-54	94.3	94.3	49.3	50.5
55-64	85.2	83.2	36.7	40.6
65+	32.2	26.9	10.5	9.5
ALL AGES 14+	79.7	76.9	36.1	37.5

* Source: *Statistical Abstract of the United States*, 1967, p. 222.

horizontal vector [**Q**], then, with all age-specific rates fixed, the Republican vote at the end of t periods would be given by $[\mathbf{Q}]\mathbf{L}^t\{\mathbf{K}\}$.

The above formulas produce an answer in total only, one not broken down by age. To retain the age distribution—say of the labor force—as a vertical vector, one would substitute for [**P**] in $[\mathbf{P}]\mathbf{L}^t\{\mathbf{K}\}$ the same participation rates written as the diagonal elements of a matrix which was elsewhere zero. If this matrix is diag (**P**), then the labor force as a vertical vector is $\text{diag}\,(\mathbf{P})\mathbf{L}^t\{\mathbf{K}\}$ after t periods or $5t$ years.

d) *Each individual moving through a succession of states.* Logically distinct from the foregoing is the set of problems where each individual moves through a succession of states and can be in only one at a time. The parity model of fertility is an example of this, where the woman who has had her first child is said to be of parity 1, who has had her second, of parity 2, etc. The notion can be extended to zero parity, defined as women who are married but have not yet had their first child, and to minus-one parity, women not yet married.

The practical importance of nuptiality as well as parity was stressed by Karmel (1950) in his discussion of the work of Whelpton. Age-parity-specific rates are likely to fluctuate more than age-specific rates. In some circumstances this fluctuation may not be meaningful: in the early 1940's a sharp rise occurred in the United States marriage rate, and soon thereafter, in first births; the age-parity adjusted figure was more influenced by this rise in first births than was the general age-adjusted rate where first births were diluted with births of other orders. If increase of births due to concentration of marriages is not really an increase of fertility, then it would be wrong so to interpret the rise in the age-parity adjusted rate. An age-parity-nuptiality-adjusted rate meets this point, and we now proceed to illustrate it.

The model has been worked out by E. M. Murphy (1965), and applied on the computer in a 51 $\times$ 51 matrix recognizing five-year age groups, but for purposes of exposition Murphy deals with only three ages and three parities. To apply this simple version, one might make one parity group consist of unmarried women, another of married women who have had one child, the third of married women who have had more than one child. Alternatively, the first group could consist of married or unmarried women without children, the second of women with one or two children, the third of women with three or more children. However the condensation is determined, three parity groups and three ages give nine combinations of age and parity, except that the second and third parities at the first age may be disregarded. The population of women is thus conceived as being divided into the seven classes or states of age and parity:

		Parity p	
	1	2	3
1	k_{11}	—	—
Age a 2	k_{21}	k_{22}	k_{23}
3	k_{31}	k_{32}	k_{33}

The transitions which are possible will be identified as follows:

From age 1 to age 2 Transition from state	Probability of transition	*From age 2 to age 3* Transition from state	Probability of transition
11 to 21	$p_{11\to21}$	21 to 31	$p_{21\to31}$
11 to 22	$p_{11\to22}$	21 to 32	$p_{21\to32}$
11 to 23	$p_{11\to23}$	21 to 33	$p_{21\to33}$
		22 to 32	$p_{22\to32}$
		22 to 33	$p_{22\to33}$
		23 to 33	$p_{23\to33}$

(14.1.8)

There are thus 9 nonzero elements for survivorship in the 7×7 transition matrix **P**, spread as shown in (14.1.9) over the second to seventh rows of the matrix. In addition, there are seven elements, m_{ap}, for the probability of a *female* birth to a woman of age a and parity p during the next period of 15 years; these are shown in the top row. The arrangement of the elements is arbitrary as long as the matrix and vector are consistent with one another, and in our vector the parities are given in numerical order within ages.

$$\mathbf{PK} = \begin{bmatrix} m_{11} & m_{21} & m_{22} & m_{23} & m_{31} & m_{32} & m_{33} \\ p_{11\to21} & 0 & 0 & 0 & 0 & 0 & 0 \\ p_{11\to22} & 0 & 0 & 0 & 0 & 0 & 0 \\ p_{11\to23} & 0 & 0 & 0 & 0 & 0 & 0 \\ 0 & p_{21\to31} & 0 & 0 & 0 & 0 & 0 \\ 0 & p_{21\to32} & p_{22\to32} & 0 & 0 & 0 & 0 \\ 0 & p_{21\to33} & p_{22\to33} & p_{23\to33} & 0 & 0 & 0 \end{bmatrix} \begin{Bmatrix} k_{11} \\ k_{21} \\ k_{22} \\ k_{23} \\ k_{31} \\ k_{32} \\ k_{33} \end{Bmatrix}. \tag{14.1.9}$$

The operation of **P** may be checked for the desired properties. For example $p_{21\to32}$ multiplies k_{21} and adds the result to the product of $p_{22\to32}$ and k_{22}, the total being put in the sixth cell of the product vector, and constituting the new k_{32}. Other elements may be similarly checked to ensure that they behave as required (Murphy, 1965).

To study the matrix **P** we again resort to its characteristic equation $|\mathbf{P} - \lambda\mathbf{I}| = 0$. One way of evaluating the determinant $|\mathbf{P} - \lambda\mathbf{I}|$ is by subtracting suitable multiples of the diagonal and subdiagonal elements from the top row, successively removing $m_{33}, m_{32}, \ldots,$ to bring the determinant to lower diagonal form. The reader may verify by this or other procedure that the characteristic equation is

$$\begin{aligned} |\mathbf{P} - \lambda\mathbf{I}| &= \lambda^4[-\lambda^3 + \lambda^2(m_{11}) + \lambda(m_{21}p_{11\to21} + m_{22}p_{11\to22} + m_{23}p_{11\to23}) \\ &\quad + m_{31}(p_{11\to21}p_{21\to31}) + m_{32}(p_{11\to21}p_{21\to32} + p_{11\to22}p_{22\to32}) \\ &\quad + m_{33}(p_{11\to21}p_{21\to33} + p_{11\to22}p_{22\to33} + p_{11\to23}p_{23\to33})] \\ &= 0\,. \end{aligned} \tag{14.1.10}$$

Define $p_{1\to2}$ as the probability in the stationary condition of living from the first age group to the second, through any sequence of parities, and define $p_{1\to3}$ as the probability of living from the first to the third age group, through any sequence of age-parity changes; finally write $p_{2\to3}$ as $p_{1\to3}/p_{1\to2}$, without attempting to express $p_{2\to3}$ in words. The coefficient of λ^2 within the bracket in (14.1.10) is m_{11}, the probability of having a child during the next 15 years for the first age group. The coefficient of λ is the sum of the probabilities of going from the first to the second age group and then having a child, the several parities being added, and we may write the coefficient as $m_2 = p_{1\to2}\bar{m}_2$. The absolute term concerns the last age group and may be written $m_3 = p_{1\to2}p_{2\to3}\bar{m}_3 = p_{1\to3}\bar{m}_3$.

The definitions may be summarized as

$$\begin{aligned}
p_{1\to2} &= p_{11\to21} + p_{11\to22} + p_{11\to23}\,, \\
m_2 = p_{1\to2}\bar{m}_2 &= m_{21}p_{11\to21} + m_{22}p_{11\to22} + m_{23}p_{11\to23}\,, \\
p_{1\to3} = p_{1\to2}p_{2\to3} &= p_{11\to21}p_{21\to31} + p_{11\to21}p_{21\to32} + p_{11\to22}p_{22\to32} \\
&\quad + p_{11\to21}p_{21\to33} + p_{11\to22}p_{22\to33} + p_{11\to23}p_{23\to33}\,, \\
m_3 = p_{1\to2}p_{2\to3}\bar{m}_3 &= m_{31}p_{11\to21}p_{21\to31} + m_{32}(p_{11\to21}p_{21\to32} + p_{11\to22}p_{22\to32}) \\
&\quad + m_{33}(p_{11\to21}p_{21\to33} + p_{11\to22}p_{22\to33} + p_{11\to23}p_{23\to33})\,.
\end{aligned}$$

Within each coefficient the probabilities of childbearing corresponding to the several parities are weighted by the probabilities of coming into those parities. In terms of these coefficients, (14.1.10) may be shortened to

$$\lambda^4(-\lambda^3 + \lambda^2 m_{11} + \lambda p_{1\to2}\bar{m}_2 + p_{1\to2}p_{2\to3}\bar{m}_3) = 0\,, \tag{14.1.11}$$

where now all subscripts refer to ages. Equation (14.1.10) may be written even more briefly in terms of the m's without bar:

$$\lambda^4(-\lambda^3 + \lambda^2 m_{11} + \lambda m_2 + m_3) = 0\,.$$

Then (14.1.11) and hence (14.1.9) must have the same roots as the matrix,

$$\begin{bmatrix} m_{11} & \bar{m}_2 & \bar{m}_3 \\ p_{1\to2} & 0 & 0 \\ 0 & p_{2\to3} & 0 \end{bmatrix}, \tag{14.1.12}$$

bordered by four rows and four columns of zeros, where again all subscripts refer to ages. This result will be verified by the quite different multiple-decrement approach of the next section. Both here and in the multiple-decrement model the age groups are weighted internally by parity, the weights in general being different from the proportions of women in the several parities in the given age group in the observed population; the weighting within the given age group is according to the *stationary* rather than the *actual* distribution by parities.

Does the recognition of parities in fact make much difference to intrinsic rates? The answer depends on how far apart the parities of the observed women are from the parities to which the population would settle down if the observed age-parity specific rates were to continue indefinitely. For United States females, 1962, Murphy (1965) found the crude rate of increase to be 13.44 per thousand population; the age-intrinsic rate, 18.85; and the age-parity-intrinsic rate, 20.21. Evidently continuance of existing specific rates would carry the population toward the ages and parities of higher birth rates, i.e., ages in the twenties and early parities.

Note that the birth of a female child, which adds unity in the top position of the vector on the right-hand side of (14.1.9), is not necessary for a shift in parities. For our purpose parities are merely a classification of women, occurring as it happens with the birth of a (male or female) child; births added to the first element of the vector in (14.1.9), k_{11}, are of female children only, by the definition of m_{ap}. No contradiction exists if we think of parities as a perfectly general set of mutually exclusive classes among which the population shifts in a single direction. These classes could be school grades, or hair color as between youthful and gray, or the number of children a woman has had. For this last-named classification of women, data are available: registrations show tables of births by age of mother and birth order, and censuses provide a denominator by tabulating women by age and total number of children born.

A model of the educational system which recognizes stages or grades through which students successively pass is suggested by Richard Stone (1966, Chap. 9). He goes beyond the parity model to propose that higher education be regarded as an epidemic process in which changes in the demand for places depend in part on the number infected and so liable to infect others, and in part on the number not yet infected and so available to catch the infection. By likening the proceeding to an epidemic, he is able to use the theory which has been developed for the latter (Bartlett, 1960, p. 57; Bailey, 1964), and he comes out with a logistic process. The model goes on to deal with different branches of education (technical school, university, etc.) and even takes account of technological improvement in methods of instruction in any given branch.

Any of the sets of differential equations of the preceding chapter may be changed into difference equations, and this simplifies the explicit incorporation of age distributions. In particular, a difference version of the marriage model due to Kendall and Goodman and shown in (13.4.1) may be constructed. If M_t is written for the unmarried male population at (discrete) time t, and F_t and N_t for the unmarried female population and married couples respectively, the parameters converted from instantaneous rates to probabilities analogous to the life table q_x, and female dominance once more assumed, then the new form of the model is

$$\begin{aligned}
M_{t+1} &= (1 - d_m)M_t - mF_t + (b_m^\circ + d_f^\circ)N_t\,, \\
F_{t+1} &= (1 - d_f - m)F_t + (b_f^\circ + d_m^\circ)N_t\,, \\
N_{t+1} &= mF_t + (1 - d_f^\circ - d_m^\circ)N_t\,, \qquad (14.1.13)
\end{aligned}$$

where m is the (female dominant) marriage rate, and the circles signify birth and death rates in the married population. The argument behind (14.1.13) is similar to that of (13.4.1), except that the parameters now require somewhat different definitions; e.g., $1 - d_f^\circ - d_m^\circ$ in the third equation is the joint probability of survival of husband and wife. For short time units

$$M'(t) \doteq M(t+1) - M(t) .$$

If $\mathbf{A}$ is the matrix of coefficients in (14.1.13) and $\{\mathbf{K}_t\}$ the vertical vector,

$$\{\mathbf{K}_t\} = \begin{Bmatrix} M_t \\ F_t \\ N_t \end{Bmatrix} ,$$

then (14.1.13) may be written in matrix form as $\{\mathbf{K}_{t+1}\} = \mathbf{A}\{\mathbf{K}_t\}$, and analyzed by the same algebra as were the matrices of Chapter 3. How would a model with male marriage dominance be written? With intermediate dominance?

To take account of age in the marriage model (14.1.13) requires only a reinterpretation of the symbols. Suppose $\mathbf{M}_t$ is a column vector giving the number of males in successive age groups, and $\mathbf{I} - \mathbf{d}_m$ is a square matrix with nonzero elements in its subdiagonal only, these giving the probabilities of survivorship on the appropriate male life table; $\mathbf{b}_m^\circ$ is also a square matrix but with nonzero elements in its first row, and similarly for females and for the other coefficients. Allowance for survivorship of widows and widowers to the end of the time interval will also be incorporated. With these changes of interpretation, the equation

$$\{\mathbf{K}_{t+1}\} = \mathbf{A}\{\mathbf{K}_t\}$$

stands for the marriage model (14.1.13) with n age groups recognized, $\mathbf{A}$ being $3n \times 3n$ in size. Judah Matras (1966) proposed a similar device of putting matrices within matrices to analyze mobility by age.

All of the above models are deterministic, in the sense that they suppose that the application of a certain death rate d_m to a population M_t will result in exactly $M_t d_m$ deaths. J. H. Pollard (1966) has shown how to construct matrices that will yield variances as well as expected values, and his method may be applied to any linear model in which the coefficients may be interpreted as probabilities; a simple example appears in Section 16.4 below.

The question of ergodicity, of the steady state that would be reached by a population to which the rates in question apply over an extended period of time, may be raised in connection with any projection process. For the life table the steady state population distribution is the L_x column; for the population of a single sex with given births and deaths, specified respectively by age at childbearing and age at death, a proof of ergodicity is contained in Chapter 5. What about the age-parity-specific case? It turns out that here also a steady state will be reached. Linder (1938) has shown this for a population in which rates are given and maintained constant simultaneously by age, marital status, parity, duration of marriage, and difference of age between husband and wife. His generalization of Lotka's theorem reads: "A population in which the probabilities of death, marriage, and divorce, as well as fertility, remain constant will grow exponentially after a sufficiently long period of time. In that condition the percent of women of given age, marital status, parity, duration of marriage, and difference of age from their husbands will remain constant" (1938, p. 146). The proof is based on properties of difference equations and need not be reproduced here. The reader may infer the nature of the limiting distribution by extending the analysis which led to (14.1.12).

14.2. MULTIPLE DECREMENT

The Life Table Analyzed by Parity

The alternative discussion of parity by the integral equation, or continuous approach, rests on a generalization of the life table. It follows from Chapter 1 that the life table age distribution is what would exist in the steady state if the observed age-specific death rates applied and births were sufficient merely to replace deaths. This way of treating mortality may be extended to the passing of women through the conditions of marriage and parity as well as (finally) death. Starting with the continuous version of the life table, and applying the observed fraction of women marrying to each $l(x)$, the number living to age x, then (disregarding widowhood and divorce) a column called $l^{(0)}(x)$ may be constructed of the women who are of zero parity, married but not yet having had their first child. We need to exclude from $l^{(0)}(x)$ the women who have had a child. If $m^{(i)}(x)\,dx$ is the probability of childbirth between ages x and $x + dx$ to women of ith parity, i.e., the probability of an $(i + 1)$th child, and $\mu(x)\,dx$ the probability of death between ages x and $x + dx$, then at each age we have

$$l^{(0)}(x + dx) = l^{(0)}(x) - l^{(0)}(x)m^{(0)}(x)\,dx + l^{(-1)}(x)m^{(-1)}(x)\,dx - l^{(0)}(x)\mu(x)\,dx\,, \tag{14.2.1}$$

where $l^{(-1)}(x)$ are single women and $m^{(-1)}(x)$ is the probability of marrying; similarly for $l^{(i)}(x + dx)$.

Equation (14.2.1) expresses the condition that the number of married women of zero parity at age $x + dx$ is equal to the number at age x, less the number who have a child and so pass on to first parity, plus the newly married who come from the $l^{(-1)}(x)$ unmarried at the marriage rate $m^{(-1)}(x)$, less the deaths. Given a set of $m^{(i)}(x)$ (the chance (assumed fixed) of going on to the $(i + 1)$th parity) for each parity and age, the $l^{(i+1)}(x)$ can be calculated from the $l^{(i)}(x)$, and would represent a stationary condition just as does the $l(x)$ column of the ordinary life table.

In practice (Jordan, 1952, Chap. 15) the data are given in finite age groups, and we cannot simply equate the central rates $m^{(i)}(x)\,dx$ with probabilities $q_x^{(i)}$ of having the $(i + 1)$th child in the next period of time and age for a woman of exact age x. We face the same problem here that we do in the ordinary or single-decrement life table—finding a set of q_x from the m_x, or more exactly, from the observed age-specific rates M_x. The principle of iterating to the data, used to construct a life table in Chapter 1, may be extended to multiple decrement.

Do the $l^{(i)}(x)$ also resemble the number living of the life table in permitting the calculation of probabilities? By analogy to $l(x+n)/l(x)$, the probability of a person x years of age being alive n years later, $l^{(i+j)}(x+n)/l^{(i)}(x)$ might seem to be the probability that a person of x years and with i children is alive n years later and has $i+j$ children, but reflection will show that this is not generally true. However, our application will be to the probability that a girl child just born will be alive and of ith parity in x years. Probabilities for individuals aged zero are correctly given by $l^{(i)}(x)/l_0$; the numerator here cannot include any individuals not implicitly "exposed" in the denominator.

14.3. THE INTEGRAL EQUATION MODIFIED TO ALLOW FOR BIRTH ORDER

We seek an analog to Lotka's integral equation (5.1.2):

$$B(t) = \int_0^\beta B(t-x)\frac{l(x)}{l_0}m(x)\,dx = \int_0^\beta B(t-x)\phi(x)\,dx\,, \qquad (14.3.1)$$

in which $l(x)m(x)/l_0$, the births in the stationary population of radix one at age x, would be replaced by terms which represent the probability that a female child survives to age x, during which time she has i children of both sexes, and at age x has her $(i+1)$th child (female), added through all i representing female children. Instead of $l(x)m(x)/l_0$ we would have for age x,

$$\sum_{i=0}^{\gamma-1}\frac{l^{(i)}(x)}{l_0}m_f^{(i)}(x)\,, \qquad (14.3.2)$$

where γ is the largest number of children any one woman has, and $m_f^{(i)}(x)$ is the probability at age x of having a female child after i children of either sex. Equation (14.3.2) is the distribution which would result from the indefinite continuance of the (given) age-parity-specific birth rates and the death rates of the year under study. We have written $m_f^{(i)}(x)$ with a subscript f for female in (14.3.2) to remind ourselves that it is not the same as the probability of having the next child used to construct $l^{(i)}(x)$—that was the probability of a child of either sex.

The new net maternity function is

$$\phi_P(x) = \frac{\sum_{i=0}^{\gamma-1} l^{(i)}(x)m_f^{(i)}(x)}{l_0}\,, \qquad (14.3.3)$$

and gives the required age-parity-specific analog to (14.3.1):

$$B(t) = \int_0^\beta B(t-x)\phi_P(x)\,dx\,. \qquad (14.3.4)$$

We may, as in Chapter 5, try

$$B(t) = Qe^{rt}$$

and obtain a characteristic equation,

$$\psi_P(r) = \int_0^\beta e^{-rx}\phi_P(x)\,dx = 1\,, \tag{14.3.5}$$

whose real root in r would be the age-parity-specific intrinsic rate. The complete solution of (14.3.4) for the unknown function $B(t)$ proceeds exactly as for (5.1.2). The reader will be able to show in what sense (14.3.5) is a continuous version of (14.1.10).

We have thus arrived at two methods of establishing the age-parity model—the matrix and the integral equation—and have suggested their equivalence. The integral equation requires as a preliminary the working out of the multiple-decrement table for women according to parity (of both male and female children) and age; once the $l^{(i)}(x)$ are available, say in five-year intervals, the rest of the calculation of (14.3.5) proceeds without difficulty on the age-parity-specific probabilities of giving birth to girl children. (Describe a model in which parities are defined in terms of girl children only.)

The difference between the solution for r in the homogeneous Lotka equation (14.3.1) and the parity-specific (14.3.4) depends on the difference between the two net maternity functions:

$$\phi(x) - \phi_P(x) = \frac{l(x)}{l_0}\sum_{i=0}^{\gamma-1}\left(\frac{k^{(i)}(x)}{k(x)} - \frac{l^{(i)}(x)}{l(x)}\right)m_f^{(i)}(x)\,, \tag{14.3.6}$$

where $k^{(i)}(x)/k(x)$ is the proportion of women aged x in the actual population who have had i children, and $l^{(i)}(x)/l(x)$ the corresponding proportion in the stationary multiple-decrement table. The difference was conspicuous in the United States in the early 1940's, when a sharp rise in the marriage rate gave actual proportions of the zeroth and first parities $k^{(i)}(x)/k(x)$ much greater than the life table proportions.

While the argument of this chapter duly takes age and parity into account, it is grossly incomplete in disregarding cohorts. The fundamental shortcoming of all analysis which uses the period cross section has been pointed out by Norman Ryder (1964). To take an example which is only slightly exaggerated, suppose that in a large population over a long period of time each woman intends to have exactly three children, and that she carries out this intention during the course of her reproductive life. Suppose that after a period of uniform ages of childbearing, a change in timing occurs in the form of an advancing of the ages of childbearing. Each woman still intends to have the same number of children in total, but the younger cohorts have their children earlier. Then examination of the period rates for several successive years will show a rise in the birth rate. Such a rise does not really constitute increased fertility.

Suppose again that women vary the time at which they have children, delaying pregnancies when times are hard and advancing them when times are prosperous, but still aiming at a fixed total number of children during each woman's childbearing career. The considerable fluctuations that period births will show are not entirely devoid of demographic significance, but they must be understood as representing variations in timing of an essentially unvarying total fertility. Such considerations have given importance to surveys asking couples what their childbearing intentions are (Westoff, Potter, and Sagi, 1963; Freedman, Goldberg, and Bumpass, 1965).

The childbearing of cohorts of women is represented by density along the lifelines of a Lexis diagram (Fig. 5.1). If the net maternity function is now represented by $\phi(a, t)$, a function of age *and* time, then the integral or total along a horizontal strip will refer to the period R_0, while an integral along a diagonal strip will give the cohort R_0. Evidently the integral equation (5.1.2) is entirely a relation connecting periods and ages, taking as it does integrals along vertical and horizontal lines. In describing it, some of the imagery of cohorts was used, but these were synthetic rather than real cohorts.

Ryder (1964) has related the integral along the diagonal to the integrals along the horizontal and the vertical. This enables him to translate period into cohort information and vice versa. Not only does Ryder show the period mean as a distorted version of the cohort mean, but he also estimates the direction and amount of the distortion in terms of the mean, variance, and skewness of the age and time cross sections.

Our example of multiple decrement has been parity, in which the living population passes through states which are mutually exclusive and arranged in an irreversible sequence. A different direction of generalization of the life table is required for cause of death, where the deaths are classified into mutually exclusive categories in an arbitrary order, and where cancer and heart disease, and other combinations, may be thought of as competing for the life of the person (Chiang, 1961c). Without stopping to examine the theory for such situations, we go on to probability models, which are more interesting than the deterministic theory that has occupied us up to now, and also more difficult. For sampling purposes, first and second moments of certain distributions are required; these are the main subject of Chapter 15.

Part VI

PROBABILITY MODELS

CHAPTER 15

SAMPLING VARIANCE OF DEMOGRAPHIC CHARACTERISTICS

Sample surveys, or a registration area which is a probability sample of a territory, are commonly proposed when vital statistics are incomplete or lacking altogether. Samples may be used to assess the demographic position of underdeveloped countries and the changes in this position with the advent of birth control. In view of the need for data, surprisingly little published material exists on survey methods and sampling errors in relation to demographic characteristics. To my knowledge the literature consists of papers by Wilson (1938), Irwin (1949), Chiang (1960b), and Koop (1951), the first three concerning the life table and especially the expectation of life, the last the gross reproduction rate, all under simplified conditions. Realistic formulas are often lengthy and complicated, and in the first part of this brief treatment we will study examples of their derivation, rather than attempt an exhaustive treatment. After that we will discuss a different approach, less complicated because it permits disregard of the peculiarities of demographic characteristics.

15.1. LIFE TABLE FUNCTIONS

The "Delta-method" is a way of following the propagation of error (Deming, 1964, pp. 37 ff.). Suppose that u and v are functions of x, and that x is in error by Δx, this being the departure from the expected value $\mathscr{E}x$, the average over all samples. We will suppose the sampling unbiased so that $\mathscr{E}x$ is also the true value or parameter. Then, if the error Δx is a small quantity,

$$\Delta u = \frac{du}{dx}\Delta x\,; \qquad \Delta v = \frac{dv}{dx}\Delta x\,; \tag{15.1.1}$$

$$\Delta(uv) \doteqdot (\Delta u)v + u(\Delta v)\,; \tag{15.1.2}$$

$$\Delta(u/v) \doteqdot \frac{u}{v}\left(\frac{\Delta u}{u} - \frac{\Delta v}{v}\right); \tag{15.1.3}$$

$$\Delta e^u \doteqdot e^u\,\Delta u\,; \tag{15.1.4}$$

$$\Delta \ln u \doteqdot \frac{\Delta u}{u}\,. \tag{15.1.5}$$

These are of course the formulas used in differentiation. As long as variation is confined to a sufficiently small range that u is representable by the linear relation $u = \mathscr{E}u + (x - \mathscr{E}x)\, du/dx$, in which du/dx may be considered constant, then transposing $\mathscr{E}u$, squaring, and averaging gives

$$\text{Var}(u) = \mathscr{E}(u - \mathscr{E}u)^2 = \left(\frac{du}{dx}\right)^2 \text{Var}(x) .$$

We can make a formula for variance from any one of (15.1.1) to (15.1.5) by squaring the differentials as they stand and averaging over all samples. The result for the ratio in particular is simply stated in terms of *rel-variance* (Hansen, Hurwitz, and Madow, 1953, Vol. II, p. 51; Kish, 1965, p. 48), defined for a random variable u as

$$V_u^2 = \frac{\text{Var}(u)}{(\mathscr{E}u)^2} .$$

Then from (15.1.3) it follows that

$$V_{u/v}^2 = V_u^2 - 2r_{uv}V_uV_v + V_v^2 ,$$

where r_{uv} is the Pearsonian coefficient of correlation.

The Number Living l_x

A simple and exact derivation of the variance of l_x is obtained if the life table may be assumed to have been made by following a generation or cohort, each member of which is independently subject to the given risk of dying year by year, $1 - (\lambda_{x+1}/\lambda_x)$. The survivors to age x of l_0 births are binomially distributed. If λ_x is the expected proportion surviving to age x, the expected number surviving is $l_0\lambda_x$, and the variance of l_x among samples of l_0 births is $l_0\lambda_x(1 - \lambda_x)$ (Wilks, 1962, p. 137). Below, this result is generalized to covariances by the use of a generating function, and a coefficient of correlation is obtained in (15.1.17).

The Number Dying ${}_nd_x$ and the Probability ${}_nq_x$

If ${}_nd_x$ is obtained by observing k_x individuals at exact age x and noting how many die during the succeeding n years, and the true probability of dying is $1 - (\lambda_{x+n}/\lambda_x)$, then the variance of ${}_nd_x$ must be

$$\text{Var}({}_nd_x) = k_x\left(1 - \frac{\lambda_{x+n}}{\lambda_x}\right)\left(\frac{\lambda_{x+n}}{\lambda_x}\right). \qquad (15.1.6)$$

The observed probability of dying ${}_nq_x$ would under these circumstances be subject to variance

$$\text{Var}({}_nq_x) = \left(1 - \frac{\lambda_{x+n}}{\lambda_x}\right)\left(\frac{\lambda_{x+n}}{\lambda_x}\right)\Big/ k_x .$$

If the sample consists in l_0 children at age zero followed through life, then the expected k_x is $l_0\lambda_x$, and the variance is approximately

$$\text{Var}({}_nq_x) \doteq ({}_nq_x)(1 - {}_nq_x)/l_0\lambda_x . \qquad (15.1.7)$$

In the case of the life table number-living we make a notational distinction between the population, universe value, or parameter, λ_x, and the number obtained in a particular sample, l_x. However, it would be a strain to make the same distinction for each of ${}_nq_x$, ${}_nm_x$, etc. and this has not been attempted. The symbols on the right-hand side of formulas such as (15.1.7) should be interpreted as true values or approximations thereto; Δ will always mean the difference between the (random) observation and the true value of the parameter. The expressions which follow are simplified by omission of the subscript n referring to the age interval, for example ${}_nq_x$ being written q_x. The length of interval n will always be understood.

In practice, q_x may be obtained from m_x, the age-specific death rate, by (Chiang, 1960a)

$$q_x = \frac{nm_x}{1 + (n - a_x)m_x}, \tag{15.1.8}$$

an identity derivable from the definition of a_x in (1.1.6). In this way of constructing the life table, the errors of q_x would be traced to those of m_x by differentiating (15.1.8) to obtain

$$\Delta q_x \doteqdot q_x\left(\frac{\Delta m_x}{m_x} - \frac{(n - a_x)\,\Delta m_x}{1 + (n - a_x)m_x}\right) \tag{15.1.9}$$

from (15.1.3), assuming that a_x, the average years lived since age x by those dying in the age group x to $x + n$, is not subject to sampling error. The further assumption that the variation in the denominator of the right-hand side of (15.1.8) is negligible produces $\Delta q_x \doteqdot (q_x/m_x)\,\Delta m_x$, from which follows (Chiang, 1960b)

$$\text{Var}\,(q_x) \doteqdot \left(\frac{q_x}{m_x}\right)^2 \text{Var}\,(m_x) \doteqdot n^2\,\text{Var}\,(m_x)\,. \tag{15.1.10}$$

This leaves us just one step from the primary data D_x and K_x, whose ratio D_x/K_x is nearly m_x. By another application of (15.1.3)

$$\Delta m_x \doteqdot m_x\left(\frac{\Delta D_x}{D_x} - \frac{\Delta K_x}{K_x}\right), \tag{15.1.11}$$

and squaring provides the variance of m_x. If deaths and population are obtained independently, the cross-product term may be disregarded. If it may be assumed that the population at the middle of the period, K_x, is known exactly, then the rel-variance of m_x, defined as $\text{Var}\,(m_x)/[\mathscr{E}(m_x)]^2$, reduces to that of D_x. Alternatively, if it may be assumed that the individuals of the sample have been selected independently at random from an initial population known exactly, D_x is the sum of drawings of a binomial variable, and its variance is

$$\begin{aligned} \text{Var}\,(D_x) &= (K_x + \tfrac{1}{2}D_x)(q_x)(1 - q_x) \\ &= D_x(1 - q_x)\,, \end{aligned} \tag{15.1.12}$$

which for most ages could be approximated by D_x.

Proceeding over the argument in the reverse direction, we could start with (15.1.12), the variance of D_x, the number of deaths, and trace the effect of this variance on that of m_x by (15.1.11), and then on q_x by (15.1.10). Proceeding forward in the chain, the next link is from Δq_x to $\Delta \mathring{e}_x$.

Expectation of Life $\mathring{e}_x$

To work out the variance of the expectation of life $\mathring{e}_x$, we note how it varies with change in q_y, where y stands for the several older age groups, again of n years. For any age $y > x$ the reader can establish the identity

$$\mathring{e}_x = \frac{T_x - T_y}{l_x} + \frac{L_y}{l_x} + \frac{T_{y+n}}{l_x} = \frac{T_x - T_y}{l_x} + \frac{l_y}{l_x}\left(\frac{L_y}{l_y}\right) + \left(\frac{l_{y+n}}{l_x}\right)\mathring{e}_{y+n}\,. \qquad (15.1.13)$$

The value of $(T_x - T_y)/l_x$, the average number of years lived between age x and age y, is not affected by q_y, which pertains to ages after y. Nor is $\mathring{e}_{y+n}$, the expectation after $y + n$, affected by q_y on the assumptions of this model. Any effect of q_y on a_y is disregarded. Hence entering for L_y its value from the equation preceding (1.1.6) and writing $l_{y+n} = l_y(1 - q_y)$ gives

$$\frac{\partial \mathring{e}_x}{\partial q_y} = \frac{\partial}{\partial q_y}\left[\frac{T_x - T_y}{l_x} + \frac{l_y}{l_x}\left(\frac{nl_y - (n - a_y)\,d_y}{l_y}\right) + \frac{l_y}{l_x}(1 - q_y)\mathring{e}_{y+n}\right]$$

$$= -\frac{l_y}{l_x}\,[n - a_y + \mathring{e}_{y+n}]\,. \qquad (15.1.14)$$

Therefore, if the errors of the q_y are uncorrelated,

$$\operatorname{Var}(\mathring{e}_x) = \sum_{y \ge x}\left(\frac{\partial \mathring{e}_x}{\partial\, {}_nq_y}\right)^2 \operatorname{Var}(q_y)$$

$$= \sum_{y \ge x}\left(\frac{l_y}{l_x}\right)^2 (n - a_y + \mathring{e}_{y+n})^2 \operatorname{Var}(q_y)\,, \qquad (15.1.15)$$

and this is substantially the result obtained by Wilson (1938, p. 706) and Chiang (1960b, p. 231).

The applicability of (15.1.15) is restricted by the assumption of independence and other simplifications. The formula without allowance for intercorrelations is appropriate if individuals have been drawn into the sample at random, but not if the drawing has been of groups or clusters of individuals; the use of (15.1.15) for a clustered sample can result in gross underestimate of the variance. On the other hand, to take all cross products as well as all squares would require the estimation of some 200 correlations for $\mathring{e}_0$ in five-year age groups. However, the principle by which a complete formula may be derived is clear: the effect of variation in the primary data D_x and K_x would be followed to m_x, then to q_x, then to $\mathring{e}_x$. A simple example of the use of (15.1.14) is given below, and then an alternative procedure is suggested for following this chain on the computer and obtaining the same result for any one age group without the algebra of the last few pages.

Propagation of Error Computed Deterministically

To know how much percentage effect a one-percent change in the q_y brings about in the $\mathring{e}_x$, we modify (15.1.14) by dividing by $\mathring{e}_x$ and apply it to finite increments:

$$\frac{\Delta \mathring{e}_x}{\mathring{e}_x} = -\left(\frac{q_y}{\mathring{e}_x}\right)\left(\frac{l_y}{l_x}\right)(n - a_y + \mathring{e}_{y+n}) \frac{\Delta q_y}{q_y}. \tag{15.1.16}$$

Consider as an example $x = 30$ and $y = 40$, and data from the table for United States males in 1961,

$$\mathring{e}_{30} = 40.80\,; \qquad \frac{l_{40}}{l_{30}} = \frac{91884}{94103}\,;$$

$$\mathring{e}_{45} = 27.32\,; \qquad {}_5q_{40} = 0.02232\,,$$

and set ${}_5a_{40}$ equal to 2.5. Then the relative effect on $\mathring{e}_x$ of a small change in ${}_5q_{40}$ is

$$-\left(\frac{0.02232}{40.80}\right)\left(\frac{91884}{94103}\right)(5 - 2.5 + 27.32)\frac{\Delta\, {}_5q_{40}}{{}_5q_{40}} = -0.0159\,\frac{\Delta\, {}_5q_{40}}{{}_5q_{40}}\,,$$

according to (15.1.16). This is to say that a 1% change in ${}_5q_{40}$ will mean a 0.0159% change in $\mathring{e}_{30}$ in the opposite direction.

When the life table was actually calculated with an increment of 1% in ${}_5q_{40}$, the expectation of life at age 30 went down from 40.8040 to 40.7975, or 0.0065, a relative change of $-0.0065/40.8040 = -0.016\%$. This is an arithmetical verification of (15.1.15) for the case in which one only of the age-specific death rates is subject to error. The computer provides a general technique for ascertaining differentials by running the data as slightly modified and comparing with the original outcome. The reader will be able to extend the method to finding higher order moments and covariances.

The Stochastic Life Table by Simulation

The deterministic method of the preceding paragraphs may be paralleled by a stochastic procedure. Ronald Lee, using the University of California, Berkeley, CDC 6400, took a fixed set of q_x (those of United States females, 1964) and exposed each of 100 individuals of age zero to the risk q_0, then the survivors successively to the probabilities $q_1, q_5, q_{10}, \ldots$. The result was replicated to produce 150 tables similar to the one shown as Table 15.1, a process requiring over 200,000 random numbers, and executed in 27 seconds. (In order to save computer time a simplified method of making a life table not involving iteration was used, but it was a method uniform throughout this section and does not affect any of our conclusions.)

To each of the elements of the table now corresponds a frequency distribution. For example, the 150 values of $\mathring{e}_0$ are as shown in Table 15.2. In respect of the l_x, the d_x, and the $\mathring{e}_x$, means and variances for the 150 life tables

Table 15.1 Specimen random or simulated life table starting with 100 births, in which each individual is given a separate probability of surviving at each age; ${}_nq_x$ taken from United States females, 1964; simplified method*

AGE x	${}_nq_x$	ℓ_x	${}_nd_x$	${}_nL_x$	$\mathring{e}_x$
0	0.02107	100	2	98.5	74.01
1	0.00347	98	0	392.0	74.51
5	0.00185	98	0	490.0	70.51
10	0.00154	98	0	490.0	65.51
15	0.00274	98	0	490.0	60.51
20	0.00359	98	1	487.5	55.51
25	0.00440	97	0	484.8	51.06
30	0.00634	97	0	485.0	46.06
35	0.00929	97	0	485.0	41.06
40	0.01372	97	0	485.0	36.06
45	0.02073	97	0	486.0	31.06
50	0.03154	97	5	474.0	26.05
55	0.04510	92	7	442.9	22.31
60	0.06841	85	7	407.5	18.94
65	0.10622	78	7	372.5	15.41
70	0.15976	71	7	340.8	11.69
75	0.24798	64	23	264.4	7.64
80	0.38839	41	16	165.4	5.48
85	1.00000	25	25	59.2	2.37

* Programmed by Ronald Lee, who also provided the material for Tables 15.2 to 15.5.

were calculated from the machine-produced "observations," and a few of these means and variances are shown in Table 15.3. The mean of the distribution in Table 15.2, for example, calculated from ungrouped values, is shown as 72.84, and its variance as 3.23.

Also in Table 15.3 are the deterministic results in parentheses. For United States females, 1964, the $\mathring{e}_0$ as calculated by the same simplified method is 73.02, and the variance of $\mathring{e}_0$ by (15.1.15) is 3.14. These deterministic values are shown in parentheses just below the result of the simulation in Table 15.3, item by item.

Table 15.2 Distribution of values of $\mathring{e}_0$ in 150 random life tables, based on q_x of United States females in 1964 and 100 births

-68.99	4
69.00-69.99	4
70.00-70.99	13
71.00-71.99	29
72.00-72.99	27
73.00-73.99	34
74.00-74.99	22
75.00-75.99	13
76.00-76.99	1
77.00+	3
TOTAL	150

Table 15.3 Means and variances among 150 random life tables based on q_x of United States females in 1964 and 100 births; expected values in parentheses beneath each simulated result*

	ℓ_x		${}_nd_x$**		$\mathring{e}_x$	
AGE x	MEAN	VARIANCE	MEAN	VARIANCE	MEAN	VARIANCE
0	100.00 (100.00)	0 (0)	2.21 (2.11)	1.83 (2.06)	72.84 (73.02)	3.23 (3.14)
20	96.83 (96.96)	2.60 (2.95)	0.33 (0.35)	0.35 (0.35)	55.12 (55.22)	1.78 (1.72)
40	94.46 (94.68)	5.26 (5.03)	1.23 (1.30)	1.37 (1.28)	36.20 (36.25)	1.47 (1.33)
60	84.18 (84.57)	13.47 (13.05)	5.81 (5.79)	5.57 (5.45)	19.09 (19.10)	0.91 (0.79)
80	44.28 (44.50)	25.07 (24.70)	17.25 (17.28)	14.75 (14.30)	5.52 (5.54)	0.19 (0.29)

* Programmed by Ronald Lee and Hardeo Sahai.

** Interval n is one year for age 0 and five years for subsequent ages.

How does a mean of the 150 stochastic tables compare with the corresponding figure in the deterministic table? For l_{60} the mean of the 150 tables was 84.18, and the deterministic table by the same method gave 84.57, a difference of 0.39. If the l_{60} are normally distributed, we may consider this in relation to the "observed" variance as estimated with 149 degrees of freedom, 13.47, and find t as $0.39/\sqrt{13.47/150} = 1.3$, which has a probability of nearly 0.2 of being exceeded by chance. Alternatively, we may compare it with the theoretical variance given by $l_0(\lambda_x)(1 - \lambda_x)$ on the assumption that the latter is exact, and find $0.39/\sqrt{13.05/150}$; for assessment of this, a normal distribution is appropriate and gives nearly the same probability.

The variances obtained from the 150 stochastic tables may be compared with the theoretical results derived earlier in this chapter. The variance with 149 degrees of freedom among the 150 $\mathring{e}_{40}$ as shown in Table 15.3 is 1.47; that on (15.1.15) is 1.33; the ratio of the first to the second, 1.47/1.33, multiplied by 149, or 165, may be considered the value of a χ^2 variable with 149 degrees of freedom. The probability that χ^2 will be greater than 165 by chance is about 0.2. In the entire table the only difference significant at the five-percent level is for $\mathring{e}_{80}$.

Complete Distributions of Life Table Functions; Intercorrelations

The foregoing argument has been confined to variances, which is to say, second moments of distributions of individual numbers. Chiang (1960a) has gone further and derived the generating function of the entire number-living column of the life table. Again think of l_0 not as the arbitrary start of the life table, but as an observed number of babies who are followed through their lives. The survivors among them, l_x, are counted year by year. Suppose that they are drawn at random from a population subject to a life table whose number-living column is λ_x on a radix of unity. Then, as we saw above, for any age x the observed quantity l_x/l_0 may be viewed as a sample from the binomial distribution with parameter λ_x; hence the probability of the sample life table turning out to contain exactly l_x individuals at age x is

$$\binom{l_0}{l_x} \lambda_x^{l_x}(1 - \lambda_x)^{l_0 - l_x} .$$

The generating function is the expected value of the l_xth power of an otherwise undefined variable, t_x:

$$\mathscr{E}(t_x^{l_x}) = \sum_{l_x} \binom{l_0}{l_x} \lambda_x^{l_x}(1 - \lambda_x)^{l_0 - l_x} t_x^{l_x} = (1 - \lambda_x + \lambda_x t_x)^{l_0} .$$

The derivative of this last with respect to t_x, evaluated at $t_x = 1$, is $l_0\lambda_x$, the expected value of l_x. Subsequent derivatives will serve to calculate subsequent moments. The distribution is implicit in its generating function.

We need not confine ourselves to the single variable t_x but can set up as many such variables as there are l_x, so that together the t_x will determine the joint distribution of the l_x. It turns out that the joint generating function is

$$\mathscr{E}(t_1^{l_1}t_2^{l_2}\cdots t_\omega^{l_\omega}) = \{1 - [\lambda_1(1-t_1) + \lambda_2 t_1(1-t_2) + \lambda_3 t_1 t_2(1-t_3) + \cdots + \lambda_\omega t_1 t_2 \cdots t_{\omega-1}(1-t_\omega)]\}^{l_0}.$$

This is proved by induction (Chiang, 1960a, p. 624). Its use may be exemplified by differentiating with respect to t_x and then with respect to t_y, to obtain the joint moment about zero of l_x and l_y. Taking this second derivative and putting all the t_i equal to unity gives

$$\left.\frac{\partial^2 \mathscr{E}(t_1^{l_1}t_2^{l_2}\cdots t_y^{l_y})}{\partial t_x \partial t_y}\right|_{t_i=1} = l_0\lambda_y(1-\lambda_x) + l_0^2\lambda_x\lambda_y,$$

if $y \geq x$. From the joint moment about zero, the covariance of l_x and l_y is obtained by subtracting the product of the means; i.e., $(l_0\lambda_x)(l_0\lambda_y) = l_0^2\lambda_x\lambda_y$, which leaves

$$\text{Covar}(l_x, l_y) = l_0\lambda_y(1-\lambda_x).$$

The coefficient of correlation between l_x and l_y is

$$r_{l_x l_y} = \frac{\text{Covar}(l_x, l_y)}{\sqrt{\text{Var}\, l_x \,\text{Var}\, l_y}} = \frac{l_0\lambda_y(1-\lambda_x)}{\sqrt{l_0\lambda_x(1-\lambda_x)l_0\lambda_y(1-\lambda_y)}}$$

$$= \sqrt{\frac{\lambda_y(1-\lambda_x)}{\lambda_x(1-\lambda_y)}}, \tag{15.1.17}$$

which does not depend on l_0. Equation (15.1.17) is not symmetric between x

Table 15.4 Correlations between l_x and l_y, $x \leqq y$, among 150 random life tables based on q_x of United States females in 1964 and 100 births; expected values in parentheses beneath each simulated result

	ℓ_{20}	ℓ_{40}	ℓ_{60}	ℓ_{80}
ℓ_{20}	1.000	0.754 (0.747)	0.478 (0.418)	0.167 (0.161)
ℓ_{40}		1.000	0.620 (0.558)	0.204 (0.216)
ℓ_{60}			1.000	0.388 (0.387)
ℓ_{80}				1.000

Table 15.5 Correlations between pairs of items from random life tables with 100 births, based on q_x of United States and Mexico

UNITED STATES FEMALES, 1964

	$_5d_{40}$	$_5d_{60}$	$_5d_{80}$
$_5d_{20}$	-0.033	-0.131	-0.033
$_5d_{40}$	1.000	-0.066	-0.067
$_5d_{60}$		1.000	-0.056
	$\mathring{e}_{40}$	$\mathring{e}_{60}$	$\mathring{e}_{80}$
$\mathring{e}_{20}$	0.850	0.575	0.243
$\mathring{e}_{40}$	1.000	0.727	0.229
$\mathring{e}_{60}$		1.000	0.302

MEXICAN FEMALES, 1960

	$_5d_{40}$	$_5d_{60}$	$_5d_{80}$
$_5d_{20}$	-0.131	-0.077	+0.029
$_5d_{40}$	1.000	+0.011	-0.004
$_5d_{60}$		1.000	-0.105
	$\mathring{e}_{40}$	$\mathring{e}_{60}$	$\mathring{e}_{80}$
$\mathring{e}_{20}$	0.698	0.493	0.185
$\mathring{e}_{40}$	1.000	0.623	0.127
$\mathring{e}_{60}$		1.000	0.172

and y, and assumes that x is the younger age. [Would you have expected the correlation to be an expression symmetric in x and y?]

Ronald Lee's random experiment estimated these correlations by simulation for certain values of l_x; his results are shown for United States females, 1964, in Table 15.4. In parentheses are the values of r from (15.1.17), using the deterministic λ_x.

Table 15.6 Correlations of ${}_5q_x$ among 83 male life tables representing observations on developed countries subsequent to 1945 of Sec. 4.2

	${}_5q_{25}$	${}_5q_{30}$	${}_5q_{35}$	${}_5q_{40}$	${}_5q_{45}$	${}_5q_{50}$	${}_5q_{55}$
${}_5q_{20}$	0.926	0.838	0.772	0.709	0.621	0.474	0.330
${}_5q_{25}$	1.000	0.956	0.891	0.840	0.732	0.589	0.418
${}_5q_{30}$		1.000	0.942	0.910	0.808	0.666	0.503
${}_5q_{35}$			1.000	0.973	0.903	0.789	0.655
${}_5q_{40}$				1.000	0.948	0.863	0.740
${}_5q_{45}$					1.000	0.949	0.851
${}_5q_{50}$						1.000	0.952
${}_5q_{55}$							1.000

The correlations for l_x are positive: where l_x on a table happens to be higher than average, l_y is also likely to be higher, the correlation diminishing as the distance $y - x$ increases. The correlation of the ${}_5d_x$ is negative and small, as appears in Table 15.5, where calculation is made from the same 150 random tables for the United States. The correlation of the $\mathring{e}_x$ shown in the same table is positive and larger. To show the extent to which such correlations vary from one experiment to another, corresponding results are presented also for Mexico, females, 1960.

The correlations here obtained are among random drawings from a population of given q_x. They would be expected to be zero among the q's and among the m's, for which the age groups vary almost independently. A quite different kind of correlation, perhaps of greater demographic interest, is that among observed life tables. In Section 4.2 we took up a brief statistical analysis of three sets of life tables computed by William Cummings. The third of his sets consisted of 83 tables for males from the presently developed countries of Europe, America, and Oceania for dates from 1945 onward. After constructing the tables from official death and population statistics given by age and sex, he produced among other statistical material the correlations of the q_x in all combinations. A selection from his correlations is shown in Table 15.6.

These correlations are very different from the near-zeros which would appear among q's on tables made by random drawings. Here the correlations are positive and high, and the closer the ages, the higher the correlation. That between ${}_5q_{20}$ and ${}_5q_{25}$ is 0.926; between ${}_5q_{40}$ and ${}_5q_{45}$, 0.948; between ${}_5q_{60}$ and ${}_5q_{65}$, 0.979 (not shown in the table). As a rough summary, ages five years apart correlate about 0.95; ten years apart, 0.85; twenty years apart, 0.7; thirty years apart, 0.5; forty years apart, 0.3. At the extremes of the table, ${}_5q_{80}$ correlates only 0.155 with ${}_4q_1$. Whatever special causes act on mortality in different countries seem to act at limited ranges of ages.

Standardized Rates

We saw in Section 1.1 that the comparison of mortality between two populations is analogous to a comparison of prices between two areas, in which the death rates for the several age-sex groups take the place of prices of the several commodities, and the number of persons at each age takes the place of the quantities of these commodities. If the standard population (base-year quantity) in the ith group is K'_i, then the directly standardized rate is that which results from applying the given age-sex-specific rates d_i to the standard population in a finite number of age intervals:

$$(\text{sd}) = \frac{\sum_i K'_i d_i}{K'} ,$$

where $K' = \sum K'_i$. This has the dimensions of a death rate as it stands, and becomes an aggregative base-weighted index on being divided by $d' = D'/K'$, the crude rate in the standard population, $D' = \sum D'_i$ being the absolute number of deaths at all ages.

To obtain a simple approximation to its sampling error we shall assume that

a) the standard population is arbitrary, and hence its numbers and rates are not subject to sampling error;
b) the given population is known to a higher order of precision than given deaths;
c) sampling for the several ages is independent, and hence covariances among the deaths at the several ages are zero;
d) deaths are sampled individually at random from a large universe, so that d_i is binomially distributed.

On these suppositions the variance Var (sd) of the directly standardized death rate is easily derived as

$$\text{Var (sd)} = \sum_i \left(\frac{K'_i}{K'}\right)^2 \text{Var}(d_i) = \sum_i \left(\frac{K'_i}{K'}\right)^2 d_i(1 - d_i) ,$$

and if the fraction of deaths d_i is small, this reduces to

$$\text{Var (sd)} \doteq \sum_i \left(\frac{K'_i}{K'}\right)^2 d_i .$$

The indirectly standardized rate (isd) divides the given deaths D by the application to the given age distribution K_i of the specific rates d'_i of the standard population, and multiplies by the crude rate d' of the standard:

$$(\text{isd}) = \frac{d'D}{\sum_i K_i d'_i} .$$

(Omission of d' from the numerator would give this the dimensions of an aggregative index number, and it is current-year weighted, as we saw in Section 1.1.) On the same assumptions as above, the variance of (isd) is

$$\mathrm{Var}\,(\mathrm{isd}) = \left(\frac{d'}{\sum_i K_i d_i'}\right)^2 \mathrm{Var}\, D \doteq \left(\frac{d'}{\sum_i K_i d_i'}\right)^2 D\,.$$

Since the assumptions include that the standard rates are not subject to variation, being arbitrary, and the number exposed in the given population has negligible relative sampling error, the only random element in the expression for Var (isd) is D. Wherever both the crude rate and the indirectly standardized rate (isd) may be supposed fixed multiples of D, their rel-variance (or its square root, the coefficient of variation) will be the same. The directly standardized rate (sd), on the other hand, may have larger or smaller rel-variance than the crude rate.

15.2. FERTILITY FUNCTIONS

The Net Reproduction Rate R_0

R_0 is in practice more influenced by variation in fertility than in mortality. We will assume now that the life table is somehow obtained without error. By definition, if nonzero fertility ranges from age 15 to 45,

$$R_0 = \frac{{}_5L_{15}F_{15} + {}_5L_{20}F_{20} + \cdots + {}_5L_{40}F_{40}}{l_0}\,,$$

where

$$F_x = {}_5B_x/{}_5K_x\,,$$

${}_5B_x$ being the girl births to mothers aged x to $x + 4$ at last birthday. Supposing the sample to have been drawn independently at random so that covariances are zero, we obtain

$$l_0^2\,\mathrm{Var}\,(R_0) = ({}_5L_{15})^2\,\mathrm{Var}\,(F_{15}) + ({}_5L_{20})^2\,\mathrm{Var}\,(F_{20}) + \cdots + ({}_5L_{40})^2\,\mathrm{Var}\,(F_{40})\,. \tag{15.2.1}$$

If in (15.2.1) the F's are regarded as hypergeometric variates, based on samples of n each drawn without replacement from a finite population of size N, then factors $(1 - (n/N))$ enter the variance and we have the result given by Koop (1951, p. 156). With cluster-sampling, such terms as $2({}_5L_{15})({}_5L_{20})\,\mathrm{Covar}\,(F_{15}, F_{20})$ would have to be added to (15.2.1).

If both deaths and births have been obtained by samples, then the departure of R_0 from its expected value is

$$\Delta l_0 R_0 = \sum_{x=15}^{40} (F_x\,\Delta\,{}_5L_x + {}_5L_x\,\Delta F_x)\,,$$

and the variance of R_0 will not only include terms for variance due to mortality and to fertility, but also for the correlations between births and survivorships at correponding ages and at different ages.

The Intrinsic Rate of Natural Increase *r*

A slight novelty arises in calculation of the variance of the intrinsic rate, taken as the solution in r of the equation

$$l_0\psi(r) = \sum_{x=\alpha}^{\beta-5} (e^{-(x+2.5)r} {}_5L_x F_x) = l_0 \,. \qquad (15.2.2)$$

Applying the Delta-method to the three factors of each term of $\psi(r)$,

$$l_0 \, \Delta\psi(r) = \sum_{x=\alpha}^{\beta-5} e^{-(x+2.5)r} {}_5L_x F_x \left(-(x + 2.5) \, \Delta r + \frac{\Delta \, {}_5L_x}{{}_5L_x} + \frac{\Delta F_x}{F_x} \right), \qquad (15.2.3)$$

by an obvious extension of (15.1.2).

But we know that $\psi(r)$ in (15.2.2) does not vary, being equal to unity as the condition on r in the characteristic equation $\psi(r) = 1$. Thus it is permissible to equate (15.2.3) to zero and move the term in Δr to the other side of the equality, so that

$$\Delta r \sum_{x=\alpha}^{\beta-5} (x + 2.5) e^{-(x+2.5)r} {}_5L_x F_x = \sum_{x=\alpha}^{\beta-5} e^{-(x+2.5)r} {}_5L_x F_x \left(\frac{\Delta \, {}_5L_x}{{}_5L_x} + \frac{\Delta F_x}{F_x} \right). \qquad (15.2.4)$$

On the left the perturbation in r is multiplied by l_0 times the mean age at childbearing in the stable population, A_r. If the mean age at childbearing may be treated as a constant in relation to Δr, $\Delta_5 L_x$, and ΔF_x, and (15.2.4) is squared and averaged on both sides and then divided through by $l_0 A_r^2$, the square of the coefficient of Δr, the result is the variance of the intrinsic rate. Alternatively, the variance of r may be obtained from $Tr = \ln R_0$ of Section 5.6, using the variance of R_0 given above.

The Intrinsic Birth Rate *b*

The variance of the intrinsic birth rate b follows from that of r. The rate b is $m(a)$ weighted by the age distribution $e^{-ra}p(a)$ as in (7.1.8):

$$b = \frac{\int_\alpha^\beta e^{-ra} p(a) m(a) \, da}{\int_0^\omega e^{-ra} p(a) \, da} \,,$$

and if r is such that the numerator equals unity, then

$$b = \frac{1}{\int_0^\omega e^{-ra} p(a) \, da} \,.$$

Hence

$$\frac{\partial b}{\partial r} = b \, \frac{\int_0^\omega a e^{-ra} p(a) \, da}{\int_0^\omega e^{-ra} p(a) \, da} = b\bar{A}_r \,,$$

or b times the mean age $\bar{A}_r$ in the stable population. For English and Welsh women in 1961, $b = 0.01931$, and $\bar{A}_r = 33.73$, making

$$\partial b/\partial r = (0.01931)(33.73) = 0.651 .$$

The variance of b would be $(0.651)^2 = 0.424$ times the variance of r.

15.3. A SIMPLIFIED APPROACH TO COMPLEX SAMPLES

In practice, samples are stratified, nested, and otherwise elaborated in the interest of efficiency; further data obtained from outside the survey are often incorporated in ratio or regression estimates, again in the interest of efficiency; finally, the characteristics of which we require the variances in demography are themselves very elaborate functions of the primary data. The reader who wishes to convince himself of the last point may try to set down $\mathring{e}_x$, the expectation of life at age x, as an explicit function of the number of deaths and population at the several ages from x to the end of life. In view of elaborate sample designs, complex estimates, and functions which involve considerable manipulation of the primary totals ${}_nD_x$ and ${}_nB_x$ estimated from the sample, the formulas presented up to this point are not likely to find much application in surveys, and when they are applied it will be with such simplifying assumptions that they may give a grossly wrong estimate of the error. This suggests the use of some practical methods introduced into surveys in fields other than population, where similar difficulties are encountered.

Suppose that two survey organizations have independently carried out unbiased probability surveys in a given population to estimate a parameter X, which could be the intrinsic rate, the expectation of life at age 0, or any other. The samples and the estimation procedures may be as complex as efficiency requires; we need not even know what methods they used, aside from their both being approximately unbiased, independent, of roughly the same variance, and distributed more or less normally. Suppose that the first one estimates X_1 and the second, X_2, and the user wishes to take advantage of both their estimates. Then his best estimate is $(X_1 + X_2)/2$, and the variance of this is in turn estimated by $[(X_1 - X_2)/2]^2$.

One degree of freedom falls short of desirable precision, but further degrees are usually available. With access to the survey records of the two organizations, one can split each survey into two parts, in such fashion that each might have been drawn independently, and so attain three degrees of freedom. It may be difficult to do this so that administrative variation is included in the error, but the U. S. Bureau of the Census Current Population survey secures a part of such error. It splits the whole sample two ways, and does this some 40 times (Bureau of the Census, 1964). The errors are not entirely independent, but each adds some information. Going through the complex estimating procedure 80 times takes about 24 hours of the time of a very powerful computer, but it does produce an honest sampling error, with the equivalent of about 25 degrees of freedom.

The sample could be grouped by pairs of strata of the original population, and estimates made from the sample for each of the strata. Then the estimate of the total would be

$$(X_1 + X_2) + (X_3 + X_4) + \cdots$$

and the variance of this would be estimated by

$$(X_1 - X_2)^2 + (X_3 - X_4)^2 + \cdots \qquad (15.3.1)$$

Equation (15.3.1) has an upward bias due to inclusion in the variance of the difference between the members of paired strata, a part of the variance which has been eliminated from the estimate itself. An alternative is to divide the original design systematically into a number of independent subsamples and then find the variance among estimates made from these (Deming, 1956).

The practical sampler pursues efficiency of estimation at the cost of bias. To take an exaggerated example, suppose we had chosen a random sample consisting of one state of the United States in order to estimate the present (1967) population. We count its 1967 population, say Y_i, and are then faced with the choice of a factor for raising this. We first think of 50, which is the reciprocal of the probability with which the state was chosen; the estimate $\hat{Y} = 50Y_i$ is unbiased in the sense that the average of such estimates over many samplings would give the true figure. Alternatively, the ratio of the 1960 population of the United States to the 1960 population of the selected state, say X/X_i, would give $\hat{Y} = (X/X_i)Y_i$. This is biased in that the average of many samplings would not equal the true figure. Few people, samplers or not, would have any doubt that of the two the biased estimate is preferable. Though using one state to estimate the United States is hardly an acceptable proposal, yet the conclusion we have drawn, that of two estimates the more efficient one may be biased, is often true in sampling work.

The series of less analytical but more practical methods here referred to reaches its culmination in the "jackknife," worked out by Fred Mosteller and John Tukey on an original suggestion by Quenouille (1956), designed to remove the principal term of bias (Cochran, 1963, p. 180). The sample is divided into k subsamples. If Y is the result of making a calculation, however complex, on the entire sample, and Y_j the result of making the calculation on the sample *omitting the* jth *subsample*, which is to say on all the $k - 1$ subsamples other than the jth, then *pseudovalues* are defined by

$$Y_j^* = kY - (k - 1)Y_j\,.$$

The k pseudovalues are treated like observations; their arithmetic mean

$$\hat{Y} = \frac{\sum_{j=1}^{k} Y_j^*}{k} \qquad (15.3.2)$$

is taken for the final estimate, and the variance of this estimate is estimated as

$$\text{Var}(\hat{Y}) \doteq \frac{\hat{s}^2}{k} = \frac{\sum_{j=1}^{k}(Y_j^* - \hat{Y})^2}{(k)(k-1)}. \tag{15.3.3}$$

Confidence limits may be set assuming $\hat{Y}\sqrt{k}/\hat{s}$ distributed as t with $k - 1$ degrees of freedom.

The sense in which $\hat{Y}$ is unbiased may be studied by supposing an estimate X, based on m elements, such that

$$\mathscr{E}(X) = \mu + \frac{a}{m} + \frac{b}{m^2} + \cdots, \tag{15.3.4}$$

where μ is the parameter required and the bias is of the order of a/m. (The argument requires that the bias be a function of sample size.) For k groups, each of n observations, (15.3.4) gives for Y_j based on $(k - 1)n$ elements

$$\mathscr{E}(Y_j) = \mu + \frac{a}{(k-1)n} + \frac{b}{(k-1)^2n^2} + \cdots$$

Similarly, Y being based on kn observations,

$$\mathscr{E}(Y) = \mu + \frac{a}{kn} + \frac{b}{k^2n^2} + \cdots$$

From these it follows that the expectation of the pseudovalue Y_j^* is

$$\mathscr{E}(Y_j^*) = \mathscr{E}(kY - (k-1)Y_j) = \mu - \frac{b}{n^2k(k-1)} + \cdots,$$

the terms which remain beyond μ being clearly negligible with the size of n and k used in practice. The principal bias term has vanished.

To apply the jackknife to a simple design, suppose that we seek the intrinsic rate of natural increase r for a population on which census and registration are lacking. To gather primary data we partition the territory to be sampled into 1000 sampling units; 75 of these units are selected at random to constitute the sample; the sample is then considered as consisting of $k = 15$ groups of $n = 5$ sampling units each, the groups being randomly assembled. We define a pseudo-unit for Y_j from 14 of these groups, calculate from the observations on it the entire sequence of numbers from the observed births and deaths, through the female life table and net maternity function, and end up with r_j and the corresponding pseudovalue r_j^*. This calculation would be carried out 15 times in all, yielding 15 unbiased estimates $r_1^*, \ldots, r_{15}^*$. Replacing Y by r in (15.3.2) and (15.3.3) provides the desired estimate of r and its variance. The considerable amount of arithmetic offers no difficulty with a computer.

The jackknife is useful with area samples based on maps, whether or not preceding information in the form of out-of-date censuses and uncertain registrations of births and deaths is on hand.

Deming and Keyfitz (1967) supposed a situation in which no such material, not even maps, was on hand, and a sample of points rather than areas was to be used to determine the number of people. Adapting methods developed for wild-life surveys (Bailey, 1951; Chapman, 1955; Goodman, 1953a; Leslie, 1952), they present estimates of total population as a function of the number of individuals encountered by wandering enumerators who go out on a first occasion and meet n_1 persons, then go out on a second occasion and meet n_2, of whom n_{12} are common to the two occasions. A simple estimate of the total is obtained by applying n_2/n_{12} as a raising factor to n_1, giving n_1n_2/n_{12}. The maximum-likelihood estimate of the total population, if n_1, n_2, and n_{12} are all random variables, is $(n_1 + n_2)^2/4n_{12}$. In practice this would be a residual method, possibly of use for those missed in the initial enumeration of a regular census.

CONCLUSION

Some indication has been given of the variation of population parameters under random sampling. This is not the same as variation in the population phenomenon itself. The latter, closer to the substance of demography, is best brought out in formal stochastic models, and to these we now proceed.

CHAPTER 16

BIRTH AND DEATH PROCESSES

With the partial exception of Chapter 15, we have so far treated population processes as deterministic, accepting expected values as the inevitable outcome of each trial. The word "probability" indeed occurs, for instance in the application of the life table to ascertain whether an individual will survive, but we have lost the variation among groups to whom the same probabilities are applied. The mathematical difficulties of realistic probability models are considerable, and in this area a highly technical literature exists, to which references will be found in Bailey (1964), Bartlett (1960), and Bharucha-Reid (1960). Three models will be taken up here—the pure birth process; the birth, death, and immigration process; and the problem of the sexes. The ideas originated with Yule (1924), Feller (1939), Kendall (1949), and Goodman (1953).

A Computer Simulation

To suggest some features of probability models of population, a simple birth and death process, not recognizing age distinctions, will be reported. Suppose $\lambda = 0.0194$ and $\mu = 0.0094$, these being approximately the current crude birth and death rates of the United States. We start with 100 individuals, and for the first year we ask the random-number generator of the computer whether the first individual will live or die. We do this by calling for a four-digit number in a rectangular distribution between 0 and 1; a number less than 0.0094 is interpreted as meaning that he will die; a number from 0.0094 to 0.9999 means that he will live. The same procedure is applied to each of the other individuals. Then the question of giving birth is asked in respect of each. The result for year 0 in our first trial was 3 deaths and 1 birth (against expected 0.94 and 1.94 respectively). Subtracting the 3 deaths and adding the 1 birth gives 98 individuals at the start of year 1. Table 16.1 shows the first 15 years of the first simulation, which was continued for 100 years and then repeated 19 more times. All of this, including the drawing of 400,000 random numbers, was completed by the CDC 6400 in a little more than half a minute. I am indebted to Frank Oechsli for developing the program.

For the 100-year period the 20 simulations ended with the following numbers of individuals alive in the hypothetical closed community: 223, 224, 266,

Table 16.1 First 15 years of first simulation of birth and death process; $\lambda = 0.0194$; $\mu = 0.0094$*

YEAR	POPULATION AT BEGINNING OF YEAR	BIRTHS DURING YEAR	DEATHS DURING YEAR
0	100	1	3
1	98	1	0
2	99	0	1
3	98	1	2
4	97	5	1
5	101	2	0
6	103	2	0
7	105	3	1
8	107	2	3
9	106	1	2
10	105	3	1
11	107	2	1
12	108	2	1
13	109	2	2
14	109	5	0
15	114		

* Programmed by Frank Oechsli.

304, 298, 236, 255, 300, 192, 298, 315, 258, 290, 225, 272, 295, 261, 371, 273, 274. The mean of these numbers is 271.5, the population variance inferred from them is 1627, and standard deviation 40.3, if they are considered as a sample with 19 degrees of freedom.

How does this compare with theory? The mean, at least, is closer than we have a right to expect. The expected number at the end of 100 years is $100e^{(\lambda-\mu)100} = 271.8$, according to the theory expressed in (16.2.13b) below, and in the stable population model of Chapters 5 and 7. The variance estimated from our observations was 1627, larger than 1345 calculated from (16.2.13a), but a reference to the distribution of χ^2 for 19 degrees of freedom gives a probability of about 0.25 for an equal or greater excess. Of the 20 trials, the range 272 ± 40, or 232 to 312, embraces some 15, close to the expected number if the distribution is normal. Table 16.2 shows mean and dispersion among the 20 trials at 10-year intervals, along with the expected mean and variance at each point of time.

The corresponding pure birth process, in which $\lambda = 0.01$ and $\mu = 0.0$, gives the same expected values, but by comparing (16.1.7) and (16.2.13a) we see that the expected variance is only 1/2.88 times as great; at 100 years in the example of Table 16.2, the expected variance would be 467.

Table 16.2 Summary of 20 trials of birth and death process; $\lambda = 0.0194$; $\mu = 0.0094$*

	MEAN		VARIANCE	
TIME	OBSERVED IN SIMULATION	EXPECTED FROM (16.2.13b)	OBSERVED IN SIMULATION	EXPECTED FROM (16.2.13a)
0	100.0	100.0	0	0
10	111.9	110.5	38.7	33.4
20	123.3	122.1	52.0	77.7
30	136.9	135.0	122.9	136.1
40	149.5	149.2	217.3	211.4
50	165.0	164.9	394.8	308.2
60	181.4	182.2	489.6	431.3
70	198.0	201.4	630.4	588.2
80	221.6	222.6	950.4	786.0
90	247.2	246.0	1293.9	1034.4
100	271.5	271.8	1627.0	1344.8

* Programmed by Frank Oechsli.

After a comment on the nature and application of differentials, we turn to the development of the theory, starting with the pure birth process.

Differential Elements of Birth and Death

Common to the situations discussed below is a birth rate λ, and the probability for each individual of giving birth to a new individual of the same sex during the short interval of length dt is $\lambda\,dt$. A basic assumption throughout will be that the several individuals are independently subject to the given probabilities. Hence, for example, the chance of no births among n individuals in time dt is $(1 - \lambda\,dt)^n$; the chance of exactly one birth is $n(1 - \lambda\,dt)^{n-1}\lambda\,dt$, etc. As dt becomes indefinitely small, any expressions of which $(dt)^2$ is a factor become negligible, so that we may write $(1 - \lambda\,dt)^n \doteq 1 - n\lambda\,dt$ for the probability in time dt of 0 births, and $n\lambda\,dt$ for the probability of 1 birth. The event of two or more births in time dt will have probability of lower order of magnitude than these and may be disregarded. When more than one contingency is introduced, for example birth and death, the probabilities of each will apply to individuals again independently, and no more than one contingency need be considered in an infinitesimal period; having a birth *and* dying in time dt may be excluded, even for different individuals in a large population.

16.1. THE PURE BIRTH PROCESS AND ITS EXTENSIONS

If the probability of an individual giving birth in time dt is $\lambda\, dt$, then, as we saw, the probability of one birth among n individuals is $n\lambda\, dt$. Call $p_n(t + dt)$ the probability that the population will have arrived at number n by time $t + dt$. Then if dt is small enough, the probability $p_n(t + dt)$ is the sum of only two mutually exclusive contingencies: (a) that the population numbers n by time t and there is no birth in time t to $t + dt$, and (b) that it numbers $n - 1$ by time t and there is one birth in time t to $t + dt$. In symbols:

$$p_n(t + dt) = p_n(t)(1 - n\lambda\, dt) + p_{n-1}(t)\big((n - 1)\lambda\, dt\big)\,. \qquad (16.1.1)$$

Transposing $p_n(t)$ to the left and dividing by dt,

$$\frac{p_n(t + dt) - p_n(t)}{dt} = -p_n(t)n\lambda + p_{n-1}(t)(n - 1)\lambda\,,$$

and proceeding to the limit as dt becomes small,

$$p_n'(t) = -p_n(t)n\lambda + p_{n-1}(t)(n - 1)\lambda\,, \quad n = 1, 2, \ldots; \qquad (16.1.2)$$

in particular, for $n = 1$,

$$p_1'(t) = -p_1(t)\lambda\,,$$

and we define $p_n(t)$ as 0 for $n \le 0$.

Though (16.1.2) is an infinite set, the equation for any particular value of n may be solved without taking account of higher n. The solution (Yule, 1924) is

$$p_n(t) = e^{-\lambda t}(1 - e^{-\lambda t})^{n-1}\,, \quad n = 1, 2, \ldots, \qquad (16.1.3)$$

the probability of n individuals by time t when the initial condition is one individual, as may be verified on substitution in (16.1.2) (Furry, 1937, p. 571; Bharucha-Reid, 1960, p. 78). The total, $\sum_{n=1}^{\infty} p_n(t)$, from (16.1.3) is evidently 1 for any given time t, as is required if $p_n(t)$ is to be the probability distribution of the discrete variable n.

The expected value of n at time t must be, from (16.1.3),

$$\mathscr{E}(n) = \sum_{n=1}^{\infty} ne^{-\lambda t}(1 - e^{-\lambda t})^{n-1}\,,$$

and summing the series gives

$$\mathscr{E}(n) = e^{\lambda t}\,.$$

This is also the solution starting with one individual for the continuous deterministic case where the increase is $n\lambda$ with certainty, expressed by the condition

$$dn/dt = n\lambda\,,$$

as we have found in Eq. (13.1.2) and elsewhere. We can say for all the cases treated in this chapter, though not in general, that the deterministic model *mimics* the probability model, at least in coming up with the correct expected value.

The solution with an initial condition of one individual is unduly restricted. An easy way to extend it to several individuals is to set up a probability generating function in the form

$$\phi(z, t) = p_0(t) + p_1(t)z + p_2(t)z^2 + \cdots + p_n(t)z^n + \cdots, \tag{16.1.4}$$

similar to the generating function of Section 5.8 in that z is a variable whose exponents keep track of the coefficients by carrying them along with its powers. If the probability-generating function for an initial condition of one individual is $\phi(z, t)$, then the generating function for two individuals will be $[\phi(z, t)]^2$. For by the rules for multiplication of polynomials:

$$[\phi(z, t)]^2 = [p_0(t)]^2 + [2p_0(t)p_1(t)]z + \cdots,$$

and these coefficients of the powers of z are the chances of zero, one,... individuals at time t. The reader may satisfy himself that the rules for the combination of probabilities to find the chances of zero, one, two,... individuals at time t are the same as the rules for the multiplication of $\phi(z, t)$ by itself to find the coefficients of $z^0, z^1, z^2, \ldots$ The generating function with n_0 individuals at the outset is $[\phi(z, t)]^{n_0}$.

By differentiating the generating function (16.1.4) with respect to z,

$$\frac{\partial\phi(z, t)}{\partial z} = p_1(t) + 2p_2(t)z + 3p_3(t)z^2 + \cdots + np_n(t)z^{n-1} + \cdots,$$

and putting $z = 1$, we have the expected value of n, the number of persons by time t, whenever the series for $\phi(z, t)$ converges uniformly. If we start with one individual the rth factorial moment about zero of the distribution of n at time t can be found by differentiating $\phi(z, t)$ r times and then equating z to 1; for the second factorial moment this is

$$\mathscr{E}n(n - 1) = \left.\frac{\partial^2\phi(z, t)}{\partial z^2}\right|_{z=1}.$$

The probability of the population having n members at time t is $1/n!$ times the nth derivative with respect to z of the generating function when $z = 0$:

$$p_n(t) = \left.\frac{\phi^{(n)}(z, t)}{n!}\right|_{z=0}.$$

Starting with one individual the generating function for the pure birth process is, from (16.1.3),

$$\phi(z, t) = ze^{-\lambda t} + z^2e^{-\lambda t}(1 - e^{-\lambda t}) + z^3e^{-\lambda t}(1 - e^{-\lambda t})^2 + \cdots, \tag{16.1.5}$$

where there is no absolute term, as accords with a process whose probability of extinction is zero. Equation (16.1.5) sums to

$$\phi(z, t) = \frac{ze^{-\lambda t}}{1 - z(1 - e^{-\lambda t})} . \tag{16.1.6}$$

By differentiation and then putting $z = 1$, the reader may show that the number of individuals expected at time t is $e^{\lambda t}$ as before. He may also differentiate (16.1.6) twice to obtain $\mathscr{E}(n)(n - 1)$ and show the variance to be

$$\mathscr{E}(n)(n - 1) + \mathscr{E}n - (\mathscr{E}n)^2 = e^{\lambda t}(e^{\lambda t} - 1) . \tag{16.1.7}$$

To study the distribution $p_n(t)$ starting with n_0 individuals, we need only examine the properties of the n_0th power of the generating function $\phi(z, t)$, or

$$(\phi(z, t))^{n_0} = \left(\frac{ze^{-\lambda t}}{1 - z(1 - e^{-\lambda t})}\right)^{n_0}, \tag{16.1.8}$$

from which the several cumulants will be found to be n_0 times the cumulants starting with one individual. (See Section 5.6 for the definition of cumulant and an analogous property of the renewal equation for successive generations.)

The pure birth process can be made to serve as the model for a human population, though the fit is crude. The United States in 1962 had a female net reproduction rate of 1.633. Interpret this as an increment in each generation of 0.633 of a person for each person alive, and measure t in generations. Then $\lambda = \ln 1.633$, and the result $\mathscr{E}n = e^{\lambda t}$ tells us that the increase would be 63% per generation, just as in the deterministic model. But now we can also say what the chance is that 7 girl children just born would have 11 great-grand-children, that is, would increase to exactly 11 by the end of three generations. This is given by the coefficient of z^{11} for $t = 3$ and $n_0 = 7$ in (16.1.8), which is

$$e^{-7\lambda t}\left(\frac{(7)(8)(9)(10)}{(1)(2)(3)(4)}\right)(1 - e^{-\lambda t})^4 = 0.00249 . \tag{16.1.9}$$

Set forth the assumptions to which this result is subject. At least one of these will be relaxed in the model of the next section.

16.2. A BIRTH, DEATH, AND IMMIGRATION MODEL

We approach closer to demographic reality by positing births, deaths, and immigration (Kendall, 1949, p. 241), though still without recognizing sex or age. The birth rate is λ, the death rate μ, and immigration is ν. We think of λ and μ as probabilities to be applied to the individuals present; ν on the other hand is a fixed absolute number and not related to the population attained. (Any component of immigration that is proportional to population can be simply incorporated in λ.)

Again we start by considering the period $(0, t + dt)$ divided into $(0, t)$ and $(t, t + dt)$. The chance that there are n individuals in the population by time $t + dt$ is equal to the chance

a) that there are n individuals by time t and nothing happens between t and $t + dt$,
b) that there are $n - 1$ individuals by time t and 1 is added by birth or immigration in $(t, t + dt)$,
c) that there are $n + 1$ individuals by time t and 1 dies in $(t, t + dt)$.

These three mutually exclusive cases constitute all the possibilities, since again we are assuming dt sufficiently small that it cannot harbor two events. The process may start with zero individuals (the immigration component makes this admissible). Once again what happens to each person as the process works itself out is assumed to be independent of what happens to each other person, and the probabilites are taken to be constant as among individuals and times.

Expressing the probabilities of (a), (b), and (c) symbolically gives

$$\begin{aligned} p_n(t + dt) &= p_n(t)\big(1 - (n\lambda + n\mu + \nu)\,dt\big) \\ &\quad + p_{n-1}(t)\big((n-1)\lambda + \nu\big)\,dt + p_{n+1}(t)(n+1)\mu\,dt\,. \end{aligned} \tag{16.2.1}$$

Again transposing $p_n(t)$ from the right to the left, dividing through by dt, and proceeding to the limit as dt tends to zero,

$$\begin{aligned} p_n'(t) &= -(n\lambda + n\mu + \nu)p_n(t) + [(n-1)\lambda + \nu]p_{n-1}(t) \\ &\quad + (n+1)\mu p_{n+1}(t), \quad n = 0, 1, 2, \ldots \end{aligned} \tag{16.2.2}$$

The reader may verify that if $p_n(t)$ is defined as 0 for $n < 0$, then (16.2.2) applies for all nonnegative n including $n = 0$.

The infinite set of differential-difference equations (16.2.2) can be converted into a single equation in the probability-generating function. Multiplying the first member by 1, the second by z, the third by z^2, etc. results in the set

$$\begin{aligned} p_n'(t)z^n &= -(\lambda + \mu)p_n(t)z(z^n)' - \nu p_n(t)z^n + \lambda z^2 p_{n-1}(t)(z^{n-1})' \\ &\quad + \mu p_{n+1}(t)(z^{n+1})' + \nu p_{n-1}(t)z^n\,, \quad n = 0, 1, 2, \ldots, \end{aligned} \qquad (16.2,3)$$

where primes indicate differentiation with respect to t on the left and to z on the right. [The reader may verify (16.2.3) by observing, for example, that the first term on the right is $-(n\lambda + n\mu)p_n(t)z^n$, and so accords with (16.2.2).] Adding (16.2.3) over all n, we obtain an equation in the generating function $\phi(z, t)$ of (16.1.4):

$$\frac{\partial\phi(z, t)}{\partial t} = (\lambda z - \mu)(z - 1)\frac{\partial\phi(z, t)}{\partial z} + \nu(z - 1)\phi(z, t)\,. \tag{16.2.4}$$

Thus we have a linear partial differential equation with a term due to immigration that does not involve a derivative. The auxiliary pair of equations

(Wilson, 1958, p. 267) from which we can find the general form of solution of (16.2.4) is

$$-\frac{dt}{1} = \frac{dz}{(\lambda z - \mu)(z - 1)} = -\frac{d\phi}{\nu(z - 1)\phi}\,.$$

Solving the first,

$$-dt = \frac{dz}{(\lambda z - \mu)(z - 1)}\,,$$

the reader will obtain

$$\left(\frac{\lambda z - \mu}{z - 1}\right) e^{-(\lambda - \mu)t} = C\,, \tag{16.2.5}$$

where C is a constant. Then, solving

$$\frac{dz}{(\lambda z - \mu)(z - 1)} = -\frac{d\phi}{\nu(z - 1)\phi}\,,$$

he will find

$$K = (\lambda z - \mu)\phi^{\lambda/\nu}\,, \tag{16.2.6}$$

where K is a constant. From (16.2.5) and (16.2.6) the general solution is $K = \Phi(C)$, or

$$(\lambda z - \mu)\phi^{\lambda/\nu} = \Phi\left[\left(\frac{\lambda z - \mu}{z - 1}\right) e^{-(\lambda - \mu)t}\right], \tag{16.2.7}$$

which satisfies (16.2.4) for any Φ, as may be verified by differentiation.

Equation (16.2.7) relates our generating function ϕ to the two variables t and z, irrespective of the nature of the arbitrary function Φ and subject only to some very general restrictions, such as that Φ is differentiable. Like the arbitrary constant in an ordinary differential equation, Φ permits us to fit to a boundary condition. In this case we can come down to something specific by the initial condition of starting with 0 population at time 0, i. e., with $\phi(z, 0) = 1$. Putting $t = 0$ and $\phi = 1$ turns (16.2.7) into

$$(\lambda z - \mu) = \Phi\left(\frac{\lambda z - \mu}{z - 1}\right). \tag{16.2.8}$$

Writing Z for $[(\lambda z - \mu)/(z - 1)]$, the argument of Φ in (16.2.8), we have z in terms of Z as

$$z = \frac{Z - \mu}{Z - \lambda}\,.$$

Substituting this value for z in (16.2.8) gives

$$\lambda\left(\frac{Z - \mu}{Z - \lambda}\right) - \mu = \Phi(Z)\,,$$

or

$$\Phi(Z) = \frac{Z(\lambda - \mu)}{Z - \lambda}\,, \tag{16.2.9}$$

as the form of the function Φ.

For the final result we need only use the function specified in (16.2.9) with the argument of Φ in (16.2.7), and this alters (16.2.7) to the specific form

$$(\lambda z - \mu)\phi^{\lambda/\nu} = \frac{(\lambda - \mu)(\lambda z - \mu)}{\lambda z - \mu - \lambda(z - 1)e^{(\lambda-\mu)t}},$$

or

$$\phi = \left(\frac{\lambda - \mu}{\lambda z - \mu - \lambda(z - 1)e^{(\lambda-\mu)t}}\right)^{\nu/\lambda}, \tag{16.2.10}$$

which may be expressed in ascending powers of z by writing it

$$\phi(z, t) = \left(\frac{\lambda - \mu}{\lambda e^{(\lambda-\mu)t} - \mu}\right)^{\nu/\lambda}\left(1 - z\,\frac{\lambda(e^{(\lambda-\mu)t} - 1)}{\lambda e^{(\lambda-\mu)t} - \mu}\right)^{-\nu/\lambda} \tag{16.2.11}$$

and expanding the last factor by the binomial theorem. The probability at time t of there being zero persons is the absolute term in the expansion of (16.2.11):

$$\left(\frac{\lambda - \mu}{\lambda e^{(\lambda-\mu)t} - \mu}\right)^{\nu/\lambda}. \tag{16.2.12}$$

The reader can write down the probability of exactly one person at time t and find the expected number of persons at time t.

In the present model immigration is permitted, and thus extinction cannot occur. The population may drop down to zero, but it continues to have the probability $\nu\,dt$ of an immigrant in each interval dt, or the probability $1 - \nu\,dt$ of not receiving an immigrant. The probability of at least one immigrant in t years is $1 - e^{-\nu t}$, which approaches 1 or certainty as t becomes large. In the language of the random walk, "extinction" is not an absorbing barrier here as it is in a birth and death process. We took advantage of this in using an initial condition consisting of zero persons.

By the same token we cannot simply put $\nu = 0$ in (16.2.11) to establish the generating function for the birth and death process without immigration. It is necessary to revert to (16.2.4) and observe that it reduces to

$$\frac{\partial\phi(z, t)}{\partial t} = (\lambda z - \mu)(z - 1)\,\frac{\partial\phi(z, t)}{\partial z}.$$

The set of auxiliary equations is now

$$-dt = \frac{dz}{(\lambda z - \mu)(z - 1)},$$

which is solved as before to give (16.2.5). By following a simpler version of the argument that led to (16.2.11), the reader can verify that starting with a population of one individual, that is, with $\phi(z, 0) = z$, gives the generating function

$$\phi(z, t) = \left(\frac{\mu(e^{(\lambda-\mu)t} - 1) - z(\mu e^{(\lambda-\mu)t} - \lambda)}{\lambda e^{(\lambda-\mu)t} - \mu}\right)\left(1 - z\,\frac{\lambda(e^{(\lambda-\mu)t} - 1)}{\lambda e^{(\lambda-\mu)t} - \mu}\right)^{-1}. \tag{16.2.13}$$

He may expand (16.2.13) in ascending powers of z to establish on this slightly more realistic model the chance that 7 girl children just born will have 11 descendants at the end of three generations, given now that the net reproduction rate of 1.633 is made up of a gross reproduction rate $\lambda = \ln 1.690$ less a chance of dying $\mu = \ln(1.690/1.633) = .0343$. Compare with (16.1.9).

By differentiating (16.2.13) twice and equating z to unity, we find the first two factorial moments, $\mathscr{E}n$ and $\mathscr{E}n(n-1)$, of the survivors of the birth and death process at time t. From these the variance is obtained as

$$\mathscr{E}(n)(n-1) + \mathscr{E}n - (\mathscr{E}n)^2 = \frac{\lambda + \mu}{\lambda - \mu} e^{(\lambda-\mu)t}(e^{(\lambda-\mu)t} - 1), \quad (16.2.13a)$$

and this, along with the mean

$$\mathscr{E}n = e^{(\lambda-\mu)t}, \quad (16.2.13b)$$

constitutes an approximate description of the process.

For a given difference between λ and μ the expected value of the population at time t will not be affected by whether λ and μ are large or small. But the variance is very much affected. Suppose positive k is added to each of λ and μ. Then the exponential factors of (16.2.13a) and (16.2.13b) remain unchanged, but the reader can show that variance is $1 + 2k/(\lambda + \mu)$ times as large. If a given starting population is growing at $\frac{1}{2}\%$ per year with $\lambda = 0.045$ and $\mu = 0.040$, it will have 3.4 times as large a variance at time t as it would if it were increasing with $\lambda = 0.015$ and $\mu = 0.010$.

Extinction

The probability of extinction is obtained by putting $z = 0$ in (16.2.13) and allowing t to increase indefinitely:

$$\lim_{t\to\infty} \phi(0, t) = \lim_{t\to\infty} \frac{\mu(e^{(\lambda-\mu)t} - 1)}{\lambda e^{(\lambda-\mu)t} - \mu}. \quad (16.2.14)$$

This limit is qualitatively different when $\lambda - \mu$ is positive and when it is negative. For $\lambda > \mu$ the quantity $e^{(\lambda-\mu)t}$ increases indefinitely, and the other terms in the numerator and denominator may be neglected; the limit is μ/λ. For $\lambda < \mu$ the exponentials become negligible, and the ratio is one in the limit. Thus when the birth rate is greater than the death rate, the probability of extinction is the ratio of the death rate to the birth rate; when the birth rate is smaller than the death rate, extinction is certain.

When the process starts with n_0 persons rather than 1, the generating function in (16.2.13) (and hence its absolute term) is raised to the n_0th power. Alternatively and more directly, if there are n_0 individuals and each has a probability μ/λ that his line will die out, then the probability that all n_0 will die out is the product of the separate probabilities, $(\mu/\lambda)^{n_0}$, still assuming the lines develop independently and only one sex is considered.

Of special interest is the case $\lambda = \mu$, which corresponds to the deterministic model denoted as "stationary" in Chapter 1. The argument for ascertaining the probability of extinction must again be modified, for (16.2.14) as it stands is indeterminate with $\lambda = \mu$. The reader may show that when λ approaches μ from below in (16.2.14), the double limit $\lim_{\lambda\to\mu}\{\lim_{t\to\infty}[\phi(0, t)]\}$ is equal to one. He will also be able to obtain the same result by having λ approach μ from above.

Thus extinction is certain in a stationary population consisting initially of one person. By a similar limiting process extinction may also be shown to be certain in a population initially consisting of n_0 individuals, no matter how large n_0 is, provided the n_0 is given in advance. We face the paradox that a population which on the deterministic model is called stationary, in which the probability of birth is equal to that of death, has a probability of extinction equal to one. The so-called stationary population is certain to disappear, and this no matter how large it may be at the outset, as soon as we shift from a deterministic to a probability form of analysis.

However, this is only true when the same condition (equal chance of birth and death) applies to all individuals. If there is some subgroup of the n_0 that has a positive $\lambda - \mu$, then it will have a chance of extinction less than one. The condition of homogeneity is essential to the argument of the preceding paragraph.

Although the probability of extinction is unity, yet even for a small starting population it may take a considerable time for extinction to occur. Frank Oechsli has computed 50 replications of an instance in which the starting population was 1, and both λ and μ were 0.2; this may be thought of as a population initially of 1 person, dealt with in 10-year cycles, in which the birth rate was 20 per thousand per year, and the death rate also 20 per thousand per year. Running the program for 100 ten-year cycles is the equivalent of running for 1000 years. The resulting extinction times were as follows, translated into years:

Period of extinction (Years)	No. of cases
-10	11
10–19	8
20–29	5
30–39	2
40–49	3
	29

In addition, there were single cases of extinction after 60, 60, 70, 80, 80, 90, 90, 130, 150, 180, 180, 210, 220, 230, 410, 570, 600, 740, and 960 years. In two instances, extinction was not attained by the end of 1000 years, at which time the two populations contained 10 and 17 individuals. Either one of these last cases could go on for thousands of years more, even with the minimum starting value of one individual. In fact the expected time to extinction is $(-\mu/\lambda)\ln(1-\lambda/\mu)$, which is infinite for $\lambda = \mu$.

On the female age-specific fertility and mortality of the United States in 1965, the intrinsic rates of birth and death are $1000\lambda = 21.29$ and $1000\mu = 8.64$, and hence the chance μ/λ of the line of female descent of a given woman dying out is 0.41. This quantity varies considerably with movement in the intrinsic birth and death rates. In 1959–61 they were, respectively, $1000\lambda = 27.65$ and $1000\mu = 6.52$, and on these the probability of extinction of a female line is down to 0.24. For 1939–41, $1000\lambda = 15.78$, $1000\mu = 14.84$, and the probability of extinction μ/λ rises to 0.94 (officially adjusted births used for all periods). The branching process of Chapter 18 is a more precise way of finding the probability of extinction, but it requires data on the probability of a woman having 0, 1, 2, ... daughters. [What set of such probabilities does the present birth and death process implicitly assume?]

16.3. THE PROBLEM OF THE SEXES TREATED STOCHASTICALLY

The probability analysis of the problem of the sexes, treated deterministically in Chapter 13, is an extension of the foregoing ideas. We will discuss the trajectory (in the sense of a probability distribution at each moment of time) of a population which starts with a given number of males and females, assuming sex-specific birth and death rates, and some kind of dominance, which is to say some rule for attaching births to parents. In our exposition, births will be attached to females only; the restriction is not essential, but it would be tedious to remove it. The entire original literature on this subject seems to consist of a few paragraphs at the end of a paper by Leo A. Goodman (1953b), on which the following account is based. We will later see how this result fits into a very general procedure due to John H. Pollard (1966).

The problem is to find the probability distribution of numbers of males and females at time t in a population which starts with m_0 males and f_0 females and in which male and female death rates are d_m and d_f and male and female birth rates b_m and b_f. If the number of females is f, the probability of a male birth in time dt will be $fb_m\,dt$, and of a female birth $fb_f\,dt$; b_m is best made equal to b_f multiplied by the ratio of males to females at birth.

We seek for time t the probabilities of all combinations of m and f, the numbers of males and females, denoting the probability of extinction by time t as $p_{0,0}(t)$, the probability of zero males and one female by time t as $p_{0,1}(t)$, etc. (The first subscript of p will always stand for males and the second for females.) The probability $p_{m,f}(t+dt)$ that there will be a population consisting of m males and f females at the end of the period $(0, t+dt)$ must be equal to the sum of the probabilities for the five mutually exclusive cases:

a) that there be m males and f females by time t and no births and no deaths in $(t, t+dt)$,

b) that there be $m - 1$ males and f females by time t and one male birth in $(t, t + dt)$,
c) that there be m males and $f - 1$ females by time t and one female birth in $(t, t + dt)$,
d) that there be $m + 1$ males and f females by time t and one male death in $(t, t + dt)$,
e) that there be m males and $f + 1$ females by time t and one female death in $(t, t + dt)$.

Expressed in the symbols defined above this means that

$$p_{m,f}(t + dt) = \big(1 - (md_m + fd_f + fb_m + fb_f)\,dt\big)p_{m,f}(t) \qquad (16.3.1a)$$
$$+ b_m f p_{m-1,f}(t)\,dt \qquad (16.3.1b)$$
$$+ b_f(f - 1)p_{m,f-1}(t)\,dt \qquad (16.3.1c)$$
$$+ d_m(m + 1)p_{m+1,f}(t)\,dt \qquad (16.3.1d)$$
$$+ d_f(f + 1)p_{m,f+1}(t)\,dt \qquad (16.3.1e)$$

$m = 0, 1, 2, \ldots, f = 0, 1, 2, \ldots,$ where the five lines correspond to the five possibilities previously lettered (a) to (e). Subtracting $p_{m,f}(t)$ from both sides, dividing through by dt, and proceeding to the limit as dt tends to zero, (16.3.1) becomes the doubly infinite set of linear first-order differential equations with constant coefficients:

$$\frac{dp_{m,f}(t)}{dt} = -(md_m + fd_f + fb_m + fb_f)p_{m,f}(t) \qquad (16.3.2a)$$
$$+ b_m f p_{m-1,f}(t) \qquad (16.3.2b)$$
$$+ b_f(f - 1)p_{m,f-1}(t) \qquad (16.3.2c)$$
$$+ d_m(m + 1)p_{m+1,f}(t) \qquad (16.3.2d)$$
$$+ d_f(f + 1)p_{m,f+1}(t) \qquad (16.3.2e)$$

$m = 0, 1, 2, \ldots, f = 0, 1, 2, \ldots.$ So as not to have to think about what happens to (16.3.2) for small m and f, we define $p_{m,f}(t)$ as zero for all m or f negative.

As before, we create a probability-generating function. The typical member, $p_{m,f}(t)$, of the doubly infinite set is multiplied by $z_1^m z_2^f$, where again the numbers z_1 and z_2 have no meaning outside of the fact that the probability of m males and f females is associated with the coefficient of $z_1^m z_2^f$. The function $\phi(z_1, z_2, t)$ is defined by

$$\phi(z_1, z_2, t) = \sum_{m,f=0}^{\infty} p_{m,f}(t) z_1^m z_2^f \,. \qquad (16.3.3)$$

With the help of this function we shall be able to condense the doubly infinite set, Eqs. (16.3.2), into one single equation. Multiplication of (16.3.2) by $z_1^m z_2^f$

gives, after addition through all m and f,

$$\frac{\partial\phi}{\partial t} = -d_m z_1 \frac{\partial\phi}{\partial z_1} - (d_f + b_m + b_f)z_2 \frac{\partial\phi}{\partial z_2} \tag{a}$$

$$+ b_m z_1 z_2 \frac{\partial\phi}{\partial z_2} \tag{b}$$

$$+ b_f z_2^2 \frac{\partial\phi}{\partial z_2} \tag{c}$$

$$+ d_m \frac{\partial\phi}{\partial z_1} \tag{d}$$

$$+ d_f \frac{\partial\phi}{\partial z_2} \tag{e}$$

and collecting together the coefficients of $\partial\phi(z_1, z_2, t)/\partial z_1$ and $\partial\phi(z_1, z_2, t)/\partial z_2$ on the right-hand side we have a relatively simple equation which describes the entire process:

$$\frac{\partial\phi}{\partial t} = d_m(1 - z_1)\frac{\partial\phi}{\partial z_1} + \big(-(b_m + b_f + d_f)z_2 + b_m z_1 z_2 + b_f z_2^2 + d_f\big)\frac{\partial\phi}{\partial z_2}. \tag{16.3.4}$$

The direct solution of (16.3.4) by the method exemplified in (16.2.3) leads to auxiliary ordinary differential equations whose variables cannot be separated. Since we cannot solve for $\phi(z_1, z_2, t)$, we turn our attention to relations among moments.

Moments are found by differentiating (16.3.4), which we will here suppose permissible. The first derivative of (16.3.4) with respect to z_1 is

$$\frac{\partial^2\phi}{\partial t\,\partial z_1} = -d_m \frac{\partial\phi}{\partial z_1} + d_m(1 - z_1)\frac{\partial^2\phi}{\partial z_1^2} + b_m z_2 \frac{\partial\phi}{\partial z_2} + \big(-(b_m + b_f + d_f)z_2 + b_m z_1 z_2 + b_f z_2^2 + d_f\big)\frac{\partial^2\phi}{\partial z_1\,\partial z_2}.$$

This shakes down considerably when we put $z_1 = z_2 = 1$:

$$\frac{\partial^2\phi}{\partial t\,\partial z_1} = -d_m \frac{\partial\phi}{\partial z_1} + b_m \frac{\partial\phi}{\partial z_2}. \tag{16.3.5}$$

Now $\partial\phi/\partial z_1$, evaluated at $z_1 = 1$, $z_2 = 1$, is $\mathscr{E}m$, the expected number or first moment of males at time t; the left-hand side of (16.3.5) is the derivative with respect to time of the first moment for males; hence (16.3.5) is the same as

$$d(\mathscr{E}m)/dt = -d_m\mathscr{E}m + b_m\mathscr{E}f. \tag{16.3.6}$$

In exactly the same way, with perfectly straightforward differentiation and subsequently making $z_1 = z_2 = 1$, we obtain the other four equations in the moments about zero (after converting from factorial to ordinary):

$$d(\mathscr{E}f)/dt = (b_f - d_f)\mathscr{E}f, \tag{16.3.7}$$

$$d(\mathscr{E}m^2)/dt = -2d_m\mathscr{E}m^2 + 2b_m\mathscr{E}mf + d_m\mathscr{E}m + b_m\mathscr{E}f, \tag{16.3.8}$$

$$d(\mathscr{E}mf)/dt = (b_f - d_f - d_m)\mathscr{E}mf + b_m\mathscr{E}f^2, \tag{16.3.9}$$

$$d(\mathscr{E}f^2)/dt = 2(b_f - d_f)\mathscr{E}f^2 + (b_f + d_f)\mathscr{E}f. \tag{16.3.10}$$

Equations (16.3.6) through (16.3.10) are a deterministic account of a stochastic process. To see how the means and variances change over time, the trajectory has been computed, using Taylor's theorem to second derivatives as in Section 13.2, and now advancing by intervals of $h = 0.1$ of a year for 250 years. The constants are those for Belgium, 1960:

$$1000b_m = 18.175; \quad 1000b_f = 17.309; \quad 1000d_m = 12.190; \quad 1000d_f = 10.930.$$

An excerpt from the output is given as Table 16.3.

Various properties of the process as t approaches 250 years may be noted:

a) $\mathscr{E}f$ is rising geometrically; the four other moments somewhat less rapidly than geometrically;
b) The ratio of increase over 0.1 of a year is 1.00064 for each of $\mathscr{E}m$ and $\mathscr{E}f$, corresponding to an exponential rate of 0.0064 on an annual basis. These accord with an ultimate stable rate suggested by the input of
$$b_f - d_f = 0.006379;$$
c) The three second moments are increasing at more than double the rate of the first moments, so that the second moments are roughly tending to multiples of the squares of the first moments;
d) The coefficient of correlation between m and f seems headed toward unity.

The 250 years of the table is not long enough for these relations to show exactly. Further speculation on them is unnecessary, however, since Eqs. (16.3.6) through (16.3.10) can be solved explicitly. They are a linear homogeneous set whose unknowns are the five first and second moments, and are dealt with especially easily because of the form which their coefficients take. Entering the trial solution a_ie^{rt}, $i = 1, 2, \ldots, 5$, for the five unknowns in (16.3.6) through (16.3.10) and then dividing by e^{rt} gives five linear homogeneous equations in r, and the condition for consistency among these is the determinantal equation obtained by eliminating the a_i:

$$\begin{vmatrix} -r - d_m & b_m & 0 & 0 & 0 \\ 0 & -r + b_f - d_f & 0 & 0 & 0 \\ d_m & b_m & -r - 2d_m & 2b_m & 0 \\ 0 & 0 & 0 & -r + b_f - d_f - d_m & b_m \\ 0 & b_f + d_f & 0 & 0 & -r + 2(b_f - d_f) \end{vmatrix} = 0. \tag{16.3.11}$$

Table 16.3 Path of first and second moments in two-sex process, starting with one female and traced from (16.3.6) ··· (16.3.10) in steps of 0.1 of a year, using Taylor's theorem to second derivatives; data of Belgium, 1960*

TIME YEARS	$\mathscr{E}$(m)	$\mathscr{E}$(f)	VAR(m)	COVAR (m,f)	VAR(f)	PEARSON r
0.0	0	1	0	0	0	0
5.0	0.0913	1.0321	0.0917	0.0067	0.1477	0.0573
10.0	0.1801	1.0652	0.1832	0.0273	0.3099	0.1145
20.0	0.3513	1.1347	0.3758	0.1142	0.6817	0.2257
30.0	0.5153	1.2088	0.5967	0.2695	1.1252	0.3289
40.0	0.6739	1.2876	0.8638	0.5029	1.6514	0.4211
50.0	0.8284	1.3716	1.1953	0.8262	2.2729	0.5013
60.0	0.9804	1.4611	1.6093	1.2526	3.0041	0.5697
70.0	1.1310	1.5564	2.1253	1.7974	3.8616	0.6274
80.0	1.2815	1.6580	2.7640	2.4782	4.8642	0.6759
90.0	1.4331	1.7661	3.5479	3.3153	6.0334	0.7166
100.0	1.5867	1.8813	4.5024	4.3320	7.3935	0.7508
125.0	1.9865	2.2034	7.8271	7.8433	11.8228	0.8153
150.0	2.4212	2.5805	12.9494	13.1860	18.1860	0.8593
175.0	2.9053	3.0222	20.6188	21.1034	27.2509	0.8903
200.0	3.4540	3.5395	31.8707	32.6294	40.0795	0.9130
225.0	4.0831	4.1453	48.1382	49.1986	58.1378	0.9300
249.9	4.8068	4.8518	71.2940	72.6860	83.3296	0.9430
250.0	4.8099	4.8549	71.4043	72.7976	83.4486	0.9431

* Programmed by Hardeo Sahai.

The five roots of (16.3.11) may be seen without calculation to be $-d_m$; $b_f - d_f$; $-2d_m$; $b_f - d_f - d_m$; $2(b_f - d_f)$. The general solution for the five expected values which are the unknowns in (16.3.6) through (16.3.10) is made up of the sum of its $a_{ij}e^{r_jt}$ for the several values of r_j which satisfy (16.3.11):

$$a_{i1}e^{-d_mt} + a_{i2}e^{(b_f-d_f)t} + a_{i3}e^{-2d_mt} + a_{i4}e^{(b_f-d_f-d_m)t} + a_{i5}e^{2(b_f-d_f)t}, \quad i = 1, 2, 3, 4, 5, \tag{16.3.12}$$

and the set of solutions would include 25 arbitrary constants. However, grouping the equations shows that 13 of the constants must be zero. We can solve for $\mathscr{E}f$ by itself, so it can have only one constant; we can solve for $\mathscr{E}f$ and $\mathscr{E}m$

without considering second moments, so $\mathscr{E}m$ can have only two constants; we can solve for $\mathscr{E}f$ and $\mathscr{E}f(f-1)$ without considering males, so $\mathscr{E}f(f-1)$ can have only two constants, etc. In short, Set (16.3.6) through (16.3.10) is decomposable or reducible, in a sense suggested by the nonnegative matrices of (2.1.12) and Section 3.2, although the matrix we are now dealing with differs from these earlier cases in containing negative elements.

The a_{ij} depend on the initial conditions, and in our first attack we make these just one female. It is easy enough to establish the several moments when $m_0 = 0$ and $f_0 = 1$: they are all 0 at $t = 0$ except $\mathscr{E}f = 1$.

Because Set (16.3.6) through (16.3.10) is decomposable we can dispense with general methods of solution which are available for linear differential equations with constant coefficients (Gantmacher, 1959, Vol. II, p. 116; Friedman, 1956, p. 120). If the solution is carried out in the sequence:

$$\begin{aligned}
&1)\ (16.3.7) \text{ for } \mathscr{E}f;\\
&2)\ (16.3.6) \text{ for } \mathscr{E}m \text{ and } (16.3.10) \text{ for } \mathscr{E}f^2, \text{ in either order};\\
&3)\ (16.3.9) \text{ for } \mathscr{E}mf;\\
&4)\ (16.3.8) \text{ for } \mathscr{E}m^2,
\end{aligned} \tag{16.3.13}$$

where the only option in the ordering is between $\mathscr{E}m$ and $\mathscr{E}f^2$, then the simple method that produced (13.2.5) may be followed. In fact, we already have solved for $\mathscr{E}f$ and $\mathscr{E}m$ in Chapter 13, and introducing the result of each successive solution in the next equation of Sequence (16.3.13) requires no new principle and yields all the a_{ij} of (16.3.12).

However, the values of the a's do not quite provide the means and variances which we seek. We want $\text{Var}(m) = \mathscr{E}(m - \mathscr{E}m)^2 = \mathscr{E}m^2 - (\mathscr{E}m)^2$, $\mathscr{E}(f - \mathscr{E}f)^2 = \mathscr{E}f^2 - (\mathscr{E}f)^2$, and $\mathscr{E}(m - \mathscr{E}m)(f - \mathscr{E}f) = \mathscr{E}mf - \mathscr{E}m\mathscr{E}f$, and the results for these which finally emerge after straightforward though extended algebra are

$$\begin{aligned}
\mathscr{E}m &= \frac{b_m}{d_m + b_f - d_f}\left(e^{(b_f-d_f)t} - e^{-d_m t}\right); \qquad \mathscr{E}f = e^{(b_f-d_f)t};\\
\text{Var}(m) &= \frac{(b_f + d_f)b_m^2}{(d_m + b_f - d_f)^2}\left(\frac{e^{2(b_f-d_f)t}}{b_f - d_f} - \frac{e^{-2d_m t}}{2d_m + b_f - d_f} + \frac{2e^{(b_f-d_f-d_m)t}}{d_m}\right)\\
&\quad + b_m e^{(b_f-d_f)t}\left(\frac{1}{d_m + b_f - d_f} - \frac{2b_m(b_f + d_f)}{d_m(b_f - d_f)(2d_m + b_f - d_f)}\right)\\
&\quad - \frac{b_m e^{-d_m t}}{d_m + b_f - d_f};\\
\text{Covar}(m, f) &= \frac{b_m(b_f + d_f)}{d_m + b_f - d_f}\left(\frac{e^{2(b_f-d_f)t}}{b_f - d_f} + \frac{e^{(b_f-d_f-d_m)t}}{d_m}\right) - \frac{b_m(b_f + d_f)e^{(b_f-d_f)t}}{d_m(b_f - d_f)};\\
\text{Var}(f) &= \frac{b_f + d_f}{b_f - d_f}\, e^{(b_f-d_f)t}\left(e^{(b_f-d_f)t} - 1\right).
\end{aligned} \tag{16.3.14}$$

Verify from (16.3.14) the asymptotic properties (a) through (d) suggested above by Table 16.3, the computed trajectory of Eqs. (16.3.6) through (16.3.10).

So far our work has been based on the initial condition of one female. To start with f_0 females rather than 1 requires no more adjustment to the above results than multiplying means, variances and covariance by f_0.

To start with m_0 males and zero females is a pure death process on our assumption of female dominance. The reader may show that at time t the expected male population will be $m_0e^{-d_mt}$ and the variance of the number of males $m_0(e^{-d_mt} - e^{-2d_mt})$.

We are now ready to write down the five moments for time t when the process starts with m_0 males and f_0 females. Appealing to the assumption that the several lines of descent of the population develop independently, we add the moments for an initial m_0 males and zero females to the moments for an initial zero males and f_0 females, to obtain for time t:

$$\mathscr{E}m = m_0e^{-d_mt} + f_0\frac{b_m}{d_m + b_f - d_f}(e^{(b_f-d_f)t} - e^{-d_mt}),$$

$$\mathscr{E}f = f_0e^{(b_f-d_f)t}. \tag{16.3.15}$$

(The identical equations (13.2.5) and (13.2.2) were found for the corresponding deterministic problem.) The variance of males is f_0 multiplied by Var (m) in (16.3.14) plus $m_0(e^{-d_mt} - e^{-2d_mt})$. The variance of females and the covariance are simply Var (f) and Covar (m, f) of (16.3.14) multiplied by f_0.

Simulation for Complex Processes

Joginder Kumar has simulated (Table 16.4) the two-sex process with female-dominant data derived from Belgium, 1960, for which intrinsic rates are as shown in the preceding example. He applied these probabilities to each individual in each five-year time period over 50 years in five-year cycles, and replicated 100 times, each time with an initial population of 100 males and 100 females. The experiment gave for the population by sex at the end of 50 years the hundred replications summarized in the second column of Table 16.4.

We now compare (16.3.14) and (16.3.15) with the results of this experiment. To do this multiply by 100 the values of moments at $t = 50$ (Table 16.3) to obtain the contributions to theoretical values in respect of the initial hundred females. For the initial hundred males, the contribution to $\mathscr{E}m$ is $100e^{-50d_m}$, and to Var (m) is $100e^{-50d_m}(1 - e^{-50d_m})$. These, added to the means and variances corresponding to $f_0 = 100$, $m_0 = 0$, make up the first column of Table 16.4.

The comparison is thus contained in the first two columns of Table 16.4. The four one-variable moments seem to agree, while the covariance and correlation appear to be significantly higher in the expected column than in the simulated. A larger test is evidently required to confirm the theory in detail.

Kumar also did the simulation by age in five-year groups, as reported in the third column of Table 16.4 which may be called a stochastic female-dominant projection by age. Again probabilities were applied to individuals, but within

Table 16.4 Moments of two-sex process after 50 years by (16.3.14) and as simulated; initial population 100 of each sex; 100 replications; data of Belgium, 1960*

	EXPECTED BY (16.3.14) WITHOUT AGE	SIMULATED WITHOUT AGE	SIMULATED WITH AGE
&(M(50))	137.20	132.51	141.88
&(F(50))	137.16	136.45	144.52
VAR(M(50))	144.34	133.97	99.79
COVAR(M,F)	82.62	51.80	31.41
VAR(F(50))	227.29	235.03	214.57
PEARSON r	0.456	0.292	0.215

* Programmed by Joginder Kumar.

age groups. The elements of the matrix **L** of (2.1.9) were interpreted as probabilities, which involved some approximation since they were derived as expected values. The difference is important insofar as a time period of five years is sufficiently long that a woman could have two children in it; both Orcutt *et al.* (1961) and Horvitz (1967) used one-month periods to avoid this difficulty.

The variances in the simulation recognizing age appear to be significantly lower than in that not recognizing age. Insofar as conclusions may be drawn from this experiment, the result seems analogous to the reduction of variance in stratified sampling.

16.4. A GENERAL EXPRESSION FOR VARIANCES IN LINEAR POPULATION MODELS

J. H. Pollard (1966) shows how the Leslie matrix of Chapters 2 and 3 can be made to give variances and higher moments rather than just expected values. His method is applicable to refashioning any linear deterministic model of the kind discussed in Chapters 12 and 13, provided only that its coefficients may be interpreted as probabilities. Although his very general technique would serve to make a probability version of highly complex deterministic models, we again will confine the present illustration to the simplest case: the interaction of the sexes, with female dominance and not recognizing age, whose differential equation representation is given as (16.3.6) through (16.3.10). The disadvantage for exposition of recognizing more variables is only that the matrices increase in the number of their elements as the square of the number of elements in the initial deterministic formulation. Ten variables (e. g., 10 ages up to 49, or married, single, widowed, divorced, and separated for each of the two sexes) would mean a 10×10 deterministic matrix, and a 110×110 matrix to give expected values and variances.

We start with a pair of differential equations showing the relations of expected values, here (16.3.6) and (16.3.7), or the equivalent (13.2.1). To translate the derivatives into changes over a short but finite period of time h we need only suppose that numbers at time $t + h$ differ from those at time t by the quantities on the right-hand side of Eqs. (16.3.6) and (16.3.7) multiplied by h. Then the numbers of the two sexes at time $t + h$ are equal to

$$\begin{aligned} M(t + h) &= (1 - hd_m)M(t) + hb_m F(t) ; \\ F(t + h) &= (1 + hb_f - hd_f)F(t) . \end{aligned} \tag{16.4.1}$$

If the vector

$$\begin{Bmatrix} M(t) \\ F(t) \end{Bmatrix}$$

be written $\mathbf{N}(t)$, and the 2×2 matrix of coefficients in (16.4.1) be written $\mathbf{A}$, then (16.4.1) is simply $\{\mathbf{N}(t + h)\} = \mathbf{A}\{\mathbf{N}(t)\}$, where

$$\mathbf{A} = \begin{bmatrix} a_{11} & a_{12} \\ a_{21} & a_{22} \end{bmatrix} = \begin{bmatrix} 1 - hd_m & hb_m \\ 0 & 1 + hb_f - hd_f \end{bmatrix} .$$

We will suppose that h is incorporated in the rates and need not be shown separately in what follows; this is the same as changing the unit of time to h.

Now think of the second moments about zero as arranged one below the other in dictionary order, to constitute the vector

$$\{\mathbf{C}(t)\} = \begin{Bmatrix} c_{11}(t) \\ c_{12}(t) \\ c_{21}(t) \\ c_{22}(t) \end{Bmatrix} .$$

Define also the direct product $\mathbf{A} \times \mathbf{A}$ (read $\mathbf{A}$ cross $\mathbf{A}$) as the matrix obtained by multiplying each element of $\mathbf{A}$ by the whole matrix $\mathbf{A}$.

Remembering that we are making the time unit short enough that two events cannot take place in it, so that all products $d_m d_f$, etc., are zero, the matrix $\mathbf{A} \times \mathbf{A}$ from (16.4.1) is readily worked out, and equals

$$\mathbf{A} \times \mathbf{A} = \begin{bmatrix} a_{11}a_{11} & a_{11}a_{12} & a_{12}a_{11} & a_{12}a_{12} \\ a_{11}a_{21} & a_{11}a_{22} & a_{12}a_{21} & a_{12}a_{22} \\ a_{21}a_{11} & a_{21}a_{12} & a_{22}a_{11} & a_{22}a_{12} \\ a_{21}a_{21} & a_{21}a_{22} & a_{22}a_{21} & a_{22}a_{22} \end{bmatrix}$$

$$= \begin{bmatrix} 1 - 2d_m & b_m & b_m & 0 \\ 0 & 1 + b_f - d_f - d_m & 0 & b_m \\ 0 & 0 & 1 + b_f - d_f - d_m & b_m \\ 0 & 0 & 0 & 1 + 2(b_f - d_f) \end{bmatrix} . \tag{16.4.2}$$

Let us compare the matrix $\mathbf{A} \times \mathbf{A}$ of (16.4.2) with the lower right-hand 3×3 portion of the matrix whose determinant is shown in (16.3.11). To replace the r by 1 is the equivalent of translating the system (16.3.11) from differential to finite form. The fourth row of (16.3.11) corresponds to the moment c_{12}; suppose that we add another identical row to represent the same moment written as c_{21}. Since the matrix $\mathbf{A} \times \mathbf{A}$ is to multiply the vector of moments $\mathbf{C}$, $2b_m$ in the third line of (16.3.11) is equivalent to two elements, each equal to b_m, in the first row of (16.4.2), one in the second column and one in the third column.

By such considerations the recurrence formula for the expected values and second moments of (16.3.6) through (16.3.10) may be written for a finite interval as

$$\begin{Bmatrix} \mathbf{N}(t+1) \\ \mathbf{C}(t+1) \end{Bmatrix} = \begin{bmatrix} \mathbf{A} & 0 \\ \mathbf{B} & \mathbf{A} \times \mathbf{A} \end{bmatrix} \begin{Bmatrix} \mathbf{N}(t) \\ \mathbf{C}(t) \end{Bmatrix}, \tag{16.4.3}$$

where by looking back to (16.3.6) through (16.3.10) we can see that $\mathbf{B}$ has to be equal to

$$\mathbf{B} = \begin{bmatrix} d_m & b_m \\ 0 & 0 \\ 0 & 0 \\ 0 & b_f + d_f \end{bmatrix}.$$

The effect of $\mathbf{B}$ is to add a multiple of the expected values to the mean squares, while leaving the cross-products where they would be with simple multiplication by $\mathbf{A} \times \mathbf{A}$. Pollard shows that the same recurrence equation (16.4.3) relates the vector consisting of the means, variances, and covariances.

A proof has been provided here only for the two-sex problem with female dominance, but the result (16.4.3) has great generality. Construct equations for means, variances, and covariance with mixed dominance, recognizing the sexes without age or marital status.

A sophisticated literature now exists on the problem for which a special case has been dealt with in this section. Proceeding by a much more thorough, as well as more general, argument than that by which we established (16.3.14) and (16.3.15), Goodman (1967b) has recently extended his earlier work to the two-sex age-dependent stochastic model. On the other side, Pollard, in research so far unpublished, has used his direct matrix product to compute means, variances, and covariances of models recognizing a large number of age, sex, and marital status groups within the population.

16.5. DISTRIBUTION OF THE SEX RATIO

The distribution of the sex ratio at time t in the model of Section 16.3 is formally analogous to the distribution of a ratio in random sampling. As a first approximation to the expected value of the sex ratio we can divide the expected number of males by the expected number of females, which is what the deterministic model does. However, this is biased, just as the ratio estimate in random sampling is biased (Cochran, 1963, p. 161). If the departure of m from its mean, $m - \mathscr{E}m$, is called Δm, and $f - \mathscr{E}f = \Delta f$, then $\mathscr{E}(\Delta m) = \mathscr{E}(\Delta f) = 0$, and

$$\mathscr{E}\left(\frac{m}{f}\right) = \mathscr{E}\left(\frac{\mathscr{E}m + \Delta m}{\mathscr{E}f + \Delta f}\right) = \frac{\mathscr{E}m}{\mathscr{E}f}\left[\mathscr{E}\left(\frac{1 + \Delta m/\mathscr{E}m}{1 + \Delta f/\mathscr{E}f}\right)\right]$$

$$\doteq \frac{\mathscr{E}m}{\mathscr{E}f}\left\{\mathscr{E}\left[1 - \frac{\Delta m\,\Delta f}{\mathscr{E}m\mathscr{E}f} + \left(\frac{\Delta f}{\mathscr{E}f}\right)^2\right]\right\},$$

so that finally

$$\mathscr{E}\left(\frac{m}{f}\right) \doteq \frac{\mathscr{E}m}{\mathscr{E}f} - \frac{\text{Covar}\,(m, f)}{(\mathscr{E}f)^2} + \frac{\mathscr{E}m\,\text{Var}\,(f)}{(\mathscr{E}f)^3}, \qquad (16.5.1)$$

the approximation being close if variances are small in comparison with expected values, and higher moments negligible. Reference to (16.3.14) shows that as t becomes large $[\text{Covar}\,(m, f)]/(\mathscr{E}f\mathscr{E}m)$ tends to $(b_f + d_f)/(b_f - d_f)$, and the same for $[\text{Var}\,(f)]/(\mathscr{E}f)^2$. Hence as t beomes large the last two terms of the right-hand side of (16.5.1) cancel out to give $\mathscr{E}(m/f) = \mathscr{E}m/\mathscr{E}f$. Goodman (1967b) shows that this is also true for the more interesting general case where the two-sex process is age-dependent.

The reader may apply the same technique to find the variance of the sex ratio in terms of the same five moments of m and f:

$$\text{Var}\left(\frac{m}{f}\right) = \frac{\text{Var}\,(m)}{(\mathscr{E}f)^2} - \frac{2\mathscr{E}m\,\text{Covar}\,(m, f)}{(\mathscr{E}f)^3} + \frac{(\mathscr{E}m)^2\,\text{Var}\,(f)}{(\mathscr{E}f)^4}, \qquad (16.5.2)$$

in whose derivation the quantity $[\mathscr{E}(m/f) - (\mathscr{E}m/\mathscr{E}f)]^2$ is neglected. Use (16.3.14) to prove that as t becomes large $\text{Var}\,(m/f)$ tends to zero. This also is proved by Goodman (1967b) for the age-dependent two-sex process.

The three instances treated in this chapter—the pure birth process; the birth, death, and immigration process; the sexes—are somewhat arbitrarily chosen out of a very large number of models. Much more variety is found in the reviews by Bartlett (1960) and Bailey (1964). Bartlett (1955 and 1957) has also developed techniques for handling stochastically the competitive and predator-prey models discussed deterministically in Chapter 12. Important as this work is, considerations of space and of the special application to large human populations which is a main interest of this book compel us to turn away now in order to examine certain quite different models which have been used for conception and birth.

CHAPTER 17

POPULATION DISTRIBUTIONS AND INDIVIDUAL BEHAVIOR

17.1. STOPPING RULES

Effect on Family Size

Models for population may be founded on the notion that individuals follow some rule in their decision to have further children. To start with the simplest rules, what is the distribution by family size of couples that continue to have children until they have one son? until they have two sons? until they have one son and one daughter? until they have two sons and two daughters? If the proportion p of births are males and q are females ($p + q = 1$), then the reader may verify the distribution for these cases as given in Table 17.1, where it is supposed that birth control is complete, that the sex of each child is independent of the sexes of other children in the family, and that the calculation is confined to fertile couples.

We may state the result of Table 17.1 in general form by noting (Sheps, 1963, p. 70) that if parents stop after α sons and β daughters, then the chance that they will have $n = \alpha + \beta + k$ children, $k \geq 0$, is made up of two parts:

1. The chance that they will have $\alpha + k$ sons and $\beta - 1$ daughters, in all possible orders, which is

$$\binom{\alpha + \beta + k - 1}{\beta - 1} p^{\alpha+k} q^{\beta-1},$$

   and then have a final daughter (probability q);

2. The chance that they will have $\alpha - 1$ sons and $\beta + k$ daughters, in all possible orders, which is

$$\binom{\alpha + \beta + k - 1}{\alpha - 1} p^{\alpha-1} q^{\beta+k},$$

   and then have a final son (probability p).

The two outcomes are mutually exclusive, and therefore the chance of $n = \alpha + \beta + k$ children is the sum of their probabilities:

$$\binom{n-1}{\beta-1} p^{n-\beta} q^{\beta} + \binom{n-1}{\alpha-1} p^{\alpha} q^{n-\alpha}. \qquad (17.1.1)$$

Table 17.1 Probability distribution of fertile couples by number of children, when certain stopping rules are in effect

NO. OF CHIL-DREN	STOP AT 1 SON (1)	STOP AT 2 SONS (2)	STOP AT 1 SON AND 1 DAUGHTER (3)
1	p	0	0
2	qp	p^2	$pq + pq$
3	q^2p	$\binom{2}{1}qp^2$	$p^2q + pq^2$
4	q^3p	$\binom{3}{1}q^2p^2$	$p^3q + pq^3$
5	q^4p	$\binom{4}{1}q^3p^2$	$p^4q + pq^4$
.	.	.	.
.	.	.	.
n	$q^{n-1}p$	$\binom{n-1}{1}q^{n-2}p^2$	$p^{n-1}q + pq^{n-1}$
.	.	.	.
.	.	.	.

Means and variances of the sizes of such families may be readily calculated. For the first column, where people stop with one son, the mean number of children is

$$\mathscr{E}n = p + 2qp + 3q^2p + 4q^3p + \cdots = \frac{p}{(1-q)^2} = \frac{1}{p}. \qquad (17.1.2)$$

The reader may show by similar calculation that the variance of number of children n for this stopping rule is

$$\operatorname{Var}(n) = 1/p^2 - 1/p = q/p^2. \qquad (17.1.3)$$

Means for random variables are additive. Whatever expected number of girls come between the start and the first boy will equal the number between the first and second boy, etc. It follows from this and (17.1.2) that the couple who stop after α boys will average α/p children. Variances for independent random variables are additive, so from (17.1.3) the variance of total children born among parents stopping with α boys is $\alpha q/p^2$. [Can we derive the mean and variance for α boys and β girls by similar addition?]

To calculate moments of the distributions for a stopping rule involving boys and girls, probability-generating functions are useful. Using Table 17.1, we multiply the row corresponding to one child by s, to two children by s^2, to three children by s^3, etc., and the row corresponding to n children by s^n. When this is done for Column (3) and the results added, we have for couples stopping with one son and one daughter $\phi(s)$, the expected value of s^n

$$\begin{aligned}\phi(s) &= (pq + pq)s^2 + (p^2q + pq^2)s^3 + \cdots + (p^{n-1}q + pq^{n-1})s^n + \cdots \\ &= pqs^2\left(\frac{1}{1 - ps} + \frac{1}{1 - qs}\right). \qquad (17.1.4)\end{aligned}$$

We need merely differentiate (17.1.4) with respect to s and put $s = 1$ to find the mean:

$$\mathscr{E}n = 1/qp - 1 = 1/q + 1/p - 1\,. \qquad (17.1.5)$$

If $p = q = \frac{1}{2}$, the expected size of family is three. If p and q are somewhat different from $\frac{1}{2}$, say $p = \frac{1}{2} + \varepsilon$ and $q = \frac{1}{2} - \varepsilon$, then the expected number of children is

$$\mathscr{E}n = 1/p + 1/q - 1 \doteqdot 3 + 16\varepsilon^2\,, \qquad (17.1.6)$$

or slightly more than three. (For the United States in 1965, ε was 0.0115.) Still considering families that stop with one son and one daughter, the reader may show that an expected $\frac{1}{2} - 2\varepsilon^2$ of couples will have two children; $\frac{1}{4} - \varepsilon^2$ will have three children;

$$\left(\frac{1}{2}\right)^{n-1} + \frac{\varepsilon^2}{2^{n-2}}(n - 1)(n - 4)$$

will have n children, if we may neglect third and higher powers of ε.

The generating function for total children $n \geq \alpha + \beta$ to couples which stop after α sons and β daughters is obtained from (17.1.1). Prove that the probability of $n \geq \alpha + \beta$ children is the coefficient of s^n in

$$g(s) = \left(\frac{qs}{1 - ps}\right)^\beta + \left(\frac{ps}{1 - qs}\right)^\alpha,$$

where terms of lower power than $s^{\alpha+\beta}$ are disregarded. Put $\alpha = 1$ and $\beta = 1$ and reconcile the result with (17.1.4), bearing in mind that stopping short of one son and one daughter has been eliminated from (17.1.4).

This model can be used to find the extent to which inability of parents to influence the sex of their unborn children will cause families to be larger in communities where the sex of children is important. If fertile couples want one boy, then the mean number of children they will have to bear is $1/p = 2 - 4\varepsilon$. If they insist on at least one boy and one girl they will average almost 50% more children than if they were satisfied with two children regardless of sex.

These results are modified when an upper limit ω is set on the total number of children a couple will have. The reader may show the modification in (17.1.4), (17.1.5), and (17.1.6), where one child of each sex is wanted but the couple is not willing to have more than ω children altogether to attain this (Sheps, 1963).

A somewhat different argument applies to couples who want a certain number of grown-up children with given probability in the face of child and young-adult mortality. If the probability of a child's dying is d and they have α boys, then the probability that all will not die is $1 - d^\alpha$. If the object is to ensure that at least one son will survive with probability $1 - \delta$ (to maintain the farm) then the number of sons α is determined by $d^\alpha = \delta$, or $\alpha = \ln \delta / \ln d$. If $d = \frac{1}{2}$ and $\delta = \frac{1}{32}$, the required number of male births is $\alpha = 5$, and combining this with the argument of the previous paragraphs gives required total children as $n = \alpha/p$, or nearly 10. Such calculations of sex preference and survival assurance in the next following generation, carried out less formally and with decidedly subjective estimates of the constants, undoubtedly influence individual birth policy in the face of sex and mortality. If the father wishes to establish a family planning policy that would ensure his entire line of male descent with given probability, he would have to refer to the birth and death processes of Chapter 16, or to the branching process of Chapter 18.

The reader may investigate the consequences of rules such as those above for the population net reproduction rate and the intrinsic rate of natural increase.

Effect on the Sex Ratio

In a population using birth control, where couples decide how many children they will have and prefer boys, can their decisions affect the sex ratio of births? It is easy to say (Winston, 1932) that the desire for sons will result in more boy babies, but more careful analysis of the probability mechanism is required. Goodman (1961a) has provided a systematic consideration of the consequences of parents' following different rules in deciding to have or not to have another child.

Suppose as before that the chance of a birth's being a boy is p and of its being a girl is $q = 1 - p$, and that these are the same for all couples, independently, and for all orders of birth. Then consider Rule I: Couples stop having children on the birth of the first boy. The proportion of couples that have just one child, a boy, is p; the proportion that have one girl and one boy is qp; the proportion that have two girls and one boy is q^2p, etc. If the total number of couples under consideration is n, then their expected distribution by number of children will be Column (2) in Table 17.2. If no limit is placed on family size, the ratio of boy births to total births in the population will be the total of Column (3) in Table 17.2 divided by the total of Column (4); that is,

$$\frac{np + nqp + nq^2p + \cdots}{np + 2nqp + 3nq^2p + \cdots}$$

Table 17.2 Distribution of *n* couples by number of children, showing expected births, when couples stop having children on birth of first boy

NUMBER OF CHILDREN (1)	COUPLES (2)	BOYS (3)	TOTAL CHILDREN OF BOTH SEXES (4)
1	np	np	np
2	nqp	nqp	2nqp
3	nq^2p	nq^2p	$3nq^2p$
4	nq^3p	nq^3p	$4nq^3p$
.	.	.	.
.	.	.	.

which reduces to p, as one would expect. The sex ratio of births is unaffected by the application of Rule I in a community where all couples have the same probability of bearing boy children. It is equally unaffected, among homogeneous couples, by any other stopping rule or combination of rules; as long as having children meets the conditions of a fair gambling game, parents cannot alter the chances of winning boys by choosing their time of entering and leaving.

Though the proportion of boys among all children, or among first children, second children, or any birth order specified in advance cannot be affected by decisions on whether to have a further child, nothing prevents parents from determining the probability of the last child's being a boy; on Rule I that probability would be certainty.

A quite different matter is the average proportion of boys in a family, as R. C. Lewontin pointed out to me. This will not be p. Taking the first column of Table 17.1, where each couple is supposed to stop with the first son, the proportion of boys in one-child families is 1, in two-child families is $\frac{1}{2}$, in three-child families is $\frac{1}{3}$, etc. The average proportion of boys is obtained by multiplying these figures by the relative frequency of one-, two-, three-, ... child families:

$$1p + (\tfrac{1}{2})qp + (\tfrac{1}{3})q^2p + \cdots = -(p \ln p)/q\,,$$

from the Taylor series for the expansion of the natural logarithm of $1 - q$. If $p = q = \frac{1}{2}$, we have

$$\frac{-p \ln p}{q} = \frac{(-\frac{1}{2})(-0.693)}{\frac{1}{2}} = 0.693$$

(very different from $\frac{1}{2}$) as the average proportion of boys in a family. If $p = \frac{1}{2} + \varepsilon$, the average will be seen to be $0.693 + 0.773\varepsilon$, provided ε is small.

All of the above is on the supposition that the probability of having a boy is the same from one couple to another. Weiler (1959) and Goodman (1961a) analyze the consequences of preference for boys in a population using birth control in which couples have different probabilities of producing boys. Suppose that the ith couple has a probability p_i of having a boy on a given birth, this being fixed for all births to it, and that the couple follows Rule I of stopping after it has a boy. Then the expected number of boy children to that couple will be 1, and the expected total number of children according to (17.1.2) will be $1/p_i$. If n couples follow Rule I, they will have an expected n boys out of $\sum_1^n 1/p_i$ children, or a proportion of male births

$$\frac{\sum 1}{\sum 1/p_i} = \frac{n}{\sum 1/p_i}. \tag{17.1.7}$$

This is the harmonic mean of the p_i, and we will refer to it as (hp). Call (ap) the arithmetic mean of the p_i, i.e., $(ap) = \sum p_i/n$. The harmonic mean of a set of positive numbers (not all identical) is less than their arithmetic mean [how is this proved?], so that (17.1.7) or (hp) must be less than $\sum p_i/n = (ap)$, the expected proportion of boys among parents who follow no stopping rule related to the sex of their children.

This shows that the desire of couples for sons expressed in Rule I will have the effect of *diminishing* the proportion of boy births by $(ap) - (hp)$, as against what they would have attained by following no stopping rule at all. The result does not seem paradoxical if one considers that Rule I leads to larger families for those couples that have a tendency to produce girls. If couples want to increase their expected proportion of boys, they would stop at the first *girl* (Goodman's Rule III). This would be as though they were testing whether they were boy-producers or girl-producers, and those that found they were boy-producers then contributed more children. [Can you suggest a more efficient test for individual parents to follow—one that would provide a higher proportion of boys to the community?]

This section has been concerned with the distribution of total births and boy births among women. In the following section the sequence of births to individual women will be studied, disregarding the sex of the child.

17.2. BIRTHS AS A SEQUENCE IN TIME

The simplest stochastic model for reproduction involves a fixed probability in each short period, the probability being the same for all women considered, and with no allowance for the infertile period following conception; these conditions, like those of the preceding section, give rise to a geometric distribution.

Sheps (1964) starts with this case, counting time in units of one menstrual cycle, which at an average of 29.5 to 30.0 days can be referred to as a month. The time-scale will be set to zero at the beginning of the first month of exposure, and a conception counted at the end of the month in which it occurs, so that a conception in the first month will be said to occur after one *trial*, or a *delay* of zero months. The probability that conception does not take place in the first month and does take place in the second is qp; that it does not take place in the first $r - 1$ months and does take place in the rth is $q^{r-1}p$, which will be called r trials and a delay of $r - 1$ months. The distribution of trials is formally identical with that of number of children among parents who stop at one son (Column (2) of Table 17.1). The mean number of trials is $1/p$ (with a mean delay of $q/p = (1/p) - 1$); the variance among trials or delays is q/p^2, from (17.1.3); the probability-generating function of the number of trials is

$$g(s) = ps/(1 - qs) .$$

[What is the probability-generating function of delays?]

The model as presented above is restricted by the assumption that all women have the identical probability of conceiving in any time interval. Sheps goes on to allow for heterogeneity in the probability of conception, making p a variable so that the proportion of fecund women having a probability of conception per month between p and $p + dp$ is $\phi(p)\,dp$ $(0 < p < 1)$. For the ith woman, whose probability is p_i per month, the mean number of trials w_i would be $1/p_i$. (Nonfecund women, for whom $p_i = 0$, are omitted in this analysis.) The expected number of trials averaged over all women is

$$\mathscr{E}w = \frac{\sum_1^n 1/p_i}{n} , \qquad (17.2.1)$$

n being the number of women in the population. For the continuous distribution of p, the mean expected number of trials is

$$\mathscr{E}w = \int_0^1 \phi(p)/p\,dp .$$

Thus $1/\mathscr{E}w$ is the harmonic average of the p. Equation (17.2.1) says that the average number of trials is the reciprocal of the harmonic mean of the probabilities of giving birth in one month for the individual woman. Since the harmonic mean is less than the arithmetic mean, $\mathscr{E}w$ is greater than the reciprocal of the arithmetic mean. This proves that heterogeneity, without change of average of the p_i, increases the mean number of trials. [Express the formulas and results in terms of delays.]

Given certain forms of the distribution $\phi(p)$, the mean and variance of the distribution of expected waiting times may be calculated from the mean and variance of the probability p of conceiving in a given month. R. G. Potter and M. P. Parker (1964) show the usefulness of the Pearson Type I or incomplete beta distribution for so translating a mean and variance of probabilities into those for waiting times. The proportion of couples having fecundability between zero and p is taken as

$$F(p) = \int_0^p \phi(p)\,dp = \frac{\int_0^p p^{a-1}(1-p)^{b-1}\,dp}{\int_0^1 p^{a-1}(1-p)^{b-1}\,dp}, \tag{17.2.2}$$

the denominator being $B(a, b)$, the beta function with arguments a and b. Using

$$B(a, b) = \frac{\Gamma(a)\Gamma(b)}{\Gamma(a+b)},$$

and the relation of successive values of the gamma function $\Gamma(a)$,

$$\Gamma(a) = (a-1)\Gamma(a-1),$$

the reader may show that the mean fecundability

$$\mathscr{E}p = \frac{\int_0^1 p^a(1-p)^{b-1}\,dp}{\int_0^1 p^{a-1}(1-p)^{b-1}\,dp}$$

reduces to

$$\mathscr{E}p = \frac{\Gamma(a+1)\Gamma(b)}{\Gamma(a+b+1)}\Big/\frac{\Gamma(a)\Gamma(b)}{\Gamma(a+b)} = \frac{a}{a+b}. \tag{17.2.3}$$

He may show that the expected value of the square of p is

$$\mathscr{E}(p^2) = \frac{(a+1)(a)}{(a+b+1)(a+b)},$$

and its variance, $\mathrm{Var}(p) = \mathscr{E}[p - \mathscr{E}(p)]^2$, is

$$\mathrm{Var}(p) = \frac{ab}{(a+b+1)(a+b)^2}. \tag{17.2.4}$$

The expected number of trials is, by a similar argument, equal to

$$\mathscr{E}w = \mathscr{E}\left(\frac{1}{p}\right) = \frac{a+b-1}{a-1}, \quad a > 1. \tag{17.2.5}$$

Comparing this with the corresponding value if all women have the same probability, that is,

$$\mathscr{E}w = \frac{1}{\mathscr{E}p} = \frac{a+b}{a},$$

we see that for $a > 1$ and $b > 0$,

$$\frac{a+b-1}{a-1} > \frac{a+b}{a},$$

so that once again, variation of women about the given mean probability increases the expected waiting time. The reader may show that the graduation by the beta function permits expression of the mean number of trials in terms of the first two moments of the probabilities of conception:

$$\mathscr{E}w = \mathscr{E}\left(\frac{1}{p}\right) = 1 + \left(\frac{2\mathscr{E}p}{1 - \mathscr{E}p} - \frac{\mathscr{E}(p^2)}{\mathscr{E}p - \mathscr{E}(p^2)}\right)^{-1}.$$

The expected value of the variance of trials or waiting times is shown by Potter and Parker (1964) to be

$$\operatorname{Var}(w) = \frac{(ab)(a + b - 1)}{(a - 1)^2(a - 2)}, \quad a > 2. \tag{17.2.6}$$

Note the difference between the variance among observed individual waiting times (17.2.6) and the variance $\mathscr{E}(1/p)^2 - (\mathscr{E}\,1/p)^2$ among the expected waiting times for individual women. Derive an expression for the latter and show that it is $1/a$ multiplied by (17.2.6).

Our chief interest here is in an inference on the p from the w. We want to know the distribution of susceptibility p, given observations on the waiting time w. We solve (17.2.5) and (17.2.6) in terms of the mean and variance of the observed waiting times to find estimates $\hat{a}$ and $\hat{b}$ of a and b respectively:

$$\hat{a} = \frac{2\,\widehat{\operatorname{Var}}(w)}{\widehat{\operatorname{Var}}(w) - (\hat{\mathscr{E}}(w))^2 + \hat{\mathscr{E}}(w)},$$

$$\hat{b} = (\hat{\mathscr{E}}(w) - 1)(\hat{a} - 1), \tag{17.2.7}$$

where we have replaced $\operatorname{Var}(w)$ and $\mathscr{E}w$ by their estimates from the observations. Potter and Parker (1964, p. 108) use the observations $\hat{\mathscr{E}}w = 5.47$ months and $\widehat{\operatorname{Var}}(w) = 89.98$ to find $\hat{a} = 2.75$ and $\hat{b} = 7.82$ from (17.2.7). From these numbers the distribution of p can be traced out in detail, always supposing the beta function to be appropriate. The estimated mean of p is 0.260 from (17.2.3) and the estimate of its standard deviation, 0.129 from (17.2.4). The model can be used to make prognostications on individual women based on their previous waiting time. The authors show that prompt conceivers are apt to conceive promptly again, while a majority of the slow conceivers will not be so slow the next time.

William Brass (1958) fitted the Poisson distribution and also considered it unrealistic to make its constant, λ, the same for all women. He starts out by assuming that for a given woman the parameter λ is fixed and the probability of zero births in time t is $e^{-\lambda t}$, of one birth is $\lambda t e^{-\lambda t}$, of two births $[(\lambda t)^2/2!]e^{-\lambda t}$, etc. The generating function of the Poisson distribution is easily shown to be $\mathscr{E}s^r = e^{-\lambda t + \lambda t s}$ (Kendall and Stuart, 1958, Vol. 1, p. 125). Brass then assumes that the λ's are distributed among women according to a Pearson Type III curve, the incomplete gamma function: the proportion of women of parameter λ to $\lambda + d\lambda$ is taken as $(a^k e^{-a\lambda}\lambda^{k-1}\,d\lambda)/\Gamma(k)$. The contribution of the women between

λ and $\lambda + d\lambda$ to the generating function of family size must equal the product

$$(e^{-\lambda t+\lambda ts})[(a^k e^{-a\lambda}\lambda^{k-1}\,d\lambda)/\Gamma(k)]\,, \tag{17.2.8}$$

and integrating out λ from (17.2.8) results in

$$[(a+t-st)/a]^{-k}\,, \tag{17.2.9}$$

which is the generating function of the negative binomial distribution (Kendall and Stuart, 1958, Vol. 1, p. 130). The probability of r, the coefficient of s^r in the expansion of (17.2.9), may be written as

$$\left(\frac{a}{a+t}\right)^k \frac{\Gamma(k+r)}{\Gamma(k)r!}\left(\frac{t}{a+t}\right)^r. \tag{17.2.10}$$

Now that we have the theoretical distribution (17.2.10) in terms of the parameters a, t, and k, it is necessary only to estimate these from actual data. By successively differentiating the moment-generating function (17.2.9) with respect to s and putting $s = 1$, we have the factorial moments about zero:

$$\mu'_{[1]} = \frac{tk}{a}\,, \qquad \mu'_{[2]} = \frac{t^2k(k+1)}{a^2}\,, \tag{17.2.11}$$

and, solving for k and for t/a,

$$k = \frac{\mu'^2_{[1]}}{\mu'_{[2]} - \mu'^2_{[1]}}\,, \qquad \frac{t}{a} = \frac{\mu'_{[2]} - \mu'^2_{[1]}}{\mu'_{[1]}}\,, \tag{17.2.12}$$

which is all that we need. The probability distribution of r represented as (17.2.10) looks as though it contains three parameters, but in fact it has only two, because a and t do not enter except as a ratio.

Now to apply this to data for the United States, 1960. The quantities calculated from the "Actual" column of Table 17.3 are

$$\begin{aligned} \mu'_{[1]} &= 2.304 & \mu'^2_{[1]} &= 5.308 \\ \mu'_{[2]} &= 6.641 & \mu'_{[2]} - \mu'^2_{[1]} &= 1.333 \\ k &= 3.982 & \frac{a}{t} &= 1.728 \end{aligned} \tag{17.2.13}$$

$$\left(\frac{a}{a+t}\right)^k = 0.1622\,.$$

For example $\mu'_{[2]}$ is

$$\begin{aligned}[(0)(937) + (0)(1)(1010) + (1)(2)(1283) + \cdots \\ + (6.5)(7.5)(274)]/5190 = 6.641\,.\end{aligned}$$

From these it is easy to work out the terms of the distribution (17.2.10), $r = 0$, 1, 2, ..., given in the right-hand column of Table 17.3. At $r = 2$ children, for example, from (17.2.10) we have

$$\left(\frac{0.1622\Gamma(3.982+2)}{\Gamma(3.982)2!}\right)\left(\frac{1}{1+1.728}\right)^2$$

$$= \frac{(0.1622)(4.982)(3.982)}{2}(0.3666)^2$$

$$= 0.2162 .$$

and multiplying this by 5190 gives 1122 as shown.

The fitted curve has decidedly too few women with zero children, which reflects, as Brass points out, that the model takes no account of the possibility of genuine sterility to which a part of any population is subject. Brass meets this by fitting a truncated negative binomial; he drops the 0 frequency from the comparison. Table 17.3 suggests special preference for two and five children

Table 17.3 Fitting of negative binomial to children ever born to women 45–49, United States, 1960 (thousands)

CHILDREN EVER BORN r	WOMEN REPORTING	
	ACTUAL*	FITTED**
TOTAL	5,190	5,190
0	937	842
1	1,010	1,229
2	1,283	1,122
3	819	821
4	463	525
5	404	306
6 AND OVER	274†	345

* Source: United Nations *Demographic Yearbook* 1963, p. 454.

** The fitted distribution is

$$5190(0.6334)^{3.982}\frac{\Gamma(r+3.982)}{\Gamma(3.982)r!}(0.3666)^r$$

$$= 841.8\underbrace{(3.982)(4.982)\cdots(2.982+r)}_{r \text{ factors}}\frac{(0.3666)^r}{r!} .$$

† Taken as having a mean of 7.5 children, which may be checked by the graduation and shown to be slightly high.

on the part of parents. In addition, the top end of the fitted distribution is too high; it has too many women with six children and over. Brass goes on to fit a curve with an allowance for pregnancy, during which the risk of conception is zero. For women with six children this nonexposure eliminates 5 or so years of the 20- or 25-year childbearing period, thus accounting for a 20% difference in number of children for such women. Periods of nonexposure are the theme of the following section.

17.3. ALLOWANCE FOR THE NONFECUND PERIOD OF PREGNANCY

Probability processes involving delay have been discussed in several contexts. Dandekar (1955) assumed that accidents are subject to a Poisson distribution, except that for a number of days after each accident the person affected was out of the factory and therefore not at risk. Neyman (1949) supposed that a fishing boat had a fixed chance at any moment of sighting a school of fish, except that after one was sighted, just $h - 1$ hours were spent fishing it, and the chance of sighting another was zero during that time. Dandekar went on to make the application to the birth process with fixed waiting time after each conception. Singh (1963) derives best asymptotically normal estimates of the parameters, and finds a reasonably good fit to Dandekar's data on the distribution of the number of children born to women in the age group 21–25 for Kolhapur, India.

Instead of reporting on these, I shall translate some of their ideas into matrix terms (Feller, 1957, Chap. 15). We begin with an illustration simple enough that matrices are superfluous: Bernoulli trials, each with probability p of success and q of failure independent of the outcome in other months, described by the matrix $\mathbf{P}$,

$$\mathbf{P} = \begin{bmatrix} p & q \\ p & q \end{bmatrix}.$$

The probabilities of success and failure in any month may be represented by the two elements of the vector $\mathbf{\Pi}$; suppose the zeroth month is known to be a failure with certainty, so that $\mathbf{\Pi}_0 = [0 \quad 1]$. The probability vector a month later is

$$\mathbf{\Pi}_1 = \mathbf{\Pi}_0\mathbf{P} = [0 \quad 1]\begin{bmatrix} p & q \\ p & q \end{bmatrix} = [p \quad q]. \tag{17.3.1}$$

If the zeroth month was a success, $\mathbf{\Pi}_1 = [p \quad q]$ as before, an independence property characteristic of Bernoulli trials. The probabilities for the tth month are $\mathbf{\Pi}_t = \mathbf{\Pi}_0\mathbf{P}^t$, and this also may easily be shown not to depend on $\mathbf{\Pi}_0$, as well as not depending on t. In (17.3.1) and later, a horizontal vector is postmultiplied by a matrix; in Chapter 3 vertical vectors were premultiplied by matrices. The difference in presentation merely reflects the notational styles of different parts of the literature. Translate (17.3.1) into the vertical vector form, and give the general rule for such translation.

When the process of conception and birth is looked at in discrete terms, and points of time are called ovulations or months, then (17.3.1) constitutes the description of a process in which the probability for any month is independent of that of the preceding months. A distinct advance is made in the model by supposing that what happens in any month does depend on the preceding months.

Let the chance of conception be p if there has been no conception in the preceding nine months or if there was a conception just nine months ago, and 0 if there has been a conception in the preceding eight months. We recognize 10 states: E_0, a conception this month; E_1, a conception last month; E_2, a conception 2 months ago; . . .; E_9, the last conception exactly 9 months ago and a birth now; (in the same state E_9 of being subject to conception in our simplified model are women whose last conception was 10 or more months ago or never). The chance $p_{0,1}$ of going from E_0 to E_1 is 1 (disregarding mortality); in general the chance of going from E_i to E_{i+1} in one month is $p_{i,i+1} = 1$, $i = 0, \ldots, 8$; while $p_{9,0} = p$ and $p_{9,9} = q$. All other transitions have zero probability. A woman in E_9, say, who is now having a birth *or* who has not had a conception in the preceding nine months will be represented by $\mathbf{\Pi}_0 = [0 \quad 0 \quad 0 \cdots 1]$, a suitable starting point. Then the probabilities of the several transitions may be arranged as a matrix $\mathbf{P}$, and the probabilities of the states at time t are

$$\mathbf{\Pi}_t = \mathbf{\Pi}_0\mathbf{P}^t = [0 \quad 0 \quad 0 \cdots 0 \quad 1]\begin{bmatrix} 0 & 1 & 0 \cdots 0 & 0 \\ 0 & 0 & 1 \cdots 0 & 0 \\ 0 & 0 & 0 \cdots 0 & 0 \\ \vdots & & & \vdots \\ 0 & 0 & 0 \cdots 0 & 1 \\ p & 0 & 0 \cdots 0 & q \end{bmatrix}^t. \tag{17.3.2}$$

The products of the initial vector $\mathbf{\Pi}_0$ (containing 10 elements of which 9 are zero) and the powers of the 10×10 matrix are successively

$$\begin{aligned} \mathbf{\Pi}_0 &= [0 \quad 0 \quad 0 \cdots 1], \\ \mathbf{\Pi}_0\mathbf{P} &= [p \quad 0 \quad 0 \cdots q], \\ \mathbf{\Pi}_0\mathbf{P}^2 &= [qp \quad p \quad 0 \cdots q^2], \\ \mathbf{\Pi}_0\mathbf{P}^3 &= [q^2p \quad qp \quad p \cdots q^3], \\ &\vdots \end{aligned} \tag{17.3.3}$$

A stochastic matrix is *regular* if its elements fill up as it is taken to powers, so that there is some n at and above which $\mathbf{P}^n$ consists entirely of positive (nonzero) terms, a condition which may be written $\mathbf{P}^n > 0$. This means that transition is possible by some route from any state to any other state. That this should be so is plain from the conditions of our formulation, which permit a woman to go from any stage of pregnancy to any other. From the 6th month to the 5th month would take at least 9 months; from the 6th to the 6th at least

10 months. The reader may prove formally that **P** of (17.3.2) is regular by an adaptation of the argument of Section 4.3. A regular chain is *ergodic*—it will stabilize, and the stable values in the ultimate vector, $\mathbf{\Pi}_\infty = \mathbf{\Pi}_0\mathbf{P}^\infty$, will not depend on the starting vector (Kemeny and Snell, 1960, Sec. 2.4).

The distribution of a group of women among the states at stability can be worked out by a set of linear equations. For if the stable $\mathbf{\Pi}_\infty$ is

$$\mathbf{\Pi}_\infty = [\pi_0 \quad \pi_1 \quad \pi_2 \cdots \pi_9] ,$$

the condition of stability is the matrix equation

$$\mathbf{\Pi}_\infty = \mathbf{\Pi}_\infty\mathbf{P} ,$$

which is the same as the nine homogeneous equations,

$$\begin{aligned} \pi_0 &= p\pi_9 , \\ \pi_1 &= \pi_0 , \\ \pi_2 &= \pi_1 , \\ &\vdots \\ \pi_8 &= \pi_7 , \end{aligned} \tag{17.3.4}$$

and these, along with the nonhomogeneous condition on the probabilities of an exhaustive set of nonoverlapping events,

$$\pi_0 + \pi_1 + \cdots + \pi_9 = 1 , \tag{17.3.5}$$

may be solved for the π's to give

$$\pi_0 = \pi_1 = \cdots = \pi_8 = p/(9p + 1)$$

and

$$\pi_9 = 1/(9p + 1) .$$

The stable vector is thus

$$\mathbf{\Pi}_\infty = \left[\frac{p}{9p+1} \quad \frac{p}{9p+1} \cdots \frac{p}{9p+1} \quad \frac{1}{9p+1}\right] . \tag{17.3.6}$$

If the nonfecundable period is $h - 1$ months, then the 9's in (17.3.6) are replaced by $(h - 1)$'s. Further analysis of the general form of $\mathbf{P}^t$ defined in (17.3.2) is possible in terms of the latent roots of **P**, found from $|\mathbf{P} - \lambda\mathbf{I}| = 0$, a determinantal equation which the reader may evaluate as

$$|\mathbf{P} - \lambda\mathbf{I}| = \lambda^h - q\lambda^{h-1} - p = 0 . \tag{17.3.7}$$

Unity is the dominant root of (17.3.7), and an asymptotic approximation corresponding to the leading term of (3.2.23) may be found by the method used for the different problem of Section 3.2. Roger Avery has pointed out that the matrix of (17.3.2) may be generalized to take account of miscarriage by replacing the 1's by probabilities of continuing pregnancy, and entering the complements of these in the last column.

If the object is merely to ascertain the real stable vector (17.3.6), an alternative and less technical line of reasoning is available. Suppose the probability of conception for a woman who is not pregnant in any given month is p. Then the mean number of trials for each success is $1/p$, as we saw in Section 17.2. If the nonsusceptible period is $h - 1$ months, supposed not subject to any (random or other) variation, then the mean time from one pregnancy to the next is $h - 1 + 1/p$ months. Among a large group of women with this mean interval, the pregnancy rate, which is the same as the proportion in their first month of pregnancy, is

$$\frac{1}{h - 1 + 1/p} = \frac{p}{(h - 1)p + 1}, \tag{17.3.8}$$

in agreement with the first element of (17.3.6) when $h = 10$. Similarly for the proportion of women who are in the second, the third, . . . , the $(h - 1)$th month of pregnancy; if every pregnancy goes to term and childbirth, then among a large group, after the process has been under way for some time, the same number of women will be in each of the $h - 1$ states. And if $p/[(h - 1)p + 1]$ are in each of the states of pregnancy, or $(h - 1)p/[(h - 1)p + 1]$ in all, then the remainder, or

$$1 - \frac{(h - 1)p}{(h - 1)p + 1} = \frac{1}{(h - 1)p + 1}, \tag{17.3.9}$$

must be in the hth state, that of nonpregnancy or susceptibility. This somewhat intuitive argument approximately justifies (17.3.6).

For a numerical example of the results (17.3.8) and (17.3.9), suppose a nonsusceptible period of $h - 1 = 9$ months, and $p = 0.18$ the probability of conception in any given month. Then the asymptotic conception rate (equal to the birth rate for a large population) per month will be

$$0.18/[9(0.18) + 1] = 0.0687 .$$

If contraception is now universally used with 50% efficacy, then p goes down to 0.09, and the birth rate to $0.09/(9(0.09) + 1) = 0.0497$ per month, a reduction of 28%. If, on the other hand, 50% of the population uses contraceptives with 100% efficacy, the reduction in the birth rate is 50%. (See Tietze (1962) for measures of contraceptive efficacy.)

Such rates may be translated into expected numbers of children during a 20-year = 240-month reproductive lifetime. The p of 0.18, disregarding the nonfecund period, gives $240 \times 0.18 = 43$ births; allowance for the nonfecund period reduces this to the more reasonable maximum of $240 \times 0.0687 = 16.5$. If 50% of women use contraceptives with 100% efficacy after having two children, the average will go down to $\frac{1}{2}(16.5 + 2.0) = 9.2$; if all women use contraception with 50% efficacy after two children, the average will be

$$2.0 + (240 - 28)(0.0497) = 12.5 ,$$

where we allow 28 months for two infertile periods of 9 months each and two waiting periods of 5 months each.

The argument leads to a policy of persuading women to use contraception effectively. If (say in one country) $1 - e$ is the efficacy with which all women use contraception, and (in another country) $1 - \alpha$ is the proportion of women using contraception with perfect efficacy (the remainder using no contraception), then for equivalent effect on the asymptotic birth rate we have

$$\frac{0.18e}{9(0.18e) + 1} = \alpha \frac{0.18}{9(0.18) + 1}$$

or, on dividing by 0.18 and taking reciprocals,

$$1.62 + \frac{1}{e} = \frac{2.62}{\alpha},$$

a linear relation in reciprocals. For small changes $\Delta\alpha$ and Δe we have

$$\frac{\Delta e}{e^2} = 2.62 \frac{\Delta\alpha}{\alpha^2},$$

so that at the margin a change in e of $2.62e/\alpha$ percent would be required to equal the effect of a 1% change in α. This is assuming a nine-month infertile period, which is undoubtedly on the low side. Mindel Sheps (1967, p. 13) supposes a period of 18 months; the reader will see on his own desk calculator how much the above conclusions are strengthened by the longer nonsusceptible period. Draw the curve of $1 - e$ against $1 - \alpha$ for various periods.

The infertile interval of pregnancy is less important where parents have had all the children they want and are aiming at 100% contraception (Tietze, 1962). The effects of attaining only 95% efficacy may well be surprising. Suppose that 95% effectiveness brings the probability of conception in any particular month to 0.01. Then the probability of avoiding all births for 20 years, or 240 months, is only $(0.99)^{240} = 0.09$, a number not affected by the nonsusceptible period. The expected number of births in 20 years is $240(0.01) = 2.4$, say on the binomial distribution, disregarding the infecundable period of pregnancy. It would be only slightly reduced by taking account of this period—to about $240[0.01/(0.09 + 1)] = 2.2$. Fertile couples who use contraception all the time and can attain only 95% contraceptive effectiveness can expect more than two children in 20 years under the suppositions made here. If they want an expected three children, then only for $3/p = 17$ months plus the three periods of pregnancy in the course of 20 years could they hazard using no contraception at all; for 196 months they would have to be careful.

Further issues, for which formal analysis could be useful, are raised by the important distinction between family planning, which permits women to have the number of children they want, and population planning, by which the total number is held down to what can be collectively supported (Davis, 1967). The relation between social variables on the one hand and intermediate variables, including the use of contraception, on the other is presented by Davis and Blake (1956) in a classic article.

The usefulness of allowing for a nonfertile period in thinking about the process of conception and birth, and especially in considering the effect of contraception, justifies the presentation of one further derivation. The difference-equation technique published by D. Basu (1955) throws further light on the preceding argument.

Suppose the overall probability of conception for month n is P_n. If no conception occurred at time zero, of which the chance is q, then all later probabilities are the same, except that they may equally be measured from time one. In respect to this possibility P_n is qP_{n-1}. If a conception did occur at time zero, of which the chance is p, then later probabilities from time h onward are the same, but now measured from time h, and in respect of this P_n is equal to pP_{n-h}. Combining these two mutually exclusive and exhaustive possibilities on P_0 gives

$$P_n = qP_{n-1} + pP_{n-h}\,, \quad n > 0\,, \tag{17.3.10}$$

where we define $P_n = 0$, $n < 0$. (This succinct way of justifying (17.3.10) by considering three time scales is due to D. Sharma.)

If the generating function of the P_n is

$$\phi(s) = P_0 + P_1 s + P_2 s^2 + \cdots\,,$$

then multiplying the recurrence equation (17.3.10), containing P_n on the left, by s^n, $n = 0, 1, 2, \ldots$ and adding, results in

$$\phi(s) = p + qs\phi(s) + ps^h\phi(s)\,, \tag{17.3.11}$$

and solving for $\phi(s)$, we have

$$\phi(s) = p/(1 - qs - ps^h)\,. \tag{17.3.12}$$

If s is put equal to $1/\lambda$, then (17.3.12) becomes

$$\frac{p\lambda^h}{\lambda^h - q\lambda^{h-1} - p}\,,$$

whose denominator is identical with the left-hand side of (17.3.7). [What does this show?]

The roots of the hth degree polynomial equation $ps^h + qs - 1 = 0$ are 1 and negative or complex numbers of absolute value *greater* than 1, as may be shown by an adaptation of the argument following (5.2.3), used for the integral equation in Chapter 5. Go through the proof, starting by putting

$$s = e^x(\cos y + i \sin y)$$

in $ps^h + qs = 1$, equating real parts, and comparing with the equation at the real root $s = 1$.

Dividing out the right-hand side of (17.3.12) in ascending powers of s would provide as the coefficients of s the probabilities, regarded from an initial zero point, of a conception in the zeroth, first, second, etc. month. While this may be done to check the procedure, it does not bring us closer to a solution. But the form of (17.3.12) suggests that the analysis of Section 5.8 may be applicable. The generating function is simplified by development in partial fractions, the denominator being factored into $(1 - s)R(s)$, where $R(s)$ has roots s_i in s such that $|s_i| > 1$. If we think of the fractions $-A_i/(s - s_i)$ which would emerge, and imagine them as expanded in ascending powers of (s/s_i), it becomes plain that their influence on the solution diminishes as the power of (s/s_i) rises, which is to say as time goes on. Ultimately only the term As^t corresponding to the root equal to 1 is retained, and it constitutes the *asymptotic* solution, in somewhat the sense that $u_t s^t$, where $u_t = 1/[s_1^{t+1}F'(s_1)]$ is the first term of (5.8.6), constitutes the solution for large t of the set of Eqs. (5.8.2). We require to know A explicitly.

The partial-fraction decomposition of $\phi(s)$ from (17.3.12) may be written

$$\phi(s) = \frac{p}{1 - qs - ps^h} = \frac{A}{1 - s} + \frac{B(s)}{R(s)},$$

and multiplying across by $1 - s$ and taking the limit as s tends to 1 gives for the constant A

$$A = p \lim_{s\to 1}\left(\frac{1 - s}{1 - qs - ps^h}\right) = -p\Big/\left.\frac{d(1 - qs - ps^h)}{ds}\right|_{s=1} = \frac{p}{q + hp}. \tag{17.3.13}$$

The asymptotic expansion is obtained by disregarding $B(s)/R(s)$:

$$\begin{aligned}\phi(s) &= \frac{p}{1 - qs - ps^h} \sim \frac{A}{1 - s}\\ &= \frac{p}{q + hp}(1 + s + s^2 + s^3 + \cdots);\end{aligned}$$

that is, the probability of a conception in any month is

$$p/(q + hp) = p/(1 + (h - 1)p), \tag{17.3.14}$$

which agrees with the result of the earlier argument, as expressed in (17.3.8) or, for $h = 10$, in (17.3.6). As in Chapter 5, the complex roots (obtained by equating the denominator $R(s)$ to zero, and omitted in this treatment) would produce waves of diminishing amplitude in the approach to the asymptotic probability (17.3.14).

Mindel Sheps shows in unpublished work that this approach may readily be extended to take account of fetal loss, at least where the loss occurs at a fixed time, say w for wastage, after conception. Suppose π to be the probability for a susceptible woman of initiating a conception that will result in miscarriage w months later, p the probability of a conception that will result in a live birth, and $q = 1 - \pi - p$. Then in place of (17.3.10) we obtain for P_n, the probability of a conception leading to a live birth in month n:

$$P_n = 0\,, \quad n < 0\,,$$
$$P_0 = p\,,$$
$$P_n = qP_{n-1} + \pi P_{n-w} + pP_{n-h}\,, \quad n > 0\,.$$

Now multiplying P_n by s^n and adding gives

$$\phi(s) = p + qs\phi(s) + \pi s^w \phi(s) + ps^h \phi(s)\,,$$

and by transposing the solution in $\phi(s)$ is seen to be

$$\phi(s) = \frac{p}{1 - qs - \pi s^w - ps^h}\,. \tag{17.3.15}$$

Equation (17.3.12) is the special case where π, the chance of wastage, is zero.

The asymptotic probability of conception that leads to a live birth, obtained by disregarding the partial fractions beyond the first, is given by the coefficients of s in the leading term $A/(1 - s)$, i.e., by A. This is ascertained from (17.3.15) by taking a derivative as before:

$$A = \lim_{s \to 1} \left(\frac{(1 - s)p}{1 - qs - \pi s^w - ps^h} \right) = \frac{p}{q + \pi w + ph}\,, \tag{17.3.16}$$

comparable with (17.3.14) (Sheps and Perrin, 1963, p. 1035).

Three different formulations have produced the identical results (17.3.6), (17.3.8), and (17.3.14) for the asymptotic pregnancy rate, and each could be made to produce (17.3.16). The ultimate probability of being in a given month of pregnancy, $p/(9p + 1)$ or $p/[(h - 1)p + 1]$, is obtained by yet other means by Henry (1957, 1961) and Dandekar (1955).

The Type I Counter

We may require to know more about the distribution of pregnancies over a given time interval. For variances and higher moments the asymptotic solution above will not suffice. Feller (1948) provides an elegant analysis of the Type I counter for radioactive particles, working from a renewal equation similar to (5.1.1). Secondary accounts of Feller's method are to be found in Bharucha-Reid (1960, p. 299) and Fisz (1962, Chap. 5). Sheps (1967) reviews the extensive literature on models of conception and birth.

17.4. SIMULATION

Louis Henry (1953a, 1957, 1961) pioneered the study of stochastic models for reproduction. He secures the results of the present chapter and develops a model in which birth order plays a central part. Perrin and Sheps (1964) consider a stochastic process recognizing five states—not only fecundable and pregnant, but also three kinds of infecundability in addition to pregnancy, namely those following fetal loss, stillbirth, and live birth. It improves on earlier versions in being in continuous time (rather than the discrete time of most of the preceding exposition), and it also makes the infertile interval due to wastage a random variable. Sheps and Menken (1967) provide a classification, summary, and reconciliation of the diverse and extensive literature.

At a certain point in the construction of probability models the mathematics becomes intractable, and it is natural to turn to simulation. Sheps (1967), Perrin and Sheps (1965), Sheps and Ridley (1965b), and Hyrenius (1964) have designed simulations of pregnancy and birth. Orcutt *et al.* (1961) carried through a promising larger simulation which included not only birth and death, but also the formation of households and entry into the labor force. Most recently Horvitz *et al.* (1967) have undertaken an extensive simulation which should result in new findings on fertility and population growth.

CHAPTER 18

THE BRANCHING PROCESS AS A POPULATION MODEL

The branching process has its roots in Francis Galton's discussion of "the decay of the families of men who occupied conspicuous positions in past times." Few of the great writers and statesmen of the past have descendants living today. People have pointed to this as evidence "that a rise in physical comfort and intellectual capacity is necessarily accompanied by a diminution in fertility." But if "by the ordinary law of chances, a large proportion of families are continually dying out, it evidently follows that, until we know what that proportion is, we cannot estimate whether any diminution of surnames among the families whose history we can trace is or is not a sign of their diminished fertility" (Galton and Watson, 1874, p. 138). The mature statement of the theory, based on the hundreds of papers available and his own contributions, is provided by Harris (1963). Applications in nuclear physics and in chemistry have become important. Here is one of a number of instances of a method devised for the study of man proving fruitful in the study of nature.

After a single main result in terms of the iterated function (18.1.2) below, a method of using the computer to calculate distributions in successive generations will be described, and the results of specimen calculations exhibited.

18.1. BRANCHING THEORY

The starting point is a set of probabilities $\pi_0, \pi_1, \pi_2, \ldots$, that a man has no sons, one son, two sons, etc., or that a woman has no daughters, one daughter, etc. These probabilities are taken to apply independently to each individual, whether the family into which he was born was large or small. We can calculate probabilities for grandsons: the chance of zero grandsons in the male line must be π_0 (the chance that a man has no son) plus the chance that he has a son who has no son, $\pi_1\pi_0$, plus the chance that he has two sons neither of whom has a son, $\pi_2\pi_0^2$, etc. For any other outcome—say exactly four great grandsons—one could similarly follow all the possible (mutually exclusive) routes and add the probabilities of these together.

The Iterated Function

Watson's device for solving the problem formulated by Galton was a generating function which systematizes the calculation of probabilities. He studied

$$f(s) = \pi_0 + \pi_1 s + \pi_2 s^2 + \cdots, \tag{18.1.1}$$

which the reader may contrast with the quite different generating function $F(s)$ of (5.8.3) or $\phi(s)$ used in (17.3.11). Among other differences the sum of the probabilities here, $f(1)$, must equal 1. [What is the value of $F(1)$ of (5.8.3)?] Evidently $f(0)$ is the chance of zero sons, which is to say the probability of extinction in the first generation. The distribution of the number of sons to two men is given by the coefficients of the powers of s in

$$\begin{aligned}[f(s)]^2 &= (\pi_0 + \pi_1 s + \pi_2 s^2 + \cdots)^2 \\ &= \pi_0^2 + 2\pi_0\pi_1 s + (2\pi_0\pi_2 + \pi_1^2)s^2 + \cdots\end{aligned}$$

as may readily be verified by enumeration of the several possibilities. For example, the chance that two men will have two sons between them is $2\pi_0\pi_2 + \pi_1^2$, etc., always on the assumption of independence and the applicability of the same set of probabilities.

This provides the probability distribution of grandsons. The chance of a man having two sons is π_2; the (conditional) distribution of sons of these two is given by the coefficients of powers of s in $[f(s)]^2$. Hence, if we do not know how many sons he will have, the probabilities that he will have two, *and* that he will have zero, one, two, ... grandsons are the coefficients of $s^0, s^1, s^2, \ldots$ in $\pi_2[f(s)]^2$. The corresponding unconditional probabilities for grandsons covering the case of three sons are the coefficients of the powers of s in $\pi_3[f(s)]^3$. Hence we can say, on the assumption of fixed and independent probabilities, that the chances of zero, one, two, etc. grandsons are obtained as the coefficients of $s^0, s^1, s^2, \ldots$, in

$$\pi_0 + \pi_1[f(s)] + \pi_2[f(s)]^2 + \pi_3[f(s)]^3 + \cdots \tag{18.1.2}$$

But (18.1.2) is exactly the same as (18.1.1) with $f(s)$ taking the place of s, and may be written $f[f(s)]$ or $f_2(s)$. The iteration of $f(s)$ may be continued; the distribution of the numbers of great grandsons will be given by the coefficients of s in $f_3(s) = f(f[f(s)])$, and so forth. Each of the iterates derives from the previous one: $f_{n+1}(s) = f[f_n(s)]$, and we can iterate in lumps without affecting the answer:

$$f_{m+n}(s) = f_m[f_n(s)] = f_n[f_m(s)]\,,$$

for all integral $m > 0$, $n > 0$.

The probability of extinction is π_0 or $f(0)$ in the first generation—the sons of ego. By the second generation, grandsons, it is $f[f(0)]$ or $f_2(0)$, and by the nth generation $f_n(0)$. The probability of extinction by the $(n + 1)$th generation must be at least as great as by the nth generation. Examination of the algebraic process by which $f_{n+1}(s)$ is formed from $f_n(s)$ shows that the absolute term $f_n(0)$ may increase with n, but it can never decrease, so that $f_n(0)$ must be a monotonically nondecreasing sequence in n. Moreover, $f_n(0)$ has an upper bound, corresponding to the probability of extinction unity, and any monotonically increasing series with an upper bound must have a unique limit point.

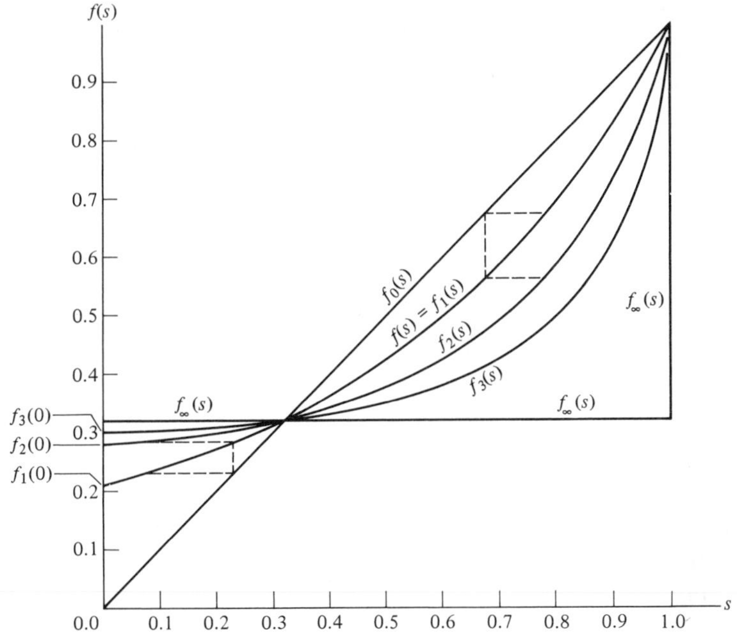

Fig. 18.1 Iterated function $f_n(s)$ for $n = 0, 1, 2, 3, \infty$, Japanese women 45–49, from 1960 census.

To find what this limit point is, we note that

a) at the limit $f_{n+1}(0)$ will equal $f_n(0)$,

b) by definition for all n, $f_{n+1}(0) = f[f_n(0)]$.

From (a) and (b) we have in the limit the equation

$$f_n(0) = f[f_n(0)] ,$$

so that the limiting value x, say, of $f_n(0)$ is the real root between 0 and 1 of

$$x = f(x) , \tag{18.1.3}$$

if that root exists (Feller, 1957, p. 275).

The successive iterates of $f(s)$ are all certain to intersect at the point where $s = f(s)$, since where $s = f(s)$ we will have $s = f[f(s)]$, etc. This and (18.1.3) fix two points on $f_\infty(s)$, a nondecreasing function of s for all $0 \leq s \leq 1$, and since their ordinates are the same, $f_\infty(s)$ must be a horizontal straight line over the interval 0 to x.

At the point of application of this theory we switch from Galton's exposition in terms of men and their sons to what the currently available data permit—women and daughters. Figure 18.1 shows the first, second, third, and ultimate

Exhibit 18.1 Distribution $\pi_0, \pi_1, \pi_2, \ldots$ of women according to number of daughters, derived from distribution $c_0, c_1, c_2, \ldots$ according to number of children (see p. 405)

With total. Children	No. of women as given	Computed as having 0, 1, 2, ... daughters			
		0	1	2	...
0	c_0	c_0			...
1	c_1	$c_1(1-g)$	$c_1 g$		...
2	c_2	$c_2(1-g)^2$	$2c_2(1-g)g$	$c_2 g^2$	...
3	c_3	$c_3(1-g)^3$	$3c_3(1-g)^2 g$	$3c_3(1-g)g^2$	...
4	c_4	$c_4(1-g)^4$	$4c_4(1-g)^3 g$	$6c_4(1-g)^2 g^2$	...
⋮	⋮	⋮	⋮	⋮	⋮
Total	c	$\pi_0 c$	$\pi_1 c$	$\pi_2 c$	...

iterates, $f_1(s)$, $f_2(s)$, $f_3(s)$, and $f_\infty(s)$, for Japanese women 45–49 years of age, as they reported the number of their children retrospectively in the census of 1960. The primary data were the distribution of women according to total children born (United Nations *Demographic Yearbook*, 1963, Table 16); from these were inferred the distribution of the same women by the number of daughters living to maturity, using a device discussed below and illustrated in Exhibit 18.1. More detailed information on the same population is provided in Table 18.1, where the change of $f_n(s)$ towards a straight line with a jump at $s = 1$ is followed up to $f_9(s)$. Calculated in double precision the curve of $f_{10}(s)$ (not shown in the table) remained between $f_{10}(s) = 0.32$ and $f_{10}(s) = 0.35$ in the whole range from $s = 0.00$ to $s = 0.98$, and then went from 0.35 to 1.00 between $s = 0.98$ and $s = 1.00$. For given finite n, the curves of $f_n(s)$ are ascending and concave upward where $s > 0$, since $f'(s)$ and $f''(s)$ are greater than 0.

The several methods for solution of the characteristic equation $\psi(r)$ of (5.2.2) in Section 5.3 are available for $s = f(s)$. The reader may apply any of these or the secant method of Section 3.2 to data for Israel, 1961 (Table 18.2). Here $s = f(s)$ is

$$s = 0.2767 + 0.3289s + 0.1949s^2 + 0.0862s^3 + 0.0509s^4 + 0.0329s^5 + 0.0183s^6 + 0.0080s^7 + 0.0026s^8 + 0.0006s^9 .$$

He will find that $s - f(s) = 0.00522$ for $s = 0.5$; $s - f(s) = -0.00202$ for $s = 0.52$; straight line interpolation gives $s - f(s) = 0$ for $s = 0.5144$. Verify that $0.5144 = f(0.5144)$.

A Matrix Formulation

Rather than program the extended algebra for handling individual probabilities by the iterated function, we express the latter as a matrix and so reduce to matrix multiplication the problem of ascertaining the chance that a line of descent contains exactly n members at x generations.

Table 18.1 Successive iterates of generating function for probability distribution of Japanese women 45–49 in 1960 by number of girl children born*

s	$f_1(s)$	$f_2(s)$	$f_3(s)$	$f_4(s)$	$f_5(s)$
0.0	0.2092	0.2752	0.3020	0.3139	0.3194
0.1	0.2375	0.2863	0.3068	0.3161	0.3204
0.2	0.2717	0.3005	0.3132	0.3191	0.3218
0.3	0.3130	0.3190	0.3217	0.3231	0.3237
0.4	0.3630	0.3434	0.3335	0.3287	0.3264
0.5	0.4238	0.3764	0.3503	0.3370	0.3304
0.6	0.4978	0.4223	0.3756	0.3499	0.3367
0.7	0.5881	0.4882	0.4160	0.3720	0.3480
0.8	0.6986	0.5868	0.4872	0.4153	0.3716
0.9	0.8339	0.7415	0.6313	0.5242	0.4404
1.0	1.0000	1.0000	1.0000	1.0000	1.0000

ENLARGEMENT OF $f_5(s)$ TO $f_9(s)$ FOR s = 0.9 TO s = 1.0

s	$f_5(s)$	$f_6(s)$	$f_7(s)$	$f_8(s)$	$f_9(s)$
0.90	0.4404	0.3861	0.3555	0.3395	0.3316
0.91	0.4545	0.3946	0.3601	0.3419	0.3328
0.92	0.4714	0.4052	0.3659	0.3449	0.3342
0.93	0.4920	0.4185	0.3734	0.3487	0.3362
0.94	0.5175	0.4357	0.3834	0.3540	0.3388
0.95	0.5497	0.4588	0.3973	0.3615	0.3426
0.96	0.5913	0.4908	0.4177	0.3729	0.3485
0.97	0.6467	0.5377	0.4500	0.3919	0.3586
0.98	0.7229	0.6115	0.5073	0.4287	0.3793
0.99	0.8327	0.7399	0.6296	0.5227	0.4393
1.00	1.0000	1.0000	1.0000	1.0000	1.0000

$$f_1(s) = \pi_0 + \pi_1 s + \pi_2 s^2 + \dots = 0.20917 + 0.25838s + 0.23595s^2 + 0.15933s^3 + 0.08275s^4 + 0.03567s^5 + 0.01331s^6 + 0.00420s^7 + 0.00106s^8 + 0.00016s^9 + 0.00002s^{10}.$$

* Programmed by Thomas G. Donnelly and William Taylor.

Table 18.2 First six elements of first ten rows of infinite matrix **P** for Israeli females 45–49, 1961*

1.0000	0	0	0	0	0	...
0.2767	0.3289	0.1949	0.0862	0.0509	0.0329	...
0.0765	0.1820	0.2160	0.1759	0.1229	0.0853	...
0.0212	0.0755	0.1345	0.1618	0.1535	0.1287	...
0.0059	0.0279	0.0662	0.1055	0.1295	0.1338	...
0.0016	0.0096	0.0286	0.0569	0.0861	0.1075	...
0.0004	0.0032	0.0114	0.0272	0.0490	0.0722	...
0.0001	0.0010	0.0043	0.0119	0.0250	0.0425	...
0.0000	0.0003	0.0016	0.0049	0.0118	0.0228	...
0.0000	0.0001	0.0005	0.0019	0.0052	0.0113	...
⋮	⋮	⋮	⋮	⋮	⋮	⋮

* Programmed by Andrea Tyree.

Still with the restrictions that age is disregarded, that we are following a single sex, say females, and that the generations are to be the unit of counting, we call the state of having no daughters during the course of one's life E_0, of having one daughter E_1, of having two daughters E_2, ... Then the vector which represents the probabilities of attaining these states by the end of a woman's reproductive life will be

$$\mathbf{\Pi} = [\pi_0 \quad \pi_1 \quad \pi_2 \cdots] \equiv [\Pr E_0 \quad \Pr E_1 \quad \Pr E_2 \cdots].$$

Think of an infinite matrix **P**, post-multiplying the vector **Π**, if necessary made infinite by filling out with zeros, to carry any generation into the next generation. For carrying the first generation into the second we have

$$\mathbf{\Pi P} = [\pi_0 \quad \pi_1 \quad \pi_2 \quad \pi_3 \cdots] \begin{bmatrix} 1 & 0 & 0 & \cdots \\ \pi_0 & \pi_1 & \pi_2 & \cdots \\ \pi_0^2 & 2\pi_1\pi_0 & 2\pi_2\pi_0 + \pi_1^2 & \cdots \\ \pi_0^3 & 3\pi_1\pi_0^2 & \cdot & \cdot \\ \cdot & \cdot & \cdot & \cdot \\ \cdot & \cdot & \cdot & \cdot \end{bmatrix}. \qquad (18.1.4)$$

To construct **P**, one simple formula (18.1.5 below) is required, based on the fact that the entry in the jth cell of the ith row is the coefficient of s^{j-1} in $(\pi_0+\pi_1 s+\pi_2 s^2+\cdots)^{i-1}$ (Galton and Watson, 1874, p. 140). The members of each row are obtained by multiplying those above and to the left by π_0, π_1, π_2, etc. Thus the first element of the fourth row is the first element of the third multiplied by π_0; the second element of the fourth row is the second of the third multiplied by π_0 plus the first multiplied by π_1; the third is the third element of the third multiplied by π_0 plus the second of the third multiplied by π_1 plus the first of the third multiplied by π_2, etc. In general

$$p_{ij} = \pi_0 p_{i-1,j} + \pi_1 p_{i-1,j-1} + \pi_2 p_{i-1,j-2} + \cdots \tag{18.1.5}$$

Then **P** will represent the transition from one woman existing with certainty,

$$\mathbf{\Pi} = [0 \quad 1 \quad 0 \quad 0 \quad 0 \cdots],$$

to the probabilities of 0, 1, 2, ... daughters. The probabilities for numbers of daughters being $\mathbf{\Pi P}$, then for 0, 1, 2, ... granddaughters through daughters the probabilities are given by the horizontal vector $\mathbf{\Pi P}^2$; ...; for 0, 1, 2, ... female descendants through the female line in the nth generation the probabilities are $\mathbf{\Pi P}^n$. Prove that multiplication by the matrix **P**, whose numbers are calculated by (18.1.5), is the equivalent of an iteration of the generating function.

To apply this method to real data about a succession of generations, we need to know the distribution of individuals according to the number of offspring they have, all for one sex. Lotka (1931b, p. 378) uses the white population of the United States in 1920 and obtains from order of birth statistics the probability of having 0, 1, 2, 3, ... children. This takes account of all births, but has the defect of applying to a single period. We can avoid the period distortion, at least in this instance, by using a different source: the census reports of women 45–59 years of age on the number of live births they have ever had. The advantage of referring to a cohort is here accompanied by the disadvantage of omitting from the analysis women who die before age 45–49. Confining the analysis to women 45–49 distorts the distribution by omitting portions on the left, i.e., at the smaller numbers of children.

We need the number of children of the same sex as the parent who live long enough to become parents in their turn. What is available from the United Nations (*Demographic Yearbook*, 1963, Table 16) is only the distribution of women by children (of both sexes together) ever born, and we must apply a device due to Lotka (1931b, p. 379; 1939c, p. 131) to approximate the distribution of women by number of daughters.

Suppose that the proportion of women who have no children is c_0, who have one child is c_1, who have two children is c_2, etc., and that the proportion of births which are girls is g, equal to 0.48793 for the United States in 1959–61 according to official registrations. Then we can say that all of the c_0 women have no daughters. Of the c_1 mothers of one child, the proportion with a daughter is g, so that an expected gc_1 of all women have one child which is a daughter. Of the c_2 mothers of two children, there will be an expected g^2c_2 with two daughters; $2g(1-g)c_2$ with one daughter; $(1-g)^2c_2$ with no daughters. Proceeding in this way (Exhibit 18.1) we divide up all the c's into classes according to number of daughters in a binomial distribution.

One further adjustment is required, to allow for the possibility of death before the age of reproduction is attained. We suppose for all individuals the same average chance of surviving to the age of reproduction. For the United States official life tables of 1959–61, we find that l_{25}/l_0 is 0.96418. This may be applied in the same way as the sex ratio; in fact, it can be incorporated as a factor in the g of the preceding step. If we think of the probability of a birth being not just a girl, but a girl who survives to the age of 25, to replace the g used previously, then no further change is required in the procedure.

The distribution of women by number of daughters as obtained by this method is shown for Israel, 1961, by the second row of Table 18.2. Table 18.2 as a whole is a portion of the matrix **P** as constructed by the computer. In principle both the matrix **P** and the vector **Π** are infinite in size; our approximation was 150×150 for the former and 150×1 for the latter, requiring 22,500 cells of storage for **P** and 150 for **Π**.

The probability distribution for successive generations appears in the successive rows of Table 18.3, each being the vector **Π** of (18.1.4) after multiplication by $\mathbf{P}^x$. The reader may verify the transition from one row to the next, at least for the first few generations and numbers of descendants. For example, the probability of one ($n = 1$) great granddaughter ($x = 3$) is obtained as the inner product of the row for granddaughters in Table 18.3 ($x = 2$) by the second column of the matrix **P** of Table 18.2:

$$(0.3847)(0) + (0.1519)(0.3289) + (0.1224)(0.1820) + \cdots = 0.0811\,,$$

in agreement with the second element of the third row of Table 18.3.

By the thirteenth generation the probability of extinction is as high as 0.5134 for Israel, while the probability of still having just one descendant is as low as 0.0007. The highest single probability aside from zero is of twenty descendants, but even that is only 0.00077 (not shown in the table). A similar calculation for United States women 45–49 in 1960 shows the probability of zero descendants to be 0.79878; of one, 0.00594; of two, 0.00611, by the thirteenth generation. As further generations are taken into account, these probabilities would continue to diminish, down to a limit of zero for any one given nonzero number of descendants. Either one's line is extinguished or one has hundreds or thousands of descendants.

18.2. ABRIDGED METHOD OF FINDING PROBABILITY OF EXTINCTION

The probability of extinction may be expressed in simple terms by supposing a geometric progression in the $\pi_0, \pi_1, \pi_2, \ldots$ If the entire series forms a geometric progression with common ratio g,

$$\pi_0 = \pi\,; \quad \pi_1 = \pi g\,; \quad \pi_2 = \pi g^2\,, \ldots,$$

Table 18.3 Probability of *n* female descendants in the *x*th generation for Israeli females 45–49, 1961*

x	n = 0	n = 1	n = 2	n = 3	n = 4	n = 5	n = 6	n = 7	n = 8	. . .
1	0.2767	0.3289	0.1949	0.0862	0.0509	0.0329	0.0183	0.0080	0.0026	. . .
2	0.3847	0.1519	0.1224	0.0844	0.0645	0.0506	0.0387	0.0286	0.0208	. . .
3	0.4384	0.0811	0.0737	0.0595	0.0514	0.0451	0.0391	0.0333	0.0282	. . .
4	0.4681	0.0466	0.0451	0.0392	0.0361	0.0336	0.0311	0.0284	0.0258	. . .
5	0.4856	0.0280	0.0280	0.0254	0.0242	0.0234	0.0224	0.0212	0.0200	. . .
6	0.4962	0.0172	0.0176	0.0164	0.0159	0.0157	0.0153	0.0148	0.0144	. . .
7	0.5028	0.0108	0.0112	0.0105	0.0104	0.0103	0.0102	0.0100	0.0098	. . .
8	0.5069	0.0068	0.0071	0.0067	0.0067	0.0067	0.0067	0.0067	0.0066	. . .
9	0.5095	0.0043	0.0045	0.0043	0.0043	0.0044	0.0044	0.0044	0.0043	. . .
10	0.5112	0.0028	0.0029	0.0028	0.0028	0.0028	0.0028	0.0028	0.0028	. . .
11	0.5123	0.0018	0.0018	0.0018	0.0018	0.0018	0.0018	0.0018	0.0018	. . .
12	0.5130	0.0011	0.0012	0.0011	0.0011	0.0012	0.0012	0.0012	0.0012	. . .
13	0.5134	0.0007	0.0008	0.0007	0.0007	0.0008	0.0008	0.0008	0.0008	. . .
. . .	. . .	. . .	. . .	. . .	. . .	. . .	. . .	. . .	. . .	. . .

* Programmed by Andrea Tyree.

then since the sum of the probabilities equals unity,

$$\pi_0 + \pi_1 + \pi_2 + \cdots = \pi + \pi g + \pi g^2 + \cdots = \pi/(1-g) = 1\,, \qquad (18.2.1)$$

and $\pi = 1 - g$. Moreover the mean number of daughters m is found from

$$\begin{aligned} m &= \pi_1 + 2\pi_2 + \cdots = \pi g + 2\pi g^2 + \cdots \\ &= \pi g/(1-g)^2 = g/(1-g) \end{aligned} \qquad (18.2.2)$$

by applying (18.2.1), and hence

$$g = m/(1+m)\,; \qquad \pi = 1 - g = 1/(1+m)\,. \qquad (18.2.3)$$

Now the probability of extinction is the solution in s of

$$\begin{aligned} s = f(s) &= \pi_0 + \pi_1 s + \pi_2 s^2 + \cdots \\ &= \pi + \pi g s + \pi g^2 s^2 + \cdots \end{aligned}$$

or

$$s = \pi/(1 - gs)\,. \qquad (18.2.4)$$

Substituting the values of g and π from (18.2.3) in (18.2.4),

$$s = \frac{1/(1+m)}{1 - ms/(1+m)}$$

or

$$(ms - 1)(s - 1) = 0\,,$$

of which the admissible solution is

$$ms - 1 = 0\,, \qquad \text{or} \qquad s = 1/m = \pi/(1-\pi)\,, \qquad (18.2.5)$$

a result due to Steffensen, quoted by Lotka (1939c, p. 136). This single parameter method is unsatisfactory; for United States women 45–49 in 1960 it gives a probability of extinction of 0.6297, against 0.8209 from the full equation $s = f(s)$.

We go on to a two-parameter system worked out by Lotka (1939c, p. 130) which assumes a geometric progression from the second term π_1 onward. Here

$$\begin{aligned} 1 &= \pi_0 + \pi_1 + \pi_1 g + \pi_1 g^2 + \cdots \\ &= \pi_0 + \pi_1/(1-g)\,. \end{aligned} \qquad (18.2.6)$$

For the equation $s = f(s)$ we have

$$s = \pi_0 + \pi_1 s/(1 - gs)\,. \qquad (18.2.7)$$

Eliminating π_1 from (18.2.6) and (18.2.7) and disregarding the root $s = 1$ gives

$$s = \pi_0/g\,. \qquad (18.2.8)$$

Lotka establishes g by least squares from $\pi_1, \pi_2, \ldots$ Alternatively, one may

Table 18.4 Probability of extinction of female line by 13th generation; probability of ultimate extinction by (18.2.10) and by polynomial equation $s = f(s)$; five female cohorts at ages 45–49 reporting number of children ever born

	EXTINCTION BY 13TH GENERATION USING MATRIX* (18.1.4)	ULTIMATE EXTINCTION BY			
		GEOMETRIC PROGRESSION AFTER FIRST TERM (18.2.10)			POLYNOMIAL EQUATION**
		π_0	π_1	PROBABILITY OF EXTINCTION	$s = f(s)$
HUNGARY 1960	0.7020	0.3432	0.3269	0.6834	0.7130
ISRAEL 1961	0.5134	0.2766	0.3289	0.5071	0.5144
JAPAN 1960	0.3242	0.2092	0.2584	0.3107	0.3242
MEXICO† 1960	0.4066	0.3047	0.1569	0.3935	0.4066
U. S. 1960	0.7988	0.3864	0.3168	0.7989	0.8209

* Programmed by Andrea Tyree.
** Programmed by William Taylor.
† Ages 40–49.

eliminate g from (18.2.6) and (18.2.7) and solve for s in the quadratic

$$\frac{1}{1-\pi_0} - \frac{1}{\pi_1} = \frac{1}{s-\pi_0} - \frac{1}{\pi_1 s}, \tag{18.2.9}$$

so using only π_0 and π_1 from the data. The reader can prove that the roots of (18.2.9) are $s = 1$ (which is of no interest) and

$$s = \frac{\pi_0 - \pi_0^2}{1 - \pi_0 - \pi_1} = \frac{\pi_0}{1 - \pi_1/(1-\pi_0)}. \tag{18.2.10}$$

Table 18.4 shows fair agreement for five populations between the matrix at the thirteenth generation, the calculation by (18.2.10), and the full equation $s = f(s)$, all ways of estimating the probability of extinction.

The easiest method is (18.2.10), which requires only π_0 and π_1, calculable as two weighted averages of the distribution of women according to children born. Table 18.5 shows the detail of calculation for Peru, 1961, yielding the weighted averages $\pi_0 = 0.2024$ and $\pi_1 = 0.1816$. Then from (18.2.10) the probability of extinction is 0.262.

Table 18.5 Women aged 45–49 by number of children reported, Peru 1961, with abridged calculation on (18.2.10) of the probability of extinction of the female line showing use of method of Exhibit 18.1 to establish π_0 and π_1

$$g = \left(\frac{\text{GIRL BIRTHS}}{\text{TOTAL BIRTHS}}\right)\left(\frac{\ell_{25}}{\ell_0}\right) = \left(\frac{173,567}{358,318}\right) 0.81611 = 0.39532$$

NUMBER OF CHILDREN BORN i	HUNDREDS OF WOMEN REPORTING i CHILDREN* c_i	$(1-g)^i$	$ig(1-g)^{i-1}$
0	192	1	
1	105	0.6047	0.3953
2	115	0.3656	0.4781
3	136	0.2211	0.4336
4	148	0.1337	0.3496
5	163	0.0808	0.2643
6	198	0.0489	0.1918
9†	816	0.0108	0.0635
TOTAL WOMEN REPORTING	1873		

$$\pi_0 = \sum_i c_i(1-g)^i / \sum_i c_i = 0.2024$$

$$\pi_1 = \sum_i ic_i g(1-g)^{i-1} / \sum_i c_i = 0.1816$$

$$\text{PROBABILITY OF EXTINCTION} \doteq \frac{\pi_0}{1 - \pi_1/(1-\pi_0)} = 0.262$$

* Source: United Nations *Demographic Yearbook*, 1963, p. 455.
† Seven and over.

18.3. EFFECT OF CHANGE IN DISTRIBUTION ON THE PROBABILITY OF EXTINCTION

The variation among populations in the probability of extinction is surprisingly great; those used for illustration in this chapter range from Peru's 0.26 (Table 18.5) to the United States' 0.82 (Table 18.4). The probability of extinction depends on the fraction of individuals who have no children or only one child, rather than on the average number of children they have. The average could be just over one girl child, but if every woman had a surviving girl child the probability of extinction would be zero. The average reported by Mexican women 40–49 was 4.331 children, and the probability of extinction was 0.41; Japanese women 45–49 reported fewer children than Mexican on the average, 3.916, but their probability of extinction was also lower, 0.32 by the thirteenth generation, due to less variation among women.

The change in the probability of extinction with a small change in the probability π_i of having i children is found from the equation $s = f(s)$. Differentiating both sides with respect to π_i gives

$$\frac{ds}{d\pi_i} = \frac{df(s)}{d\pi_i} + \frac{df(s)}{ds} \cdot \frac{ds}{d\pi_i} = s^i + f'(s)\frac{ds}{d\pi_i},$$

from which the solution for $ds/d\pi_i$ is

$$\frac{ds}{d\pi_i} = \frac{s^i}{1 - f'(s)}.$$

But this is too simple in neglecting the fact that $\sum \pi_i = 1$. Since the total of the probabilities must add to unity, we cannot increase π_i without an equal change elsewhere. Suppose that we lower π_j by δ, the amount by which we raise π_i, $i < j$. Then by a double application of the above argument, the change in s is

$$\Delta s = \left(\frac{s^i - s^j}{1 - f'(s)}\right)\delta. \tag{18.3.1}$$

The result (18.3.1) shows that if we shift any part of the probability distribution from π_j down to π_i, $i < j$, we increase the probability of extinction. (To prove this we need the fact that $1 - f'(s)$ is positive for s which satisfies $s = f(s)$.) If i and j are both large, the effect is small, and it is smaller, the closer i and j are to each other and the lower the value of s. If $i = 0$ and j is large enough that s^j is negligible, then the effect is greatest, the probability of extinction being increased by $1/[1 - f'(s)]$ times the increase in π_0. Show for the Israeli data of Table 18.2, in which the equation $s = f(s)$ is satisfied by $s = 0.5144$ and $f'(0.5144) = 0.6423$, that a shift of 0.01 from π_1 to π_0 would increase the probability of extinction by 0.0136; that the same shift from π_9 to π_8 would increase the probability of extinction by only 0.000067.

We could in this way take two actual populations, say Peru and Israel, and "explain" or decompose the difference in their probabilities of extinction in terms of the differences of the several π.

What distribution of girl children to individual women is implicit in the birth process of Section 16.1? In the birth and death process? Why is the probability of extinction as calculated on the branching process more precise than that of Section 16.1?

The present chapter has discussed only one "type," a single sex of a human population undifferentiated by age or other characteristic. Extension of the argument to several types, which may be ages, sexes, marital conditions, animal species, or combinations of these, appears in the work of Bartlett (1955), Harris (1963), Pollard (1966), and Goodman (1967b). The most unrestricted population model so far developed is the Galton-Watson multitype branching process, of which a special case appeared in Section 16.4. Its general analysis includes mathematical ideas beyond the scope of this book.

CONCLUSION

As this treatment of the mathematics of population comes to a close after five years of almost continuous work, I am more than ever conscious of the gaps in it. Not only are some important themes omitted altogether, but many of those that are included are covered incompletely. I thought it best to work out in some detail such basic matters as the matrix and integral-equation representations of a population trajectory and stop with a superficial account of stochastic processes, though the latter are both mathematically and demographically important—the reason was partly lack of space, partly an attempt to keep the mathematics at the level of elementary calculus and elementary matrix algebra. Some topics, such as curve fitting (Chapter 9) and its application to interpolation (Chapter 10), have been briefly treated simply because a large secondary literature is already available, and modern interest has in any case shifted elsewhere.

Many important issues are represented only by questions addressed to the reader, which he can answer on his scratch pad as he reads. No apology is needed for asking the reader to fill in the algebraic manipulation for a proof in which all the necessary assumptions are explicitly contained on the page in front of him. He needs to participate in the development of the argument, and the book is already lengthy. On the other hand, compactness in presentation and the length of the jump from one step to the next may sometimes reach the point where the track through an argument is lost, and this is a matter for apology. The average pace at which I can fill in the argument in detail to a class is about one printed page an hour, and for the lone reader to explain it to himself is likely to take at least that long, unless he is already familiar with the material. Not many beside the author will follow every page with this degree of attention; the provision of a list of the principal symbols, following the bibliography, should make the chapters in some degree separately readable.

The grossest omission is the lack of material bridging the gaps between demography and econometrics, demography and genetics, demography and ecology, and demography and sociology. The techniques here presented are being used in interstitial fields, and a few items introducing these extensions have been included in the following bibliography. Many problems call for research, to which it is hoped the methods of the preceding exposition will be found applicable.

BIBLIOGRAPHY

Abramowitz, M., and I. A. Stegun (eds.). *Handbook of Mathematical Functions.* Washington, D. C.: National Bureau of Standards Applied Mathematics Series No. 55, 1965.

Aitken, A. C. *Determinants and Matrices.* 9th ed. New York: Interscience Publishers, 1956.

Allen, R.G.D. *Mathematical Analysis for Economists.* 1st ed., 1938. London: Macmillan, 1962.

Andrewartha, H. G., and L. C. Birch. "The Lotka-Volterra theory of interspecific competition," *Australian Journal of Zoology,* I (1953), 174–177.

——. *The Distribution and Abundance of Animals.* Chicago: University of Chicago Press, 1954.

Arriaga, E. A. "New abridged life tables for Peru: 1940, 1950–51, and 1961," *Demography,* III (1966), 218–237.

Bailey, N. T. J. "On estimating the size of mobile populations from capture-recapture data," *Biometrika,* XXXVIII (1951), 293–306.

——. *The Elements of Stochastic Processes with Applications to the Natural Sciences.* New York: John Wiley & Sons, 1964.

Bajema, C. "Estimation of the direction and intensity of natural selection in relation to human intelligence by means of the intrinsic rate of natural increase," *Eugenics Quarterly,* XIII (1966), 306–315.

Barclay, George W. *Techniques of Population Analysis.* New York: John Wiley & Sons, 1958.

Bartlett, M.S. *An Introduction to Stochastic Processes with Special Reference to Methods and Applications.* Cambridge: Cambridge University Press, 1955.

——. "On theoretical models for competitive and predatory biological systems," *Biometrika,* XLIV (1957), 27–42.

——. *Stochastic Population Models in Ecology and Epidemiology.* New York: John Wiley & Sons, 1960.

——, C. Gower, and P. H. Leslie. "A comparison of theoretical and empirical results for some stochastic population models," *Biometrika,* XLVII (1960), 1–11.

——, and D. G. Kendall. "On the use of the characteristic functional in the analysis of some stochastic processes occurring in physics and biology," *Proceedings of the Cambridge Philosophical Society,* XLVII (1951), 65–76.

Basu, D. "A note on the structure of a stochastic model considered by V. M. Dandekar," *Sankhya,* XV (1955), 251–252.

Beard, R. E. "Some notes on approximate product-integration," *Journal of the Institute of Actuaries,* LXXIII (1947), 356–416.

Beers, Henry. "Six-term formulas for routine actuarial interpolation," *Record American Institute of Actuaries,* XXXIII (1944), 245–260.

BERNARDELLI, H. "Population waves," *Journal of Burma Research Society*, XXXI, Part I (1941), 1–18.

BESHERS, JAMES. *Population Processes in Social Systems.* New York: Free Press, 1967.

BHARUCHA-REID, ALBERT T. *Elements of the Theory of Markov Processes and Their Applications.* New York: McGraw-Hill, 1960.

BISHIR, JOHN. "Maximum population size in a branching process," *Biometrics*, XVIII (1962), 394–403.

BLALOCK, H. M., Jr. *Causal Inferences in Non-experimental Research.* Chapel Hill, N.C.: University of North Carolina Press, 1964.

BLUMEN, I., M. KOGAN, and P. J. MCCARTHY. *The Industrial Mobility of Labor as a Probability Process.* Vol. VI of Cornell Studies of Industrial and Labor Relations. Ithaca, N. Y.: Cornell University Press, 1955.

BOGUE, D. J. *Principles of Demography.* New York: John Wiley & Sons, 1968.

——, and EVELYN KITAGAWA. *Techniques of Demographic Research.* New York: John Wiley & Sons, 1968.

BOOTH, ANDREW D. *Numerical Methods.* 2nd ed. London: Butterworth's Scientific Publications, 1957.

BORTKIEWICZ, L. V. "Die Sterbeziffer und der Frauenüberschuss in der stationären und in der progressiven Bevölkerung," *Bulletin de l'Institut International de Statistique*, XIX (1911), 63–138.

——. *Bevölkerungswesen.* Leipzig: Teubner, 1919.

BOULDING, K. E. "Toward a general theory of growth," *Canadian Journal of Economics and Political Science*, XIX (1953), 326–340.

——. *A Reconstruction of Economics.* New York: Science Editions, 1962.

BOURGEOIS-PICHAT, JEAN. *Mesure de la Fécondité des Populations.* (INED, Cahier 12.) Paris: Presses Universitaires de France, 1950.

——. "Utilisation de la notion de population stable pour mesurer la mortalité et la fécondité des populations des pays sous-développés," *Bulletin de l'Institut International de Statistique* (Actes de la 30ᵉ Session), 1957.

——. I. "Définition d'une population stable et étude expérimentale de ses propriétés caractéristiques"; II. "Calcul des caractéristiques des populations stables"; III. "Une géneralization du concept de population stable"; IV. "Le réseau de populations stables type intermédiaire"; (Unpublished ms., mimeographed, April, 1962.)

BOWLEY, A. L. "Births and population of Great Britain," *Journal of the Royal Economic Society*, XXXIV (1924), 188–192.

BRASS, W. "The estimation of total fertility rates from data for primitive communities," *World Population Congress, 1954*, 263–270. New York: United Nations.

——. "Simplified methods of fitting the truncated negative binomial distribution," *Biometrika*, XLV (1958), 59–68.

——. "The distribution of births in human populations," *Population Studies*, XII (1958), 51–72.

BROWN, A. W. "A note on the use of a Pearson Type III function in renewal theory," *Annals of Mathematical Statistics*, XI (1940), 448–453.

BURGDÖRFER, F. "Dynamik d. künft. Bevölkerungsentwickl. im Deutschen Reich," *Algemeines Statistisches Archiv*, XXII (1932), 168.

BURKS, BARBARA S. "Statistical method for estimating the distribution of sizes of completed fraternities in a population represented by a random sampling of individuals," *Journal of the American Statistical Association*, XXVIII (1933), 388–394.

BURNSIDE, W. S., and A. W. PANTON. *The Theory of Equations.* 2 vols., 7th rev. ed., 1912 and 1928. New York: Dover Publications, 1960.

CANNAN, E. "The probability of a cessation of the growth of population in England and Wales during the next century," *The Economic Journal*, V (1895), 505–515.

CARLSON, J. F., and J. R. OPPENHEIMER. "On multiplicative showers," *Physical Review*, LI (1937), 220–231.

CHAPMAN, D. G. "Population estimation based on change of composition caused by selective removal," *Biometrika*, XLII (1955), 279–290.

CHEMICAL RUBBER PUBLISHING COMPANY. *Standard Mathematical Tables.* 12th ed. Cleveland, Ohio: Chemical Rubber Publishing Co., 1959.

CHIANG, C. L. "Competition and other interactions between species," in O. Kempthorne (ed.), *Statistics and Mathematics in Biology.* Ames, Iowa: Iowa State College Press, 1954, pp. 197–215.

———. "A stochastic study of the life table and its applications: I. Probability distributions of the biometric functions," *Biometrics*, XVI (1960a), 618–635.

———. "A stochastic study of the life table and its applications: II. Sample variance of the observed expectation of life and other biometric functions," *Human Biology*, XXXII (1960b), 221–238.

———. "Standard error of the age-adjusted death rate," *Vital Statistics—Special Reports*, XLVII (1961a), 275–285 (U. S. Department of Health, Education and Welfare, National Vital Statistics Division).

———. "A stochastic study of the life table: III. The follow-up study with the consideration of competing risks," *Biometrics*, XVII (1961b), 57–78.

———. "On the probability of death from specific causes in the presence of competing risks," *Proceedings of the Fourth Berkeley Symposium on Mathematical Statistics and Probability*, VI (1961c), 169–180.

———. *Introduction to Stochastic Processes in Biostatistics.* New York: John Wiley & Sons, 1968.

CHRYSTAL, GEORGE. *Textbook of Algebra.* New York: Dover Publications, 1961.

CLARK, C., and R. E. DYNE. "Applications and extensions of the Karmel formula for reproductivity," *Economic Record*, XXII (1946), 23–39.

COALE, ANSLEY J. "The effects of changes in mortality and fertility on age composition," *Milbank Memorial Fund Quarterly*, XXXIV (1956), 79–114.

———. "How the age distribution of a human population is determined," *Cold Spring Harbor Symposia on Quantitative Biology*, XXII (1957a), 83–89.

———. "A new method for calculating Lotka's *r*—the intrinsic rate of growth in a stable population," *Population Studies*, XI (1957b), 92–94.

———. "Increases in expectation of life and population growth," *Proceedings of the International Population Conference, Vienna 1959* (Union internationale pour l'étude scientifique de la population), 36–41.

———. "Estimates of various demographic measures through the quasi-stable age distribution," *Emerging Techniques in Population Research*: Proceedings of the 1962 Annual Conference of the Milbank Memorial Fund, 175–193.

COALE, ANSLEY J. "Convergence of a human population to a stable form." Annual Meeting of Population Association of America, 1967.

——, and P. DEMENY. *Regional Model Life Tables and Stable Populations.* Princeton, N. J.: Princeton University Press, 1966a.

——. *Methods of Estimating Fertility and Mortality from Censuses of Population.* Princeton, N. J.: Office of Population Research, 1966b.

——, and M. ZELNICK. *New Estimates of Fertility and Population in the United States.* Princeton, N. J.: Princeton University Press, 1963.

COCHRAN, W. G. *Sampling Techniques.* 2nd ed. New York: John Wiley & Sons, 1963.

CODDINGTON, E. A., and N. LEVINSON. *Theory of Ordinary Differential Equations.* New York: McGraw-Hill, 1955.

COLE, L. C. "Population cycles and random fluctuations," *Journal of Wildlife Management*, XV (1951), 233–252.

——. "The population consequences of life history phenomena," *Quarterly Review of Biology*, XIX (1954), 103–137.

——. "Dynamics of animal population growth," in M. C. Sheps and J. C. Ridley (eds.), *Public Health and Population Change: Current Research Issues.* Pittsburgh: University of Pittsburgh Press, 1965.

——. *Ecology.* San Francisco: Freeman (in press).

COLEMAN, J. S. *Introduction to Mathematical Sociology.* London: Free Press of Glencoe (Macmillan), 1964.

CONSAEL, R., and A. LAMENS. "Processus Markoviens d'embranchement en démographie," *Bulletin of the International Statistical Institute*, XXXVII (1960), 271–289.

COX, DAVID. R. *Renewal Theory.* New York: John Wiley & Sons, 1962.

COX, P. R. "Projection of population size and age-sex structure," *Proceedings of the World Population Conference, 1965*, Summary Report, I, 253. New York: United Nations, 1966.

CZUBER, E. *Wahrscheinlichkeitsrechnung und ihre Anwendung auf Fehlerausgleichung, Statistik und Lebensversicherung.* 2 vols. Leipzig: Teubner, 1921, 1923.

DANDEKAR, V. M. "Certain modified forms of binomial and Poisson distributions," *Sankhya*, XV (1955), 237–251.

DARWIN, J. H. "Population differences between species growing according to simple birth and death processes," *Biometrika*, XL (1953), 370–382.

——. "The behavior of an estimator for a simple birth and death process," *Biometrika*, XLIII (1956), 23–31.

DAVIS, HAROLD T. *Introduction to Nonlinear Differential and Integral Equations.* First pub., 1960. New York: Dover Publications, 1962.

DAVIS, KINGSLEY. "Population policy: Will current programs succeed?" *Science*, CLVIII (1967), 730–739.

——, and JUDITH BLAKE. "Social structure and fertility: An analytic framework," *Economic Development and Cultural Change*, IV (1956), 211–235.

DE BACH, P., and H. S. SMITH. "Are population oscillations inherent in the host-parasite relations?" *Ecology*, XXII (1941), 363–369.

DEEVEY, E. S., Jr. "Life tables for natural populations of animals," *Quarterly Review of Biology*, XXII (1947), 283–314.

DEMENY, PAUL. "Estimation of vital rates for populations in the process of destabilization." (Mimeographed ms., 1964.)

DEMING, W. EDWARDS. *Statistical Adjustment of Data.* First pub., 1943. New York: Dover Publications, 1964.

———. "On simplifications of sampling design through replication with equal probabilities and without stages," *Journal of the American Statistical Association*, LI (1956), 24–53.

———, and N. KEYFITZ. "Theory of surveys to estimate total population," *Proceedings of the World Population Conference, 1965*, III, 141–144. New York: United Nations, 1967.

DHARMADHIKARI, S. W. "A generalization of a stochastic model considered by V. M. Dandekar," *Sankhya*, XXVI, Series A (1964), 31–38.

DOBBERNACK, W. and G. TIETZ. "Die Entwicklung von Personengesamtheiten vom Standpunkt der Sozialversicherungstechnik," *Twelfth International Congress of Actuaries*, IV (1940), 233–253.

DOETSCH, G. *Einführung in Theorie und Anwendung der Laplace-Transformation.* Basel: Birkhäuser Verlag, 1958.

DORN, HAROLD F. "Pitfalls in population forecasts and projections," *Journal of the American Statistical Association*, XLV (1950), 311–334.

DUBLIN, L. I., and A. J. LOTKA. "On the true rate of natural increase as exemplified by the population of the United States, 1920," *Journal of the American Statistical Association*, XX (1925), 305–339.

———, A. J. LOTKA, and M. SPIEGELMAN. *Length of Life.* New York: Ronald Press, 1949.

DUNCAN, O. D. "Occupation trends and patterns of net mobility in the United States," *Demography*, III (1966), 1–18.

———, R. P. CUZZORT, and BEVERLEY DUNCAN. *Statistical Geography.* Glencoe, Illinois: Free Press, 1961.

DURAND, J. D. "World population estimates, 1750–2000," *Proceedings of World Population Conference, 1965*, II, 17–22. New York: United Nations, 1967a.

———. "The modern expansion of world population," *Proceedings of the American Philosophical Society*, CXI (1967b), 136–159.

EDWARDS, A. W. F. "Sex-ratio data analysed independently of family limitation." (Typewritten ms., 1965.)

ELDERTON, W. P. *Frequency Curves and Correlation.* 3rd ed. Cambridge: The University Press, 1938.

ELTON, CHARLES. *The Ecology of Animals.* London: Methuen & Company, 1933.

ERRINGTON, P. "Predation and vertebrate populations," *Quarterly Review of Biology*, XXI (1946), 144–177.

EULER, L. "Recherches générales sur la mortalité et la multiplication," *Mémoires de l'Académie Royale des Sciences et Belles Lettres*, XVI (1760), 144–164.

FADDEEVA, V. N. *Computational Methods of Linear Algebra.* Trans., C. D. Benster. New York: Dover Publications, 1959.

FELLER, W. "Die Grundlagen der Volterraschen Theorie des Kampfes ums Dasein in wahrscheinlichkeitstheoretischer Behandlung," *Acta Biotheoretica*, V (1939), 11–40.

———. "On the integral equation of renewal theory," *Annals of Mathematical Statistics*, XII (1941), 243–267.

———. "On probability problems in the theory of counters," in *Studies and Essays* (presented to R. Courant on his 60th birthday). New York: Interscience Publishers, 1948, pp. 105–115.

FELLER, W. "Diffusion processes in genetics," *Proceedings of the Second Berkeley Symposium on Mathematical Statistics and Probability* (1951), 227–246.

———. *An Introduction to Probability Theory and its Applications.* Vol. 1, 2nd ed. New York: John Wiley & Sons, 1957.

FINN, R. K. "Accounting for periodicities in biology," *Bull. Math. Biophysics*, XVI (1954), 181–182.

FISHER, R. A. *The Genetical Theory of Natural Selection.* First pub., 1930. New York: Dover Publications, 1958.

FISZ, MAREK. *Probability Theory and Mathematical Statistics.* New York: John Wiley & Sons, 1963.

FLIEGER, WILHELM, SVD. *A Re-examination of the Demographic Transition in the Light of Newly Collected Data.* Ph. D. dissertation, Department of Sociology, University of Chicago, 1967.

FOERSTER, H. v., P. M. MORA, and L. W. AMIOT. "Doomsday: Friday, 13 November, A. D. 2026," *Science*, CXXXII (1960), 1291–1295.

FORT, T. *Finite Differences and Difference Equations in the Real Domain.* Oxford: Oxford University Press, 1948.

FRAZER, R. A., W. J. DUNCAN, and A. R. COLLAR. *Elementary Matrices.* Cambridge: The University Press, 1963.

FREEDMAN, R., D. GOLDBERG, and L. BUMPASS. "Current fertility expectations of married couples in the United States: 1963," *Population Index*, XXXI (1965), 3–20.

FREEMAN, HARRY. *Finite Differences for Actuarial Students.* Cambridge: The University Press, 1962.

FRIEDMAN, B. *Principles and Techniques of Applied Mathematics.* New York: John Wiley & Sons, 1956.

FROBENIUS, G. "Über Matrizen aus nicht negativen Elementen," *Sitz. Preuss. Akad.* (1912), 456–477.

FRÖBERG, CARL-ERIK. *Introduction to Numerical Analysis.* Reading, Massachusetts: Addison-Wesley, 1965.

FURRY, W. H. "On fluctuation phenomena in the passage of high energy electrons through lead," *Physical Review*, LII (1937), 569–581.

GALTON, F., and H. W. WATSON. "On the probabilty of extinction of families," *Journal of the Anthropological Institute*, VI (1874), 138–144.

GANTMACHER, F. R. *The Theory of Matrices*, trans. K. A. Hirsch. 2 vols. New York: Chelsea Publishing Co., 1959.

GAUSE, G. F. *La Théorie mathématique de la lutte pour la vie.* (Actualités Scientifiques, No. 277.) Paris: Hermann, 1935a.

———. "Experimental demonstration of Volterra's periodic oscillations in the numbers of animals," *Journal of Experimental Biology*, XII (1935b), 44–48.

———, and A. A. Witt. "Behavior of mixed populations and the problem of natural selection," in W. E. Hazen (ed.), *Readings in Population and Community Ecology.* Philadelphia: W. B. Saunders Co., 1964, pp. 108–121.

GERSHENSON, H. *Measurement of Mortality.* Chicago: Society of Actuaries, 1961.

GLASS, D. V., and E. GREBENIK. *The Trend and Pattern of Fertility in Great Britain, A Report on the Family Census of 1946.* Vol. 6 of Papers of the Royal Commission on Population. London: H. M. Stationery Office, 1954.

GOLDBERG, SAMUEL. *Introduction to Difference Equations.* New York: Science Editions, 1961.

GOODMAN, L. A. "Population growth of the sexes," *Biometrics*, IX (1953a), 212–225.

——. "Sequential sampling tagging for population size problems," *Annals of Mathematical Statistics*, XXIV (1953b), 56–69.

——. "Some possible effects of birth control on the human sex ratio," *Annals of Human Genetics* (London), XXV (1961a), 75–81.

——. "Statistical methods for the mover-stayer model," *Journal of the American Statistical Association*, LVI (1961b), 841–868.

——. "Some possible effects of birth control on the incidence of disorders and on the influence of birth order," *Annals of Human Genetics* (London), XXVII (1963), 41–52.

——. "On the statistical analysis of mobility tables," *American Journal of Sociology*, LXX (1965), 564–585.

——. "Population growth of the sexes when the age-specific rates for males and females are different: I. The expected pattern of growth." (Unpublished ms., 1967a.)

——. "Population growth of the sexes when the age-specific rates for males and females are different: II. A stochastic model." (Unpublished ms., 1967b.)

——. "On the reconciliation of mathematical theories of population growth," *Journal of the Royal Statistical Society*, CXXX, Series A (General) (1967c), 541–553.

——. "The probabilities of extinction for birth-and-death processes that are age-dependent or phase-dependent," *Biometrika*, LIV (1967d).

——. "On the age-sex composition of the population that would result from given fertility and mortality conditions," *Demography*, IV (1967e).

——. "An elementary approach to the population projection-matrix and to the mathematical theory of population growth," *Demography*, V (1968a).

——. "Stochastic models for the population growth of the sexes," (Unpublished ms. 1968b.)

GRABILL, WILSON. "Lecture on Aitken's iteration process," given at Population Research and Training Center, University of Chicago, May, 1965. (Mimeographed.)

GREVILLE, T. N. E. "Short methods of constructing abridged life tables," *Record of the American Institute of Actuaries*, XXXII, Part I (1943), 29–42.

——. "A generalization of Waring's formula," *Annals of Mathematical Statistics*, XV (1944a), 218–219.

——. "The general theory of osculatory interpolation," *Transactions of the Actuarial Society of America*, XLV (1944b), 202–265.

——. "United States abridged life tables, 1945." *Vital Statistics Special Reports:* Selected Studies of the Public Health Agency, National Office of Vital Statistics, XXIII (April 15, 1947), 243–247.

——. *Methodology of the National, Regional, and State Life Tables for the United States: 1959–61.* Washington, D. C.: United States Department of Health, Education, and Welfare, National Center for Health Statistics, Public Health Publication No. 1252, Vol. I, No. 4, October 1967.

HADWIGER, H. "Zur Berechnung der Erneuerungsfunktion nach einer Formel von V. A. Kostitzin," *Mitteilungen der Vereinigung schweizerischer Versicherungsmathematiker*, XXXIV (1937), 37–43.

——. "Zur Frage des Beharrungszustandes bei kontinuierlich sich erneuernden Gesamtheiten," *Archiv für mathematische Wirtschafts- und Sozialforschung*, V (1939a), 32–34.

HADWIGER, H. "Über die Integralgleichungen der Bevölkerungstheorie," *Mitteilungen der Vereinigung schweizerischer Versicherungsmathematiker*, XXXVIII (1939b), 1–14.

———. "Eine analytische Reproduktionsfunktion für biologische Gesamtheiten," *Skandinavisk Aktuarietidskrift*, XXIII (1940), 101–113.

———. "Eine Formel der mathematischen Bevölkerungstheorie," *Mitteilungen der Vereinigung schweizerischer Versicherungs mathematiker*, XLI (1941), 67–73.

———, and W. RUCHTI. "Über eine spezielle Klasse analytischer Geburtenfunktionen," *Metron*, XIII, 4 (1939), 17–26.

———, and W. RUCHTI. "Darstellung der Fruchtbarkeit durch eine biologische Reproduktionsformel," *Archiv Mathematische Wirtschafts- und Sozialforschung*, VII (1941), 30–40.

HAJNAL, J. "Aspects of recent trends in marriage in England and Wales," *Population Studies*, I (1947a), 72–92.

———. "The analysis of birth statistics in the light of the recent international recovery of the birth-rate," *Population Studies*, I (1947b), 137–164.

———. "Some comments on Mr. Karmel's paper, 'The relations between male and female reproduction rates'," *Population Studies*, II (1948), 354–360.

———. "The prospects for population forecasts," *Journal of the American Statistical Association*, L (1955), 309–322.

———. "The ergodic properties of nonhomogeneous finite Markov chains," *Proceedings of the Cambridge Philosophical Society*, LII (1956), 67–77.

———. "Weak ergodicity in nonhomogeneous Markov chains," *Proceedings of the Cambridge Philosophical Society*, LIV (1958), 233–246.

HALDANE, J. B. S. "A mathematical theory of natural and artificial selection," *Proceedings of the Cambridge Philosophical Society*, XXIII (1927), 607–615.

HANSEN, M. H., W. N. HURWITZ, and W. G. MADOW. *Sample Survey Methods and Theory*. 2 vols. New York: John Wiley & Sons, 1953.

HARRIS, THEODORE E. *The Theory of Branching Processes*. Englewood Cliffs. N. J.: Prentice-Hall, 1963.

HARTREE, D. R. *Numerical Analysis*. 2nd ed. Oxford: Clarendon Press, 1958.

HAUSER, P. M. "The use of sampling for vital registration and vital statistics," *Bulletin of the World Health Organization*, XI (1954), 5–24.

———, and O. D. DUNCAN (eds.). *The Study of Population*. Chicago: University of Chicago Press, 1959.

HAWKINS, D., and S. ULAM. *Theory of Multiplicative Processes*, I. Los Alamos Scientific Laboratory, LADC-265, 1944.

HAZEN, WILLIAM E. (ed.). *Readings in Population and Community Ecology*. Philadelphia: W. B. Saunders Co., 1964.

HENDERSON, R. *Mathematical Theory of Graduation*, Actuarial Studies, No. 4. Chicago: Society of Actuaries, 1938.

HENRY, LOUIS. "Fondements théoriques des mesures de la fécondité naturelle," *Revue de l'Institut International de Statistique*, XXI (1953a), 135–151.

———. *Fécondité des mariages: Nouvelle méthode de mesure*. Paris: Institut National d'Etudes Demographiques, 1953b.

———. "Fécondité et famille. Modèles mathématiques I," *Population*, XII (1957), 413–444.

———. "Fécondité et famille. Modèles mathématiques II," *Population*, XVI (1961), 27–48 and 261–282.

HERGLOTZ, G. "Über die Integralgleichungen der Elektronentheorie," *Mathematische Annalen*, LXV (1908), 87–106.

HERMALIN, A. I. "The effect of changes in mortality rates on population growth and age distribution in the United States," *Milbank Memorial Fund Quarterly*, XLIV (1966), 451–469.

HERTZ, P. "Die Bewegung eines Elektrons unter dem Einflusse einer stets gleich gerichteten Kraft," *Mathematische Annalen*, LXV (1908), 1–86.

HICKMAN, J. C. "A statistical approach to premiums and reserves in multiple decrement theory," *Transactions of the Society of Actuaries*, XVI, Part I (1964), 1–16.

HILDEBRAND, F. B. *Introducton to Numerical Analysis*. New York: McGraw-Hill, 1956.

HORVITZ, D. G., F. GIESBRECHT, and P. A. LACHENBRUCH. "Microsimulation of vital events in a large population." Paper presented at meeting of Population Association of America, Cincinnati, 1967.

HOUSEHOLDER, ALTON S. *Principles of Numerical Analysis*. New York: McGraw-Hill, 1953.

HYRENIUS, H. "La mesure de la réproduction et de l'accroissement naturel," *Population*, III (1948), 271–292.

———. "Reproduction and replacement," *Population Studies*, IV (1951), 421.

———, and I. ADOLFSSON. *A Fertility Simulation Model*. Goteborg, Sweden: University of Goteborg, Demographic Institute Reports, 2, 1964.

INCE, E. L. *Ordinary Differential Equations*. First pub., 1926. New York: Dover Publications, 1956.

IRWIN, J. O. "The standard error of an estimate of expectational life," *Journal of Hygiene*, XLVII (1949), 188–189.

JAFFE, A. J. *Handbook of Statistical Methods for Demographers*, U. S. Bureau of the Census. Washington, D. C.: U. S. Government Printing Office, 1951.

JOHNSON, N. L. "Systems of frequency curves generated by methods of translation," *Biometrika*, XXXVI (1949), 149–176.

JOHNSTON, J. *Econometric Methods*. New York: McGraw-Hill, 1963.

JORDAN, C. *Calculus of Finite Differences*. 2nd ed. New York: Chelsea Publishing Co., 1947.

JORDAN, C. W. *Life Contingencies*. Chicago: Society of Actuaries, 1952.

JOSHI, D. D. "Les processus stochastiques en démographie," *Publ. Inst. Statist. Univ. Paris*, III (1954), 153–177.

———. "Stochastic models utilized in demography," *Proceedings, World Population Conference, 1965*, III, 227–233. New York: United Nations, 1967.

KAPLAN, E. L., and PAUL MEIER. "Nonparametric estimation from incomplete observations," *Journal of the American Statistical Association*, LIII (1958), 457–481.

KAPLAN, WILFRED. *Ordinary Differential Equations*. Reading, Mass.: Addison-Wesley, 1958.

———. *Operational Methods for Linear Systems*. Reading, Mass.: Addison-Wesley, 1962.

KARLIN, SAMUEL, and J. MCGREGOR. "The differential equations of birth and death processes and the Stieltjes moment problem," *Transactions of the American Mathematical Society*, LXXXV (1957a), 489–546.

———. "The classification of birth and death processes," *Transactions of the American Mathematical Society*, LXXXVI (1957b), 366–400.

———. "Linear growth, birth, and death processes," *Journal of Mathematics and Mechanics*, IV (1958), 643–662.

KARMEL, P. H. "The relations between male and female reproduction rates," *Population Studies*, I (1947), 249–274.

——. "An analysis of the sources and magnitudes of inconsistencies between male and female net reproduction rates in actual populations," *Population Studies*, II (1948a), 240–273.

——. "The relations between male and female nuptiality in a stable population," *Population Studies*, I (1948b), 353–387.

——. "A note on P. K. Whelpton's calculation of parity adjusted reproduction rates," *Journal of the American Statistical Association*, XLV (1950), 119–124.

KEMENY, J. G. and J. L. SNELL. *Finite Markov Chains.* New York: Van Nostrand Co., 1960.

KENDALL, DAVID G. "On the generalized birth-and-death process," *Annals of Mathematical Statistics*, XIX (1948a), 1–15.

——. "On some modes of population growth leading to R. A. Fisher's logarithmic series distribution," *Biometrika*, XXXV (1948b), 6–15.

——. "On the role of variable generation time in the development of a stochastic birth process," *Biometrika*, XXXV (1948c), 316–330.

——. "Stochastic processes and population growth," *Journal of the Royal Statistical Society*, B, XI (1949), 230–264.

——. "An artificial realization of a simple 'birth-and-death' process," *Journal of the Royal Statistical Society*, B, XII (1950), 116–119.

——. "Les processus stochastiques de croissance en biologie," *Ann. Inst. H. Poincaré*, XIII (1952), 43–108.

KENDALL, MAURICE G., and ALAN STUART. *The Advanced Theory of Statistics.* 3 vols. New York: Hafner Publishing Company, 1958.

KERNER, E. H. "On the Volterra-Lotka principle," *Bulletin of Mathematical Biophysics*, XXIII (1961), 141–157.

KEYFITZ, N. "Estimating the trajectory of a population," *Proceedings of the Fifth Berkeley Symposium on Mathematical Statistics and Probability*, IV (1965), 81–113.

——, D. NAGNUR, and D. SHARMA. "On the interpretation of age distributions," *Journal of the American Statistical Association*, LXII (1967), 862–874.

KIMBALL, A. W. "Disease incidence estimation in populations subject to multiple causes of death," *Bulletin of the International Statistical Institute*, Uppsala, 1957, pp. 1–12.

KIMELDORF, G. S., and D. A. JONES. "Bayesian graduation," *Transactions of the Society of Actuaries*, XIX (1967), 66–112.

KISH, LESLIE. *Survey Sampling.* New York: John Wiley & Sons, 1965.

KITAGAWA, EVELYN M. "Standardized comparisons in population research," *Demography*, I (1964), 296–315.

KNIBBS, GEORGE H. "The mathematical theory of population, of its character and fluctuations, and of the factors which influence them...," *Census of the Commonwealth of Australia, April, 1911*, I, Appendix A, 1–466.

——. "The growth of human populations and the laws of their increase," *Metron*, V (1925), 147–162.

KOBER, H. *Dictionary of Conformal Representations.* New York: Dover Publications, 1952.

KOOP, J. C. "Notes on the estimation of gross and net reproduction rates by methods of statistical sampling," *Biometrics*, VII (1951), 155–166.

KOSTITZIN, V. A. *Symbiose, parasitisme, et évolution.* (Actualités Scientifiques et Industrielles, No. 96.) Paris: Hermann, 1934.

KUNSTADTER, PETER, ROALD BUHLER, F. F. STEPHAN, and C. F. WESTOFF. "Demographic variability and preferential marriage patterns," *American Journal of Physical Anthropology*, XXI (1963), 511–519.

LAH, IVO. "Generalization of Yastremsky's formula for analytical graduation of fertility rates," *Journal of the Royal Statistical Society*, XX, Part I (1958), 100–104.

——. "Analytische Ausgleichung der aus den Ergebnissen der Volkszählungen berechneten demographischen Tafeln," *International Union for the Scientific Study of Population Conference*, 1959, pp. 192–201.

LAMENS, A. "Sur le processus non-homogène de naissance et de mort à deux variables aléatoires," *Acad. roy. Belg., Bull. classe sci.*, ser. 5, XLIII (1957), 711–719.

——, and R. CONSAEL. "Sur le processus non-homogène de naissance et de mort," *Acad. roy. Belg., Bull. classe sci.*, ser. 5, XLIII (1957), 597–605.

LEDERMAN, W., and G. E. H. REUTER. "Spectral theory for the differential equations of simple birth and death processes," *Philosophical Transactions of the Royal Society*, A, CCXLVI (1954), 321–369.

LEFKOVITCH, L. P. "An extension of the use of matrices in population mathematics," *Biometrics*, XXI (1965), 1–18.

LEIBENSTEIN, H. *A Theory of Economic Demographic Development.* Princeton, N. J.: Princeton University Press, 1954.

LESLIE, P. H. "On the use of matrices in certain population mathematics," *Biometrika*, XXXIII (1945), 183–212.

——. "Some further notes on the use of matrices in population mathematics," *Biometrika*, XXXV (1948a), 213–245.

——. "On the distribution in time of the births in successive generations," *Journal of the Royal Statistical Society*, CXI, Part I (1948b), 44–53.

——. "The estimation of population parameters obtained by means of the capture-recapture method, II," *Biometrika*, XXXIX (1952), 363–388.

——, and J. C. GOWER. "The properties of a stochastic model for two competing species," *Biometrika*, XLV (1958), 316–330.

——, and T. PARK. "The intrinsic rate of natural increase of *Triboleum castaneum* Herbst," *Ecology*, XXX (1949), 469–477.

LEWIS, E. G, "On the generation and growth of a population," *Sankhya*, VI (1942), 93–96.

LEWONTIN, R. C., and L. C. DUNN. "The evolutionary dynamics of a polymorphism in the house mouse," *Genetics*, XLV (1960), 705–722.

LEXIS, W. *Einleitung in die Theorie der Bevölkerungs-Statistik.* Strasbourg: Trubner, 1875.

LI, C. C. *Population Genetics.* Chicago: University of Chicago Press, 1955.

LINDER, A. "Die Vermehrungsrate der stabilen Bevölkerung," *Archiv Mathematische Wirtschafts- und Sozialforschung*, IV (1938), 136–156.

——. "Fruchtbarkeit, Sterblichkeit und Bevölkerungszahl," *Mitteilungen Verein schweizerischer Versicherungsmathematiker*, XLII (1942), 35.

LOPEZ, ALVARO. *Problems in Stable Population Theory.* Princeton, N. J.: Office of Population Research, 1961.

——. "Asymptotic properties of a human age distribution under a continuous net maternity function." Paper delivered at Annual Meeting of Population Association of America, 1967.

LORIMER, F., and F. OSBORN. *Dynamics of Population.* New York: Macmillan, 1934.

LOTKA, ALFRED J. "Relation between birth rates and death rates," *Science*, N. S. XXVI (1907a), 21–22.

——. "Studies on the mode of growth of material aggregates," *American Journal of Science*, XXIV (1907b), 199–216.

——. "The stability of the normal age distribution," *Proceedings of the National Academy of Sciences*, VIII (1922), 339–345.

——. *Elements of Physical Biology.* Baltimore: Williams & Wilkins, 1925. (Republished by Dover Publications, 1956.)

——. "The progressive adjustment of age distribution to fecundity," *Journal of the Washington Academy of Sciences*, XVI (1926), 505–513.

——. "The progeny of a population element," *American Journal of Hygiene*, VIII (1928), 875–901.

——. "The spread of generations," *Human Biology*, I (1929a), 305–320.

——. "Biometric functions in a population growing in accordance with a prescribed law," *Proceedings of the National Academy of Sciences*, XV (1929b), 793–798.

——. "The structure of a growing population," *Human Biology*, III (1931a), 459–493.

——. "The extinction of families," *Journal of the Washington Academy of Sciences*, XXI (1931b), 377, 453.

——. "Orphanhood in relation to demographic factors," *Metron*, IX (1931c), 37–109.

——. "Zur Dynamik der Bevölkerungsentwicklung," *Allgemeines Statistisches Archiv*, XXII (1932a), 587–588; XXIII (1933), 98–99.

——. "The growth of mixed populations: Two species competing for a common food supply," *Journal of the Washington Academy of Sciences*,XXI (1932c) 461–469.

——. "Industrial replacement," *Skandinavisk Aktuarietidskrift*, (1933a), 51–63.

——. "Applications de l'analyse au phénomène démographique," *Journal de la Société de Statistique de Paris*, LXXIV (1933b), 336–341.

——. *Théorie analytique des associations biologiques.* Part I. Principes. (Actualités Scientifiques et Industrielles, No. 187.) Paris: Hermann et Cie, 1934.

——. "The geographic distribution of intrinsic natural increase in the United States and an examination of the relation between several measures of net reproductivity," *Journal of the American Statistical Association*, XXXI (1936), 273–294.

——. "Population analysis: A theorem regarding the stable age distribution," *Journal of the Washington Academy of Sciences*, XXVII (1937), 299.

——. "Some recent results in population analysis," *Journal of the American Statistical Association*, XXXIII (1938), 164–178.

——. "A contribution to the theory of self-renewing aggregates, with special reference to industrial replacement," *Annals of Mathematical Statistics*, X (1939a), 1–25.

——. "On an integral equation in population analysis," *Annals of Mathematical Statistics*, X (1939b), 144–161.

——. *Théorie analytique des associations biologiqes.* Part II. Analyse démographique avec application particulière à l'espèce humaine. (Actualités Scientifiques et Industrielles, No. 780.) Paris: Hermann & Cie, 1939c.

——. "The place of the intrinsic rate of natural increase in population analysis," *Proceedings of the 8th American Scientific Congress.* Washington, D. C. (1940).

——. "The progeny of an entire population," *Annals of Mathematical Statistics*, XIII (1942), 115–126.

LOTKA, ALFRED J. "Population analysis as a chapter in the mathematical theory of evolution," in W. E. LeGros Clark, and P. B. Medawar (eds.). *Essays on Growth and Form.* New York: Oxford University Press, 1945, pp. 355–385.

———. "Application of recurrent series in renewal theory," *Annals of Mathematical Statistics* XIX (1948), 190–206.

LOVITT, W. V. *Linear Integral Equations.* First pub., 1924. New York: Dover Publications, 1950.

MAKEHAM, W. M. "On the law of mortality," *Journal of the Institute of Actuaries*, XIII (1860), 325–358.

MATRAS, JUDAH. "Social mobility and social structure: Some insights from the linear model." Sixth World Congress of Sociology, Evian, France, 1966.

MILBANK MEMORIAL FUND. *Emerging Techniques in Population Research.* New York: Milbank Memorial Fund, 1963.

MILLER, KENNETH S. *An Introduction to the Calculus of Finite Differences and Difference Equations.* New York: Henry Holt & Co., 1960.

MILLER, M. D. *Elements of Graduation.* Chicago: American Institute of Actuaries, 1949.

MILNE, WILLIAM EDMUND. *Numerical Calculus.* Princeton, N. J.: Princeton University Press, 1949.

MOORE, FELIX. "The construction of abridged life tables." (Unpublished ms., 1968.)

MORAN, P. A. P. "Some remarks on animal population dynamics," *Biometrics*, VI (1950), 250–258.

———. *The Statistical Processes of Evolutionary Theory.* Oxford: Clarendon Press, 1962.

MOSER, C. "Beiträge zur Darstellung von Vorgängen und des Beharrungszustandes bei einer sich erneuernden Gesamtheit," *Bulletin de l'Association des Actuaires Suisses*, XXI (1926), 1–24.

MOULTON, FOREST RAY. *Differential Equations.* First pub., 1930. New York: Dover Publications, 1958.

MOYAL, J. E. "The general theory of stochastic population processes," *Acta Mathematica*, CVIII (1962a), 1–31. Applied Mathematics and Statistics Lab., Stanford University, Technical Report No. 7.

———. "Multiplicative population chains," *Proceedings of the Royal Society*, A, CCLXVI (1962b), 518–526.

MUIR, THOMAS. *A Treatise on the Theory of Determinants.* Rev. by W. H. Metzler, 1933. New York: Dover Publications, 1960.

MURPHY, EDMUND M. "A generalization of stable population techniques." Unpublished Ph. D. dissertation, Dept. of Sociology. University of Chicago, 1965.

MYERS, R. J. "The validity and significance of male net reproduction rates," *Journal of the American Statistical Association*, XXXVI (1941), 275–282.

MCCRACKEN, DANIEL D. and WILLIAM S. DORN. *Numerical Methods and FORTRAN Programming.* New York: John Wiley & Sons, 1964.

MCKENDRICK, A. G. "Applications of mathematics to medical problems," *Proceedings of the Edinburgh Mathematical Society*, XLIV, I (1926), 98–130.

NELDER, J. A. "The fitting of a generalization of the logistic curve," *Biometrics*, XVII (1961), 89–110.

NEWCOMBE, H. B. "Pedigrees for population studies; a progress report," *Cold Spring Harbor Symposia on Quantitative Biology*, XXIX (1964), 21–30.

NEYMAN, J. "On the problem of estimating the number of schools of fish," *University of California Publications in Statistics*, I (1949), 21–36.

NEYMAN, J., T. PARK, and E. L. SCOTT. "Struggle for existence. The *Tribolium* model: Biological and statistical aspects," *Proceedings of the Third Berkeley Symposium on Mathematical Statistics and Probability*, IV (1956), 41–79.

NICHOLSON, A. J. "An outline of the dynamics of animal population," *Australian Journal of Zoology*, II (1954), 9–65.

NÖRLAND, N.E. *Vorlesungen über Differenzenrechnung*. Berlin: Verlag von Julius Springer, 1924.

NOTESTEIN, FRANK W., *et al*. *The Future Population of Europe and the Soviet Union*. Geneva: League of Nations, 1944.

ORCUTT, GUY H., *et al*. *Microanalysis of Socioeconomic Systems: A Simulation Study*. New York: Harper & Row, 1961.

OTTER, RICHARD. "The multiplicative process," *Annals of Mathematical Statistics*, XX (1949), 206–224.

PARK, T. "Experimental studies of interspecies competition. I. Competition between populations of the flour beetles *Tribolium confusum* Duval and *Tribolium castaneum* Herbst," *Ecological Monographs*, XVIII (1948), 265–308.

——. "Experimental studies of interspecies competition. II. Temperature, humidity, and competition in two species of *Tribolium*," *Physiological Zoology*, XXVII (1954), 177–238.

——. "Beetles, competition, and population," in W. E. Hazen, ed., *Readings in Population and Community Ecology*. Philadelphia: W. B. Saunders Co., 1964, pp. 132–142.

PARZEN, E. *Stochastic Processes*. San Francisco: Holden-Day, 1962.

PEARL, R. *Studies in Human Biology*. Baltimore: Williams and Wilkins, 1924.

——. *The Biology of Population Growth*. New York: Alfred A. Knopf, 1925.

____, T. PARK, and J. R. MINER. "Experimental studies on the duration of life. XVI. Life tables for the flour beetle *Tribolium confusum* Duval," *American Naturalist*, LXXV (1941), 5–19.

——, and L. J. REED. "On the rate of growth of the population of the United States since 1790 and its mathematical representation," *Proceedings of the National Academy of Science*, VI (1920), 275–288.

PERLIS, S. *Theory of Matrices*. Reading, Massachusetts: Addison-Wesley, 1952.

PERRIN, E. B., and M. C. SHEPS. "Human reproduction: A stochastic process," *Biometrics*, XX (1964), 28–45.

——. "A mathematical model for human fertility patterns," *Archives of Environmental Health*, X (1965), 694–698.

PERRON, OSKAR. "Zur Theorie der Matrizen," *Mathematische Annalen*, LXIV (1907), 248–263.

PIERPONT, JAMES. *Functions of a Complex Variable*. First pub., 1914. New York: Dover Publications, 1959.

PINNEY, E. *Ordinary Difference-Differential Equations*. Berkeley: University of California Press, 1958.

PITT-RIVERS, G. H. (ed.). *Problems of Population*. International Union for the Scientific Investigation of Population Problems. London: Allen & Unwin, 1932.

POLLARD, Alfred H. "The measurement of reproductivity," *Journal of the Institute of Actuaries*, LXXIV (1948), 288–305.

——. "The measurement of the intensity of marriage," *Journal of the Institute of Actuaries Stud. Soc.*, II (1953), 21–30.

POLLARD, J. H. "On the use of the direct matrix product in analysing certain stochastic population models," *Biometrika*, LIII (1966), 397–415.

POTTER, R. G. and M. P. PARKER. "Predicting the time required to conceive," *Population Studies*, XVIII (1964), 99–116.

PREINREICH, G. A. D. "The theory of industrial replacement," *Skandinavisk Aktuarietidskrift* (1939), 1–9.

PRESSAT, ROLAND. *L'Analyse démographique: méthodes, résultats, applications.* Paris: Presses Universitaires de France, 1961.

PRETORIUS, S. J. "Skew bi-variate frequency surfaces, examined in the light of numerical illustrations," *Biometrika*, XXII (1930), 109–223.

PYKE, RONALD. "Markov renewal processes: Definitions and preliminary properties," *Annals of Mathematical Statistics*, XXXII (1961), 1231–1242.

QUENOUILLE, M. H. "Notes on bias in estimation," *Biometrika*, XLIII (1956), 353–360.

QUENSEL, C. E. "Changes in fertility following birth restriction," *Skandinavisk Aktuarietidskrift* (1939), 177–199.

RAINVILLE, E. D. *The Laplace Transform: an Introduction.* New York: Macmillan, 1963.

RALSTON, A. *A First Course in Numerical Analysis.* New York: McGraw-Hill, 1965.

———, and H. S. WILF. *Mathematical Methods for Digital Computers.* New York: John Wiley & Sons, 1960.

RAO, C. Radhakrishna. *Advanced Statistical Methods in Biometric Research.* New York: John Wiley & Sons, 1952.

RASHEVSKY, NICHOLAS. *Mathematical Biophysics. Physico-Mathematical Foundations of Biology.* 2 vols. 3rd rev. ed. New York: Dover Publications, 1960.

REED, LOWELL J. and MARGARET MERRELL. "A short method for constructing an abridged life table," *American Journal of Hygiene*, XXX (1939), 33–62.

RHODES, E. C. "Population mathematics, I, II, and III," *Journal of the Royal Statistical Society*, CIII (1940), 61–89, 218–245, and 362–387.

RICHTER, HANS. "Untersuchungen zum Erneurungsproblem," *Mathematische Annalen*, CXVIII (1941), 145–194.

ROGERS, ANDREI. "Estimating interregional population and migration operators from interregional population distributions." Annual Meeting of the Population Association of America, 1967.

———. *Matrix Analysis of Interregional Population Growth and Distribution.* Berkeley: University of California Press, 1968.

RYDER, N. B. "The translation model of demographic change," *Emerging Techniques in Population Research* (39th Annual Conference of the Milbank Memorial Fund, 1962). New York: Milbank Memorial Fund, 1963.

———. "The process of demographic translation." *Demography*, I, No. 1 (1964) 74–82.

SAUVY, ALFRED. *Théorie générale de la population.* Vol. I. *Economie et population.* Vol. II. *Biologie sociale.* Paris: Presses Universitaires de France, 1952, 1954.

SAXENA, G. B. "Estimates of birth rate and expectation of life in India on the basis of quasi-stability," *Proceedings of World Population Conference, 1965*, III, 203–204. New York: United Nations, 1967.

SCARBOROUGH, JAMES B. *Numerical Mathematical Analysis.* 4th ed. Baltimore: Johns Hopkins Press, 1958.

SCHULTHESS, HARALD. "Über das Erneuerungsproblem bei Verwendung eines analytischen Sterbegesetzes," *Bulletin de l'Association des Actuaires Suisses*, XXXIII (1937), 69.

SEMENOFF, N. *Chemical Kinetics and Chain Reactions.* Oxford: Oxford University Press, 1935.

SHARPE, F. R., and A. J. LOTKA. "A problem in age-distribution," *Philosophical Magazine*, Ser. 6, XXI (1911), 435–438.

SHEPS, MINDEL C. "Effects on family size and sex ratio of preferences regarding the sex of children," *Population Studies*, XVII (1963), 66–72.

——. "On the time required for conception," *Population Studies*, XVIII (1964),85–97.

——. "Uses of stochastic models in the evaluation of population policies," *Proceedings of the Fifth Berkeley Symposium on Mathematical Statistics and Probability.* IV (1967), 115–136.

——, and J. A. MENKEN. "A survey of probability models for family building." Paper presented at meeting of the Biometrics Society, Washington, D. C., 1967.

——, and E. B. PERRIN. "Changes in birth rates as a function of contraceptive effectiveness: Some applications of a stochastic model," *American Journal of Public Health*, LIII (1963), 1031–1046.

——. "Further results from a human fertility model with a variety of pregnancy outcomes," *Human Biology*, XXXVIII (1966), 180–193.

——, and J. C. RIDLEY (eds.). *Public Health and Population Change: Current Research Issues.* Pittsburgh: University of Pittsburgh Press, 1965a.

——. "Studying determinants of natality: Quantitative estimation through a simulation model," *Proceedings of World Population Conference, 1965*, III, 265. New York: United Nations, 1967.

SIMON, HERBERT. *Models of Man.* New York: John Wiley & Sons, 1957.

SINGH, S. N. "Probability models for the variation in the number of births per couple," *Journal of the American Statistical Association*, LVIII (1963), 721–727.

SIRKEN, M. G. *Comparison of Two Methods of Constructing Abridged Life Tables by Reference to a "Standard" Table.* U. S. Department of Health, Education and Welfare, National Center for Health Statistics, Series 2, No. 4, 1964.

SKELLAM, J. G. "Random dispersal in theoretical populations," *Biometrika*, XXXVIII (1951), 196–218.

——. "Studies in statistical ecology. I. Spatial patterns," *Biometrika*, XXXIX (1952), 346–362.

SLOBODKIN, L. B. "An algebra of population growth," *Ecology*, XXXIV (1953), 513–519.

——. *Growth and Regulation of Animal Populations.* New York: Holt, Rinehart and Winston, 1961.

SMIRNOV, V. I. *Advanced Calculus.* Vol. II of *A Course of Higher Mathematics.* Trans., D. E. Brown. Reading, Mass.: Addison-Wesley, 1964.

SMITH, WALTER L. "Renewal theory and its ramifications," *Journal of the Royal Statistical Society*, Series B, XX (1958).

SPENGLER, J. J. "The economist and the population question," *American Economic Review*, LVI (1966), 1–24.

——, and O. D. DUNCAN (eds.). *Demographic Analysis: Selected Readings.* Glencoe, Ill.: Free Press, 1956.

SPIEGELMAN, MORTIMER. *Introduction to Demography.* 2nd ed. Cambridge, Mass.: Harvard University Press, 1968.

SPURGEON, E. F. *Life Contingencies.* Cambridge: The University Press, 1932.

STEFFENSEN, J. F. *Interpolation.* Baltimore: Williams and Wilkins, 1927.

STEPHAN, F. F. "The expected value and variance of the reciprocal and other negative powers of a positive Bernoullian variate," *Annals of Mathematical Statistics*, XVI (1945), 50–61.

STOLNITZ, G. J. *Life Tables from Limited Data: A Demographic Approach.* Princeton: Princeton University Press, 1956.

STONE, RICHARD. "Population mathematics, demand analysis and investment planning." University of Cambridge, Department of Applied Economics, Reprint Series, No. 176. Published in Polish in *Przeglad Statystyczny*, VIII (1961), 1–9.

——. "A model of the educational system," *Minerva*, III (Winter, 1965), 172–186.

——. *Mathematics in the Social Sciences and Other Essays.* Cambridge, Massachusetts: M. I. T. Press, 1966.

SUNDBÄRG, GUSTAV. *Bevölkerungsstatistik Schwedens 1750–1900.* Stockholm: Norstedt, 1907.

TABAH, LEON. "Algunos modelos teóricos y numéricos de población." Centro Latinoamericano de Demografia, Santiago, Chile, 1964. Serie B, E/CN. CELADE/B. 1. (Unpublished)

——. "Relationships between age structure, fertility, mortality and migration. Population replacement and renewal," *United Nations World Population Conference, 1965*, background paper B. 7/15/E/476.

TÄCKLIND, SVEN. "Elementare Behandlung von Erneuerungsproblem für den stationären Fall," *Skandinavisk Aktuarietidskrift*, XXVII (1944), 1–15.

——. "Fourieranalytische Behandlung von Erneuerungsproblem," *Skandinavisk Aktuarietidskrift*, XXVIII (1945), 68–105.

THOMPSON, W. R. "On the reproduction of organisms with overlapping generations," *Bull. Ent. Res.*, XXII (1931), 147–172.

——. "Biological control and the theories of the interaction of populations," *Parasitology*, XXXI (1939), 299–388.

THOMPSON, W. S., and P. K. WHELPTON. *Population Trends in the United States.* New York: McGraw-Hill, 1933.

TIETZE, C. "Pregnancy rates and birth rates," *Population Studies*, XVI (1962), 31–37.

TURNBULL, H. W. *The Theory of Determinants, Matrices, and Invariants.* 3rd ed. New York: Dover Publications, 1960.

UNITED STATES BUREAU OF THE CENSUS. *The Current Population Survey: A Report on Methodology.* Technical Paper No. 7. Washington, D.C.: U.S. Government Printing Office, 1963.

——. *Statistical Abstract of the United States: 1965.* 86th ed. Washington, D. C., 1965.

UNITED STATES DEPARTMENT OF HEALTH, EDUCATION AND WELFARE. *United States Life Tables: 1959–61.* Washington, D. C.: National Center for Health Statistics, Public Health Publication No. 1252, Vol. I, No. 1, December, 1964.

UNITED NATIONS. *Age and Sex Patterns of Mortality: Model Life Tables for Underdeveloped Countries.* New York: 1955.

——. *Methods for Population Projections by Sex and Age.* Population Studies No. 25. New York, 1956.

——. *Demographic Yearbook.* 13th to 17th issues, proofs of 18th issue. New York: United Nations International Publications Service, 1961–1966.

VAN DER POL, B., and H. BREMMER. *Operational Calculus.* 2nd ed. Cambridge: Cambridge University Press, 1964.

VEIT, K. P. "Stationary population methods," *Transactions of the Society of Actuaries*, XVI, Part I (1964), 233–264.

VERHULST, P. F. "Notice sur la loi que la population suit dans son accroissement," *Correspondance mathématique et physique publiée par A. Quételet* (Brussels), X (1838), 113–121.

VINCENT, P. "Potentiel d'accroissement d'une population stable," *Journal de la Société de Statistique de Paris*, LXXXVI (1945), 16–29.

———. "De la mesure du taux intrinsèque d'accroissement naturel dans les populations monogames," *Population*, I (1946), 699–712.

VOLTERRA, VITO. "Variazioni e fluttuazioni del numero d'individui in specie animali conviventi," *Memorie della R. Accademia Nazionale dei Lincei*, anno CCCXXIII, II (1926), 1–110.

———. "Principes de biologie mathématique, I. Les fondements de la théorie de la lutte pour la vie," *Acta Biotheoretica*, III (1937), 1–35.

———, and U. D'ANCONA. *Les associations biologiques au point de vue mathématique.* (Actualités Scientifiques et Industrielles, 243.) Paris: Hermann et Cie, 1935.

WANGERSKY, P. J., and W. J. CUNNINGHAM. "Time lag in population models," *Cold Spring Harbor Symposium on Quantitative Biology*, XXII (1957), 329–338.

WARING, E. "Problems concerning interpolation," *Philosophical Transactions of the Royal Society*, LXIX (1779), 59–67.

WAUGH, W. A. O'N. "An age-dependent birth and death process," *Biometrika*, XLII (1955), 291–306.

WEILER, H. "Sex ratio and birth control," *American Journal of Sociology*, LXV (1959), 298–299.

WESTOFF, C. F., R. G. POTTER, and P. C. SAGI. *The Third Child: A Study in the Prediction of Fertility.* Princeton: Princeton University Press, 1963.

WHELPTON, P. K. "An empirical method of calculating future population," *Journal of the American Statistical Association*, XXXI (1936), 457–473.

———. "Reproduction rates adjusted for age, parity, fecundity, and marriage," *Journal of the American Statistical Association*, XLI (1946), 501–516.

———. *Forecasts of the Population of the United States, 1945–1975.* U. S. Bureau of the Census. Washington, D. C.: U. S. Government Printing Office, 1947.

———. "Comments on Mr. Karmel's note on P. K. Whelpton's calculation of parity adjusted reproduction rates," *Journal of the American Statistical Association*, XLV (1950), 125–135.

———. *Cohort Fertility: Native White Women in the United States.* Princeton, N. J.: Princeton University Press, 1954.

WICKSELL, S. D. "Nuptiality, fertility, and reproductivity," *Skandinavisk Aktuarietidskrift*, (1931), 125–157.

WIDDER, D. V. *The Laplace Transform.* Princeton: Princeton University Press, 1946.

———. *Advanced Calculus.* New York: Prentice-Hall, 1947.

WIELANDT, HELMUT. "Unzerlegbare, nicht negative Matrizen," *Mathematische Zeitschrift*, LII (1950), 642–648.

WILKS, SAMUEL S. *Mathematical Statistics.* New York: John Wiley & Sons, 1962.

WILLERS, FR. A. *Practical Analysis: Graphical and Numerical Methods.* Trans., R. T. Beyer. New York: Dover Publications, 1948.

WILSON, E. B. "Mathematics of growth," *Cold Spring Harbor Symposia on Quantitative Biology*, II (1934), 199–202.

Wilson, E. B. "The standard deviation of sampling for life expectancy," *Journal of the American Statistical Association*, XXXIII (1938), 705–708.

——, and M. M. Hilferty. "Size of completed families," *Journal of the American Statistical Association*, XXX (1935), 577–580.

Wilson, Edwin Bidwell. *Advanced Calculus.* New York: Dover Publications, 1958.

Winsor, C. P. "Mathematical analysis of growth of mixed populations," *Cold Spring Harbor Symposia on Quantitative Biology*, II (1934), 181–189.

Winston, S. "Birth control and the sex-ratio at birth," *American Journal of Sociology*, XXXVIII (1932), 225–231.

Wolfenden, H. H. *Population Statistics and their Compilation.* First pub., 1925. Chicago: University of Chicago Press, 1954.

Woofter, T. J. "Completed generation reproduction rates," *Human Biology*, XIX (1947), 133–153.

——. "The relation of the net reproduction rate to other fertility measures," *Journal of the American Statistical Association*, XLIV (1949), 501–517.

Wynne-Edwards, V. C. *Animal Dispersion in Relation to Social Behavior.* Edinburgh: Oliver and Boyd, 1962.

Yates, F. *Sampling Methods for Censuses and Surveys.* 3rd ed. London: Charles Griffin and Co., 1960.

Yerushalmy, J. "The age-sex composition of the population resulting from natality and mortality conditions," *Milbank Memorial Fund Quarterly*, XXI (1943), 37–63.

Yntema, L. *Mathematical Models of Demographic Analysis.* Leiden: J. J. Groen & Zoon, 1952.

Yule, G. U. "A mathematical theory of evolution based on the conclusions of Dr. J. C. Willis, F. R. S." *Philosophical Transactions of the Royal Society*, B, CCXIII (1924), 21–87.

——. "The growth of population and the factors which control it," *Journal of the Royal Statistical Society*, LXXXVIII, Part I (1925), 1–58.

Zwinggi, Ernst. "Beiträge zu einer Theorie des Bevölkerungswachstums," *Bulletin de l'Association des Actuaires Suisses*, XXIV (1929), 95–104.

——. "Zur Methodik der Bevölkerungsvorausberechung," *Zeitschrift für schweizerische Statistik und Volkswirtschaft*, LXIX (1933), 255.

——. "Entwicklung von Personengesamtheiten, Zusammenfassender Bericht," *Twelfth International Congress of Actuaries*, III (1940), 263–273.

LIST OF SYMBOLS

Symbol	Definition	Chapter
A_r	Average age of mothers at childbearing in the stable population: $A_r = \int_\alpha^\beta a e^{-ra} p(a) m(a)\, da$	5
$\bar{A}_r$	Average age in the stable population: $\bar{A}_r = \dfrac{\int_0^\omega a e^{-ra} p(a)\, da}{\int_0^\omega e^{-ra} p(a)\, da}$	7
a	As subscript or argument of a function stands for age. Used interchangeably with x	5
${}_na_x$	Average number of years lived between ages x and $x + n$ by those dying in that age interval	1
$\mathbf{B}$	Matrix of eigenvalues; the jth element of its ith row is $b_{ij} = \lambda_j^{-i+1}, \quad i, j = 1, 2, \ldots, 9;$ that is, b_{ij} is the $(-i + 1)$th power of the jth eigenvalue	8
$\mathbf{B}$	Matrix with nonzero elements in its first row only, representing births	4
${}_nB_x$	Number of births to women aged x to $x + n$, or x to $x + n - 1$ at last birthday	2
$B(t)$	Number of births as a function of time; usually on the assumption that age-specific birth and death rates remain constant	5
b	Intrinsic birth rate, i.e., birth rate in stable population: $b = \dfrac{1}{\int_0^\omega e^{-ra} p(a)\, da}$	7
b_m, b_f	Parameter birth rate for males and females respectively in two-sex probability process	13
c_i	Proportion of women having exactly i children	18
c_i	The weight of the ith stable vertical vector in the decomposition of $\{\mathbf{K}^{(0)}\}$, as in $\{\mathbf{K}^{(0)}\} = c_1\{\mathbf{K}_1\} + c_2\{\mathbf{K}_2\} + \cdots + c_n\{\mathbf{K}_n\}$	3

Symbol	Definition	Chapter
$c(a)$	Proportion of (male or female) population at age a: $$c(a) = \frac{k(a)}{K}$$	7
$c(a, t)$	Same as $c(a)$ when variation with time is considered	7
D	Number of observed deaths at all ages, usually of one sex	1
D	Degree of male dominance	13
${}_nD_x$	Deaths observed between ages x and $x + n$, that is, ages x to $x + n - 1$ at last birthday	1
d	Intrinsic death rate, i.e., death rate in stable population	7
d_m, d_f	Parameter death rate for males and females respectively in two-sex probability process	13
${}_nd_x$	Number dying in the stationary population between ages x and $x + n$: $${}_nd_x = l_x - l_{x+n}$$	1
E_i	ith state (pregnant or not and month of pregnancy)	17
$\mathscr{E}$	Expected or average value	15
e	Base of natural logarithms, equal to 2.7182818...	1
$\mathring{e}_x$ or $\mathring{e}(x)$	Complete (i.e., including fractions of a year) expectation of life at age x: $$\mathring{e}(x) = \frac{T(x)}{l(x)}$$	1
$F(s)$	Generating function of the probabilities f_i: $$F(s) = f_0 + f_1s + f_2s^2 + \cdots$$	5
$F(t)$	Number of females at time t in two-sex model	13
${}_nF_a$	Age-specific childbearing rate for women aged between a and $a + n$: $${}_nF_a = \frac{\int_a^{a+n} k(x)m(x)\,dx}{\int_a^{a+n} k(x)\,dx}$$	2
f	Number of females, a random variable in the two-sex population process	16
f_i	Probability of a girl child now born surviving and having a daughter at exact age $5i$	5
f_x^z	Separation factor, the fraction of deaths under one year of age which are to births of the preceding calendar year $z - 1$	1
$f(s)$	Generating function for the probabilities π_i of i sons to a man or daughters to a woman: $$f(s) = \pi_0 + \pi_1s + \pi_2s^2 + \cdots$$	18
$f_n(s)$	Generating function iterated n times: $$f_n(s) = f(f_{n-1}(s))$$	18

Symbol	Definition	Chapter
$f(\lambda)$	Characteristic function of matrix **M**: $f(\lambda) = \lvert\mathbf{M} - \lambda\mathbf{I}\rvert$	3
$G(t)$	Children born at time t to women already living at time 0, $t \geq 0$	5
g	Proportion of births which are girls; proportion of births which are girls *and* survive to age 25	18
$g_a^{(t)}$	Number of individuals of given sex a years of age at last birthday at time t	4
H	Karmel's measure such that the difference between male and female intrinsic rates is estimated by $(r_m - r_f) \doteqdot -\dfrac{\ln H}{T}$ H is defined as weighted harmonic mean of ${}_5H_x$, the weights being the net maternity function	13
${}_5H_x$	Karmel's measure for the five-year age interval x to $x + 4$: ${}_5H_x = \dfrac{{}_5K_x^*}{{}_5K_x} \Big/ \dfrac{s_5L_x^*}{{}_5L_x}$	13
H	The matrix constituted of the stable row vectors $[\mathbf{H}_i]$ set one below the other: $\mathbf{H} = \begin{Bmatrix} [\mathbf{H}_1] \\ [\mathbf{H}_2] \\ \vdots \\ [\mathbf{H}_n] \end{Bmatrix}$	3
$[\mathbf{H}_i]$	ith horizontal vector (eigenvector), corresponding to λ_i; it satisfies $[\mathbf{H}_i]\mathbf{M} = \lambda_i[\mathbf{H}_i]$	3
$[\bar{\mathbf{H}}_i]$	ith horizontal stable vector of projection matrix after normalization	3
$h - 1$	Nonfecundable period, assumed fixed for all women	17
i	The rate of interest per annum	1
i	Unity on imaginary axis for complex numbers: $i = \sqrt{-1}$	3
(isd)	Indirectly standardized death rate	1
K	The matrix constituted of the stable column vectors $\{\mathbf{K}_i\}$ set side by side: $\mathbf{K} = [\{\mathbf{K}_1\}\{\mathbf{K}_2\} \cdots \{\mathbf{K}_n\}]$	3
K	Population of all ages, usually of one sex	1
$\{\underline{\mathbf{K}}\}$	Vertical vector of age distribution, but with the nine age groups reduced to three: $\underline{k}_1 = k_1 + k_2 + k_3$ is the population under 15 years of age	2

Symbol	Definition	Chapter
$\{\mathbf{K}_i\}$	The ith vertical stable vector (eigenvector), corresponding to λ_i; it satisfies $$\mathbf{M}\{\mathbf{K}_i\} = \lambda_i\{\mathbf{K}_i\}$$	3
$\{\underline{\mathbf{K}}_i\}$	ith vertical stable vector of projection matrix in 15-year age groups	3
$\{\bar{\mathbf{K}}^{(0)}\}$	Observed age distribution, usually for one sex and represented as a vertical vector in five-year age groups: $$\{\bar{\mathbf{K}}^{(0)}\} = \begin{Bmatrix} {}_5K_0 \\ {}_5K_5 \\ \vdots \\ {}_5K_{85} \end{Bmatrix},$$ sometimes including only ages to end of reproductive span, in which case it is written without a bar	2
$\{\mathbf{K}^{(t)}\}$	Vertical vector of (observed, $t = 0$, or projected, $t > 0$) age distribution, ages 0 to β at time t	2
${}_nK_x$	Number of individuals in the observed population between exact ages x and $x + n$, or between ages x and $x + n - 1$ at last birthday: $${}_nK_x = \int_0^n k(x + t)\, dt$$	1
${}_nK_x^{(t)}$	${}_nK_x$ at time t	1
k_i	Number of women (or men) of the ith age group	2
k_{ij}	Number of women of ith age group and jth parity	14
$k(x)$	Ordinate at x of continuous curve representing population by age	1
$k(x, t)$	$k(x)$ at time t	7
$\mathbf{L}$	Projection matrix to the end of life; in representation with an age interval of five years $\mathbf{L}$ is 18×18	2
$\bar{L}_0$	Life table total population on radix unity: $\bar{L}_0 = \mathring{e}_0$	7
$\bar{L}_i/\bar{L}_0$	ith moment about zero of the life table number living: $$\frac{\bar{L}_i}{\bar{L}_0} = \frac{\int_0^\omega a^i l(a)\, da}{\int_0^\omega l(a)\, da}$$	7
${}_nL_x$	Number living in life table between ages x and $x + n$: $${}_nL_x = \int_0^n l(x + t)\, dt$$ (n omitted when context makes clear that 1 or 5 is intended)	1
l_0	Radix of the life table, arbitrarily chosen	1
l_0	Number starting life together in cohort constituting sample; not arbitrary	15

Symbol	Definition	Chapter
$l(x)$ or l_x	Expected survivors to age x from l_0 births of given sex at observed age-specific death rates	1
$l_x^{(i)}$	The number of persons left alive at age x in the ith category of a life table in which several decrements are admitted	14
ln	Natural or Napierian logarithm	1
M	Observed crude death rate: $M = D/K$	1
$\mathbf{M}$	The part of matrix $\mathbf{L}$ applicable up to the end of the reproductive span of ages; in the five-year representation $\mathbf{M}$ may be 9×9, 10×10, or 11×11, depending on whether births are shown for ages of mother up to 45, 50, or 55	2
$\underline{\mathbf{M}}$	The matrix $\mathbf{M}$ as reduced from the 9×9 form to a 3×3 approximation for 15-year age groups. The jth element of the ith row of $\mathbf{M}$ is m_{ij}, of $\underline{\mathbf{M}}$ is $\underline{m}_{ij}$	2
$\mathbf{M}^{(0)}, \mathbf{M}^{(1)}, \mathbf{M}^{(2)}, \ldots$	Values of the projection matrix supposed to apply over successive intervals of time	4
${}_nM_x$	Observed age-specific death rate for individuals—usually of one sex—between exact ages x and $x + n$	1
${}_nM'_x$	Age-specific death rate applicable to a population increasing at given rate r, as calculated from life table and r	1
$M(t)$	Number of males at time t in deterministic model	13
$\dfrac{M}{F} = \dfrac{M(\infty)}{F(\infty)}$	Stable sex ratio: $\dfrac{M}{F} = \lim\limits_{t\to\infty} \dfrac{M(t)}{F(t)}$	13
m	Number of males, a random variable, in the two-sex population process	16
$m_f^{(i)}(x)$	The probability at age x of having a female child after i children of either sex	14
$m_{ij}^{(n)}$	The jth element of the ith row of $\mathbf{M}^n$, the nth power of the matrix $\mathbf{M}$	2
$m(a)$	Continuous function representing fertility; the probability of a woman giving birth between a and $a + da$ is $m(a)\,da$, if mortality is excluded	5
${}_nm_x$	Age-specific death rate in the life table population: ${}_nm_x = {}_nd_x/{}_nL_x$	1
$\mathbf{N}$	The projection matrix $\mathbf{M}$ deflated by removal of the real component: $\mathbf{N} = \mathbf{M} - \lambda_1\mathbf{Z}_1$	3
$N(t)$	Population at time t	9
$N_1(t)$	Number of first species at time t, e.g., prey in Volterra model	12
$N_2(t)$	Number of second species at time t, e.g., predator in Volterra model	12

Symbol	Definition	Chapter
n	The number in the population by time t, a random variable	16
$[\mathbf{P}]$	Horizontal vector of participation rates (e.g., in labor force) at the several ages	14
$\mathbf{P}$	Matrix of transition probabilities; p_{ij} is the probability of going from the ith to the jth state	17
$\mathbf{P}^{(r)}$	Product of projection matrices for r periods: $\mathbf{P}^{(r)} = \mathbf{M}^{(r)}\mathbf{M}^{(r-1)} \dots \mathbf{M}^{(1)}$	4
p	Probability of conception in a given month's exposure for a woman in the fertile state; probability that a given birth will be male; p is fixed for all members of the population	17
p_i	Probability for the ith couple that a given birth will be male; probability of conception for the ith woman, per month	17
p_{ij}	Probability of going from ith to jth state in a given month	17
$p_{ij\to kl}$	Probability of transition from ith age and jth parity to kth age and lth parity during unit time period	14
$p_{m,f}(t)$	Probability of m males and f females having been reached by time t in two-sex probability process	16
$p_n(t)$	The probability that the population has reached n in number by time t	16
$p(a)$	Probability of surviving from birth to age a: $p(a) = l(a)/l_0$; $p(a)$ is the number-living column in a life table of radix 1	5
${}_np_x$	Probability of living n years more for an individual of exact age x: ${}_np_x = 1 - {}_nq_x = \dfrac{l_{x+n}}{l_x}$	1
Q_s	Coefficient of e^{r_st} in solution of the integral equation $B(t) = G(t) + \int_0^t B(t-a)p(a)m(a)\,da$: $B(t) = \sum_{s=1}^{\infty} Q_s e^{r_st}$	5
q	Probability of no conception in a given month's exposure: $q = 1 - p$; also used for probability that a given birth will be female	17
q_i	Probability for the ith family that a given birth will be female	17
${}_nq_x$	Probability of dying within n years for individual now of exact age x: ${}_nq_x = {}_nd_x/l_x$	1
R_0	Net reproduction rate, i.e., the expected number of girl children to which a girl child now born will give birth, based on observed survivorship and fertility rates: $R_0 = \int_\alpha^\beta p(a)m(a)\,da$	5

Symbol	Definition	Chapter
R_i	Moment of the net maternity function $p(a)m(a)$: $$R_i = \int_\alpha^\beta a^i p(a)m(a)\,da$$ Strictly, $p(a)m(a)$ is not a distribution, since its integral is R_0 rather than unity; usually we consider the distribution $p(a)m(a)/R_0$, of which the ith moment about zero is R_i/R_0	6
r	Rate of increase; intrinsic rate of natural increase; the variable of the function $\psi(r)$ in the characteristic equation $\psi(r) = 1$	1
r_m, r_f	Male and female intrinsic rates	14
$r_1, r_2, r_3, \ldots$	Roots of $\psi(r) = 1$; r_1 is real; all other r are complex, and their real parts are less than r_1	5
${}_nr_x$	Rate of increase supposed for ages x to $x + n$, inferred from observed age distribution as $${}_nr_x = \frac{1}{2n} \ln \left(\frac{{}_nK_{x-n}/{}_nL_{x-n}}{{}_nK_{x+n}/{}_nL_{x+n}} \right)$$	1
$\mathbf{S}$	Matrix representing survivorship whose only nonzero elements are in its subdiagonal	4
s	Sex-ratio at birth: ratio of male to female births in given period; also called masculinity of births	13
(sd)	Standardized death rate by the direct method	1
T	Length of generation, defined by $e^{rT} = R_0$	6
T_x	Sum of ${}_nL_x$ from age x to the end of life: $$T_x = {}_nL_x + {}_nL_{x+n} + \cdots + {}_nL_{\omega-n} = \int_0^{\omega-x} l(x+t)\,dt$$	1
Th	Thompson's index: $$\text{Th} \doteq \frac{{}_5K_0/{}_{30}K_{15}}{{}_5L_0/{}_{30}L_{15}}$$ approximately equal to the net reproduction rate R_0	7
$T(x)$	Integral of $l(x)$ from age x to the end of life: $$T(x) = \int_0^{\omega-x} l(x+t)\,dt$$	1
$U(s)$	Generating function of the quantities u_i: $$U(s) = u_0 + u_1 s + u_2 s^2 + \cdots$$	5
u	Real part of root λ of $\|\mathbf{M} - \lambda\mathbf{I}\| = 0$	3
u_t	Total children at time t in all generations in partial fraction model	5
v	Imaginary part, i.e., coefficient of $i = \sqrt{-1}$, in complex root of $\|\mathbf{M} - \lambda\mathbf{I}\| = 0$: $$\lambda = u + iv$$	3

Symbol	Definition	Chapter
V	Total reproductive value of a (one-sex) population	3
v_x	Reproductive value of a woman of exact age x: $$v_x = \frac{1}{l_x}\int_x^\beta e^{-r_1(a-x)} l(a)m(a)\,da$$	3
w_i	Expected waiting time to conception for ith woman: $$w_i = 1/p_i$$	17
$\mathscr{E}(w)$	Mean expected waiting time to conception: $$\mathscr{E}(w) = \frac{1}{n}\sum\frac{1}{p_i}$$	17
Var (w)	Variance of expected waiting time to conception: $$\text{Var}(w) = \frac{1}{n}\sum\left(\frac{1}{p_i} - \mathscr{E}w\right)^2$$	17
x	Age; frequently a discrete variable with values at five-year intervals, 0, 5, 10, . . .	1
x	Real part of complex root r of the equation $\psi(r) = 1$	3
y	Imaginary part, i.e., coefficient of $i = \sqrt{-1}$, in complex root r of $\psi(r) = 1$	3
$[y_1, y_2]$	Divided difference: $$[y_1, y_2] = \frac{y_2 - y_1}{x_2 - x_1}$$	10
$\mathbf{Z}_1, \mathbf{Z}_2, \ldots$	Stable matrices in the analysis of the projection matrix, corresponding to $\lambda_1, \lambda_2, \ldots$; they satisfy $\mathbf{MZ}_i = \lambda_i\mathbf{Z}_i$, and are idempotent ($\mathbf{Z}_i^n = \mathbf{Z}_i$)	3
α	Youngest age of reproduction, or else age which is the multiple of 5 just below youngest age of reproduction	2
β	Highest age of reproduction, or age which is the multiple of 5 just above highest age of reproduction	2
β_1	Pearson's measure of skewness: $\beta_1 = \mu_3^2/\mu_2^3$	6
β_2	Pearson's measure of kurtosis: $\beta_2 = \mu_4/\mu_2^2$	6
Δl_x	First difference of l_x, usually taken over five-year interval: $$\Delta l_x = l_{x+5} - l_x = -{}_5d_x$$	1
κ_i	ith cumulant, usually of the net maternity function divided by R_0. For $i = 1$, κ_i is the same as μ or μ_1', the first moment about zero; for $i = 2, 3$, it is the same as the corresponding moment about the mean ($\kappa_2 = \mu_2 = \sigma^2$, $\kappa_3 = \mu_3$); for $i = 4$, it is $\kappa_4 = \mu_4 - 3\mu_2^2$	5
$\mathbf{\Lambda}$	The diagonal matrix whose ith element reading from the upper left is λ_i, the ith root of $\lvert\mathbf{M} - \lambda\mathbf{I}\rvert = 0$	3

Symbol	Definition	Chapter
λ	An eigenvalue; the variable of $f(\lambda)$ in the determinantal equation $f(\lambda) = \|\mathbf{M} - \lambda\mathbf{I}\| = 0$	3
λ	Instantaneous birth rate in birth and death process; the probability of each individual giving birth in time t to $t + dt$ is $\lambda\, dt$	16
λ_x	In sampling problems the parameter probability of surviving from birth to age x; in the observations, l_x is the number surviving to age x out of a sample of l_0 born	15
λ_1	The real root of the determinantal equation $\|\mathbf{M} - \lambda\mathbf{I}\| = 0$; in the matrix used in population analysis it is the root of largest absolute value	3
λ_2, λ_3	The second and third roots of $\|\mathbf{M} - \lambda\mathbf{I}\| = 0$ in absolute value; usually complex	3
μ	The instantaneous death rate; probability of dying for each individual between t and $t + dt$ is $\mu\, dt$	16
μ	Mean age of childbearing in the stationary population: $\mu = R_1/R_0$	6
$\bar{\mu}$	Mean age in the stationary population: $\bar{\mu} = \bar{L}_1/\bar{L}_0$	9
$\mu(x)$	Force of mortality at age x: $\mu(x) = -\dfrac{1}{l(x)}\dfrac{dl(x)}{dx}$	1
$\mathbf{\Pi}_t$	Vector containing probabilities of the several states at time t	17
π_i	Probability of the ith state in the stable condition	17
π_i	Probability that a man has i sons or a woman i daughters	18
σ^2	Variance of ages of mothers at childbearing in the stationary population: $\sigma^2 = \dfrac{R_2}{R_0} - \left(\dfrac{R_1}{R_0}\right)^2$	6
$\bar{\sigma}^2$	Variance of ages in the stationary population: $\bar{\sigma}^2 = \dfrac{\bar{L}_2}{\bar{L}_0} - \left(\dfrac{\bar{L}_1}{\bar{L}_0}\right)^2$	9
$\phi(a)$	The net maternity function: $\phi(a) = p(a)m(a)$. The probability (at birth) that a girl child will survive and herself have a girl child between ages a and $a + da$ is $\phi(a)\, da$	5
$\phi(s)$	Generating function of P_i: $\phi(s) = P_0 + P_1 s + P_2 s^2 + \cdots$	17

Symbol	Definition	Chapter
$\phi_p(x)$	Net maternity function recognizing decrement classes, for instance parities, when the distribution of the population among the classes is stationary	14
$\phi(z, t)$	A probability generating function for the $p_n(t)$: $\phi(z, t) = p_0(t) + p_1(t)z + p_2(t)z^2 + \cdots$	16
$\psi(r)$	Discounted value of future births to a girl child as of the time of her birth: $\psi(r) = \int_\alpha^\beta e^{-ra}p(a)m(a)\,da$ Often used in characteristic equation for r: $\psi(r) = 1$	5
ω	Last age of life table: $l_\omega = 0$	17

General

Subscripts are used for the argument of a function thought of as a discrete variable, and parentheses for a continuous argument. For instance, the life table number surviving to quinquennial age x is l_x, $x = 0, 5, 10, 15, \ldots$; to age a (a member of a continuous set of values), it is $l(a)$.

A subscript on the lower left means the length of an interval, usually of age. For instance, ${}_5L_x$ is the number of individuals of a given sex in the stationary population between exact ages x and $x + 5$. When the context makes clear that an interval of one year, or of five years, is intended, the 1 or 5 on the lower left is omitted.

A superscript on the upper right stands for time: thus the population at time t between ages x and $x + n$ is ${}_nK_x^{(t)}$. For projections over a five-year period, the unit for t is five years, while the units for x and n are single years. E_x^z is the exposure at age x last birthday during calendar year z.

A bar above, $\bar{\kappa}_i$, is used to distinguish cumulants of age distribution from those of the distribution of ages at childbearing.

Symbols for the one-sex process described in terms of females are equally applicable to males; R_0, for example, is the expected number of sons to a boy child just born, calculated on observed age-specific birth and death rates.

The power of a matrix $\mathbf{A}$ is $\mathbf{A}^t$, of which the jth element of the ith row is $a_{ij}^{(t)}$.

$\lvert A\rvert$, $\lvert\mathbf{A}\rvert$	Absolute value of A if A is a scalar, real or complex. Determinant if $\mathbf{A}$ is a square matrix.
$\doteq$	Approximately equal to.
$\sim$	Asymptotically equal to.
*	Laplace transform; improved value in an iterative process; male characteristic when necessary to distinguish male from female.

Table of e^x for calculation of exponentials and logarithms

x*	0.000	0.001	0.002	0.003	0.004
0.00	1.000 000	1.001 001	1.002 002	1.003 005	1.004 008
0.01	1.010 050	1.011 061	1.012 072	1.013 085	1.014 098
0.02	1.020 201	1.021 222	1.022 244	1.023 267	1.024 290
0.03	1.030 455	1.031 486	1.032 518	1.033 551	1.034 585
0.04	1.040 811	1.041 852	1.042 894	1.043 938	1.044 982
0.05	1.051 271	1.052 323	1.053 376	1.054 430	1.055 485
0.06	1.061 837	1.062 899	1.063 962	1.065 027	1.066 092
0.07	1.072 508	1.073 581	1.074 655	1.075 731	1.076 807
0.08	1.083 287	1.084 371	1.085 456	1.086 542	1.087 629
0.09	1.094 174	1.095 269	1.096 365	1.097 462	1.098 560

x	0.005	0.006	0.007	0.008	0.009
0.00	1.005 013	1.006 018	1.007 025	1.008 032	1.009 041
0.01	1.015 113	1.016 129	1.017 145	1.018 163	1.019 182
0.02	1.025 315	1.026 341	1.027 368	1.028 396	1.029 425
0.03	1.035 620	1.036 656	1.037 693	1.038 731	1.039 770
0.04	1.046 028	1.047 074	1.048 122	1.049 171	1.050 220
0.05	1.056 541	1.057 598	1.058 656	1.059 715	1.060 775
0.06	1.067 159	1.068 227	1.069 295	1.070 365	1.071 436
0.07	1.077 884	1.078 963	1.080 042	1.081 123	1.082 204
0.08	1.088 717	1.089 806	1.090 897	1.091 988	1.093 081
0.09	1.099 659	1.100 759	1.101 860	1.102 963	1.104 066

x	0.0	0.1	0.2	0.3	0.4
0.0	1.000000	1.105171	1.221403	1.349859	1.491825
1.0	2.718282	3.004166	3.320117	3.669297	4.055200
2.0	7.389056	8.166170	9.025013	9.974182	11.02318
3.0	20.08554	22.19795	24.53253	27.11264	29.96410
4.0	54.59815	60.34029	66.68633	73.69979	81.45087
5.0	148.4132	164.0219	181.2722	200.3368	221.4064
6.0	403.4288	445.8578	492.7490	544.5719	601.8450
7.0	1096.633	1211.967	1339.431	1480.300	1635.984
8.0	2980.958	3294.468	3640.950	4023.872	4447.067
9.0	8103.084	8955.293	9897.129	10938.02	12088.38

x	0.5	0.6	0.7	0.8	0.9
0.0	1.648721	1.822119	2.013753	2.225541	2.459603
1.0	4.481689	4.953032	5.473947	6.049647	6.685894
2.0	12.18249	13.46374	14.87973	16.44465	18.17415
3.0	33.11545	36.59823	40.44730	44.70118	49.40245
4.0	90.01713	99.48432	109.9472	121.5104	134.2898
5.0	244.6919	270.4264	298.8674	330.2996	365.0375
6.0	665.1416	735.0952	812.4058	897.8473	992.2747
7.0	1808.042	1998.196	2208.348	2440.602	2697.282
8.0	4914.769	5431.660	6002.912	6634.244	7331.974
9.0	13359.73	14764.78	16317.61	18033.74	19930.37

* The argument x is the number at the beginning of the row plus the number at the top of the column. For an example of use see Table 5.3.

INDEX

ABCDE698